CHAPTER 12

$$Z = \sqrt{R^2 + X_L{}^2} \tag{12.1}$$

$$V_T = \sqrt{V_R{}^2 + V_X{}^2} \tag{12.2}$$

$$f = 1/(2\pi\sqrt{LC}) \tag{12.3}$$

$$C = 1/(4^2\pi^2 f^2 L) \tag{12.4}$$

$$L = 1/(4\pi^2 f^2 C) \tag{12.5}$$

$$\text{power factor} = P/S \tag{12.6}$$

$$\text{power factor} = P/S = \frac{VI_p}{VI} = \frac{I_p}{I} = \cos\theta \tag{12.7}$$

$$P = S\cos\theta = VI\cos\theta \tag{12.8}$$

CHAPTER 13

$$V = \sqrt{3}\ V_{LN} \tag{13.1}$$

$$\cos\theta = \frac{\text{active power of the line}}{\text{apparent power of the line}} = \frac{P}{S} \tag{13.2}$$

$$S = 1.732\ VI \tag{13.3}$$

CHAPTER 14

$$V_p = v \times N_p \text{ volts} \tag{14.1}$$

$$V_s = v \times N_s \tag{14.2}$$

$$\frac{V_p}{V_s} = \frac{N_p}{N_s} \tag{14.3}$$

$$\frac{I_p}{I_s} = \frac{V_s}{V_p} \tag{14.4}$$

$$I_p N_p = I_s N_s \tag{14.5}$$

$$Z_L = V_s/I_s \tag{14.6}$$

$$\text{percent } Z_T = \frac{Z_T}{Z_L} \times 100 \tag{14.7}$$

$$Z_T = v_s/i_s \tag{14.8}$$

CHAPTER 15

$$V_o = Kn\phi \tag{15.1}$$

$$P_{mi} = V_o I_a \tag{15.2}$$

$$\text{\% regulation} = 100 \times \frac{V_{NL} - V_{FL}}{V_{FL}} \tag{15.3}$$

CHAPTER 16

$$P_a = V_s I_a \tag{16.1}$$

$$P_{mi} = V_s I_a - I_a{}^2 R_a \tag{16.2}$$

$$P_{mi} = V_o I_a \tag{16.3}$$

$$T = \frac{9.55\ P}{n} = \frac{9.55\ P_{mi}}{n} \tag{16.4}$$

$$T = 9.55\ \frac{V_o I_a}{n} \tag{16.5}$$

$$T = 9.55\ K\phi I_a \tag{16.6}$$

$$V_o = V_s - I_a R_a \tag{16.7}$$

$$n = \frac{V_o}{K\phi} = \frac{V_s - I_a R_a}{K\phi} \text{ (exactly)} \tag{16.8}$$

$$n = \frac{V_s}{K\phi} \text{ (approximately)} \tag{16.9}$$

$$I_a = (V_s - V_o)/R_t \tag{16.10}$$

CHAPTER 17

$$s = \frac{n_s - n}{n_s} \tag{17.1}$$

$$n_s = \frac{120\ f}{p} \tag{17.2}$$

$$f_r = sf \tag{17.3}$$

CHAPTER 20

$$\delta = \alpha p/2 \tag{20.1}$$

$$\text{percent regulation} = \frac{V_o - V_N}{V_N} \times 100 \tag{20.2}$$

CHAPTER 21

$$n_s = 120\ f/p \tag{21.1}$$

$$T = kVI\cos\theta \tag{21.2}$$

CHAPTER 23

$$\alpha = I_c\ /\ I_e \tag{23.1}$$

$$\beta = I_c\ /\ I_b \tag{23.2}$$

CHAPTER 24

$$PIV = \sqrt{3}\ V_{PK} \tag{24.1}$$

$$VHz^{-1} = \frac{V_{Nameplate}}{f_{Nameplate}} \tag{24.2}$$

Canadian Edition

Basic Electricity for Industry

CIRCUITS AND MACHINES

Canadian Edition

Basic Electricity
for Industry
CIRCUITS AND MACHINES

DOUG EDGAR

The Northern Alberta Institute of Technology

PEARSON

Prentice
Hall

Toronto

National Library of Canada Cataloguing in Publication Data

Edgar, Douglas R. (Douglas Robert), 1949-
    Basic electricity for industry : Circuits and machines / Doug
Edgar—Canadian ed.

Includes index.
ISBN 0-13-035451-1

    1. Electric engineering—Textbooks. I. Title.

TK146.E34 2004   621.3   C2003-903095-4

ISBN 0-13-035451-1

Vice President, Editorial Director: Michael J. Young
Executive Editor: Dave Ward
Marketing Manager: Toivo Pajo
Developmental Editor: John Polanszky
Production Editor: Joel Gladstone
Copy Editor: Tally Morgan
Production Coordinator: Trish Ciardullo
Page Layout: Joan M. Wilson
Art Director: Mary Opper
Cover Design: Michelle Bellemare
Cover Image: Getty Images

1 2 3 4 5   08 07 06 05 04

Printed and bound in the United States.

Contents

Chapter 5: Magnetism and Electromagnets   78

Chapter 9: Inductors and Inductance   133

Chapter 10: Capacitors and Capacitance   147

Chapter 11: Basic R, L, and C Circuits   162

Chapter 12: Solving Single-Phase Ac Circuits   175

Chapter 13: Three-Phase Circuits   194

Chapter 14: Transformers   208

Chapter 15: Direct Current Generators   238

Chapter 18: Selection and Application of Three-Phase Induction Motors   300

Chapter 19: Synchronous Motors   316

Chapter 20: Synchronous Generators   334

Chapter 21: Single-Phase Motors   356

Chapter 22: Industrial Motor Control   376

Appendices

Index   467

Preface

The Canadian Edition of *Basic Electricity for Industry: Circuits and Machines* is a textbook specifically adapted to meet the needs of Canadian industry. This book has been written to appeal to a variety of readers and cater to several levels of education. It is intended for community colleges and survey courses for non-electrical engineering students at the technical institute and university level. It is also well adapted to industrial apprenticeship training programs. Industrial workers involved in the maintenance, upkeep, and repair of electrical apparatus will find this book to be a useful reference text. Technicians and engineers filling administrative, supervisory, or sales positions will also find this reference helpful.

In creating a text for the Canadian market, many considerations were taken into account. First and foremost, the text is written in clear and concise language, free of any unnecessary jargon, and presents an approach to electrical machines and the fundamental electrical laws that students with little or no prior knowledge in the field will appreciate.

The presentation is simple and assumes only an elementary knowledge of algebra and trigonometry. Consistent notation and methods of explanation are used throughout so students are presented with a clear and coherent picture. This simplicity, however, is achieved without sacrificing any technical rigour. An electrical engineer familiar with differential equations, Maxwell's laws of electromagnetism, and sophisticated methods of solving circuits will find nothing in this book that is at odds with his or her knowledge.

The text also includes a number of features especially for the Canadian instructor and student, such as the use of electron current flow, SI units, and references to Canadian standards.

Teaching electron current flow has become increasingly popular with instructors. Electron current flow not only more closely reflects our current understanding of the movement of electrical charge, but also makes semiconductor theory easier for students to grasp.

The text has been thoroughly reorganized, grouping together those chapters with introductory concepts and those chapters devoted to the theory and operation of electrical machines. Two new chapters have been added to the Canadian Edition of *Basic Electricity for Industry.* Chapter 23, Semiconductor Devices, introduces students to the most common semiconductor devices used in industry: the rectifying diode, basic transistor switching circuits, and silicon controlled rectifiers. Chapter 24, Variable Frequency Drives, introduces students to the basic concept of variable frequency drives, which have revolutionized the control of single and polyphase electric motors.

In addition to the technical and structural changes, the pedagogy has been significantly improved. Each chapter now includes the following features:

- CHAPTER OUTLINES present a quick overview of the key topics, by heading, covered in each chapter.

- LEARNING OBJECTIVES help students focus their reading and study of each chapter.

- EXAMPLES throughout the text provide students with ample opportunities to review and practise new concepts and applications.

- KEY TERMS are highlighted throughout the text and reproduced in the margins, with definitions provided at the end of each chapter.

- SUMMARIES at the end of every chapter provide a quick recap of the major topics covered in the chapter.

- TEST YOUR KNOWLEDGE multiple-choice questions at the end of every chapter test students on key chapter points. Answers are provided in Appendix A at the end of the book.

- QUESTIONS AND PROBLEMS at the end of every chapter challenge students to put into practice concepts that they've learned throughout the chapter. Answers are provided in Appendix A at the end of the book.

- APPENDICES include unique and easy-to-use conversion charts and a table summarizing the properties of round copper conductors.

An Instructor's Manual is also available to instructors who adopt *Basic Electricity for Industry*.

Basic Electricity for Industry is easily adapted to a variety of learning programs. In semester one of two semester programs, Chapters 1 through 12 introduce students to the concepts of dc and ac circuits and devices. In the second semester, Chapters 13 through 24 cover three-phase circuits, single and three-phase machines, basic semiconductor theory, and the control of ac motors using variable frequency drives. Students with a strong mathematics and physics background can cover the 24 chapters in a single semester. The text is also easily adapted to any of the four-year provincial apprenticeship programs.

I would like to acknowledge the assistance of numerous reviewers in every province, especially Gary Miller (Fanshawe College), Frank Bowick (Algonquin College), Dave Dewar (Durham College), and John Jenness (Kwantlen University College). Their advice and suggestions made a significant contribution to this edition of *Basic Electricity for Industry*.

Many companies provided photographs that have contributed to the book's content and level of interest and I am grateful to each of them. I would like to thank the staff of Pearson Education Canada, and in particular Developmental Editor John Polanszky and Editorial Coordinator Joel Gladstone, for their professional and enthusiastic support in the production of this Canadian Edition.

Doug Edgar

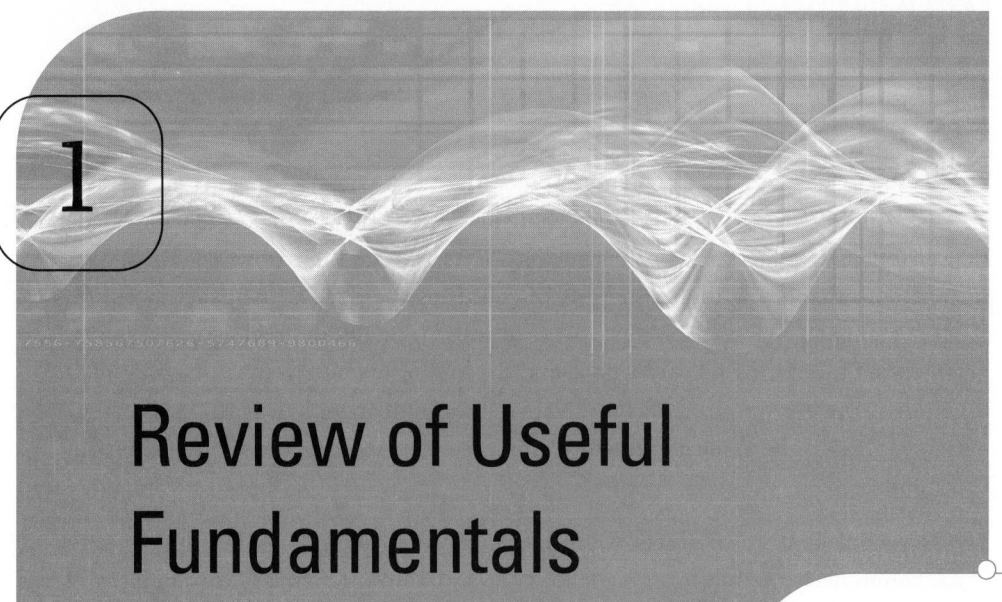

1

Review of Useful Fundamentals

LEARNING OBJECTIVES

Upon completion of this chapter you will be able to:

- Describe the SI standard of units and convert between the SI standard and the Imperial system

- Solve problems involving work, power, and energy

- Explain the relationship between the torque and speed of an electric motor

- Calculate efficiency of a system

- Explain the effect of acceleration and deceleration on a motor and its load

1.1 Introduction

One would normally expect that a book on electricity would cover only electrical subjects. However, motors, generators, contactors, and other electrical devices produce thermal and mechanical effects, as well as electrical effects. Consequently, we cannot limit our study to electrical subjects alone, but must also have an understanding of elementary mechanics and heat.

1.2 Units, the SI

Lord Kelvin once said that when you can measure what you are speaking about, and express it in numbers, you know something about it. Units are the measuring sticks that enable us to express quantities such as mass, length, time, power, and voltage, in terms of numbers. It took hundreds of centuries to arrive at the exact measurement systems we use today. Thus, the yard was originally defined as the distance between the tip of King Edward's nose and the end of his outstretched hand. Today it can be expressed in terms of the distance that light travels in 1/327 857 019 of a second. This modern measurement of the yard is exact to better than one part in one billion!

IMPERIAL SYSTEM OF UNITS

The **Imperial system of units** comprises such familiar units as the foot, square yard, pound mass, pound force, second, volt, and kilowatt. Some of these units are related to each other by odd factors such as 12, 36, and 32.17404, and these historically developed multipliers are not very convenient to handle. For this and other reasons, a much simpler set of units was adopted by international agreement wherein the factors are all multiples of 10. This system of units, known as the **International system of units** (abbreviated **SI**) is now recognized by all countries of the world. Indeed, most countries use it as their sole system of measurement.

INTERNATIONAL SYSTEM OF UNITS (SI)

The most commonly used units of the SI are the metre, kilogram, second, and newton. (The newton corresponds to the pound force, which is the customary unit of force.) The SI comprises about 25 additional units that are used to measure quantities such as pressure, volume, magnetic flux, temperature, torque, and so forth. These units, and their relationship to the Imperial units, are listed in Table 1A. Study this table from time to time in order to become familiar with the names of the units.

One final point: there is nothing mysterious or complicated about units. For any given quantity, such as mechanical pressure, the units of the various systems are similar, differing only in size. The various units of a given quantity are therefore related to each other by simple numbers, called conversion factors. Thus, 1 pound force per square inch = 144 pounds force per square foot = 6.894 757 kilopascals = 68.947 57 millibars. The pound force per square inch is an Imperial unit, the kilopascal is an SI unit, and the millibar is a special unit used by meteorologists. (The conversion factors relating the units of different systems are shown graphically in Appendix B.)

What unit should we use, for example, in measuring a length? For short lengths we may use a unit such as the inch. However, for large distances it is preferable to use a bigger unit, such as the mile. For example, the distance between Toronto and Montreal is better expressed as 520 kilometres than as 520 000 000 millimetres. But the width of a desk is more meaningful when stated as 81 centimetres than as 0.000 81 kilometres. In effect, we don't like to use very large or very small numbers when expressing the magnitude of something. That is why we use units that are multiples (or submultiples) of a given unit. Thus, the yard is a *multiple* of the inch, equal to 36 inches. In the same way, the mil is a *submultiple* of the inch, equal to one thousandth of an inch.

Table 1A SOME COMMONLY USED QUANTITIES AND UNITS
IN THE THE SI AND IMPERIAL SYSTEMS

QUANTITY	SI UNIT AND/OR SYMBOL	IMPERIAL UNIT AND/OR SYMBOL	RELATIONSHIP BETWEEN SI AND AND IMPERIAL UNITS
mass	kilogram (kg)	pound mass (lbm)	1 kg = 2.204 lbm
length	metre (m)	foot (ft)	1 m = 3.28 ft
time	second (s)	second (s)	-
area	(m^2)	square foot (ft^2)	$1\ m^2 = 10.764\ ft^2$
volume	(kg/m^3)	cubic foot (ft^3)	$1\ m^3 = 35.31\ ft^3$
flow	(m^3/s)	(ft^3/s)	$1\ m^3/s = 35.31\ ft^3/s$
speed	(m/s)	(ft/s)	1 m/s = 3.28 ft/s
speed of rotation	(r/min)	revolution per minute (r/min)	-
frequency	hertz (Hz)	cycle per second	1 cycle per second = 1 Hz
force	newton (N)	pound force (lbf)	1 lbf = 4.448 N
torque	newton metre (N.m)	foot-pound force (ft.lbf)	1 lbf.ft = 1.356 N.m
pressure	pascal (Pa)	psi (lbf/in^2)	1 psi = 6.9 kPa
electric energy	joule (J)	kilowatt hour (kW.h)	$1\ kW.h = 3.6 \times 10^6\ J$
mechanical energy	joule (J)	(ft.lbf)	1 ft.lbf = 1.356 J
thermal energy	joule (J)	British thermal unit (Btu)	1 Btu = 1055 J
electric power	watt (W)	watt (W)	-
mechanical power	watt (W)	horsepower (hp)	1 hp = 746 W
electric potential	volt (V)	volt (V)	-
electric current	ampere (A)	ampere (A)	-
electric charge	coulomb (C)	coulomb (C)	-
electric resistance	ohm (Ω)	ohm (Ω)	-
magnetomotive force	ampere (A)	ampere-turn (At)	1 At = 1 A
magnetic flux	weber (Wb)	line or maxwell	$1\ maxwell = 10^{-8}\ Wb$
magnetic flux density	tesla (T)	$(line/in^2)$	$1\ line/in^2 = 15.5 \times 10^{-6}\ T$
inductance	henry (H)	henry (H)	-
capacitance	farad (F)	farad (F)	-
temperature	degree Celsius (°C)	degree Fahrenheit (°F)	°F = 1.8°C + 32

In the SI multiples and submultiples of units are related to each other by factors of ten. Thus, the centimetre is a submultiple of the metre, equal to 1/100 of a metre. On the other hand, the kilometre is a multiple of the metre, equal to 1000 metres.

Multiples and submultiples of 10 are conveniently expressed in exponent form. Thus, $100 = 10^2$; $1000 = 10^3$; and $1\ 000\ 000 = 10^6$. Similarly, $1/100 = 10^{-2}$; $1/1000 = 10^{-3}$; and $1/1\ 000\ 000 = 10^{-6}$.

Multiples and submultiples in the SI are designated by attaching a prefix to the "base" unit. A list of prefixes is given in Table 1B, together with the multiplier it represents. The most frequently encountered prefixes are *mega, kilo, milli*, and *micro*. The others are rarely used except in scientific work. The only exception is the centimetre, but even here, many people prefer to express "short" lengths in millimetres rather than in centimetres. For example, in mechanical work, it is quite common to express a length of 9.76 metres as 9760 mm.

1.3 Force, the Newton

FORCE

The most familiar **force** we know is the force of gravity. For example, whenever we lift a stone, we must exert a muscular effort to overcome the gravitational force that continually pulls the stone downwards. The magnitude of the force of gravity depends upon the mass of the body and where it is located. For bodies that are relatively close to the surface of the earth (within 20 km, say) the force is given by the approximate equations:

EQ. 1.1
EQ. 1.2

SI UNITS	IMPERIAL UNITS
$F = 9.8\ m$ $\qquad(1.1)$	$F = m$ $\qquad(1.2)$
where	where
F = force of gravity, in newtons (N)	F = force of gravity, in pounds force (lbf)
m = mass of body, in kilograms (kg)	m = mass of body, in pounds (lb)

There are other kinds of forces, such as the force exerted by a stretched spring, or the force we exert when pushing a stalled car. All these forces are expressed in terms of the newton (symbol N), which is the SI unit of force.

1.4 Torque, the Newton Metre (N.m)

TORQUE

Whenever a force acts on a body so as to make it twist or rotate (or tend to rotate), the body is said to be subjected to a **torque.** Torque is equal to the product of the force times the perpendicular distance between the axis of rotation and the direction of the force. For example, consider a cable wrapped around a winch having a radius r (Fig. 1.1). If the pull (force) on the cable is F, the torque exerted is given by:

EQ. 1.3
EQ. 1.4

SI UNITS	IMPERIAL UNITS
$T = Fr$ $\qquad(1.3)$	$T = Fr$ $\qquad(1.4)$
where	where
T = torque, in newton metres (N.m)	T = torque, in foot pounds force (ft.lbf)
F = force, in newtons (N)	F = force, in pounds force (lbf)
r = radius, in metres (m)	r = radius, in feet (ft)

▼ **Figure 1.1**

Torque = Fr

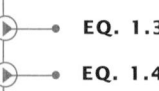

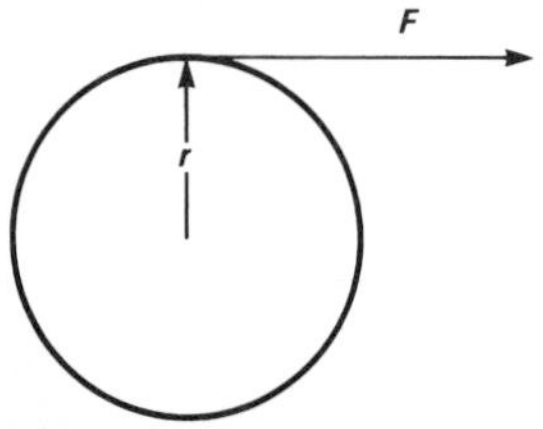

Gasoline engines and electric motors develop a torque because whenever they are coupled to a mechanical load they exert a twisting action, causing the load to rotate.

Table 1B   MULTIPLES AND SUBMULTIPLES OF SI UNITS

PREFIX	MULTIPLIER	SYMBOL	EXAMPLE
exa	10^{18}	E	2 exametres $= 2 \times 10^{18}$ metres 2 Em $= 2 \times 10^{18}$ m
peta	10^{15}	P	3 petajoules $= 3 \times 10^{15}$ joules 3 PJ $= 3 \times 10^{15}$ J
tera	10^{12}	T	4 terawatts $= 4 \times 10^{12}$ watts 4 TW $= 4 \times 10^{12}$ W
giga	10^{9}	G	1 gigajoule $= 10^{9}$ joules 1 GJ $= 10^{9}$ J
mega	10^{6}	M	1 megapascal $= 10^{6}$ Pa 1 MPa $= 10^{6}$ Pa
kilo	10^{3} or 1000	k	3 kilometres $= 3000$ metres 3 km $= 3000$ m
hecto	10^{2} or 100	h	1 hectolitre $= 100$ litres 1 hL $= 100$ L
deca	10	da	1 decatesla $= 10$ teslas 1 daT $= 10$ T
deci	10^{-1} or 1/10	d	1 cubic decimetre $=$ (metre/10)^3 $=$ metre^3/1000 1 dm^3 $= 10^{-3}$ m^3
centi	10^{-2} or 1/100	c	4 centimetre $=$ (4/100) metre 4 cm $= 0.04$ m
milli	10^{-3} or 1/1000	m	1 millimetre $= 10^{-3}$ metre 1 mm $= 0.001$ m
micro	10^{-6}	μ	1 microfarad $= 10^{-6}$ farad 1 μF $= 10^{-6}$ F
nano	10^{-9}	n	1 nanosecond $= 10^{-9}$ second 1 ns $= 10^{-9}$ s
pico	10^{-12}	p	1 picoampere $= 10^{-12}$ ampere 1 pA $= 10^{-12}$ A
femto	10^{-15}	f	1 femtometre $= 10^{-15}$ metre 1 fm $= 10^{-15}$ m
atto	10^{-18}	a	1 attojoule $= 10^{-18}$ joule 1 aJ $= 10^{-18}$ J

EXAMPLE 1.1

A motor develops a starting torque of 150 ft.lbf. If the pulley on the shaft has a diameter of 1 ft, calculate the braking force needed to prevent the motor from turning.

SOLUTION:

Because the radius is 0.5 ft, the required braking force is:

$F = T/r = 150$ ft.lbf/0.5 ft $= 300$ lbf

If the radius of the pulley were 2 ft, a braking force of 75 lbf would be enough to prevent the motor from starting.

1.5 Work, the Joule (J)

Work is a very common word, but in mechanics it has a very precise meaning. Mechanical work is said to be done when a force F moves through a distance d, with the distance measured in the same direction as the force. The work is given by the equations:

EQ. 1.5

EQ. 1.6

SI UNITS	IMPERIAL UNITS
$W = Fd$ (1.5)	$W = Fd$ (1.6)
where	where
W = work done, in joules (J)	W = work done, in foot pounds force (ft.lbf)
F = force, in newtons (N)	F = force, in pounds force (lbf)
d = distance, in metres (m)	d = distance, in feet (ft)

The SI unit of work is the joule (symbol J). It is equal to the work done when a force of 1 newton moves through a distance of 1 metre.

EXAMPLE 1.2

A person weighing 50 kg walks up a flight of stairs whose vertical height is 12 m (Fig. 1.2). What is the work done by the person?

SOLUTION:

1. The force of gravity acting downwards on the person is:
   $F = 9.8\ m = 9.8 \times 50 = 490$ newtons = 490 N
2. The work done is:
   $W = Fd = 490 \times 12 = 5880$ joules = 5880 J

EXAMPLE 1.3

A 500 lb mass is lifted through a height of 60 feet (Fig. 1.3). Calculate the work done.

SOLUTION:

In the Imperial system of units, the force of gravity, expressed in pounds force, is numerically equal to the mass, in pounds.

The force of gravity on the 500 lb mass is therefore equal to 500 pounds force. The work done is:

$W = Fd = 500$ lbf $\times$ 60 ft = 30 000 ft.lbf

▼ Figure 1.2

See Example 1.2.

▼ Figure 1.3

See Example 1.3.

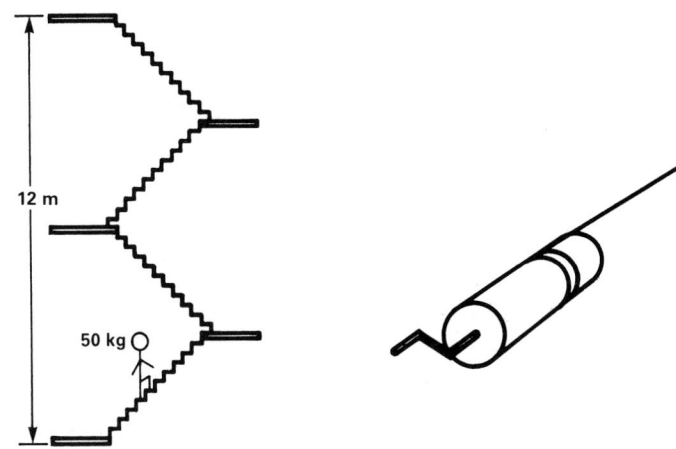

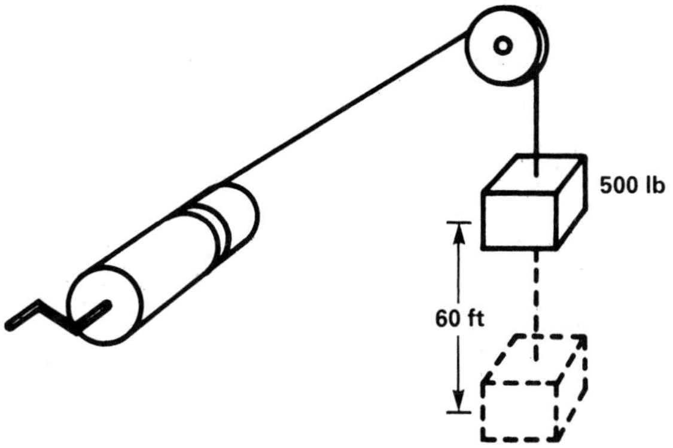

1.6 Power, the Watt (W)

Power is also a common word, but again, in mechanics, it has a very precise meaning. Power is the rate of doing work. It is given by the equations:

POWER

SI UNITS	IMPERIAL UNITS
$P = W/t$ (1.7)	$P = W/33000t$ (1.8)

EQ. 1.7

EQ. 1.8

where	where
P = power, in watts (W)	P = power, in horsepower (hp)
W = work done, in joules (J)	W = work done, in foot pounds force (ft.lbf)
t = time, in seconds (s)	t = time, in minutes (min)

The SI unit of power is the watt (symbol W). We often use the kilowatt (kW), equal to 1000 W, or the megawatt (mW), equal to one million watts. The power output of motors is usually expressed in horsepower (hp), an Imperial unit that is equal to 746 W. In the SI, however, the mechanical power of a motor is expressed in watts, even if the motor happens to be a diesel engine. Furthermore, in the SI, the rate of heat loss of a radiator, or of any warm body, is also expressed in watts. As a result, whether power is electrical, mechanical, or thermal, its value is always expressed in watts. This is one of the important simplifications afforded by the SI.

EXAMPLE 1.4

An elevator motor lifts a mass of 3730 kg through a height of 40 m in 7 s (Fig. 1.4). Calculate the power developed by the motor, in kilowatts and in horsepower.

continued

SOLUTION:

1. The lifting force is:

    $F = 9.8 \, m = 9.8 \times 3730 = 36\,554$ N (N for newtons)

2. The work done is:

    $W = Fd = 36\,554 \times 40 = 1\,462\,160$ J (J for joules)

3. The power is:

    $P = W/t = 1\,462\,160/7 = 208\,880$ W $= 208.88$ kW

4. Expressed in horsepower:

    $P = 208\,880/746 = 280$ hp

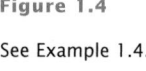

Figure 1.4

See Example 1.4.

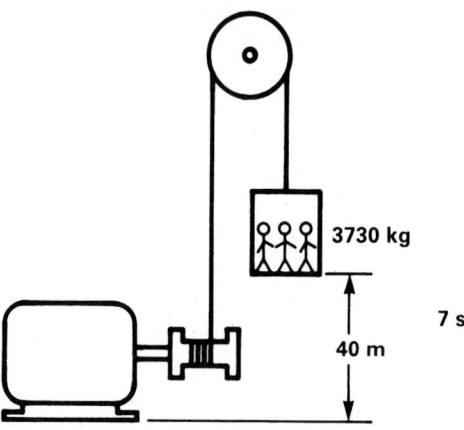

EXAMPLE 1.5

An electric locomotive exerts a pull of 1200 lbf while moving along at a speed of 40 miles per hour (Fig. 1.5). Calculate the power developed by the driving motors (note that 1 mile = 5280 ft).

SOLUTION:

1. Work done in one hour is:

    $W = Fd = 1200 \times 40 \times 5280 = 253.44 \times 10^6$ ft.lbf

2. The power is:

    $P = W/33\,000t = 253.44 \times 10^6/33\,000 \times 60 = 128$ hp

Figure 1.5

See Example 1.5.

1.7   Prony Brake

The mechanical power of a motor depends upon the torque it develops, and its speed of rotation. The power is given by the equations:

SI UNITS	IMPERIAL UNITS
$P = nT/9.55$ (1.9)	$P = nT/5252$ (1.10)
where	where
P = mechanical power, in watts (W)	P = mechanical power, in horse power (hp)
n = speed, in revolutions per minute (r/min)	n = speed, in revolutions per min (r/min)
T = torque, in newton metres (N.m)	T = torque, in foot pounds force (ft.lbf)
9.55 = constant, to take care of units	5252 = constant, to take care of units

EQ. 1.9

EQ. 1.10

We can both load up and measure the mechanical power of a motor by means of a prony brake. In its simplest form, it consists of a flat pulley mounted on the shaft of the motor, and a braking device. The device possesses brake shoes that rub on the surface of the pulley. The resultant braking force is transmitted to a radius arm having a length r (Fig. 1.6). The braking action can be increased or decreased by tightening or slackening a thumb-screw V. A spring balance measures the force F exerted at the distance r from the centre of the motor shaft. Consequently, the product Fr gives the torque developed by the motor while it is running. A tachometer measures the speed n, and so the power output can immediately be calculated, using Eq. 1.9 or 1.10.

The mechanical power of the motor is entirely converted into heat, and so the pulley heats up very quickly unless it is cooled by some means.

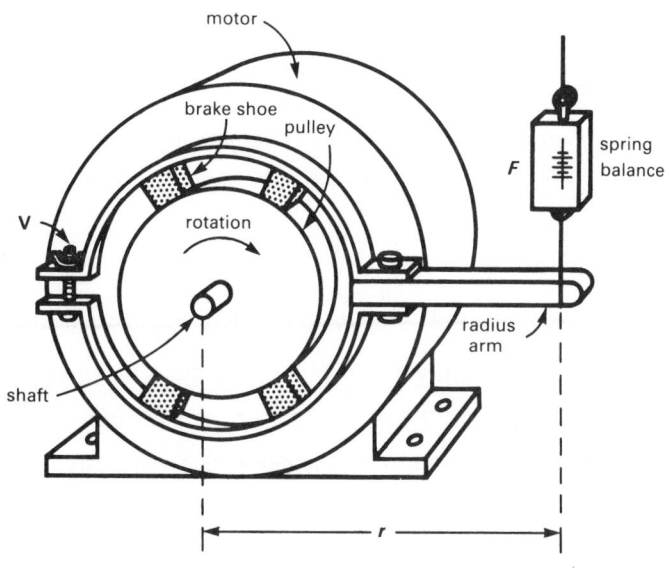

Figure 1.6

A motor can be loaded up and its power measured by means of a prony brake.

EXAMPLE 1.6

During a prony brake test on a 5 hp motor, the following readings were taken: $F = 6$ lbf, $r = 14$ inches, $n = 1720$ r/min. Calculate the torque and power developed by the motor under these conditions.

SOLUTION:

$T = Fr = 6$ lbf $\times 14/12$ ft $= 7$ ft.lbf

$P = nT/5252 = 1720 \times 7/5252 = 2.29$ hp

The motor is not fully loaded because it could actually develop a rated power output of 5 hp. To increase the power output, screw V must be tightened so that the brake shoes press more firmly against the pulley.

EXAMPLE 1.7

A small synchronous motor running at 1800 r/min has a nominal power output of 120 W. If the prony brake arm has a length of 10 cm, calculate the braking force F needed so that the motor develops its rated power output.

SOLUTION:

1. $P = nT/9.55$; therefore $120 = 1800\ T/9.55$
    and so T $= 0.637$ N.m
2. $T = Fr$; therefore $0.637 = F \times 10/100$
    and so $F = 6.37$ N

The required scale reading is 6.37 N or about 1.43 lbf. (Note that from Appendix B or Table 1A, 1 lbf = 4.448 N.)

1.8 Energy, the Joule (J)

A body is said to possess energy whenever it is capable of doing work. Indeed, all work is produced as a result of using up energy. Energy can exist in one of the forms listed below:

1. Mechanical energy (energy in a waterfall, a coiled spring, or a moving car).

2. Thermal energy (heat released by a stove, by friction, or by the sun).

3. Chemical energy (energy contained in dynamite, coal, or an electric storage battery).

4. Electrical energy (energy produced by a generator or manifested by lightning).

5. Atomic energy (energy released when the nucleus of an atom is split).

Because energy can be made to do work, energy is essentially work that is stored up. Consequently, energy, like work, is expressed in joules. We therefore come to the remarkable result that all forms of energy — mechanical, electrical, chemical, atomic, and thermal — can be expressed in the same SI unit, the joule (J).

1.9 Transformation of Energy

The law of conservation states that energy neither can be created nor destroyed. However, energy can be converted from one form to another by means of appropriate devices called *machines*. In Fig. 1.7, for example, the chemical energy contained in coal may be transformed into thermal energy by burning the coal in a steam boiler. The thermal energy contained in the steam can be transformed into mechanical energy by using a turbine. Finally, mechanical energy can be transformed into electrical energy by means of a generator. In this example, the boiler, turbine, and generator are the machines that do the energy transformation.

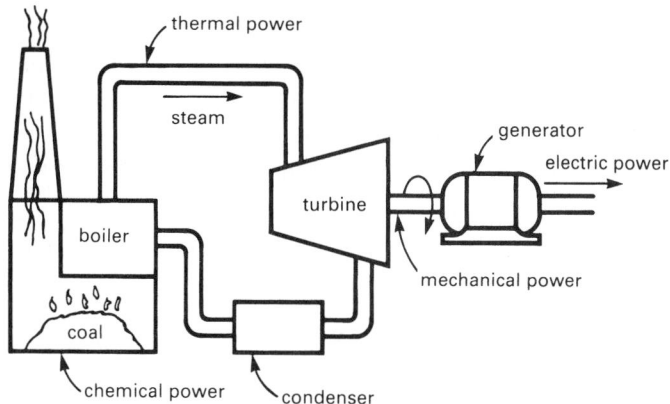

Figure 1.7

Energy is converted from one form to another by means of machines.

Unfortunately, whenever energy is transformed, the output is always less than the input because all machines have losses. These losses appear in the form of heat, causing the temperature of the machine to rise. In the case of an electric motor (Fig. 1.8) the mechanical power output (expressed in watts) is less than the electrical power input (also expressed in watts). The difference between the two increases as the motor is loaded up, which means that the losses become greater with increasing load. It follows that a motor is hotter when running at full load than at no-load. Furthermore, if the motor is loaded beyond its rated capacity, the losses may become so great that the motor overheats and the windings may burn out. This fundamental fact applies to all electric machines, no matter how they are constructed or how big they are.

1.10 Efficiency of a Machine

The **efficiency** of a machine is the ratio of the power output it delivers to the power input it receives. Because the power output is always less than the input, the

EFFICIENCY

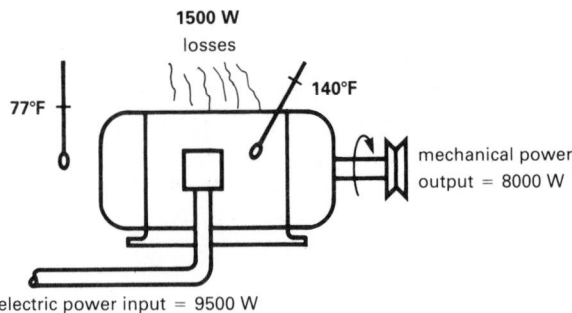

Figure 1.8

The losses in a motor cause its temperature to rise above the ambient temperature.

efficiency must be less than one. The efficiency is usually given in percent and its value is calculated by the equation:

EQ. 1.11

$$eff = 100\ P_o\ /\ P_i$$

where

eff = efficiency, in percent (%)
P_o = power output of machine, in watts (W)
P_i = power input of machine, in watts (W)

For a given machine, say a 10 hp electric motor, the efficiency varies with the load. It starts from zero at no-load, increases rapidly as the load increases, and then stays almost flat over a considerable load range. If the machine is loaded much above its normal rating, the efficiency again begins to fall, but only slightly. This typical variation of efficiency with load is shown by the graph of Fig. 1.9.

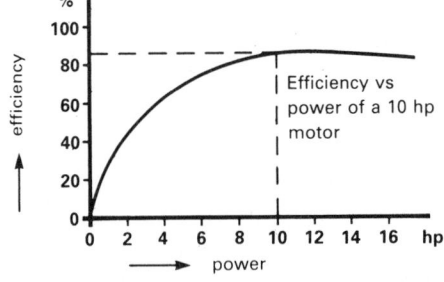

Figure 1.9

Typical efficiency versus power output of a 10 hp motor.

The efficiency of electric motors improves with size. Thus, a 1/4 hp motor has a full-load efficiency of about 60 percent, whereas a 10 000 hp motor has an efficiency of about 98 percent. Small may be beautiful, but it is always accompanied by low efficiency. For example, the motor in an electric razor has an efficiency of about 10 percent, and there is no way it can be significantly improved.

EXAMPLE 1.8

A 150 hp motor has a full-load efficiency of 91 percent. Calculate the electric power it consumes, and the losses at full load.

continued

SOLUTION:

1. The mechanical power output is:
   P_o = 150 hp = 150 × 746 = 111 900 W
2. The electric power input is:
   P_i = P_o/eff = 111 900/0.91 = 122 967 W
3. The losses are:
   $P_i - P_o$ = (122 967 − 111 900) = 11 067 W = 11.0 kW

1.11 Temperature Rise and Temperature Scales

When a body produces heat, its temperature rises above that of its surroundings. The difference between the temperature of the body and the ambient temperature is called *temperature rise.* Thus, if the temperature of a motor winding is 87°C, when the ambient temperature is 20°C, the temperature rise of the winding is (87 − 20) = 67°C. In order to ensure that electrical equipment will last a long time, upper limits have been set on temperature rise. For example, the temperature rise of transformer windings is usually limited to 55°C when the coils are immersed in oil. On the other hand, the permissible temperature rise may be as high as 105°C for specially insulated dry-type transformer windings.

The SI unit of temperature (and of temperature rise) is the degree Celsius (°C). The relationship between the SI and the Imperial unit of temperature is given by:

$$F = 1.8\ C + 32$$

EQ. 1.12

where

F = temperature, in degrees Fahrenheit (°F)
C = temperature, in degrees Celsius (°C)

EXAMPLE 1.9

A thermometer placed on a motor frame (Fig. 1.8) registers a temperature of 140°F. The ambient temperature is 77°F. Express these temperatures in °C, and calculate the temperature rise.

continued

SOLUTION:

1. The temperature of the motor frame is:
   $F = 1.8\ C + 32$
   $140 = 1.8\ C + 32$
   $C = (140 − 32)/1.8 = 108/1.8 = 60°C$

2. The ambient temperature is:

$F = 1.8\ C - 32$

$77 = 1.8\ C + 32$

$C = (77 - 32)/1.8 = 45/1.8 = 25°C$

3. The temperature rise of the frame is:

$60 - 25 = 35°C$ or $140 - 77 = 63°F$

1.12 Kinetic Energy

KINETIC ENERGY

A fast-moving train, a falling stone, or a revolving flywheel all possess a form of stored mechanical energy called **kinetic energy**. The amount of energy depends upon the mass and speed of the body: the heavier it is and the faster it goes, the greater its kinetic energy.

The kinetic energy in a moving body does not come out of the blue, but is due to the mechanical work that was previously done upon it. In other words, to bring any body up to speed, we must do mechanical work. If there is no friction or any other braking force, the amount of kinetic energy is exactly equal to the mechanical work that was previously supplied. For a given body, the kinetic energy increases as the square of the speed. Thus, if the speed is tripled, the stored kinetic energy increases nine times.

What are some of the consequences of kinetic energy? We have all observed that when we cut the power to an electric motor, the rotor and its connected load continue to turn for a certain time. If the friction is small and the rotating parts are heavy, it may take several minutes before the system comes to a halt. In effect, the system continues to run as long as it has kinetic energy. As the speed falls, the kinetic energy decreases progressively, until it finally becomes zero when the motor stops. The loss in kinetic energy, from start to finish, is exactly equal to the heat produced by friction. We can bring the system to a faster stop by increasing the friction, or braking torque. Nevertheless, the drop in kinetic energy is still the same, and consequently the total amount of heat produced remains unchanged.

Owing to the phenomenon of kinetic energy, it is impossible to bring a motor up to speed in zero time. Similarly, we cannot cause it to stop in zero time. The reason is that the accelerating torque and the braking torque would have to be infinite in each case.

1.13 Typical Torque-Speed Curves

The torque developed by machines such as electric motors, gasoline engines, and pneumatic motors usually varies with the speed. Figure 1.10 shows the typical torque-speed curve of a gasoline engine when operating at a fixed setting of the throttle. Note that when the speed is zero, the torque is also zero; consequently a gasoline engine must be equipped with a starter to get it going. The torque then increases with the speed, reaching a maximum of 300 N.m at 2000 r/min. Beyond this peak, the torque decreases gradually and finally becomes zero at 10 000 r/min.

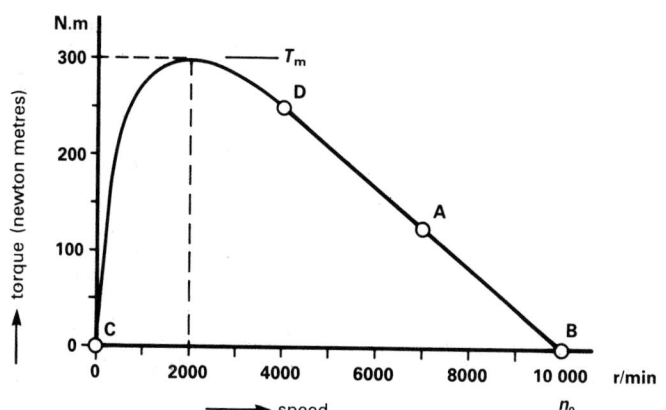

Figure 1.10

Torque-speed curve of a
gasoline engine.

The engine develops its rated power output (in horsepower) at operating point A. When it runs at no load, the operating point is B. Under normal conditions, the engine runs between no-load and full-load, which is to say somewhere along line AB. The engine can, however, deliver more than its rated power for brief periods. Such an overload situation corresponds to point D.

The torque-speed curve of an electric motor is quite similar. For example, Fig. 1.11 shows the characteristic of a three-phase induction motor. However, unlike the gasoline engine, this motor develops a substantial torque at zero speed (point C). Consequently, it is a self-starting motor.

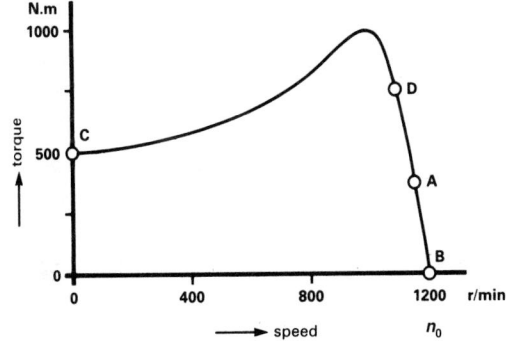

Figure 1.11

Torque-speed curve of an
induction motor.

One interesting feature is that the operating characteristic between no-load and full-load (line AB) is essentially a straight line in both cases. This linear torque-speed characteristic holds true for all electric motors.

Portion CDA of the curve represents the starting characteristic of the motor (Fig. 1.11), or of the gasoline engine (Fig. 1.10). This characteristic is important because it tells us the maximum load that can be brought up to speed. However, the starting characteristic is only important during the short time the motor is accelerating.

1.14 Power Output and Torque-Speed Curves

According to Eqs. 1.9 and 1.10, the power output of a motor is proportional to the product of its torque T and speed n. This simple fact enables us to visualize the power that a motor develops, by looking at its torque-speed curve. Referring to Fig. 1.12, suppose we select any operating point (1). The corresponding torque is T_1 and the corresponding speed is n_1. The power which the motor develops at this point is proportional to the product T_1 times n_1. But this product is equal to the area of the dotted rectangle in Fig 1.12. Consequently, the area of the rectangle is a measure of the power that the motor develops.

Figure 1.12

The power output of a motor can be visualized by means of the dotted rectangle.

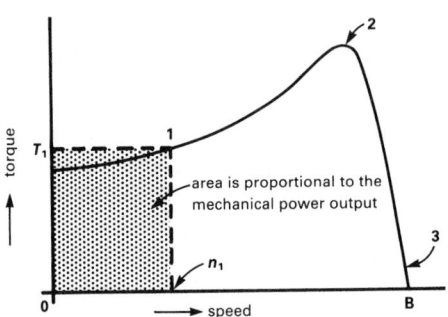

As we move along the curve, the successive "power" rectangles change in size. This gives us a visual means of evaluating the mechanical power the motor develops. Thus, as we move along the torque-speed curve of Fig 1.12, we can actually "see" that the power at low speeds (1) is small, that it reaches a maximum at operating point (2), and that it again falls off at point (3). Finally, the output power vanishes (the rectangle has zero area) when the motor reaches no-load point B.

1.15 Load Torque

Mechanical loads, just like motors, often possess distinctive torque-speed curves. Note, for example, the T–n curves of a fan and of a reciprocating pump (Figs. 1.13, 1.14).

▼ Figure 1.13

Torque-speed curve of a fan.

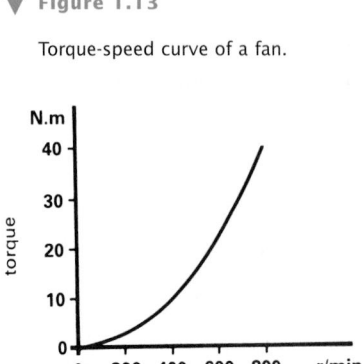

▼ Figure 1.14

Torque-speed curve of a reciprocating pump.

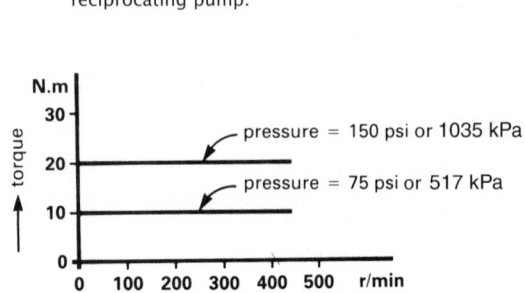

However, some loads, such as punch-presses, lathes, vibrators, and saws, have highly unusual torque-speed characteristics that cannot be described by a single curve. The reason is that such loads cover a whole spectrum of torques and speeds. Nevertheless, at any instant, the mechanical power absorbed by a load is given by Eqs. 1.9 or 1.10, where T and n are the *instantaneous* torque and speed.

1.16 Acceleration and Deceleration of a Motor and its Load

A motor and its load together constitute a system which obeys some simple, but important, mechanical laws. These laws may be stated as follows:

1. The speed of the motor is always equal to that of the load. This is so because the motor shaft is assumed to be directly coupled to the load shaft.

2. If the motor torque exceeds the load torque, the speed will increase. The reason is that the power developed by the motor then exceeds the power demanded by the load. The excess mechanical power causes the system to accelerate, which increases its kinetic energy.

3. If the motor torque is less than the load torque, the speed will decrease. The reason is that the power developed by the motor is now less than that demanded by the load. The system decelerates and in so doing it releases kinetic energy. The power absorbed by the load is then equal to the power delivered by the motor, *plus* the power released by the falling kinetic energy of the system.

4. If the motor torque is equal to the load torque, the speed remains constant. We repeat: when the torque developed by the motor is equal to the torque exerted by the load, the speed remains constant. The system does not come to a halt, as we might be inclined to believe.

With reference to items 2 and 3 above, how quickly does the speed change when the torque developed by the motor is not equal to the load torque? It depends upon two things:

a) the difference between the torques: the bigger the difference, the faster the speed will change.

b) the so-called inertia of the revolving parts: the bigger the inertia, the slower the speed will change.

A large rotor or a heavy, massive load possesses a lot of inertia, and such revolving masses do not quickly change their speed. For example, it may take several minutes to bring a large flywheel up to speed, even if the bearings are frictionless.

1.17 Summary

Upon completion of this chapter you should have learned that:

• The SI system of units is a metric system based upon the metre, kilogram, and second. It is important that you be able to convert between the SI system and the Imperial system.

- Energy is the ability to perform work. Work is performed when a force is moved through a distance. Power is the rate at which work is performed.

- The torque and speed relationship of an electric induction motor depends on the type of load being driven.

- The efficiency of a system is the ratio of the input power to the output power.

- If the torque of a motor exceeds the load torque, the motor speed will increase; if the motor torque is less than the load torque, the motor speed will decrease.

Key Terms

EFFICIENCY: The output power of a system or machine measured as a percentage of the input power.

FORCE: The effect of gravity acting on a mass.

IMPERIAL SYSTEM OF UNITS: A measurement system based upon the foot, pound, and second.

INTERNATIONAL SYSTEM OF UNITS (SI): A measurement system based upon the metre, kilogram, and second.

KINETIC ENERGY: The energy stored in a moving body, such as falling water, a floating balloon, or a rotating motor; the amount of energy stored is related to the speed of the moving body.

POWER: A measure of the rate at which work is performed.

TORQUE: Force operating in a twisting motion, such as the rotating force of a motor shaft.

Test Your Knowledge

1.1   The foot is an SI unit.

   true_____   false _____

1.2   The prefix kilo stands for
   a. 100   b. 36
   c. 1000   d. 1/1000

1.3   The prefix mega stands for
   a. 144   b. 10^6
   c. 10 000   d. 0.001

1.4   A length of 2 m is equal to
   a. 2 miles   b. 200 cm
   c. 20 mm   d. 6 ft

1.5   The symbol r/min stands for
   a. revolution per minute
   b. return per minute
   c. minimum radius
   d. radian per minute

1.6   The SI units of mass and force are respectively
   a. gram and kilogram
   b. kilogram and pascal
   c. kilogram and joule
   d. kilogram and newton

1.7   When we tighten a bolt with a wrench, the bolt is subjected to
   a. a force   b. a pressure
   c. a torque   d. power

1.8   When we push hard against a brick wall, we do a lot of work.

   true_____   false _____

1.9   The SI unit of mechanical power is expressed in
   a. newton metres   b. watts
   c. horsepower   d. joules

1.10   One horsepower is equivalent to
      a. 100 W   b. 400 N.m
      c. 746 W   d. 476 W

1.11   A prony brake is used to
      a. prevent a machine from turning
      b. measure the power of a spring
      c. measure the power of a motor
      d. produce heat

1.12   A machine is a device that can
      a. convert one form of energy into another
      b. do useful work
      c. rotate when power is applied
      d. run by itself

1.13   A machine that has an efficiency of 60 percent has a loss of
      a. 30 percent   b. 0.6
      c. 40 percent   d. torque

1.14   A car runs at a speed of 30 km/h. If its speed increases to 90 km/h, the kinetic energy increases
      a. 3 times   b. 27 times
      c. 9 times   d. not at all

1.15   Referring to Fig. 1.13, the torque at 600 r/min is about
      a. 20 N.m   b. 10 N.m
      c. 75 psi   d. 20 psi

1.16   The pump in Fig. 1.14 is operating at 400 r/min and against a pressure of 150 psi. The torque is
      a. 20 N.m   b. 10 N.m
      c. 75 psi   d. 20 psi

1.17   An electric motor drives a load at a speed of 1600 r/min. The motor exerts a torque of 60 N.m, and the load torque is 70 N.m. Under these conditions, the speed of the motor (and load) is
      a. steady at 1600 r/min
      b. increasing
      c. decreasing
      d. accelerating

1.18   A motor develops 500 hp. The equivalent power in SI units is
      a. 0.6702 W   b. 373 kW
      c. 373 kJ   d. 373 kg

1.19   A speed of 1800 r/min is equal to
      a. 109 000 r/h
      b. 30 r/h
      c. 30 r/s
      d. 1800 kHz

1.20   An automobile has a mass of 1200 kg. It exerts a downward force on the road equal to
      a. 1200 kg
      b. 11.76 kN
      c. 2600 lbf

1.21   A wrench 10 cm long exerts a torque of 12 N.m. The pull exerted on the wrench is
      a. 120 kg
      b. 12.24 kg
      c. 120 N

1.22   For Fig. 1.2 express the mass and height in SI units.
      a. 1102 kg; 18.29 m
      b. 226.7 kg; 18.29 m
      c. 196.8 m; 1102 kg

1.23   An electric motor draws 20 kW from a line for a period of 8 h. The energy absorbed by the motor is
      a. 2.5 kW/h
      b. 9.6 MJ
      c. 576 MJ

1.24   The motor shown in Fig. 1.6 is turning at 1700 r/min, and the scale reading is 25 N. If the radius arm $r = 30$ cm, the mechanical power of the motor is
      a. 1335 W
      b. 18 hp
      c. 12.75 kW

1.25   In Fig. 1.8, the efficiency of the motor is
      a. 84.2%
      b. 0.1875
      c. 57.14 W/°F

1.26   A room temperature of 77°F
corresponds to
a. 25°C
b. 60.55°C
c. 170.6°C

1.27   In Fig. 1.10, point D corresponds
to 4000 r/min and 250 N.m.
Calculate the mechanical power
of the engine.
a. 104.7 hp
b. 190.4 hp
c. 104.7 kW

1.28   Point A in Fig. 1.10 corresponds to
7000 r/min and 150 N.m. The power
developed by the engine at point A is
greater than that at point D.

        true _____   false _____

1.29   In Fig. 1.12, as we move along the
torque-speed curve from point 1 to
point 3, the mechanical power increases progressively.

        true _____   false _____

1.30   In Fig. 1.14, it takes more power to
drive the pump at 400 r/min and a
pressure of 75 psi than at 300 r/min
and 150 psi.

        true _____   false _____

2

The Nature of Electricity

LEARNING OBJECTIVES

Upon completion of this chapter you will be able to:

- Describe the structure of the atom
- Explain the nature of insulators and conductors
- Explain the nature of voltage and current
- State and apply Ohm's law
- Determine the power consumed by a load
- Determine the rate at which power is dissipated by a load
- List several ways of storing energy

2.1 Introduction

In describing circuits and machines, we will continually be using terms such as voltage, current, resistance, electric power, and electric energy. This chapter explains the meaning of these terms and how they are related. The relationship can be expressed by a few simple equations, the most important of which is Ohm's law.

Chapter Outline

2.2 Composition of Matter, Atoms, and Molecules

Let us take a block of aluminum and break it in two. Then let us select one of the pieces and again break it in two. If we were able to continue this process millions and millions of times, we would eventually reach a point at which it would be impossible to subdivide the tiny speck of aluminum any further without altering its fundamental properties. In other words, if we were to subdivide it one more time, the resulting fragments would no longer be aluminum. This smallest possible bit of aluminum is called an **atom** of aluminum.

ATOM

All substances—such as aluminum, carbon, copper, hydrogen, and oxygen—are composed of atoms, each having a particular structure that is characteristic of the substance. For most substances, however, the smallest possible bit is a *molecule.* A molecule is composed of two, three, or more atoms that act together as a group. Thus, a molecule of water is composed of two atoms of hydrogen and one atom of oxygen. A molecule of salt is composed of one atom of sodium and one atom of chlorine. Finally, a molecule of rubber consists of at least 5000 atoms of carbon and 8000 atoms of hydrogen strung out in a continuous chain.

2.3 Structure of the Atom, Nucleus, and Electrons

If we could look inside an atom, we would see that it is composed of a small, dense, central core surrounded by light, fast-moving particles rotating around the core, like planets around the sun. The core is called the **nucleus** of the atom, and the rotating particles are called electron*s*. Each electron carries a negative charge. This is the smallest electric charge that is known to exist. The nucleus carries a positive electric charge, equal to the sum of the negative charges of the orbiting electrons. It follows that the atom is electrically neutral because the negative charges exactly balance the positive charges. Experiments have shown that electric charges having the same sign repel each other, and opposite signs attract. Consequently, a force of attraction exists between each electron and the central nucleus. However, the force is greatest on those electrons that are closest to the nucleus.

NUCLEUS

The electrons fly around the nucleus in one or more distinct orbits. The first orbit is said to be full when it contains 2 electrons. The second and third orbits are full when they contain respectively 8 and 18 electrons. An atom of aluminum possesses three distinct orbits containing 2, 8, and 3 electrons (Fig. 2.1). It follows that its nucleus has a charge of $+13$. On the other hand, an atom of copper contains 29 electrons, one of which occupies the fourth orbit (Fig. 2.2).

▼ **Figure 2.1**

Atom of aluminum.

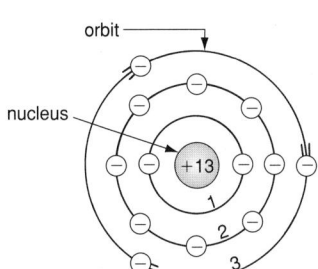

▼ **Figure 2.2**

Atom of copper.

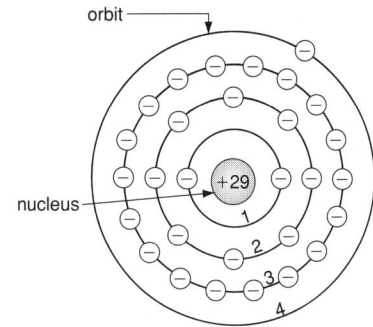

2.4 Free Electrons

We saw that an atom of aluminum has only 3 electrons in its outer orbit, compared with the "normal" number of 18. Because this outer orbit is far from being complete and the electrons it contains are distant from the nucleus, the electrons of this orbit are only weakly bound to the nucleus. The result is that in a solid piece of aluminum, these relatively **free electrons** continually jump from one atom to the next. They zigzag in every direction at high speed (Fig. 2.3). However, despite their high velocity, these free electrons never leave the piece of metal, and so the sum of the positive charges on the stationary nuclei are still balanced by the sum of the negative charges on all the electrons. As a result, the piece of aluminum remains electrically neutral. Figure 2.3 is obviously not drawn to scale because it is known that one cubic millimetre of aluminum contains nearly 10^{20} (100 000 000 000 000 000 000) free electrons. This does not include the electrons in the first and second orbits that are permanently bound to an individual nucleus.

FREE ELECTRON

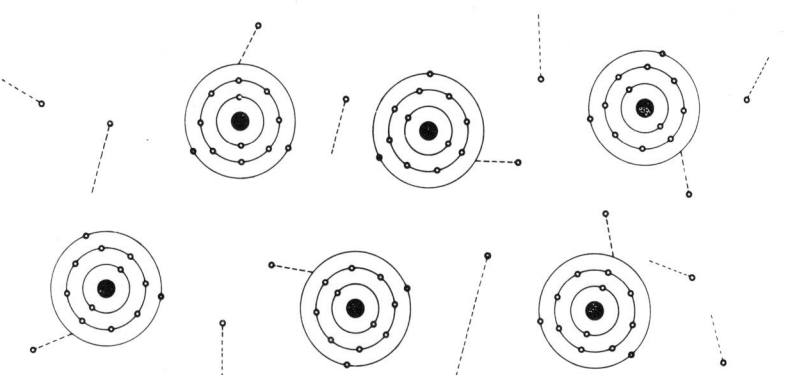

Figure 2.3

Free electrons moving inside a piece of aluminum.

If we forcibly remove some of the free electrons from a piece of aluminum, the positive charge on the nuclei is no longer balanced by the negative charge on the electrons, and so the net charge of the piece of aluminum is positive. Similarly, if we add electrons to a block of aluminum that is initially neutral, the block will possess a net negative charge.

Thus, any body is positive or negative depending upon whether it has a deficiency or a surplus of electrons.

2.5 Conductors and Insulators

Materials such as copper, aluminum, and iron contain billions upon billions of free electrons because the electrons in the outer orbits of individual atoms are only weakly bound to the nucleus. On the other hand, materials such as rubber, air, and oil have a strong hold on all their electrons — even those in the outer orbits of individual atoms. Such materials possess very few free electrons.

CONDUCTOR ●⎯ Materials having many free electrons are said to be good **conductors** of electricity.

INSULATOR ●⎯ Materials having very few free electrons are poor conductors of electricity. They are called **insulators**.

The number of free electrons per cubic centimetre is precisely the factor that determines whether a material is a good conductor of electricity or an insulator. Electrons move freely in a conductor and only with great difficulty in an insulator. Thus, if an insulator is placed between two conductors, it will prevent any movement of free electrons between them. Metals, in general, are excellent conductors.

2.6 Unit of Electric Charge, the Coulomb (C)

The electric charge on an electron is so small that it is preferable, in day-to-day calculations, to use a larger value. The practical unit of electric charge is called the coulomb (symbol C). It is equivalent to the charge of 6 241 450 380 000 000 000, or $6.241\ 450\ 38 \times 10^{18}$ electrons.

2.7 Sources of Electricity, Potential Difference (*E*)

How can we produce electricity? The secret is to establish a difference in the relative number of electrons between two points. Devices that are able to create a surplus of electrons at one point with respect to another point are called generators (or *sources*) of electricity.

This unequal distribution of electrons between two points can be achieved in several ways. It can be done chemically, as in a dry cell; mechanically, as in a rotating generator; thermally, as in a thermocouple; or optically, as in a photoelectric cell. In each case the point (or terminal) having a lack of electrons possesses a positive charge and a so-called positive polarity (+). Conversely, the point (or terminal) having a surplus of electrons possesses a negative charge and consequently a negative polarity (−).

Whenever one terminal of a device possesses a shortage of electrons and the other terminal a surplus, a difference of electric potential is said to exist between the terminals. It is represented by the symbol E. This difference of potential, or *electromotive force* (emf), may be considered to be a kind of electric pressure. By analogy, it may be compared to the difference of hydraulic pressure created between the inlet and outlet of a water pump. A generator can therefore be considered to be a sort of electron pump.

2.8 Unit of Potential Difference, the Volt (V)

The SI unit of electric potential difference (and of electromotive force) is the **volt** (symbol V). The kilovolt (kV) is a multiple of the volt, equal to 1000 V. Similarly, the millivolt (mV) is a submultiple of the volt, equal to 1/1000 V. The difference of potential, or voltage between two points, is measured with a voltmeter (Fig. 2.4).

VOLT

2.9 Electric Current (*I*)

Consider the storage cell in Fig. 2.5. The central terminal has a deficiency of electrons and it is therefore positive. On the other hand, the outer terminal has a surplus of electrons and so its polarity is negative. Because of this shortage and surplus of electrons, a voltage appears between the terminals. The voltage ranges between 1.5 V and 2 V, depending on the type of cell.

▼ **Figure 2.4a**

Panelboard ac voltmeter used in a utility company substation. *(Courtesy General Electric)*

▼ **Figure 2.4b**

Portable dc voltmeter having three scales: 150 V, 300 V, and 750 V. *(Courtesy Weston Instruments)*

Let us now connect a conductor of electricity across the terminals, as shown in Fig. 2.6. The surplus electrons at the negative terminal will repel the free electrons inside the conductor, urging them toward the positive terminal. At the same time, the positive terminal attracts these free electrons. The result is that the free electrons inside the conductor will begin to move from the negative to the positive terminal. They continue to zigzag at high speed, bumping from one atom to the next, but to this random motion is now added a gradual mass drift from the negative to the positive terminal. This mass drift of electrons is called an **electric current**. It is represented by the symbol I.

ELECTRIC CURRENT

Figure 2.5

A storage cell produces a difference of potential between its terminals.

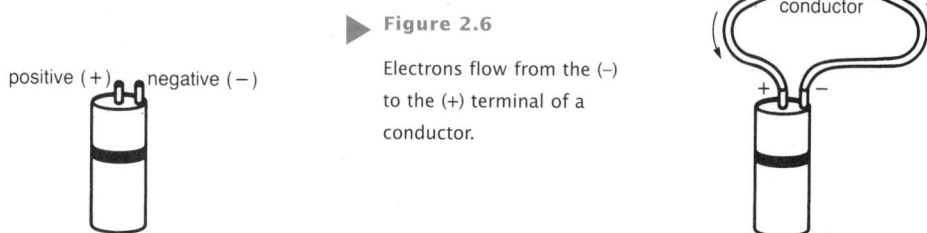

Figure 2.6

Electrons flow from the (−) to the (+) terminal of a conductor.

As shown in Fig. 2.6, the free electrons come out of the negative terminal of the cell and re-enter by the positive terminal. What happens to the electrons that enter the positive terminal? They flow through the body of the cell and eventually re-emerge at the negative terminal. Current flow is therefore a circular flow of electrons whereby they continuously move through the conductor, then through the source and back again. Inside the conductor, electrons move from the negative to the positive terminal. However, inside the source, they move from the positive to the negative terminal.

The path followed by the electrons as they flow from the negative terminal of the source to the positive terminal of the source is called an *electric circuit.* Thus, the combination of the cell and conductor shown in Fig. 2.6 constitutes an electric circuit.

2.10 Current Flow, the Ampere (A)

In the early 1750s Benjamin Franklin performed a number of electrical experiments, including his famous kite experiment. From his observations, Franklin reasoned that electricity flowed from positive to negative. Through the nineteenth century his ideas on the flow of electricity were used to explain the flow of current. Today we know that this *conventional* direction of current flow is opposite to the actual motion of the electrons. As scientists learned more about the structure of the atom in the late nineteenth and early twentieth centuries, it became obvious that current flowed from areas with an excess number of electrons, the negative terminal, to areas that were deficient in electrons, the positive terminal. This description of current flow is termed *electron flow*. We will use electron flow throughout this book (Fig. 2.6).

As you continue your study of electricity and take this knowledge to the workplace, you will encounter both current flow conventions. It is important to remember that the current flow convention used has no effect on how an electrical or electronic circuit behaves. In order to change from conventional current flow to electron current flow, one has only to change the direction of the arrow that indicates the direction of current flow. Everything else in the circuit or system remains the same.

Current flow in a conductor may be compared to the flow of water in a pipe, which can be measured in litres per second. Similarly, current flow can be measured in coulombs per second. By definition, when one coulomb of electricity moves past a point each second, the flow is equal to one ampere. The SI unit of current is the ampere (symbol A) and it is equivalent to the flow of 6.24×10^{18} electrons per second.

2.11 Measuring Voltage and Current; Voltmeter and Ammeter

Consider Fig. 2.7 in which an electric heater is connected to a source G. We can measure the current flow by inserting an ammeter directly into the line, so that all the electrons pass through the instrument. A pointer indicates the current flow in amperes. The ammeter is designed so that it does not appreciably change the current flow that existed before the ammeter was connected into the line.

To measure the difference of potential between the terminals of the heater, we connect a voltmeter across the terminals, as shown in Fig. 2.8. A pointer indicates the difference of potential in volts. A very tiny current flows through the voltmeter, but this current is negligible compared with the current flowing through the heater. Consequently, the voltmeter reading is very close to the difference of potential that existed between the terminals of the heater before the voltmeter was connected into the circuit.

It is important to remember that the circuit must be de-energized, and the line has to be "cut" in order to connect the current-measuring ammeter. The voltmeter, on the other hand, is simply connected across two terminals, without otherwise disturbing the circuit. *Caution*: an ammeter must never be connected, like a voltmeter, across the terminals of a source.

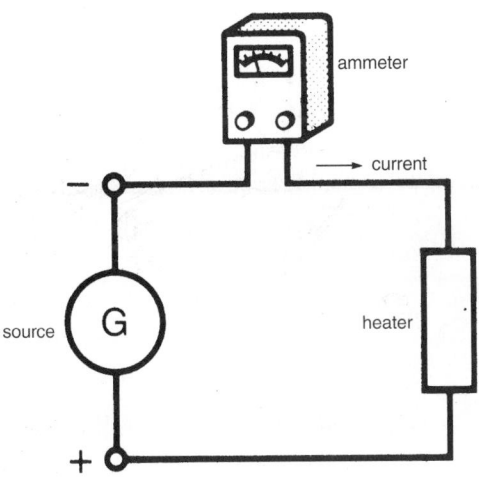

Figure 2.7

Current is measured with an ammeter.

Figure 2.8

The difference of potential is
measured with a voltmeter.

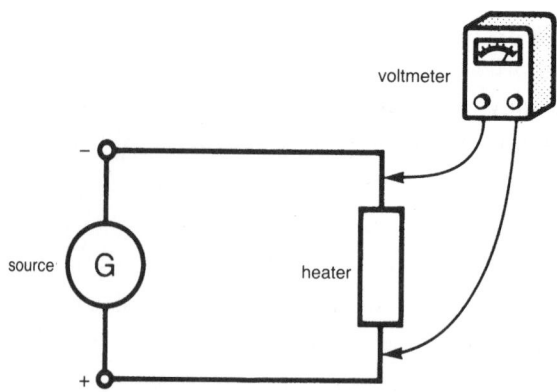

Multi-scale voltmeters and ammeters are available that can measure from micro-
volts to kilovolts and from microamperes to amperes. Some instruments have a
digital readout (Fig. 2.9); others use a pointer that moves across a calibrated scale
(Fig. 2.4).

2.12 Distinction between Sources and Loads

The flow of electric current enables us to identify a source and a load. A device that
receives electric current is called a load; a device that delivers electric current is a
source. But how can we tell whether a device is a source or a load? We can tell one
from the other by observing two things: (1) the polarity of the terminals and (2) the
direction of electron flow through the device.

The rule is very simple:

a)   If current flows out of the negative terminal, the device is a source.

b)   If current flows into the negative terminal, the device is a load.

Figure 2.11 shows an unusual electric circuit that contains devices we haven't studied yet. However, the direction of the currents and the polarities of the terminals
are given. Using the simple rule above, we immediately see that devices A, B, D are
sources, and devices C, E, F are loads. The sources deliver electric power and the
loads absorb it.

Figure 2.9

This multi-range volt-ohm-
milliameter has a digital
readout and an accuracy of
0.1%. *(Courtesy Weston
Instruments)*

2.13 Ohm's Law; the Ohm (Ω)

Consider a conductor of electricity, such as the heating element of an electric stove (Fig. 2.10). If we apply a voltage across its terminals, a certain current will flow. If we double the voltage, we discover that the current also doubles. Again, if we triple the voltage, the current triples, and so forth. The ratio of the voltage divided by the current is therefore a constant for this particular heater. We can therefore write:

$$V_{heater}/_{heater} = \text{constant (for this particular heater)}$$

The constant is a property of the heater which we call its **resistance**. The symbol for resistance is R. A heater that allows a large current to flow through it when a moderate voltage is applied across its terminals is said to have a low resistance. On the other hand, a heater (or other conductor) that allows only a small current to flow through it is said to have a high resistance.

RESISTANCE

This relationship between the voltage, current, and resistance of a conductor is known as Ohm's law. Ohm's law states:

$$R = V/I \qquad\qquad \text{EQ. 2.1}$$

where

V = voltage applied across the conductor, in volts (V)
I = resulting current that flows through the conductor, in amperes (A)
R = resistance of the conductor, in ohms (Ω)

The SI unit of resistance is the ohm (symbol Ω). By definition, the electric resistance between two terminals of a conductor is equal to one ohm when a constant difference of potential of one volt applied across the terminals produces a current of one ampere.

2.14   The Application of Ohm's Law

Now that we know Ohm's law relating V, I, and R, it is easy to find any one of these three values when we know the two others. Thus, from Eq. 2.1 we obtain two other equations:

$$I = \frac{V}{R} \quad \text{or} \quad \textbf{amperes} = \frac{\textbf{volts}}{\textbf{ohms}} \qquad\qquad \text{EQ. 2.2}$$

and

$$V = IR \quad \text{or} \quad \textbf{volts} = \textbf{amperes} \times \textbf{ohms} \qquad\qquad \text{EQ. 2.3}$$

EXAMPLE 2.1

An electric iron is connected to a 120 V source and the resulting current is 10 A. Calculate the resistance of the heater element.

continued

SOLUTION:

$$R = \frac{V}{I} = \frac{120 \text{ V}}{10 \text{ A}} = 12 \text{ ohms} = 12 \text{ }\Omega$$

EXAMPLE 2.2

A long copper wire having a resistance of 5 Ω carries a current of 20 A. Calculate the difference of potential across the ends of the wire.

SOLUTION:

$$V = IR = 20 \text{ A} \times 5 \text{ }\Omega = 100 \text{ V}$$

EXAMPLE 2.3

In Example 2.1, calculate the current flowing in the electric iron if the line voltage drops to 108 V.

SOLUTION:

The resistance of the electric iron is a property of the device which, like its weight or colour, is fixed. Because $R = 12 \text{ }\Omega$, we can write:

$$I = V/R = 108 \text{ V}/12 \text{ }\Omega = 9 \text{ A}$$

2.15 Electric Power, the Watt (W)

Consider Fig. 2.10, in which a generator G is connected to a heater. As current flows through the heater, the electrons continually bump against the stationary atoms. These repeated impacts produce heat. Because heat is a form of energy that the heater cannot produce by itself, it follows that the energy must come from the generator. Scientists have proved that the power released in the form of heat is exactly equal to the product of the voltage *V* across the heater, times the current *I* that flows through it. The electric power delivered by the generator is also equal to the difference of potential (or electromotive force) across its terminals times the current it delivers.

▶ **Figure 2.10**

Circuit composed of a generator, heater, and connecting wires.

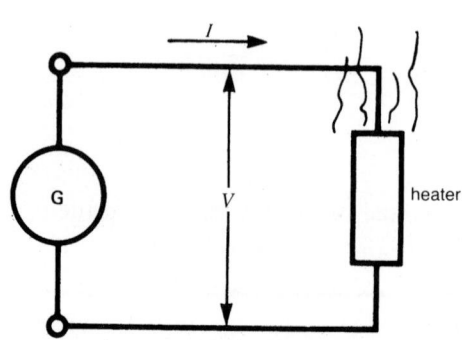

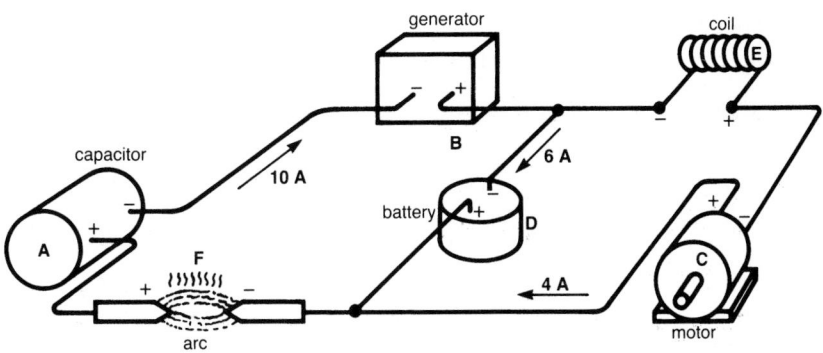

Figure 2.11

Circuit composed of various sources and loads.

We can generalize by saying that the electric power associated with a device is always given by the voltage V across it, times the current I that flows through it. We can therefore write:

$P = VI$

EQ. 2.4

where

P = power, in **watts** (W)
V = difference of potential across the device, in volts (V)
I = current flowing in the device, in amperes (A)

WATT

Equation 2.4 can be applied to any device, whether it is a heater, a dc motor, a transformer, a transistor, a coil, or an electroplating bath. Furthermore, the instantaneous electric power a device receives (or delivers) is *always* equal to the voltage V times the current I that exists at that particular instant.

2.16 Power Dissipated in a Resistance

We can calculate the power dissipated in a resistance by applying Equation 2.4, which states that $P = VI$. However, it is often useful to combine Equation 2.4, and Ohm's law as follows:

$P = VI = (IR)\, I = I^2 R$

whence

$P = I^2 R$

EQ. 2.5

Alternatively, we can write

$P = VI = V(V/R) = V^2/R$

Where

$P = V^2/R$

EQ. 2.6

Equation 2.5 tells us that the power dissipated in a conductor is proportional to the square of the current it carries. This equation is particularly useful in calculating the power losses in transmission lines, and the windings of motors and generators.

Equation 2.6 indicates that the power dissipated in a heater, for example, is proportional to the square of the voltage applied across its terminals. Thus, if the line voltage in a home decreases by 10 percent, the power output of all heating elements (hot water heaters, electric ranges, and so forth) will decrease more than 10 percent.

Equations 2.5 and 2.6 do not add anything new because both are derived from $P = VI$ and $V = IR$. Nevertheless, we will often apply Equation 2.5.

EXAMPLE 2.4

A transmission line that is 15 km long has a resistance of 3 Ω. Calculate the power loss in the line when it carries a current of 60 A.

SOLUTION:

$P = I^2R = (60)^2 \times 3 = 3600 \times 3 = 10\ 800\ W = 10.8\ kW$

2.17 Electric Energy, the Joule (J), the Kilowatthour (kWh)

In Chapter 1 we learned that mechanical power is the rate at which mechanical energy is used up. A similar definition applies to electric power. Electric power P is the rate at which electrical energy W is used: it is electrical energy divided by time; consequently, electrical energy is electric power multiplied by time. We can therefore rewrite Equation 2.7 in the form:

EQ. 2.7 $W = Pt$

where

W = electrical energy, in joules (J)
P = electric power, in watts (W)
t = time during which the power is consumed (or produced) in seconds (s)

The SI unit of electrical energy is the joule: it is equal to one watt-second. However, if power is expressed in kilowatts and time in hours, the electric energy can also be stated in kilowatthours (kWh). The kilowatthour* is not an SI unit, but it is a unit used by most electric utility companies to measure the energy consumed in business, factories, and homes.

For example, a 100 W lamp that burns for 20 seconds consumes energy equal to 100 watts × 20 seconds = 2000 watt-seconds, which is equal to 2000 joules. In the same way, a generator that develops 150 kW during a 20–hour period delivers a quantity of energy equal to 150 kW × 20 h = 3000 kWh or 10 800 MJ.

* 1 kWh = 1000 W × 3600 s = 3 600 000 Ws = 3 600 000 J = 3.6 megajoules = 3.6mJ

The cost of electrical energy equals energy consumption times the unit cost. For example, if the unit cost of electrical energy is 5.5 cents per kWh, the cost of consuming 3000 kWh would be:

Cost = energy consumption $\times$ unit cost
= 3000 kWh $\times$ 5.5¢/kWh
= \$165.00

2.18 Storing Electric Energy

Enormous quantities of chemical energy are stored in underground deposits of oil and coal. When these fuels are burned, they release thermal energy which, in turn, can be converted into electrical energy.

We can also store large quantities of mechanical energy by erecting power dams. The potential energy stored in the water behind the dam is later converted into electrical energy as the water rushes through the generator turbines.

The nuclear energy in a uranium mine is another form of stored energy. Unfortunately, no practical method exists for storing large quantities of electrical energy. Batteries, for example, do not store electrical energy. They store chemical energy, which is released in the form of electrical energy as the chemical elements are transformed. Only two devices are able to store electricity in its natural state: coils and capacitors. However, to store even moderate amounts of electrical energy, the size and cost of these devices make them economically unfeasible. For example, a coil 2 metres long, 1 metre in diameter, and weighing 2 tonnes can keep a 100 W lamp burning for only about 2 minutes.

Because it is virtually impossible to store large quantities of electricity, utility companies must produce it at the same rate it is being consumed. If the rate of consumption is only slightly different from the rate of generation, the electrical system reacts dramatically. Overvoltages, excessive currents, and speed changes are produced which immediately trip circuit breakers, bringing the electrical system to a halt. If we could one day store electrical energy as easily as chemical energy is stored in a litre of oil, the generation, transmission, and distribution of electricity would be profoundly changed.

2.19 Summary

Upon completion of this chapter you should have learned that:

• The atom is composed of a heavy central nucleus and light, fast-moving electrons.

• Conductors have a large number of free electrons and easily allow current to flow, while insulators have few free electrons and allow little current to flow.

- Voltage is a measure of potential difference and provides the "pressure" that causes current to flow through a circuit.

- Ohm's Law relates current, voltage and resistance; knowing any two of the factors, it is possible to calculate the third.

- The power consumed by a load is the product of the voltage across the load and the current flowing through it.

- The kilowatt measures the rate at which energy is dissipated by a load.

- Megajoules and kilowatt hours are common units for electrical energy billing.

- Energy is commonly stored in large amounts as chemical, mechanical and nuclear energy.

Key Terms

ATOM: The smallest fragment of an element that retains all the properties of that element.

CONDUCTOR: Any material that easily allows current to flow; conductors have a large number of free electrons.

ELECTRIC CURRENT: The movement of electrons from the negative terminal of the source to the positive terminal of the source. The unit of current is the ampere and the symbol for current is I.

FREE ELECTRON: An electron that is weakly bound to the central nucleus of an atom. Little energy is required to cause these electrons to be dislodged from their orbit about the atomic nucleus.

INSULATOR: Any material that does not allow current to pass easily. Insulators have very few free electrons.

NUCLEUS: The heavy central core of an atom. The nucleus contains positively charged protons. The number of protons equals the number of electrons orbiting the nucleus.

RESISTANCE: The opposition to the flow of current in a circuit. The unit for resistance is the ohm (Ω) and the symbol is R.

VOLT: The volt is the unit of potential difference. The symbol for the volt is V.

WATT: The watt is the unit for electric power. One watt of power equals energy consumed at the rate of one joule per second. The symbol for the watt is W.

Test Your Knowledge

2.1   An atom of iron has 26 electrons. The charge on the nucleus is
    a. zero   b. − 26
    c. + 26   d. exactly 13

2.2   Electrons repel each other.

    true _____   false _____

2.3   A material having 1000 free electrons per cubic millimetre is a good insulator.

    true _____   false _____

2.4   The unit of potential difference is the
    a. voltage
    b. ampere (A)

c. volt (E)

d. volt (V)

2.5   The unit of electric current is the

a. watt

b. electron

c. ampere

d. flow

2.6   The voltage across the terminals of a
device is 60 V, and the current
through it is 5 A. Current is flowing
into the (+) terminal. The device is a

a. load that consumes 12 W

b. source that is delivering 300 W

c. load that consumes 300 W

2.7   A conductor becomes hotter when the
current through it increases.

true _____   false _____

2.8   A resistance dissipates 12 kW when
240 V is applied to its terminals. The
current in the resistance is

a. 2.88 mA   c. 0.02 A

b. 50 A   d. 4.8

2.9   A current of 20 mA is equal to

a. 20 000 A

b. 0.2 A

c. 0.02 A

2.10   A potential difference of
2 450 000 V is equal to

a. 2.45 MV

b. 2.45 mV

c. 245 kV

2.11   The SI unit of electrical
energy is the

a. watt

b. kilowatt

c. joule

d. kilowatthour

2.12   The polarity of a terminal is positive
if it has

a. a surplus of electrons

b. an absence of electrons

c. a deficiency of electrons compared
with its neutral state

Questions and Problems

2.13   An atom of iron has 26 electrons.
How many electrons are there in the
outer orbit? Draw a diagram of the
atom, similar to that of Fig. 2.1.

2.14   A molecule of salt is composed of one
atom of sodium and one atom of chlorine. The nucleus of the sodium atom
has a charge of +11, while that of
chlorine is +17. (a) How many electrons are there in a molecule of salt?
(b) How many electrons are there in
the two inner orbits next to the nuclei?

2.15   A circuit is composed of a 12 V battery connected to a car heater. Draw a
diagram showing how a voltmeter
and ammeter should be connected
into the circuit.

2.16   An electric heater draws a current of
8 A when it is connected to a 120 V
source. Calculate (a) the power dissipated and (b) the resistance of the
heater.

2.17   In problem 2.16, if the voltage drops
to 60 V, calculate the new values of
power and resistance.

2.18   A soldering iron is connected to a
120 V outlet. Knowing that its resistance is 50 Ω, calculate the current it
draws from the line.

2.19   An average lightning stroke produces
a current of 16 kA at a voltage of
200 MV. If the duration of the stroke
is 30 μs, calculate (a) the power in
megawatts, (b) the average resistance

of the arcing path, and (c) the energy released by the stroke, in kilowatt-hours.

2.20   The magnetic coils of a 500 MW generator have a resistance of 62.6 mΩ. Calculate the voltage needed to cause a current of 4060 A to flow.

2.21   A 560 W load is run for a total of 24 hours. If the energy cost is 2.5 cents per MJ, determine the cost of operating the load.

3

Conductors, Resistors, and Insulators

LEARNING OBJECTIVES

Upon completion of this chapter you will be able to:

- Classify materials as insulators and conductors
- Explain resistivity
- Understand the thermal classification of insulators
- Calculate the dielectric strength of insulators
- Describe the Standard American Wire Gauge
- Calculate the resistance of conductors
- Explain the effect of heat on conductor resistance
- Interpret the resistor colour code
- Understand the operation of fuses
- Explain the importance of ground resistance

Chapter Outline

3.1   Classification of Materials

There is hardly any material that is not used either directly or indirectly in electrical equipment or as part of an electrical system. Copper, iron, paper, cement, gold, cotton, and numerous plastics are all used in the construction of motors, heaters, transmission lines, lamps, relays, and switches. All these materials can be grouped into two categories—conductors and insulators. The conductors, in turn, can be divided into three other categories: good conductors, not-so-good conductors (called *resistors*), and semiconductors. Semiconductors are special non-linear materials that behave as either conductors or insulators, depending upon voltage, current, and temperature.

There is no clear dividing line between conductors and resistors. For example, carbon is considered to be a conductor when used as a brush in a dc motor, but is classified as a resistor when used as a current-limiting element. Table 3A lists some of the more common electrical materials and how they are usually classified.

Table 3A   CLASSIFICATION OF MATERIALS

CONDUCTORS	RESISTORS	INSULATORS
silver	iron	air
copper	carbon	rubber
aluminum	tungsten	porcelain
brass	nichrome	paper
carbon	molybdenum	plastics
mercury	salt water	mineral oil

3.2 Resistivity of Electrical Materials, the Ohm Metre (Ω.M)

Conductors, resistors, and insulators may be distinguished from each other by the relative ease with which they conduct an electric current. They also may be classified according to their relative opposition, or **resistivity**, to the flow of electric current.

RESISTIVITY

Figure 3.1 gives an idea of the relative resistance of three identical samples of copper, nichrome, and rubber. Note that nichrome (an alloy composed of 80 percent nickel and 20 percent chromium) is about 60 times more resistive than copper is. Rubber is many million times more resistive than copper is.

OHM METRE

The SI unit of resistivity is the **ohm metre** (symbol Ω.m). It is numerically equal to the resistance of a sample of material that is one metre long and whose cross section is one square metre. For example, the resistivity of copper is $15.88 \times 10^{-9}\,\Omega.m$ at 0°C, and that of rubber is about $10^{-13}\,\Omega.m$.

Figure 3.1

Relative resistance of three materials having identical dimensions.

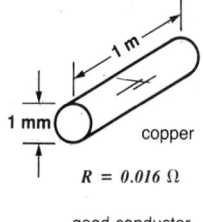

1 m		
1 mm		
copper	nichrome	rubber
$R = 0.016\,\Omega$	$R = 1.0\,\Omega$	$R = 10^{19}\,\Omega$
good conductor	resistive conductor	insulator

3.3 Solid, Liquid, and Gaseous Insulators

Solid, liquid, and gaseous insulators are used in electrical equipment. For example, solid insulators such as rubber, paper, and synthetic plastics are used to cover electrical wires and cables. Treated paper and fibre are used to prevent electrical coils from coming in contact with the iron cores of rotating machines. Some insulators are composed of several materials, such as asbestos, glass, and plastics, so they can withstand very high temperatures while retaining great strength.

In large transformers, liquid insulators such as mineral oil serve to insulate the high-voltage windings from each other and from ground. The oil also carries the heat away from the windings and prevents air from coming in contact with them. This prevents oxidation and deterioration of the insulation, and increases the useful life of the transformer.

Under normal conditions, one of the best insulators is the air that surrounds us. Its thermal properties are better than those of porcelain, it can act as a cooling agent, and, best of all, it costs nothing. However, at extremely high temperatures (between 5000°C and 50 000°C) the molecules of air begin to break down, releasing free electrons. Air then becomes a relatively good conductor, with a resistivity approaching that of salt water. This molecular breakdown, called *ionization,* occurs whenever an electric arc passes through air.

Sulfur hexafluoride (SF_6) is another important insulating gas. Its insulating properties are about ten times better than air. It is used in high-voltage circuit breakers, transformers, and short cable runs when space reduction is particularly important.

Hydrogen is a gaseous insulator used in very large turboalternators. It prevents air from coming in contact with the windings. It also acts as an excellent cooling agent to carry away the heat from the innermost parts of the machine.

3.4 Deterioration of Organic Insulators

Time and temperature are the agents that cause the gradual deterioration and ultimate failure of insulators. The rate of deterioration is further accelerated if the insulating material is in a polluted or humid atmosphere, or if it is subjected to continuous vibration.

Apart from accidental electrical and mechanical failures, the life expectancy of electrical apparatus is limited by the temperature of its insulation: the higher the temperature, the shorter its life. Tests made on many insulating materials have shown that the useful life of electrical apparatus diminishes by approximately half for every 10°C increase above its rated operating temperature. This means that if a motor has a normal life expectancy of eight years at a rated temperature of 100°C, it will have a life expectancy of four years at a temperature of 110°C, two years at 120°C, and only one year at 130°C.

3.5 Thermal Classification of Insulators

A user expects newly purchased electrical equipment to last a reasonable length of time before it has to be repaired. In general, it is felt that a useful life of about ten years is adequate. Based on these considerations, and knowing that temperature is the main factor that determines equipment life, standards-setting organizations have established five temperature grades for insulation and insulation systems. They correspond respectively to a hot-spot temperature of 105°C, 130°C, 155°C, 180°C and 220°C.* The hot-spot temperature is the temperature of the hottest spot inside a winding.

In addition to the hot-spot temperature limits, the standards specify that the ambient temperature shall not exceed 40°C.

What is the relative advantage of one insulation class over another? First, a higher temperature class enables us to get more output from a machine of a given size. For example, a motor rated at 150 hp with a 105°C insulation system can yield an output of almost 200 hp if rewound with a 155°C insulation system. However, the motor runs hotter and the high-temperature insulation is more costly.

Second, a higher temperature class enables us to build machines that can operate for years in very high ambient temperatures (above 40°C) without breaking down.

▼ **Figure 3.2**

Testing the dielectric strength of an insulator.

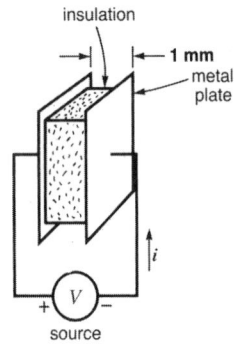

DIELECTRIC
STRENGTH

3.6 Breakdown of Solid and Gaseous Insulators

Suppose an insulator (solid, liquid, or gas) is placed between two metal plates spaced 1 mm apart. Let us apply a voltage across the plates, using an external source (Fig. 3.2). A current will flow in the circuit, but it will be exceedingly small because the insulator possesses very few free electrons. However, if we gradually raise the voltage, we eventually reach a critical point at which the insulation suddenly breaks down. In effect, the insulator suddenly becomes a conductor, and a large current will flow in the circuit.

The breakdown voltage required to produce this insulation failure depends upon the nature of the insulator and its thickness. The ratio of breakdown voltage to insulator thickness is called **dielectric strength**. It is generally expressed in kilovolts per millimetre (kV/mm). Table 3B gives the dielectric strength of several insulators.

When a solid insulator breaks down, its chemical composition is permanently damaged, and so it must be replaced. On the other hand, liquid and gaseous insulators are inherently self-healing and can usually withstand many arcing discharges.

---

* These insulation grades were formerly designated class A (105°C), class B (130°C), class F (155°C), class H (180°C), and class C (220°C and up).

Table 3B   PROPERTIES OF INSULATING MATERIALS

INSULATOR	DIELECTRIC STRENGTH	MAXIMUM OPERATING TEMPERATURE
	kV/mm	**°C**
dry air	3	2000
SF$_6$	30	—
glass	100	600
mineral oil	10	110
paper (treated)	14	120
rubber	12 to 20	65
Mylar®	400	150

EXAMPLE 3.1

A two-conductor 120 V cable used in house wiring has a 0.03 inch thermoplastic covering over each conductor (Fig. 3.3). If the dielectric strength is 25 kV/mm, calculate the voltage that could be applied between the conductors before breakdown occurs. (Note: 1 inch = 25.4 mm, by definition.)

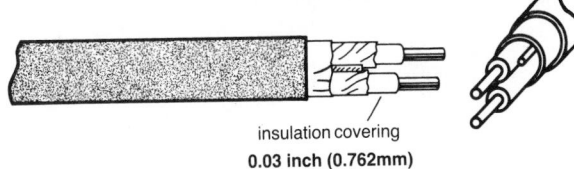

insulation covering
0.03 inch (0.762mm)

Figure 3.3

See Example 3.1.

SOLUTION:

1. The total distance between the conductors is 0.03 × 2 = 0.06 inch.
2. The distance in millimetres is 0.06 × 25.4 = 1.52 mm.
3. The approximate breakdown voltage is 1.5 mm × 25 kV/mm = 38 kV.

The breakdown voltage is much higher than that needed to withstand 120 V. A thinner insulation covering could be used, but it would not have the mechanical strength and resistance to abrasion that the thicker covering has. Thus, in low-voltage installations, the thickness of the insulation is dictated more by mechanical robustness than by voltage breakdown. In high-voltage equipment, the reverse is true.

3.7 Round Conductors, Standard American Wire Gauge

In Canada and the United States, the size of round conductors is standardized according to what is known as the Standard American Wire Gauge (abbreviation **AWG**). This standard is also called the Brown & Sharp Gauge (B & S).

AWG

According to this standard, each wire bears a gauge number that corresponds to a definite diameter. The diameter of the wire diminishes as the gauge number increases: for example, a No. 6 gauge wire is smaller than a No. 4 gauge wire. Table 3C gives the diameter and cross section of round wires corresponding to the respective gauge numbers. It also gives the weight and resistance of round copper wires. You will find it useful to memorize the following rules that apply to the AWG system:

1. A conductor that has twice the cross section of another has a gauge number that is three numbers smaller. Example: the cross section of a No. 15 wire is double that of a No. 18 wire.

2. A conductor that has ten times the cross section of another has a gauge number that is ten numbers smaller. Example: a No. 4 gauge wire has the same cross section as ten No. 14 gauge wires.

Figure 3.4 shows how to measure the conductor size using a slotted wire gauge.

After stripping all insulation (including any thin varnish covering), the bare wire is inserted into the slot that gives the best fit. The slot number corresponds to the wire size.

Figure 3.4

Method of measuring the size of a conductor using an AWG wire gauge. A No. 4 bare conductor is about to be slipped into the No. 4 slot. The wire gauge and its slots are shown full size.

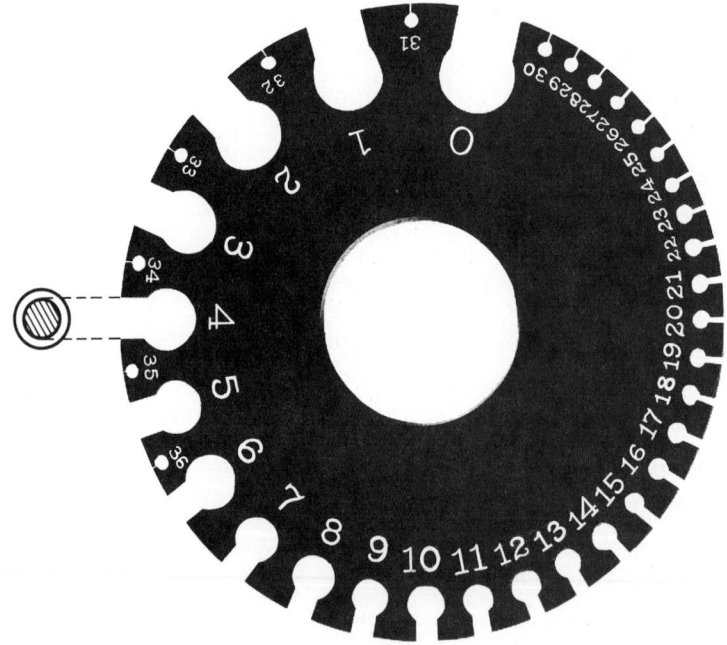

Figure 3.5

The area enclosed by the circle is 1 circular mil.

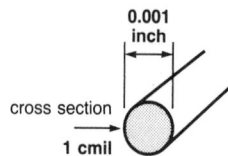

3.8 Mils, Circular Mils

The diameter of a conductor is sometimes expressed in mils instead of millimetres. The mil is a unit of length equal to one thousandth of an inch, or 0.0254 mm.

CIRCULAR MILS

Similarly, the cross section of round wires is sometimes expressed in **circular mils** instead of in square millimetres. The circular mil (cmil or CM) is equal to the area of a circle having a diameter of 1 mil (Fig. 3.5). A circular mil is equal to 0.000 506 707 mm².

The cross section of a round wire expressed in circular mils is equal to the square of its diameter expressed in mils.

EXAMPLE 3.2

Calculate the cross section of a round wire having a diameter of 0.102 inch.

SOLUTION:

1. The diameter is equal to 102 thousandths of an inch, or 102 mils.
2. The cross section is therefore:

   A = 102 mils × 102 mils = 10 404 circular mils
3. Expressed in square millimetres, the area is:

   A = 10 404 × 0.000 506 707 = 5.27 mm²

Note that conductors bigger than 0000 (or 4/0) do not bear a gauge number; they are usually identified by their cross section in thousands of circular mils (MCM). Thus, a 250 MCM conductor has a cross section of 250 000 cmil, or 126.6 mm².

3.9 Stranded Cables

A stranded wire or cable is composed of seven or more conductors so that it can provide flexibility. Its cross section is equal to the sum of the cross sections of the strands. It does not include the area of the empty spaces between the strands. Thus, a No. 10 stranded wire possesses the same net cross section (and same resistance) as a No. 10 solid wire.

3.10 Square Wires and Other Conductor Shapes

Square wires have gauge numbers that correspond to those of round wires. According to the AWG, if a square wire has the same width as the diameter of a round wire, the two bear the same gauge number (Fig. 3.6). It follows that the cross section of a square wire is about 1.25 times greater than that of a round wire having the same gauge number.

Rectangular conductors whose dimensions can be made to order are also available. They are used in the windings of large transformers and rotating machines. Some have a hollow centre so that water can be circulated inside the conductor to keep it cool.

Very large bare conductors called busbars are used to carry the heavy currents in factories and substations. Some are rectangular, with such typical dimensions as 8 mm × 150 mm, and others are pipe-shaped.

▼ **Figure 3.6**

Comparison between the cross sections of round and square conductors having the same gauge number.

No. 10 gauge round wire

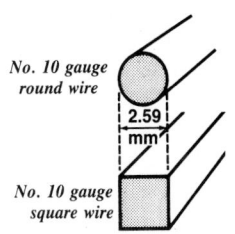

2.59 mm

No. 10 gauge square wire

3.11 Current Rating of Conductors; Ampacity

Even the best conductors have some resistance; consequently, they all heat up when they carry an electric current. The heat produced in insulated conductors is transmitted through the insulating layers and finally dissipated to the surrounding

Table 3C   PROPERTIES OF ROUND COPPER CONDUCTORS

Gauge number AWG/ B & S	Diameter of bare conductor		Cross section		Resistance mΩ/m or Ω/km		Weight g/m or kg/km	Typical diameter of *insulated* magnet wire used in relays, magnets, motors, transformers, etc.
	mm	mils	mm²	cmils	25°C	105°C		mm
250MCM	12.7	500	126.6	250 000	0.138	0.181	1126	
4/0	11.7	460	107.4	212 000	0.164	0.214	953	
2/0	9.27	365	67.4	133 000	0.261	0.341	600	
1/0	8.26	325	53.5	105 600	0.328	0.429	475	
1	7.35	289	42.4	87 700	0.415	0.542	377	
2	6.54	258	33.6	66 400	0.522	0.683	300	
3	5.83	229	26.6	52 600	0.659	0.862	237	
4	5.18	204	21.1	41 600	0.833	1.09	187	
5	4.62	182	16.8	33 120	1.05	1.37	149	
6	4.11	162	13.30	26 240	1.32	1.73	118	
7	3.66	144	10.5	20 740	1.67	2.19	93.4	
8	3.25	128	8.30	16 380	2.12	2.90	73.8	
9	2.89	114	6.59	13 000	2.67	3.48	58.6	3.00
10	2.59	102	5.27	10 400	3.35	4.36	46.9	2.68
11	2.30	90.7	4.17	8 230	4.23	5.54	37.1	2.39
12	2.05	80.8	3.31	6 530	5.31	6.95	29.5	2.14
13	1.83	72.0	2.63	5 180	6.69	8.76	25.4	1.91
14	1.63	64.1	2.08	4 110	8.43	11.0	18.5	1.71
15	1.45	57.1	1.65	3 260	10.6	13.9	14.7	1.53
16	1.29	50.8	1.31	2 580	13.4	17.6	11.6	1.37
17	1.15	45.3	1.04	2 060	16.9	22.1	9.24	1.22
18	1.02	40.3	0.821	1 620	21.4	27.9	7.31	1.10
19	0.91	35.9	0.654	1 290	26.9	35.1	5.80	0.98
20	0.81	32.0	0.517	1 020	33.8	44.3	4.61	0.88
21	0.72	28.5	0.411	812	42.6	55.8	3.66	0.79
22	0.64	25.3	0.324	640	54.1	70.9	2.89	0.70
23	0.57	22.6	0.259	511	67.9	88.9	2.31	0.63
24	0.51	20.1	0.205	404	86.0	112	1.81	0.57
25	0.45	17.9	0.162	320	108	142	1.44	0.51
26	0.40	15.9	0.128	253	137	179	1.14	0.46
27	0.36	14.2	0.102	202	172	225	0.908	0.41
28	0.32	12.6	0.080	159	218	286	0.716	0.37
29	0.29	11.3	0.065	128	272	354	0.576	0.33
30	0.25	10.0	0.0507	100	348	456	0.451	0.29
31	0.23	8.9	0.0401	79.2	440	574	0.357	0.27
32	0.20	8.0	0.0324	64.0	541	709	0.289	0.24
33	0.18	7.1	0.0255	50.4	689	902	0.228	0.21
34	0.16	6.3	0.0201	39.7	873	1140	0.179	0.19
35	0.14	5.6	0.0159	31.4	1110	1450	0.141	0.17
36	0.13	5.0	0.0127	25.0	1390	1810	0.113	0.15
37	0.11	4.5	0.0103	20.3	1710	2230	0.091	0.14
38	0.10	4.0	0.0081	16.0	2170	2840	0.072	0.12
39	0.09	3.5	0.0062	12.3	2820	3690	0.055	0.11
40	0.08	3.1	0.0049	9.6	3610	4720	0.043	0.1

air. The greater the current in the wire, the higher the temperature will be. However, to ensure a reasonable life, the temperature of the insulation must not be too high. We therefore arrive at the following important conclusion:

The maximum current a conductor can carry depends upon the highest temperature its insulation can withstand for the desired lifetime of the conductor.

Although bare conductors present no insulation problem, the current and temperature must still be kept within reasonable limits because high temperatures produce excessive oxidation and flaking of the conductor. They also create a potential fire hazard.

3.12 Canadian Electrical Code and Electrical Installations

The life expectancy of the electrical wiring in factories, buildings, and homes must be particularly long because we cannot afford to replace the conductors every ten years. For this reason, the Canadian Electrical Code specifies rather low maximum temperatures for wire and cable used in electrical installations. Depending on the type of insulation, the Canadian Electrical Code typically recognizes maximum temperatures of 60°C, 75°C, and 90°C.

A wire of a given size rated at 90°C can carry, a higher current than one having a lower temperature rating. For example, a No. 6 wire whose insulation is rated at 60°C can carry a current of 80 A in free air. The same wire with insulation rated at 90°C can carry a current of 100 A. Both conductors have the same life expectancy under the specified temperature conditions. Table 3D gives an idea of the **ampacities** (ampere capacities) of various conductor sizes.

AMPACITY

Table 3D   ALLOWABLE AMPACITIES FOR INSULATED CONDUCTORS RATED 0-2000 V SINGLE CONDUCTORS IN FREE AIR, BASED ON AN AMBIENT TEMPERATURE OF 30°C

GAUGE NUMBER	TEMPERATURE RATING OF INSULATION COVERING	
(AWG)	60°C	90°C
12	25 amperes	25 amperes
10	40	40
8	55	70
6	80	100
4	105	135
2	140	180
1/0	195	245
3/0	260	330
250 MCM	340	425

Note: The above values are derived from the National Electrical Code. The Canadian Electrical Code gives identical values.

When several insulated conductors are placed in the same conduit, the heat dissipated by each raises the temperature of the others. The ampacity of each conductor must then be reduced so as not to exceed the maximum permissible temperature. For example, the Canadian Electrical Code specifies that when three No. 6 conductors rated at 60°C are run in a conduit, the ampacity per conductor is only 55 A, compared with 80 A when they are suspended separately in free air.

3.13 Calculation of Resistance

Resistance is the physical property of a material that limits the flow of current. The unit of resistance is the ohm, named in honour of the German physicist Georg Simon Ohm. The symbol for the ohm is Greek letter omega (Ω).

For a given temperature, the resistance of a conductor depends upon its length, cross section, and resistivity. The relationship is given by the equation:

EQ. 3.1

$$R = \rho l / A$$

where:

R = resistance of the conductor, in ohms (Ω)
ρ = resistivity of the conductor, in ohm metres (Ω.m)
l = length of the conductor, in metres (m)
A = cross section of the conductor in square metres (m^2)

We recall that the SI unit of resistivity is the ohm metre. However, owing to the low resistivity of metallic conductors, we prefer to use a submultiple, the nanohm metre (nΩ.m), equal to 10^{-9} Ω.m. The resistivity of some common metals is given in Table 3E.

EXAMPLE 3.3

Calculate the resistance of a copper conductor having a length of 2 km and a cross section of 22 mm^2. Assume the resistivity is 18 nΩ.m.

SOLUTION:

Knowing that:

l = 2 km = 2000 m
A = 22 mm^2 = 22 $\times$ 10^{-6} m^2
ρ = 18 nΩ.m = 18 $\times$ 10^{-9} Ω.m

We find:

$$R = \rho \, \frac{l}{A}$$

$$= \frac{18}{10^9} \times \frac{2000}{22 \times 10^{-6}} = 1.64 \ \Omega$$

EXAMPLE 3.4

Calculate the resistance of 82 ft of No. 20 AWG nichrome wire at a temperature of 0°C.

SOLUTION:

According to Table 3C, the cross section of No. 20 gauge round wire is 1020 cmils. Furthermore, the resistivity of nichrome is 649 Ω.cmil/ft (Table 3E). The resistance of the conductor is therefore:

EQ. 3.2

$$R = \rho \, \frac{l}{A} = 649 \times \frac{82}{1020} = 52.2 \ \Omega$$

Table 3E RESISTIVITY AND TEMPERATURE COEFFICIENT OF SOME CONDUCTORS

CONDUCTOR	RESISTIVITY AT 0°C		TEMPERATURE COEFFIENT	MELTING POINT
	nΩ.m.	Ωcmil/ft	per °C	°C
silver	15.0	9.02	0.004 11	960
copper	15.9	9.56	0.004 27	1083
aluminum	26.0	15.6	0.004 39	660
tungsten	49.6	29.8	0.005 5	3410
manganin	482	290	0.000 015	1020
nichrome	1080	649	0.000 11	1400
carbon	8000 to 30 000	—	−0.000 3	3600

3.14 Resistance and Temperature

The resistance of most metallic conductors increases with temperature. The increase depends upon the so-called **temperature coefficient** of the conductor. The resistance can be calculated from the equation:

$$R_t = R_o (1 + \alpha t)$$ EQ. 3.3

where

R_t = resistance of the conductor at t °C, in ohms
R_o = resistance of the conductor at 0°C, in ohms
α = temperature coefficient of the conductor, at 0°C
t = temperature of the conductor, in °C

EXAMPLE 3.5

An aluminum transmission line has a resistance of 80 Ω at a winter temperature of 0°C. Calculate its resistance in the summer when the conductor temperature is 36°C.

SOLUTION:

From Table 3E, the temperature coefficient for aluminum is 0.00439. The resistance of the line at 36°C is:

$$R_{36°} = R_o (1 + \alpha t)$$ EQ. 3.3
$$= 80 (1 + 0.00439 \times 36)$$
$$= 80 (1 + 0.158)$$
$$= 92.6 \ \Omega$$

The resistance in summer is therefore almost 15 percent higher than in winter.

The resistance of some alloys, such as manganin, changes very little with temperature; consequently, these materials are used in precision voltmeters and ammeters and to make resistance standards.

Other alloys, such as nichrome, possess both high resistivity and a low temperature coefficient. They are used in heater elements and commercial resistors.

3.15 Classification of Resistors

Resistors can be grouped into three classes depending upon whether they operate at low, medium, or high temperature. Low temperatures are considered to be those below 155°C, medium temperatures lie between 275°C and 415°C, and high temperatures are those above 600°C.

Low-temperature resistors (below 155°C) are mainly used in electronic circuits. They are usually enclosed in boxes, and so they are rated to operate in ambient temperatures as high as 70°C. The allowable temperature rise of these resistors is therefore (155 − 70) = 85°C.

These resistors are small because they typically dissipate between 1/4 W and 10 W. They are made by depositing a thin layer of carbon on a ceramic tube or by winding nichrome wire on a porcelain support.

Some carry four coloured bands which permit us to identify the ohmic value and precision of the resistor. Thus, red and blue correspond respectively to the numbers 2 and 6. The complete colour code is given in Table 3F.

There are many types of resistors in the low-temperature category. Their properties and performance are determined by standards organizations such as EIA (Electronic Industries Association) and IEC (International Electrotechnical Commission), or by military standards (MIL specs).

Table 3F   COLOUR CODING OF RESISTORS

COLOUR	NUMERICAL VALUE OR MULTIPLIER	CODING
black	0	first band = first number
brown	1	second band = second number
red	2	third band = number of zeros
orange	3	fourth band = precision
yellow	4	
green	5	
blue	6	Example: 420 000 Ω ± 10%
violet	7	
grey	8	
white	9	
gold	± 5%	
silver	± 10%	

Medium-temperature resistors (275°C to 415°C) are those most often found in industry. They include fixed and variable resistors (called rheostats) that are designed to operate in an ambient temperature of 40°C. The power rating varies from 10 W to many kilowatts. These resistors are used to start motors, to dim lights in theatres, to vary the current in magnetic coils, and in numerous other applications, including space heating in factories and homes.

High-temperature resistors (600°C and up) are used in electric stoves and furnaces, in infrared lamps, and in incandescent light bulbs. Typical temperatures are incandescent lamp, 2600°C; industrial electric furnace, 1100°C; and red-hot stove element, 950°C.

3.16 Fuses

The melting point of a conductor is put to practical use in the construction of **fuses**. These devices usually consist of a fuse link enclosed in a fibre tube. The fuse link is indented at one, two, or three places along its length to create short, narrow bridges of relatively high resistance (Fig. 3.7). When the current exceeds the rated value, the bridges melt, thereby interrupting the circuit. Plug fuses found in homes are designed along the same principles as industrial fuses (Fig. 3.8).

When a short-circuit occurs, the current becomes very high and the tremendous heat causes the fusible element to literally explode. The fibre tube must withstand the high internal pressure and special precautions must be taken to prevent the arc from being sustained by the vapourized metal. To meet these requirements, the fuse is made longer as the operating voltage increases. Furthermore, the amount of fusible metal is kept to a strict minimum. Zinc, which melts at 420°C, is most often used.

High rupturing capacity (HRC) fuses use a thin copper or silver wire as the fusible element.

| FUSES |

▼ **Figure 3.7**

Construction of a 450 A, 600 V fuse having a renewable fuse link.

▼ **Figure 3.8**

Plug fuse rated at 15 A, 250 V.

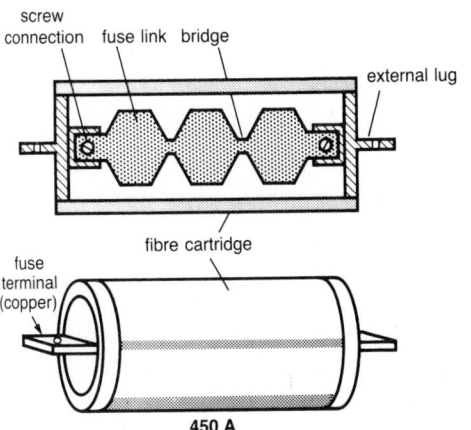

3.17 Contact Resistance

When two current-carrying conductors meet at a terminal, they may cause appreciable contact resistance and substantial I^2R losses. The heat will gradually carbonize the surrounding insulation and oxidize the metallic joint. This raises the contact resistance until a catastrophic failure occurs. Note that a low contact resistance is no guarantee that a connection will not overheat.

EXAMPLE 3.6

The terminals of a circuit breaker are bolted to a bus-bar and the contact resistance is 0.0003 Ω. If the current is 5000 A, calculate the heat dissipated.

Figure 3.9

Current flow between two ground electrodes.

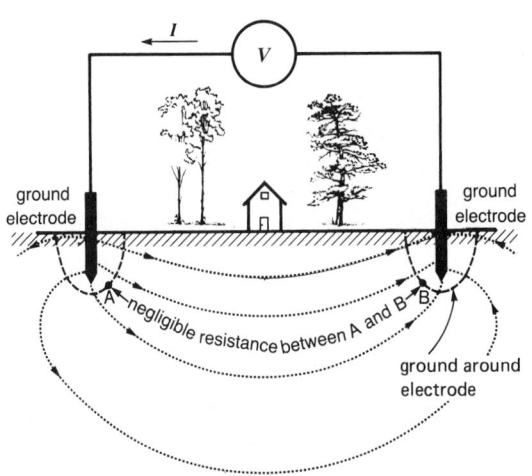

SOLUTION:

The heat released is:

EQ. 2.5 $P = I^2R$

$= 0.0003 \times (5000)^2 = 7500$ W

3.18 Resistance of the Ground

GROUND

The resistance of the **ground** is very important in electrical installations. First, for safety reasons, most electrical installations are connected to ground (earthed). Second, the ground is often used as a return conductor on some transmission lines. Unfortunately, the ground also offers a path for leakage currents, which can corrode buried metallic pipes and structures.

The resistivity of the ground ranges between 5 Ω.m and 5000 Ω.m, depending upon its composition (clay, sand, granite, etc.) and the degree of moistness. Despite its high resistivity, the ground is an excellent conductor because of the enormous cross section it offers to current flow. For example, if we apply a voltage *V* between two electrodes driven into the ground, the resulting current flows through the entire volume of the earth, following a path similar to that shown in Fig. 3.9. As a result, the resistance between the electrodes remains quite low, even though they may be many kilometres apart. The resistance of a single electrode is typically less than 25 ohms. Experience has shown that this electrode resistance is mainly concentrated in a 10-metre radius around each electrode. Beyond this circle, the resistance is negligible. Consequently, the distance between electrodes does not change the resistance between them unless the electrodes are very close.

We can reduce the resistance to a fraction of an ohm by driving the electrodes deeper into the ground or by impregnating the surrounding soil with chemicals, such as copper sulfate. When a very low ground electrode resistance is required, a steel grid, covering several square metres, can be buried in the ground.

3.19 Summary

Upon completion of this chapter you should have learned that:

- All materials can be classified as insulators or conductors. Conductors have a relatively large number of free electrons, while insulators have relatively few.

- Resistivity is based upon the resistance of a 1 metre long piece of a material with a cross section of 1 square metre. Resistivity is used to compare the conducting qualities of materials.

- There are five thermal classes for insulators. These classes allow us to match the thermal requirements for insulation to the application.

- Dielectric strength of insulators is measured in kilovolts/millimetre and it is used as a means rating the strength of insulation.

- The American Wire Gauge (AWG) is used as a means of sizing conductors. It is based on circular mils.

- Using Equation 3.1, we can calculate the resistance of conductors.

- Conductor resistance is dependent upon temperature. Using Equation 3.3, we can calculate the resistance of a material at a given temperature.

- The resistor colour code (Table 3F) was developed as a means of encoding information on small resistors used in electronic circuits.

- Fuses are protective devices designed to fail when the current reaches a specific value.

- Ground connections are used as return paths on some transmission lines and for safety reasons. It is important that ground resistance be maintained at a relatively low value.

Key Terms

AMPACITY: A contraction derived from *amp*ere cap*acity*. It is a term used to describe the current carrying capability of a conductor.

AWG: American Wire Gauge. The standard used to describe the physical size of conductors.

CIRCULAR MIL: The basic unit used in comparing the size of conductors. One circular mil is the area of a conductor that has a diameter of one mil (0.001 inches).

DIELECTRIC STRENGTH: Ratio of an insulation's breakdown voltage (in kV) to the thickness of the insulation in millimetres.

FUSES: Protective devices designed to open a circuit at a specific current level.

Fuses are devices designed to be used once.

GROUND: A point of common connection in a circuit. Usually, the ground point is electrically connected to the earth.

OHM METRE: The resistance of a given conductor with a length of one metre and a cross sectional area of one square metre.

RESITIVITY: A measure of a materials opposition to the flow of current based upon the ohm metre.

TEMPERATURE COEFFICIENT: The change in a material's resistance when the temperature changes by one degree Celsius.

Test Your Knowledge

3.1 The following metals are most commonly used as electrical conductors:
   a. silver and copper
   b. copper and aluminum
   c. iron and copper

3.2 The life expectancy of an insulator is 16 years at a temperature of 105°C. If the temperature rises to 135°C, the life expectancy will be
   a. 9.3 years
   b. 1.5 years
   c. 4 years

3.3 A piece of writing paper that is 10 cm wide, 15 cm long and 0.05 mm thick has a dielectric strength of 8 kV/mm. If placed between two copper plates and subjected to an increasing voltage, it will break down at
   a. 160 kV
   b. 400 V
   c. 120 kV

3.4 A round aluminum conductor has a diameter of about 0.032 inch. The corresponding AWG number is
   a. No. 40
   b. No. 28
   c. No. 20

3.5 A No. 12 copper conductor has a length of 3400 m. Its weight is
   a. 115.25 kg
   b. 100.3 kg
   c. 0.115 kg

3.6 A No. 15 copper wire has a length of 48 ft. Using Table 3C, its resistance at 25°C is
   a. 155.1 mΩ
   b. 155.1 Ω
   c. 508.8 mΩ

3.7 A round conductor has a diameter of 0.025 inch. Its cross section is
   a. 635 mil²
   b. 0.006 25 cmil
   c. 625 cmil

3.8   The allowable ampacity of No. 12 wire used in house wiring is limited in order to
a.   prevent fires
b.   prevent excessive voltage drop
c.   ensure a long life for the wiring system

3.9   A resistor is colour-coded brown–black–red–gold. Its value and precision are
a.   102 Ω ±5 %
b.   1000 Ω 5 %
c.   100 Ω ±5 %

Questions and Problems

3.10   Name three insulators that can withstand temperatures above 220°C.

3.11   A transformer is insulated with class H insulation. What is the maximum allowable hot-spot temperature?

3.12   An electric motor is built using a 105°C insulation system. The motor runs in a very hot location, where the ambient temperature is far above 40°C. As a result, the motor gets too hot and breaks down every 5 months. If the motor is rewound using a 155°C insulation system, how long would you expect it to last, assuming no mechanical failure?

3.13   Calculate the approximate breakdown voltage of
a.   a sheet of glass 1/8 inch thick
b.   an air gap of 1 inch

3.14   A stranded aluminum cable has a cross section of 500 MCM. Express this in square millimetres.

3.15   Why do we sometimes prefer to use a No. 10 stranded wire instead of a No. 10 solid wire?

3.16   Without referring to the wire table, what size conductor is eight times bigger than No. 10 gauge wire?

3.17   Using Table 3C, calculate the thickness of the insulation covering a No. 15 magnet wire.

3.18   A 600 A, 250 MCM extra-flexible welding cable is composed of 6300 copper wires. What is the gauge number of the strands?

3.19   A coil made of No. 22 wire has a resistance of 400 Ω at 25°C. Using Table 3C, calculate (a) the length of the wire and (b) the weight of the coil.

3.20   Using Table 3C and applying the rules of the AWG system, calculate the cross section and diameter of a No. 45 round wire.

3.21   A coil made of copper wire has a resistance of 400 ohms at 27°C. Calculate its resistance at (a) 0°C and (b) 105°C.

3.22   A 2-conductor feeder made of No. 4 copper wire has a length of 800 m. Calculate (a) the total line resistance at 25°C and (b) the voltage drop and line losses for a line current of 120 A.

3.23   Determine the value and precision of two small resistors that have the following colour code:
(a) red–red–red–silver
(b) brown–red–blue–gold

3.24   A rectangular aluminum busbar is 1/4 inch thick, 6 inches wide, and 200 feet long. Using Table 3E, calculate its resistance at 80°C.

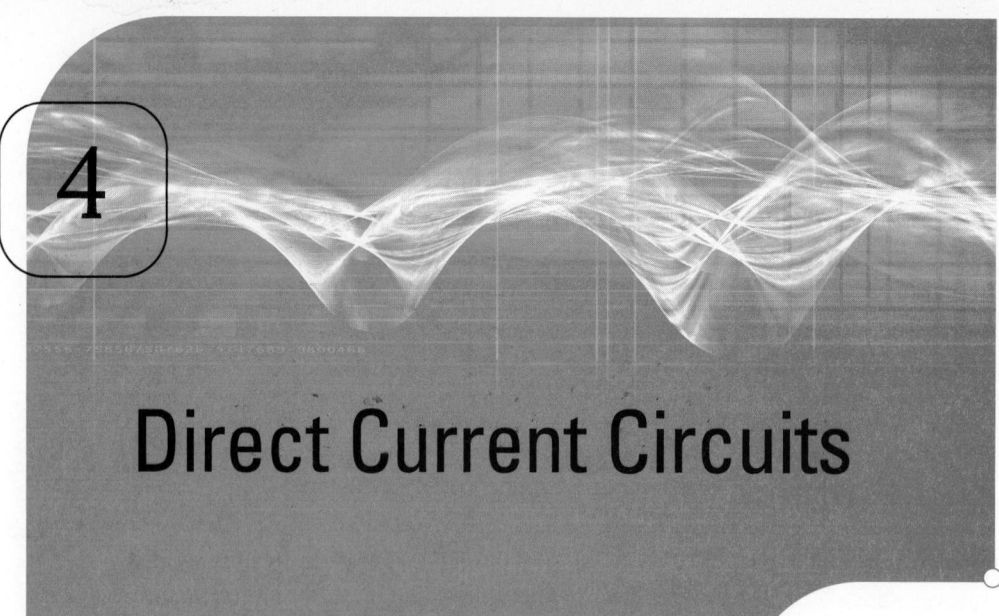

4

Direct Current Circuits

LEARNING OBJECTIVES

Upon completion of this chapter you will be able to:

- Recognize series, parallel, and series-parallel circuits

- Solve problems involving voltage, current, and resistance

- Explain power flow in a transmission line

- Describe the difference between primary and secondary cells

- Describe the operation of the lead-acid cell

- Explain how cells can be connected to increase output current and voltage

- Solve complex circuits using Kirchoff's laws

4.1 Series Circuits

Electric devices are connected in **series** when there is only one current path between the negative terminal and the positive terminal of the source. Fig. 4.1 shows a circuit composed of three lamps connected in series. If this same circuit is connected to a generator G (Fig. 4.2), a current will flow.

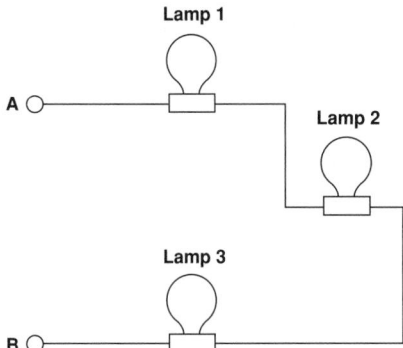

Figure

Series circı

three lamps.

Such series circuits possess three main properties:

SERIES

1. The current in each device is the same.

    In Fig. 4.2, the currents in the three devices and the generator are identical. Since there is only one current path between the terminals of the source, each electron must flow through each of the lamps. Mathematically, we can state this relationship as:

    $I_{\text{Total}} = I_{Lamp 1} = I_{Lamp 2} = I_{Lamp 3}$

    or

    $I_T = I_1 = I_2 = I_3$

2. The sum of the voltages across the individual loads is equal to the voltage across the source.

    In Fig. 4.2, voltmeters are connected across each device. If we take careful measurements, we discover that:

    $V_{\text{Total}} = V_{Lamp 1} + V_{Lamp 2} + V_{Lamp 3}$

    or

    $V_T = V_1 + V_2 + V_3$

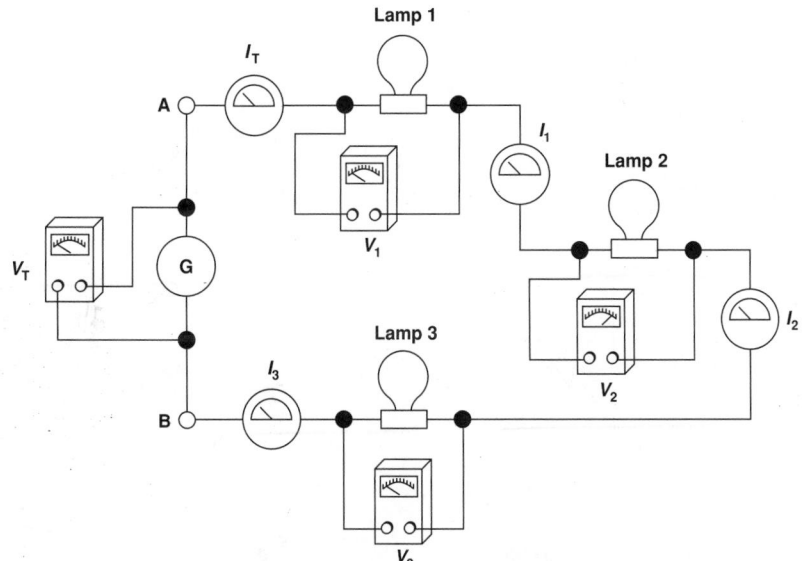

Figure 4.2

Series circuit connected to a generator G.

3. The sum of the powers absorbed by the individual loads is equal to the power supplied by the source.

   This is true because of the law of conservation of energy.

Using Fig. 4.2, we can therefore state:

$$P_{Total} = P_{Lamp\,1} + P_{Lamp\,2} + P_{Lamp\,3}$$

However, we recall that the power of each device (source or load) is equal to the product of the current it carries times the voltage across it. Consequently, we can write:

$$V_{Total}\,I_{Total} = V_{Lamp\,1}\,I_{Lamp\,1} + V_{Lamp\,2}\,I_{Lamp\,2} + V_{Lamp\,3}\,I_{Lamp\,3}$$

These three rules apply to any dc series circuit, no matter what the elements are.

In drawing electric circuits, it is useful to simplify the pictures by using a wiring diagram symbol for each device. Thus, the much simpler schematic diagram of Fig. 4.3 can represent the "real" circuit of Fig. 4.2.

4.2 Resistors in Series, Equivalent Resistance

Heaters, lamps, toasters, and other devices that do not generate an emf all possess a certain resistance, which is expressed in ohms. From a circuit standpoint, these devices are considered to be **resistors** because they oppose the flow of current to a greater or lesser degree. Even a good conductor of electricity, such as a length of copper wire, may be considered to be a resistor because it offers *some* opposition to current flow.

RESISTOR

For the circuit in Fig. 4.1, we developed two rules showing the relationship between the individual currents and voltages and the total values for each:

$$I_T = I_1 = I_2 = I_3$$

and

$$V_T = V_1 + V_2 + V_3$$

Figure 4.3

This circuit diagram is a simpler representation of the circuit in Fig. 4.2.

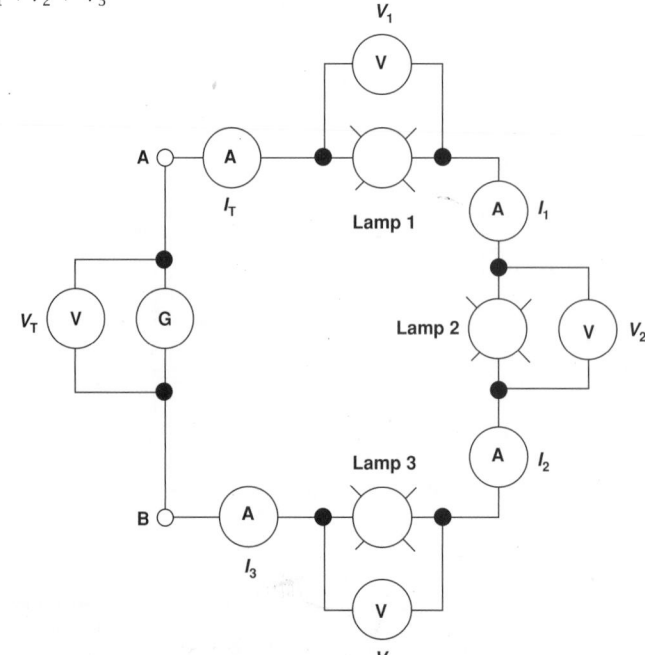

Combining these values using Ohm's law, we have:

$$\frac{V_T}{I_T} = \frac{V_1}{I_T} = \frac{V_2}{I_T} = \frac{V_3}{I_T}$$

This gives us:

$$R_T = R_1 + R_1 + R_1 \qquad\qquad \text{EQ. 4.1}$$

The total resistance (R_T) will behave, electrically, in exactly the same fashion as the circuit containing three individual resistors. Therefore, we can refer to it as an equivalent resistance.

Consider three resistors of 4 Ω, 6 Ω, and 12 Ω connected in series across a 220 V source (Fig. 4.4). The total resistance R_T of the group is equal to the sum of their individual resistances:

$$R_T = 4 + 6 + 12 = 22\ \Omega$$

Therefore, a single equivalent resistor R_T of 22 Ω could replace the three individual resistors. The reason is that if this resistor were connected across the 220 V source, it would draw the same current as the three resistors do (Fig. 4.5). Thus, the current flowing in the individual resistors is:

$$I = \frac{V}{R_T} = \frac{220\ \text{V}}{22\ \Omega} = 10\ \text{A}$$

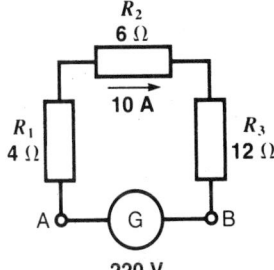

Figure 4.4

Series circuit composed of three resistors connected to a source G.

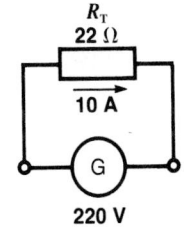

Figure 4.5

This circuit is equivalent to the series circuit of Fig. 4.4.

The 22 Ω resistor is called an equivalent resistance R_T because it represents the overall effect of the three resistors in the circuit.

What is the difference of potential across the individual resistors in Fig. 4.4? It can be found by applying Ohm's law ($V = IR$) to each element. Knowing that the current is 10 A, and referring to Fig. 4.4, we find:

for R_1, $V_1 = IR_1 = 10 \times 4 = 40$ V

for R_2, $V_2 = IR_2 = 10 \times 6 = 60$ V

for R_3, $V_3 = IR_3 = 10 \times 12 = 120$ V

for R_T, $V_T = IR_T = 10 \times 22 = 220$ V

If voltmeters were connected across each resistor, they would give readings as shown in Fig. 4.6.

Figure 4.6

Voltmeters are used to
measure the voltage across
each resistor.

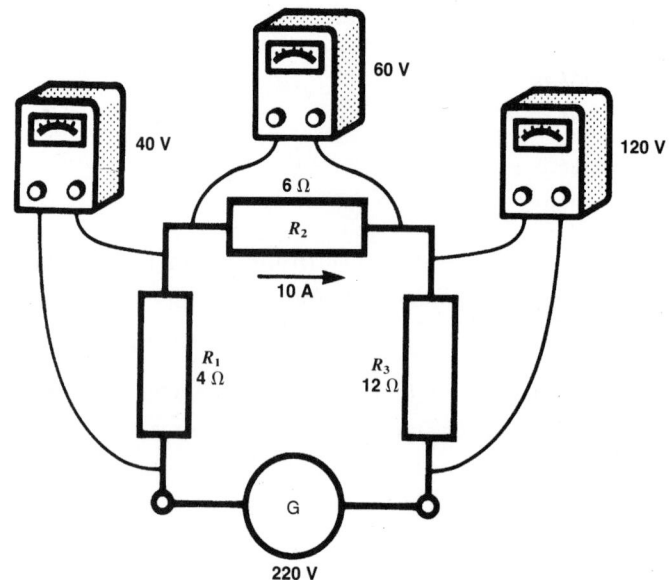

Note that $V_1 + V_2 + V_3 = 220$ V. Thus, the sum of the voltages across the resistors is equal to the voltage of the source, as it should be.

Let us now consider the power aspects of the circuit. Using $P = I^2R$, we can calculate the power dissipated in each resistor. Thus:

in R_1, $P_1 = I^2R_1 = 10^2 \times 4 = 400$ W
in R_2, $P_2 = I^2R_2 = 10^2 \times 6 = 600$ W
in R_3, $P_3 = I^2R_3 = 10^2 \times 12 = 1200$ W

Total power dissipated in the three resistors is:

$P_{load} = 400 + 600 + 1200 = 2200$ W

On the other hand, the power delivered by the source is:

$P_{source} = VI = 220 \times 10 = 2200$ W

Thus, the total power dissipated by the resistors is equal to the power supplied by the source.

EXAMPLE 4.1

Three resistors are connected in series. The voltage across one resistor is 20 volts, the resistance of the second resistor is 5 Ω, and the current through the third resistor is 3 amperes. Determine the voltage across each of the three resistors and resistance of each device.

continued

SOLUTION:

i)   The voltage across the first resistor is given: 20 V.

The voltage across R_2:

$V = I_T R_2$ (Remember that in a series circuit the current is constant, so 3 A flows
   through each of the resistors.)

   $= 3\ \text{A} \times 5\ \Omega$

   $= 15\ \text{V}$

We know that, in a series circuit, $V_T = V_1 + V_2 + V_3$.

The voltage across R_3:

$V_3 = V_T - (V_2 + V_1)$

   $= 120\ \text{V} - (20\ \text{V} + 15\ \text{V})$

   $= 85\ \text{V}$

ii) Now that we have the voltage drop across each of the resistors, we can calculate
the individual ohmic values.

$R_1 = V_1 / I_T$

   $= 20\ \text{V}/3\ \text{A}$

   $= 6.67\ \Omega$

R_2 is given as $5\ \Omega$.

$R_3 = V_3 / I_T$

   $= 85\ \text{V} / 3\ \text{A}$

   $= 28.3\ \Omega$

4.3 Parallel Circuits

Electric devices are said to be connected in **parallel** when there is more than one
current path for electrons to follow from the negative to the positive terminals of the
source. Fig. 4.7 shows the schematic diagram of a parallel circuit composed of three
lamps. These devices are effectively connected to the two common terminals A and
B. The conductors leading from terminals A and B to terminals 1, 2, 3 and 4, 5, 6 are
assumed to have negligible resistance. It follows that terminals 1, 2, 3 are *electrically*
at the same potential as terminal A, while terminals 4, 5, 6 are *electrically* at the same
potential as terminal B. Thus, from an electrical standpoint, the four terminals 1, 2,
3, A form one common terminal. The same is true of terminals 4, 5, 6, B.

Let us connect this parallel circuit to a source G. Voltages and currents will immediately appear in each device, as indicated in Fig. 4.8.

Parallel circuits, like series circuits, possess three main properties:

1.   The voltage across each device is the same.

Thus, in Fig. 4.8, we have:

$V_{Total} = V_{Lamp\,1} - V_{Lamp\,2} - V_{Lamp\,3}$

or

$V_T = V_1 - V_2 - V_3$

PARALLEL

▼ Figure 4.7

Parallel circuit composed of
three lamps.

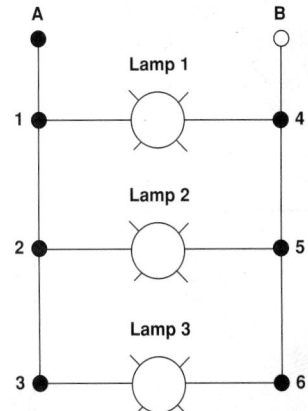

Figure 4.8

Parallel circuit connected to
a source G.

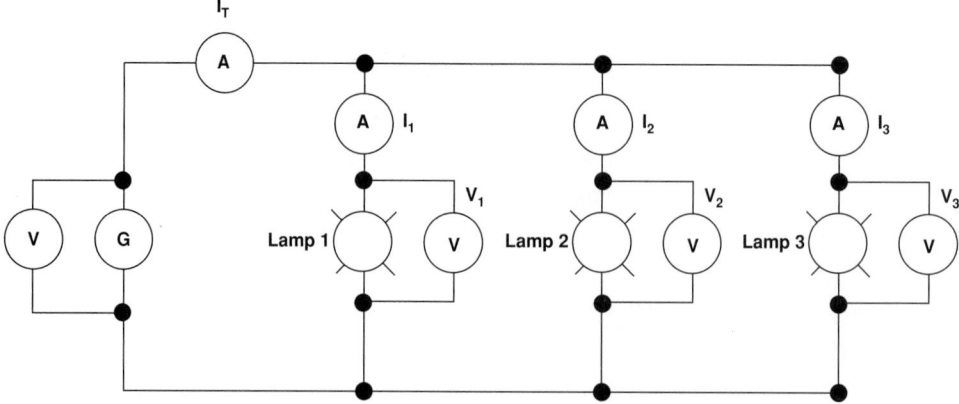

2. The sum of the currents flowing in the individual loads is equal to the current supplied by the source. Thus, in Fig. 4.8 we have:

$$I_{Total} = I_{Lamp\,1} + I_{Lamp\,2} + I_{Lamp\,3}$$

or

$$I_T = I_1 + I_2 + I_3$$

3. The sum of the powers consumed by the individual loads is equal to the power supplied by the source.

    As in the case of series circuits, we obtain:

$$P_{Total} = P_{Lamp\,1} + P_{Lamp\,2} + P_{Lamp\,3}$$

or

$$V_{Total}\, I_{Total} = V_{Lamp\,1}\, I_{Lamp\,1} + V_{Lamp\,2}\, I_{Lamp\,2} + V_{Lamp\,3}\, I_{Lamp\,3}$$

These three rules apply to any parallel circuit, no matter what the elements may be.

4.4 Resistors in Parallel, Equivalent Resistance

Resistance is a property of a device that opposes the flow of current. The opposite concept would be how easily current passes through a device. The easier it is for current to pass through a device, the lower the resistance of the device. We call this property conductance and give it the symbol G. Since G is the opposite of resistance:

$$G = \frac{1}{R}$$

A parallel circuit is a circuit with more than one current path. As we add current paths, it becomes easier and easier for current to flow. Using conductance, we can write this relationship as:

$$G_T = G_1 + G_2 + G_3$$

We can rewrite the conductance in terms of resistance as:

$$\frac{1}{R_T} = \frac{1}{R_1} + \frac{1}{R_2} + \frac{1}{R_3}$$

EQ. 4.2

To find the total resistance we must invert $\frac{1}{R_T}$ to give us:

$$R_T = \frac{1}{\dfrac{1}{R_2} + \dfrac{1}{R_2} + \dfrac{1}{R_3}}$$

Consider a 6 Ω and a 3 Ω resistor connected in parallel across the terminals of a 30 V battery (Fig. 4.9). The current in the 6 Ω resistor is

$$I_1 = \frac{V}{R_1} = \frac{30}{6} = 5\ \text{A}$$

EQ. 2.3

Similarly, the current in the 3 Ω resistor is

$$I_2 = V/R_2 = 30/3 = 10\ \text{A}$$

The total current supplied by the battery is therefore

$$I_G = I_1 + I_2 = 5 + 10 = 15\ \text{A}$$

If the two resistors were hidden under a box so that only the wires leading into the box were accessible, a technician would measure a current of 15 A and a voltage of 30 V. From these measurements, the technician would be led to believe that the box contains a resistor of $R = V/I = 30/15 = 2\ \Omega$.

We conclude that a single resistor of 2 Ω is equivalent to a 6 Ω and a 3 Ω resistor connected in parallel (Fig. 4.10).

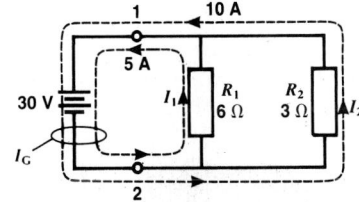

Figure 4.9

Resistors connected in parallel across a battery.

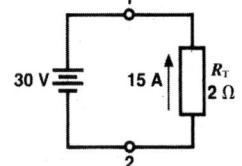

Figure 4.10

This circuit is equivalent to the parallel circuit of Fig. 4.9.

EXAMPLE 4.2

Two resistors of 6 Ω and 3 Ω are connected in parallel (Fig. 4.9). Calculate the value of the equivalent resistance.

SOLUTION:

$$\frac{1}{R_T} = \frac{1}{R_1} + \frac{1}{R_2} = \frac{1}{6} + \frac{1}{3} = 0.1666 + 0.333 = 0.4999$$

Therefore $R_T = 1/0.4999 = 2\ \Omega$

Note that the equivalent resistance (2 Ω) is lower than the lowest of the two resistances (3 Ω). The reason is that when we connect a second resistor in parallel with the 3 Ω resistor, we offer an additional path for current flow. Consequently, the resistance "seen" by the source is less than 3 Ω.

EXAMPLE 4.3

Calculate the resulting resistance when three resistors of 7 Ω, 30 Ω, and 42 Ω are connected in parallel.

SOLUTION:

$$\frac{1}{R_T} = \frac{1}{7} + \frac{1}{30} + \frac{1}{42} = 0.1429 + 0.0333 + 0.0238 = 0.2$$

$$R_T = \frac{1}{0.2} = 5 \ \Omega$$

EXAMPLE 4.4

Calculate the resistance of resistor R_2 in Fig. 4.11.

SOLUTION:

$$\frac{1}{R_T} = \frac{1}{R_1} + \frac{1}{R_2} + \frac{1}{R_3}$$

$$\frac{1}{R_2} = \frac{1}{R_T} - \left(\frac{1}{R_1} + \frac{1}{R_3} \right)$$

$$\frac{1}{R_2} = \frac{1}{4.6} - \left(\frac{1}{10} + \frac{1}{15} \right)$$

$$= 0.2167 - (0.1 + 0.067)$$

$$= 0.2167 - 0.167$$

$$= 0.0497$$

$$R_2 = 1/0.0497$$

$$= 20 \ \Omega$$

Figure 4.11

Three resistors connected in parallel for Example 4.4.

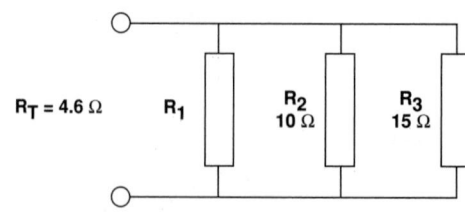

4.5   Series-Parallel Circuits

SERIES-PARALLEL

To solve a **series-parallel** circuit, we begin by looking for resistors that are directly in series or directly in parallel. We then replace these resistors by their equivalent resistance. The resulting circuit will therefore contain fewer resistors than before. If this circuit still contains resistors that are directly in series or directly in parallel, they are also replaced by a new equivalent resistance. Proceeding in this way, from circuit to circuit, we eventually end up with a circuit containing only one resistor. We can easily calculate the voltage and current in this resistor. We then work backward, moving from one circuit to the next higher up, until we have found the current and voltage in every resistor. The method is best explained by means of a numerical example.

EXAMPLE 4.5

In the circuit of Fig. 4.12, calculate the current, voltage, and power for each resistor.

SOLUTION:

We immediately recognize that the 30 Ω and 6 Ω resistors are directly in parallel. Their equivalent resistance is:

$$\frac{I}{R_T} = \frac{1}{6} + \frac{1}{30}$$

EQ. 4.3

Thus, $R_T = 5\ \Omega$

Using the 5 Ω resistor, the circuit simplifies to that of Fig. 4.13. However, we now see that the 10 Ω and 5 Ω resistors are in series, and so we can replace them with an equivalent resistance:

$$R_T = R_1 + R_2 = 10 + 5 = 15\ \Omega$$

Thus, the series-parallel circuit of Fig. 4.12 has been reduced to a single resistance of 15 Ω (Fig. 4.14).

We now work backward, using the same diagrams but inserting the voltages and currents as we go along. (To prevent confusion, we have duplicated Figs. 4.14 to 4.12 and labelled them 4.14a to 4.12a.)

In Fig. 4.14a, the current flowing in the 15 Ω resistor is:

$$I = V/R = 90/15 = 6\text{ A}$$

EQ. 2.2

Clearly, the current in Fig. 4.13a is also 6 A. The voltage across the 10 Ω resistor is:

$$V_1 = IR = 6 \times 10 = 60\text{ V}$$

The voltage across the 5 Ω resistor is

$$V_2 = IR = 6 \times 5 = 30\text{ V}$$

Moving backward to Fig. 4.12a, the voltage and current in the 10 Ω resistor are obviously the same as in Fig. 4.13a, namely 60 V and 6 A, respectively.

Next, we remember that the 5 Ω resistor replaces the 6 Ω and 30 Ω resistors in parallel. Because the voltage is the same in a parallel circuit, the voltage is 30 V across both the 6 Ω and 30 Ω resistors (Fig. 4.12a). The respective currents are:

continued

Figure 4.12

Series-parallel circuit of Example 4.4.

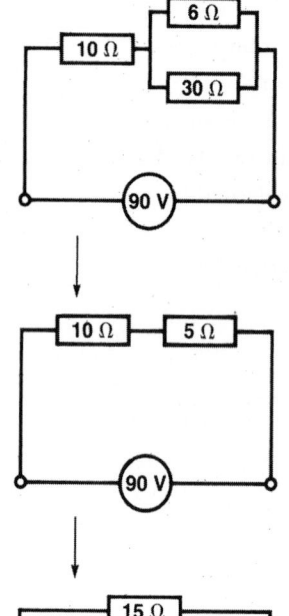

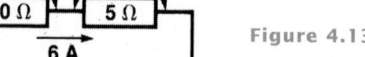

Figure 4.12a

Current in 6 Ω and 30 Ω resistors is calculated.

Figure 4.13

Resistors in parallel are replaced by the 5 Ω resistor.

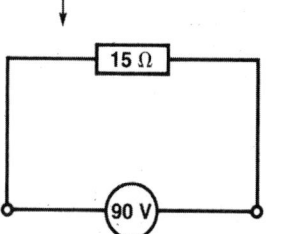

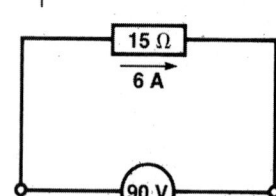

Figure 4.13a

Voltage across the 5 Ω and 10 Ω resistors is calculated.

Figure 4.14

Resistors in series are replaced by the 15 Ω resistor.

Figure 4.14a

Current in 15 Ω resistor is calculated.

$$I_1 = V/R = 30/6 = 5 \text{ A}$$

$$I_2 = 30/30 = 1 \text{ A}$$

Knowing the voltages and currents (Fig. 4.12a), we can calculate the power dissipated in each resistor:

in the 10 Ω resistor: $P = VI = 60 \text{ V} \times 6 \text{ A} = 360 \text{ W}$

in the 6 Ω resistor: $P = VI = 30 \text{ V} \times 5 \text{ A} = 150 \text{ W}$

in the 30 Ω resistor: $P = VI = 30 \text{ V} \times 1 \text{ A} = 30 \text{ W}$

Total power dissipated: $= 360 + 150 + 30 = 540 \text{ W}$

As a check on our calculations, we calculate the power supplied by the source:

$$P = VI = 90 \text{ V} \times 6 \text{ A} = 540 \text{ W}$$

Thus, the generator power is indeed equal to the total power dissipated by the three resistors.

4.6 Energy Flow in a Simple Transmission Line

The purpose of a transmission line is to carry electric energy from a source to a distant load. Figure 4.15 shows a two-conductor line connecting a generator G to a motor M. The generator is driven by a gasoline engine and it generates a terminal voltage of 100 V. The potential difference across the motor terminals is assumed to

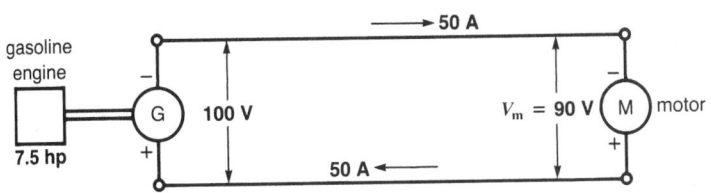

Figure 4.15

Motor connected to a source by means of a transmission line.

be 90 V, and the line current is 50 A. Note that current flows out of the (−) terminal of the generator and into the (−) terminal of the motor. Therefore, the generator is definitely a source and the motor is definitely a load.

The transmission line voltage at the motor end is less than at the generator end, and the so-called **voltage drop** is 100 V − 90 V = 10 V. The voltage drop (also called *IR* drop) occurs because the two line conductors have a certain amount of resistance. We can calculate the value of this resistance by reasoning as follows. The voltage drop for both conductors is 10 V. Therefore, the voltage drop for one conductor is 5 V. Knowing that the line current is 50 A, the resistance for one conductor is $R = V/I = 5/50 = 0.1 \ \Omega$.

VOLTAGE DROP	

The voltage between the line conductors decreases uniformly from 100 V at the generator end to 90 V at the motor end. Thus, the difference of potential at the centre of the line is 95 V.

Let us now calculate the power of each element in the circuit:

1. The generator supplies power $P_G = VI = 100 \times 50 = 5000$ W.

2. The motor receives power $P_M = VI = 90 \times 50 = 4500$ W.

3. The difference between P_M and P_G (500 W) is due to **line losses**. The losses are dissipated as heat in the transmission line. (We also could have calculated the line losses from $P = I^2R$. Thus, the loss in one conductor is $P = I^2R = 50^2 \times 0.1 = 250$ W, or 500 W for both conductors.)

LINE LOSSES	

4.7 Example of a Short-Circuit

Suppose that the lines in Fig. 4.15 accidentally touch each other inside the terminal box of the motor. The current in the line is now limited only by the resistance of the two conductors, namely 0.2 Ω. Consequently, the current will suddenly rise to $I = V/R = 100/0.2 = 500$ A. The generator output will jump to $P = VI = 100 \times 500 = 50\ 000$ W, which is far above normal. This power is entirely dissipated as heat in the conductors, and they will become intensely hot in a matter of seconds (Fig. 4.16). Such a **short-circuit** is dangerous because it may cause a fire or burn out the generator.

SHORT-CIRCUIT	

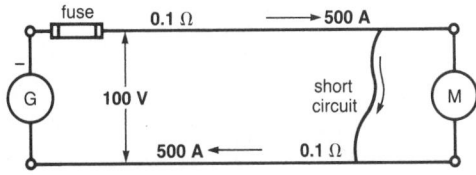

Figure 4.16

A short-circuit can produce high currents and intense heat.

To prevent such disasters we place a *fuse* in series with the line. When the current reaches an abnormally high value, the fuse melts, and the current is interrupted automatically before any damage is done. A fuse is therefore a very important safety device.

4.8 Primary and Secondary Cells

Electric cells are sources of electricity that transform chemical energy into electrical energy. When several cells are connected together to produce either a higher voltage, a greater current, or more power, the combination is called an electric battery.

When a cell delivers electrical energy, it undergoes a progressive chemical change. In the so-called **primary cell**, the chemical change is permanent. As a result, when the chemical material in such a cell is completely transformed, the cell becomes "dead" and has to be thrown away.

PRIMARY CELL

In the case of a **secondary cell**, the original chemical composition can be partly restored by circulating current through the cell in a direction opposite to that of the discharge current. Secondary cells can be recharged several hundred times before they, too, have to be discarded.

SECONDARY CELL

Primary and secondary cells contain three major components: a positive plate called the anode, a negative plate called the cathode, and a conductive base or acid solution called the electrolyte.

The most commonly used primary cell is the alkaline cell. This cell is able to supply current for a longer period than the older carbon-zinc dry cells and at lower temperatures. The alkaline cell has a manganese dioxide anode and a zinc metal cathode, which forms the outer case. The electrolyte is potassium hydroxide paste. The construction of an alkaline cell is shown in Fig. 4.17.

Figure 4.17

The construction of an alkaline primary cell.

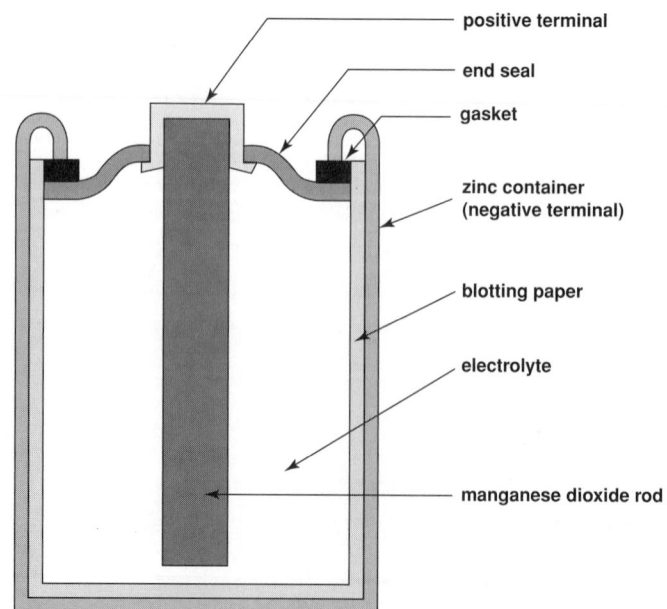

- positive terminal
- end seal
- gasket
- zinc container (negative terminal)
- blotting paper
- electrolyte
- manganese dioxide rod

The lead-acid cell is the most widely used secondary cell. It is used in most cars and is commonly found in industrial standby power systems. It is capable of delivering relatively high load currents for short time periods and moderate currents for longer time periods. The time period depends upon a number of factors, such as temperature, state of charge, and the level of load current.

The lead-acid cell is made from a porous lead plate that forms the cathode and a porous lead oxide plate which forms the anode. The electrolyte is sulphuric acid. The construction of a simple lead-acid cell is shown in Fig. 4.18.

When two electrons are removed from the lead plate, positive lead **ions** are formed. Ions are atoms that have lost or gained electrons. Negative ions have gained electrons, while positive ions have a deficit of electrons. The lead ions combine with negative sulphate ions to form lead sulphate. The lead sulphate forms a layer on the surface of the negative plate. Chemically, we can write this as:

Positive lead ions + negative sulphate ions → lead sulphate

When the lead oxide for the positive plate is formed, the lead atoms share four electrons with the oxygen. This means that the lead dioxide molecule needs four electrons to have a neutral charge. When the two electrons from the negative plate pass through the load and enter the positive plate, they are captured by one of the lead atoms. But now the lead atoms cannot hold onto the oxygen atoms. The oxygen atoms move into the electrolyte, where they combine with hydrogen atoms in the acid. This can be written as:

Lead oxide + 2 electrons → lead + oxygen

In the electrolyte, one oxygen atom freed from the positive plate combines with two hydrogen atoms to form one molecule of water:

1 oxygen + 2 hydrogen → water

ION

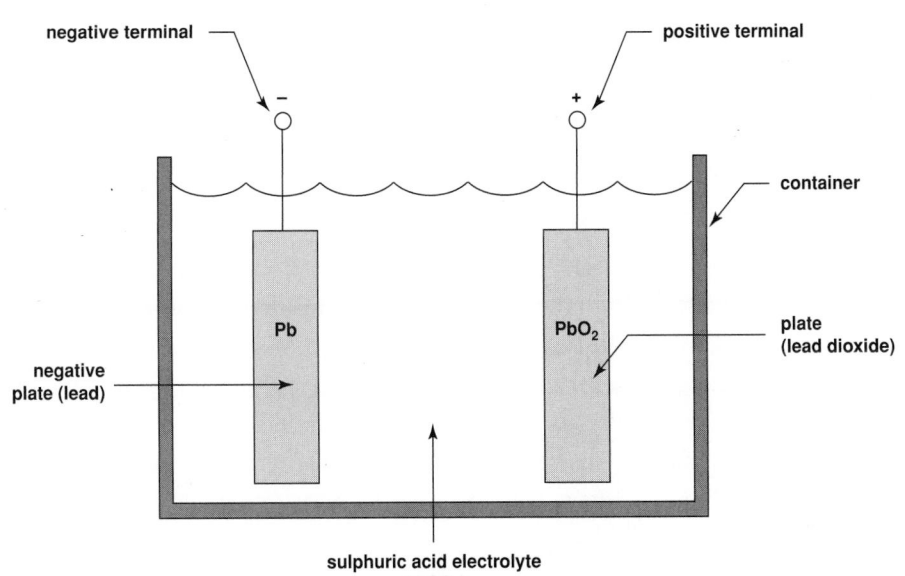

negative terminal

positive terminal

container

plate
(lead dioxide)

Pb

PbO$_2$

negative
plate (lead)

sulphuric acid electrolyte
(H_2SO_4)

Figure 4.19

In order to increase the
current output, a number of
plates are connected in
parallel.

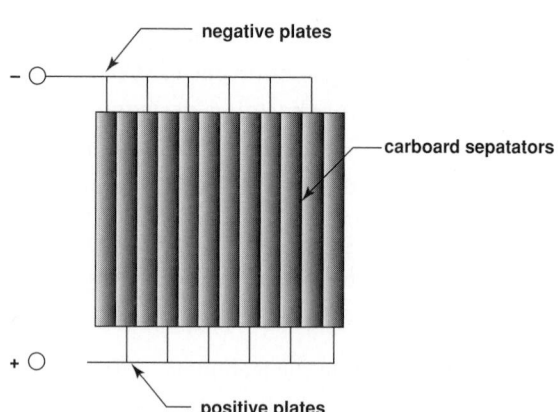

The reaction only happens as long as the plates are in contact with the sulphuric acid electrolyte. As the lead sulphate layer builds up on the negative plate, the reaction slows and the power output of the cell decreases. Recharging the cell will reverse the chemical reactions and restore the original materials.

The amount of current a cell can produce is related to the area of the plates. In order to increase the current output, each cell is made from a number of plates connected in parallel, as shown in Fig. 4.19.

4.9   The Ampere Hour (A.h)

There are about a dozen basic types of cells of commercial importance. They produce dc voltages that range from about 1.5 V to 2.5 V on **open-circuit**—that is, with no load connected to the terminals. The energy a cell can deliver depends upon its size and chemical composition. For example, a standard carbon-zinc flashlight cell delivers about 150 kJ per kilogram; a car battery delivers about 80 kJ per kilogram.

| OPEN-CIRCUIT |

The capacity of a cell or battery is usually expressed in terms of the number of **ampere hours** (A.h) it can deliver. Thus, if a 12 V car battery has a capacity of 40 A.h, it can supply 1 A for 40 h, or 2 A for 20 h, and so forth. Assuming an average terminal voltage of 12 V, this represents a quantity of energy equal to 40 A.h × 12 V = 480 W.h = 480 × 3600 W.s = 1 728 000 J = 1728 kJ.

| AMPERE HOUR |

All batteries possess a certain amount of internal resistance, usually a few milliohms. As a result, the terminal voltage under load is less than at no-load. For normal battery loading, the drop in voltage is seldom more than 10 percent of the open-circuit voltage. However, as the battery charge is depleted, the internal resistance rises. This means that as current is drawn from the battery, the voltage drop across the internal resistance also rises and the terminal voltage decreases. Therefore, the battery voltage should always be measured under load.

EXAMPLE 4.6

A dry cell produces an emf of 1.5 V on open-circuit. It has an internal resistance of 0.2 Ω. Calculate the current and the terminal voltage when the cell is connected to a resistor of 1 Ω (Fig. 4.20).

SOLUTION:

The cell can be represented by a source of 1.5 V in series with a resistance of 0.2 Ω (Fig. 4.21). Note that A and B are the actual terminals of the cell. Point X is not accessible, but exists only in the circuit diagram.

1. The total resistance of the circuit is:

    $R = 1.0 + 0.2 = 1.2\ \Omega$ **EQ. 4.1**

2. The current is $I = V/R = 1.5/1.2 = 1.25$ A

3. The difference of potential across the load (and across the cell terminals) is:

    $V = IR = 1.25 \times 1.0 = 1.25$ V

4. The internal voltage drop of the cell is $(1.5 - 1.25) = 0.25$ V

▼ **Figure 4.20**

See Example 4.6.

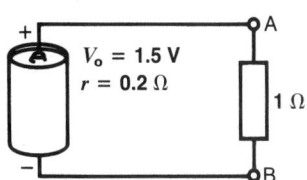

▼ **Figure 4.21**

Equivalent circuit of Fig. 4.20.

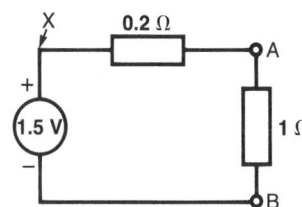

4.10 Cells in Series

Cells are connected in series to create a source of higher emf. The emf of the battery is equal to the sum of the emfs of the individual cells. Furthermore, the internal resistance of the battery is equal to the sum of the internal resistances of the individual cells.

Connections are made from the positive terminal of one cell to the negative terminal of the next until only two terminals are left — one positive, the other negative. Fig. 4.22 shows three cells connected in series.

The cells should be of the same type and have the same ampere hour capacity. If the cells are not identical, some will become discharged earlier than others, and so the battery is rendered useless before all the cells have released their available energy. This also applies to cells connected in parallel.

▼ **Figure 4.22**

Cells connected in series.

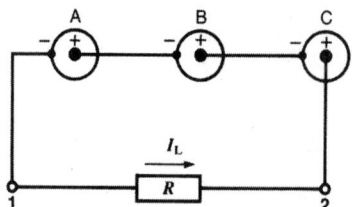

▼ **Figure 4.22**

Cells connected in series.

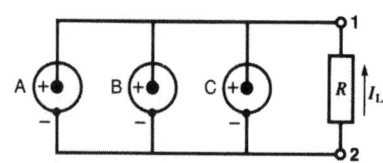

▼ **Figure 4.23**

Cells connected in parallel.

4.11 Cells in Parallel

Cells have to be connected in parallel whenever the load current is greater than the rated current of a single cell. Cells are also connected in parallel whenever we have to store a large quantity of energy. In a parallel connection, all the positive terminals are connected together to make a single positive terminal. Similarly, all the negative terminals are connected to make a single negative terminal (Fig. 4.23). If, by accident, we should connect one cell in reverse, all the cells will become discharged in a few seconds by a heavy circulating current. The reason is that a reversed cell produces the same effect as a short-circuit across the cells. If the cells happen to be primary cells, they will all be destroyed in less than a minute.

4.12 Cells Connected in Series-Parallel

Cells are connected in series-parallel to produce the desired emf and to store the required amount of energy. Fig. 4.24 shows two groups of four cells connected in series. The groups themselves are connected in parallel.

▶ **Figure 4.24**

Cells connected in series-parallel. See Example 4.7.

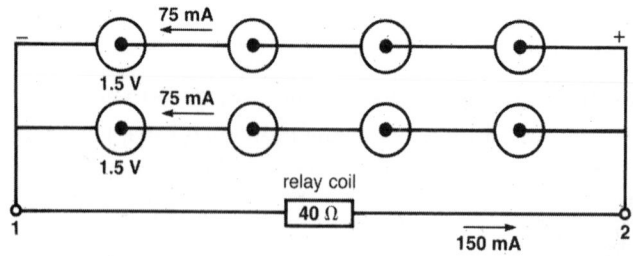

EXAMPLE 4.7

The coil of a relay is rated at 6 V and has a resistance of 40 Ω. The coil has to operate off a battery for at least 400 h. Dry cells rated at 1.5 V and having a capacity of 40 A.h are available. How many cells are needed, and how should they be connected?

continued

SOLUTION:

Four cells have to be connected in series to produce 6 V (4×1.5 V = 6 V). The load current drawn by the relay coil is

$I = V/R = 6/40 = 0.15$ A = 150 mA

During the 400 h operating period, the battery must deliver at least 400 h $\times$ 0.15 A = 60 A.h. Because one group of four cells in series can deliver only 40 A.h, we must use two such groups in parallel, thus yielding 80 A.h. This capacity is more than we need, but it is better to be on the safe side. The current flowing through the battery and load is shown in Fig. 4.24.

4.13 Charging a Secondary Battery

When a secondary battery supplies power to a load, current flows out of the negative terminal (Fig. 4.25). To recharge the battery, we have to force current into the negative terminal, as shown in Fig. 4.26. This is done by connecting the (–) terminal of a battery charger to the (–) terminal of the battery. The charger voltage V_c is slightly greater than battery voltage V_b. As a result, current flows into the (–) terminal of the battery, causing it to charge up.

According to our basic definition for a source and load, the battery is actually a load in Fig. 4.26. It receives energy from the charger and this energy restores the battery to its former chemical state.

We now see that a source, such as a battery, can also behave as a load, depending upon the direction of current flow. We shall encounter this surprising dual behaviour in other circuits and machines.

When a secondary cell such as a lead-acid cell is being recharged, it releases hydrogen, a flammable gas. Battery rooms must therefore be well ventilated to prevent possible explosions. Particular care must also be taken to keep away from the extremely corrosive and blinding sulfuric acid.

Figure 4.25 ◄

Current flow when battery is discharging.

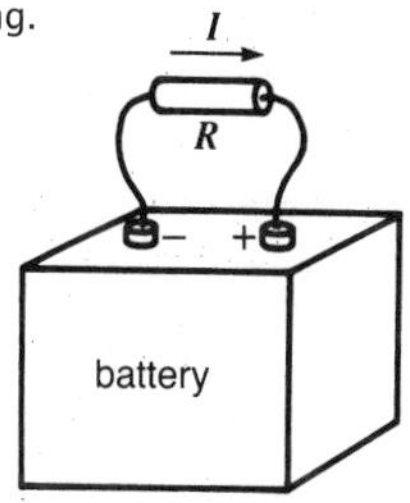

Figure 4.26 ◄

Current flow when battery is charging.

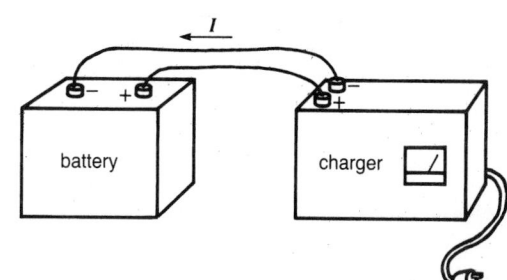

4.14 Kirchhoff's Voltage and Current Laws

Most circuits can be solved using the methods covered in the previous sections. Other circuits, however, are more complex, and a systematic method must be used to solve them. This method is based upon two laws, known as Kirchhoff's voltage law (KVL) and Kirchhoff's current law (KCL).

KIRCHHOFF'S VOLTAGE LAW

Kirchhoff's voltage law states that the algebraic sum of the voltages around any closed loop is zero. In essence, this means that the sum of all the voltage rises is equal to the sum of all the voltage drops as we move around a circuit loop. This is much the same as a mountain climber who starts from a given point, takes a random walk over hills and valleys, and then comes back to the starting point. The sum of all the uphill vertical distances the climber covers is obviously equal to all the downhill vertical distances.

KIRCHHOFF'S CURRENT LAW

Kirchhoff's current law states that the algebraic sum of the currents that arrive at a point is zero. This means that the sum of the currents that arrive at a terminal is equal to the sum of the currents that leave it.

To understand how KCL is applied, consider seven currents that flow into and out of a common terminal T, as shown in Fig. 4.27. The sum of the currents that arrive at the terminal is $I_1 + I_3 + 3$. The sum of the currents that leave is $I_2 + I_5 + 10 + I_4$. Using KCL the equation is:

$$I_1 + I_3 + 3 = I_2 + I_5 + 10 + I_4$$

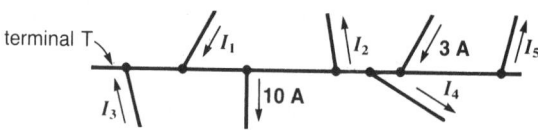

Figure 4.27

Circuit illustrating Kirchhoff's current law.

4.15 Voltage Rises and Voltage Drops

To understand how KVL is applied, we first define what is meant by a voltage rise and a voltage drop. Consider a voltage V having the polarities given in Fig. 4.28. Imagine that we move from terminal A to terminal B. Because this is a move from (–) to (+), it is considered to be a voltage drop. (Recall that electrons are negative.) If we move from B to A, this is a move from (+) to (–), which is considered to be a voltage rise. The magnitude of the voltage rise (or drop) is equal to V.

Voltage rises and voltage drops are also produced when currents flow through a resistance.

Thus, suppose a current I is flowing through a resistor R in the direction shown in Fig. 4.29a. Clearly, the voltage across the resistor is equal to IR. Because current always flows from (–) to (+) in a resistor, we indicate these polarities, as shown in Fig. 4.29b. Now if we move from terminal C to terminal D, we go from (+) to (–) which gives us a voltage rise. If we move from D to C, we obtain a voltage drop. The magnitude of the voltage rise (or drop) is equal to IR.

▼ **Figure 4.28**

Defining voltage rise and voltage drop.

▼ **Figure 4.29a**

Current flowing in a resistor produces a voltage across its terminals.

▼ **Figure 4.29b**

Currents produce a voltage rise or voltage drop.

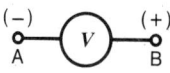

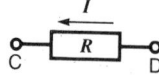

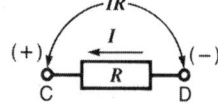

4.16 Applying Kirchhoff's Laws

Let us apply these principles to solve the circuit of Fig. 4.30. It is composed of two resistors, and of three sources — 10 V, 20 V, and 30 V — having the polarities shown. It is not obvious in which direction the currents will flow, so let us *assume* that I_1 flows from C to B, and I_2 flows from D to B (Fig. 4.31). This enables us to put (–) and (+) signs on the 10 Ω and 5 Ω resistors. Furthermore, the voltage across each resistor is equal to 10 I_1 and 5 I_2, *as* shown.

We are now ready to apply Kirchhoff's voltage law because every element in the circuit has polarity marks, and the magnitude of the voltage across each element is indicated.

Think of yourself as being an electrical-mountain climber starting at any point, such as A. You are allowed to move along any loop you please, but you must come back to your starting point. As you cross the electrical hills and valleys, you record all the voltage rises and voltage drops. Then you equate their sum.

Referring to Fig. 4.31, and starting from point A, let us move clockwise around the outer loop. It is composed of the three sources and the 5 Ω resistor. As we move from B to D, across the 5 Ω resistor, we experience a voltage rise equal to 5 I_2. Then, as we cross the 30 V source, we have a voltage drop. Next, as we pass C and cross the 20 V source, it gives us a voltage rise. Finally, we cross the 10 V source, which

▼ **Figure 4.30**

Solving a more complex circuit.

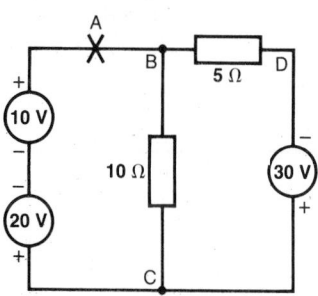

▼ **Figure 4.31**

Applying KVL to the circuit of Fig. 4.30.

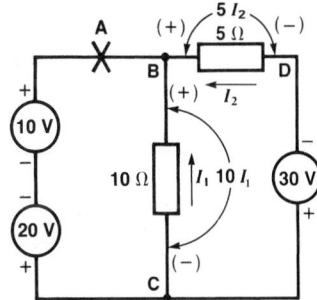

gives us a voltage drop and brings us back to the starting point. We list the voltage rises and voltage drops, and find their sum, as follows:

voltage drops = 30 + 10 = 40
 voltage rises = 5 I_2 + 20

Equating these sums, we obtain:

$$20 + 5\ I_2 = 40$$

And so   5 I_2 = 20

Therefore I_2 = 4 A

To find I_1 we again start at point A, but travel over the left-hand loop. It consists of the 10 V and 20 V sources and the 10 Ω resistor. This time, to show our versatility, let us move counterclockwise (ccw) around the loop. We again record the voltage rises and voltage drops, and find their sum:

voltage drops = 20 + 10 I_1
 voltage rises = 10

Equating the sums, we find

$$20 + 10\ I_1 = 10$$
$$10\ I_1 = -10$$
$$I_1 = -1 \text{A}$$

Current I_1 is equal to 1 A, but it has a negative sign. This means that the current actually flows in the direction opposite to what we had assumed. The actual current flows are shown in Fig. 4.32.

The remaining current I_3 can be found by using Kirchhoff's current law. The sum of the currents that leave at point B is (I_3 + 1). The sum of the currents that arrive at point B is obviously 4 A. Consequently,

$I_3 + 1 = 4$
And so
$I_3 = 3$ A

Figure 4.32

Currents in the circuit of Fig. 4.30.

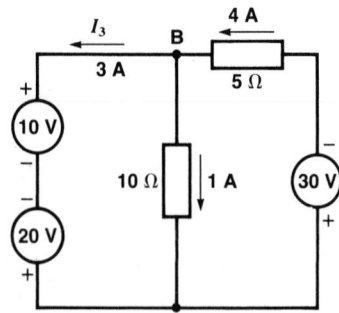

4.17 Summary

Upon completion of this chapter you should have learned that:

● series circuits are circuits that have only one current path, while parallel circuits have more than one current path. In series-parallel circuits, a portion of the circuit is connected in series and other portions are connected in parallel.

- Problems involving voltage, current, and resistance in series, parallel and series-parallel circuits can be solved using Ohm's law and Kirchoff's laws.

- When current flows through a transmission line, there will be a voltage drop across the resistance of the transmission line, and the line resistance will also consume some power.

- Primary cells, such as the alkaline cell, are disposable, while secondary cells, such as the lead-acid cell, can be recharged.

- A chemical process allows a lead-acid cell to produce current. This process is reversible. Passing a current from the positive battery terminal to the negative battery terminal can reverse the chemical charges.

- Cells can be connected in series to increase voltage output, or they can be connected in parallel to increase output current.

- Kirchoff's laws can be used to determine the current through any portion of a complex circuit or the voltage across any component in a complex circuit.

Key Terms

AMPERE HOUR: A means of rating cells and batteries based upon the amount of current they can supply for a period of one hour.

ION: Atom that has gained or lost electrons.

KIRCHOFF'S CURRENT LAW: The sum of the currents flowing into a point will equal the sum of the currents flowing out of a point.

KIRCHOFF'S VOLTAGE LAW: The sum of the voltages around a closed loop will be zero.

LINE LOSS: The power, in watts, consumed by the resistance of a conductor.

OPEN-CIRCUIT: A circuit with a total resistance that approaches an infinite value. As a result, no current will flow. An example is an open switch connected in series with a lamp.

PARALLEL: Any circuit in which there is more than one current path is a parallel connected circuit.

PRIMARY CELL: A chemical cell that cannot be recharged. An alkaline cell is an example.

RESISTOR: A device whose primary characteristic is resistance. Examples of resistors include light bulbs, electric toasters and electric radiant heaters.

SECONDARY CELL: A chemical cell that can be recharged by causing a reverse current to flow. A lead-acid cell is an example of a secondary cell.

SERIES: Any circuit in which there is only one current path is a series connected circuit.

SERIES-PARALLEL: Any circuit in which a portion of the circuit is series connected and other portions are connected in parallel.

SHORT-CIRCUIT: A circuit connection in which the total resistance is close to zero ohms. Short-circuits result in excessive current, which can damage equipment and wiring. They often present a safety hazard.

VOLTAGE DROP: The decrease in load voltage due to the resistance of the transmission lines.

Test Your Knowledge

4.1 A series circuit is composed of several loads and a single source. The sum of the currents in the loads is equal to the current supplied by the source.

true_____   false_____

4.2 Four *identical* resistors are connected in series across a 120 V source. The current in one of the resistors is 8 A. The power dissipated by one resistor is
a. 240 W
b. 960 W
c. 240 J
d. 15 W

4.3 A current of 360 A feeds 20 identical resistors connected in parallel. The current in each resistor is
a. 360 A
b. 18 A
c. 7200 A

4.4 Three resistors of 7 Ω, 42 Ω and 30 Ω are connected in parallel. The equivalent resistance is
a. 79 Ω
b. 0.2 Ω
c. 5 Ω

4.5 Thirty resistors of 60 Ω each are connected in parallel. The equivalent resistance is
a. 2 Ω
b. 0.5 Ω
c. 60 Ω

4.6 A primary cell can be recharged by using a battery charger.

true_____   false_____

4.7 When recharging a secondary battery, the positive battery terminal is connected to the negative terminal of the battery charger.

true_____   false_____

4.8 In Fig. 4.24 there is a voltage drop in going from terminal 1 to terminal 2.

true_____   false_____

4.9 Three batteries have voltages of 6 V, 12 V, and 20 V, respectively. If they are connected in series in every possible way, the highest and lowest voltages are
a. 38 V and 6 V
b. 20 V and 6 V
c. 38 V and 2 V

4.10 When identical cells axe connected in series, the ampere hour capacity of the battery is equal to the ampere hour capacity of one cell.

true_____   false_____

4.11 When identical cells are connected in parallel, the ampere hour capacity of the battery is equal to the sum of the ampere hour capacities of the cells.

true_____   false_____

Questions and Problems

4.12 In Fig. 4.22, each cell produces 2 V, and load resistance R is 4 Ω. Calculate (a) the load current I_L and (b) the power supplied by each cell.

4.13 In Fig. 4.23, each cell produces 2 V, and load resistance R is 2 Ω. Calculate (a) the load current I_L and (b) the power supplied by each cell.

4.14 In Fig. 4.22, each cell produces an open-circuit voltage of 2 V and has an internal resistance of 0.1 Ω. If the capacity of each cell is 60 A.h and R is 1.7 Ω, calculate (a) the voltage across the resistor, (b) the voltage across the terminals of each cell, and (c) the time to discharge the battery.

4.15 In Fig. 4.23, each cell produces an open-circuit voltage of 1.5 V and has an internal resistance of 0.3 Ω. If the capacity of each cell is 2 A.h and R is 100 Ω, calculate (a) the voltage across the resistor and (b) the time to discharge the battery.

4.16 Primary cells are available having a rating of 1.5 V, 20 A.h. Using these cells, we wish to make a 30 V battery having a rating of at least 110 A.h. How many cells are required, and how must they be connected?

4.17 A home is equipped with nine 10-watt lamps. Calculate the total current if the line voltage is 120 V.

4.18 A 25 Ω resistor is connected in series with a relay coil having a resistance of 80 Ω. If 42 V is applied to the circuit, calculate (a) the current in the coil and (b) the power dissipated in the resistor.

4.19 Two resistors of 20 Ω and 30 Ω are connected in series across a 1.5 kV source. Calculate (a) the voltage across the 30 Ω resistor and (b) the power supplied by the source.

4.20 Two resistors of 60 Ω and 40 Ω are connected in series. The voltage across the 40 Ω resistor is 50 V. Calculate (a) the voltage of the source and (b) the power dissipated in the 60 Ω resistor.

4.21 Fill in the empty spaces in the following table. Each case involves only one resistor.

CASE NUMBER	1	2	3	4	5
P	100 W		200 W	100 kW	2 W
E		10 V		1 kV	
R		1000 Ω	800 Ω		10^6 Ω
I	10 A				

4.22 In Fig. 4.33, calculate the current in the 12 Ω resistor, using KVL and KCL.

4.23 In Fig. 4.34, determine the magnitude and direction of the current that flows in conductor x.

▼ Figure 4.33

See Problem 4.22.

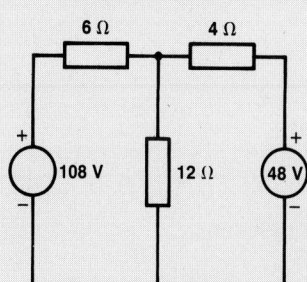

▼ Figure 4.34

See Problem 4.23.

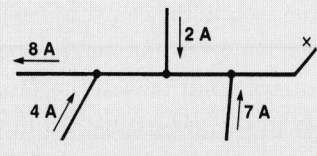

5

Magnetism and Electromagnets

LEARNING OBJECTIVES

Upon completion of this chapter you will be able to:

- Describe the properties of permanent magnets
- Describe the properties of electromagnets
- List several applications for electromagnets
- Explain how the magnetic circuit affects an electromagnet
- Describe how torque is created in a magnetic circuit
- Describe hysteresis losses
- Explain how hysteresis develops torque

5.1   Magnetic Polarity, N and S Poles

If we tie a string around the centre of a permanent magnet and suspend it from the ceiling, one end of the magnet will always point toward the geographic North Pole, the other to the geographic South Pole. The two ends of the bar magnet are therefore different. The end

that points toward the north is called a **magnetic** north **pole** (N). Similarly, the end
that points toward the south is called a magnetic south pole (S).

MAGNETIC POLE

5.2 Magnetic Attraction and Repulsion

Suppose we have two bar magnets A and B whose magnetic north and south poles
have been identified in the manner we have just explained. If we bring the N pole
of magnet A near the S pole of magnet B, we discover that the poles are attracted
to each other. On the other hand, if we bring the S pole of magnet A near the S pole
of magnet B, the poles repel each other. By doing more experiments with magnets
of different types and sizes, we always observe the same behaviour. We can therefore state a basic law of magnetism: **poles of opposite polarity attract each
other, and poles of the same polarity repel each other.**

The law of repulsion and attraction can explain why one end of a bar magnet always
points toward the geographic North Pole. The reason is that a magnetic S pole
exists near the geographic North Pole. Similarly, a magnetic N pole exists near the
geographic South Pole. These magnetic poles are created by enormous electric currents that circulate within the earth's core.

Navigators formerly applied this magnetic effect by using a compass to circum-
navigate the earth. A compass is a sensitive instrument that consists of a very small
bar magnet pivoted on its centre. One end of the compass needle always points
north; this permitted the sailors to find their way.

5.3 Lines of Force; the Weber (Wb)

If a compass is placed near a bar magnet, the N pole of the compass will be repelled
by the N pole and attracted by the S pole of the magnet. Similarly, the S pole of the
compass needle is attracted by the N pole and repelled by the S pole of the magnet. The effect of these forces causes the compass needle to point in a definite
direction, which depends upon where the compass is placed.

Suppose we have dozens of tiny compasses to experiment with. Starting from a
point A on the bar magnet, let us string out a series of compasses so that the needles follow each other, head to tail. We discover that the needles trace a curved path
that extends from A to B (Fig. 5.1). Similarly, if we start at another point such as X,
we obtain a new path which ends up at point Y.

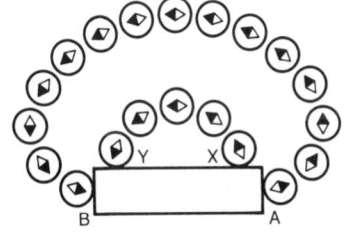

Figure 5.1

Compass needles
indicate the shape of
the flux line.

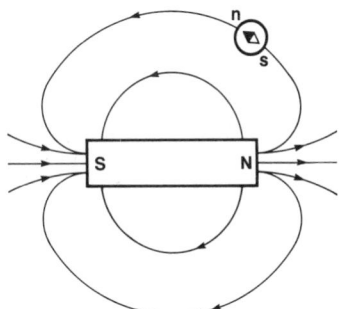

Figure 5.2

Magnetic field around
a bar magnet.

FLUX LINES

Fig. 5.2 shows some of the many paths that can be traced out in this way. They are called **flux lines**, or magnetic lines of force. The entire space surrounding the bar magnet is filled with these lines. The sum total of the lines is called a magnetic field.

Although magnetic lines of force do not actually exist, they are very useful in representing a magnetic field. In the same way that the weather forecaster on television uses arrows and curves to illustrate the direction and strength of the wind, we use lines to indicate the direction and strength of a magnetic field.

In some measurement systems, the line of force (or maxwell) is the unit of magnetic flux. However, the SI unit of magnetic flux is the weber symbol (Wb). One weber is equal to 10^8 lines; consequently, 1 line = 10^{-8} Wb = 0.01 microwebers (μWb).

5.4 Properties of Lines of Force

To simplify the study of magnetism, lines of force are assumed to have a direction. The direction is that indicated by the N pole of a compass needle. As shown in Fig. 5.3, the flux lines around a bar magnet are therefore directed from the N pole to the S pole. Consequently, a flux line always comes out of a N pole and enters by a S pole. Each flux line is assumed to pass right through the bar magnet, forming an individual, closed loop.

Michael Faraday, a nineteenth century British physicist, also found it useful to assume that flux lines have the following properties:

1. They behave as if they were tightly stretched elastic bands that mutually repel each other.

2. They never cross each other.

3. They always tend to follow the shortest (or easiest) path.

The flux lines are not affected in any way if we bring a piece of material, such as aluminum, glass, copper, or cement, near the magnet. The flux lines pass through such materials as if they weren't there. The only substances that affect the lines are iron, nickel, cobalt, and their alloys. Such substances are called magnetic materials, and we shall learn more about them later.

Figure 5.3

Flux lines come out of the N pole and enter by the S pole.

Figure 5.4

When a bar magnet is cut in two, N and S poles are created in each part.

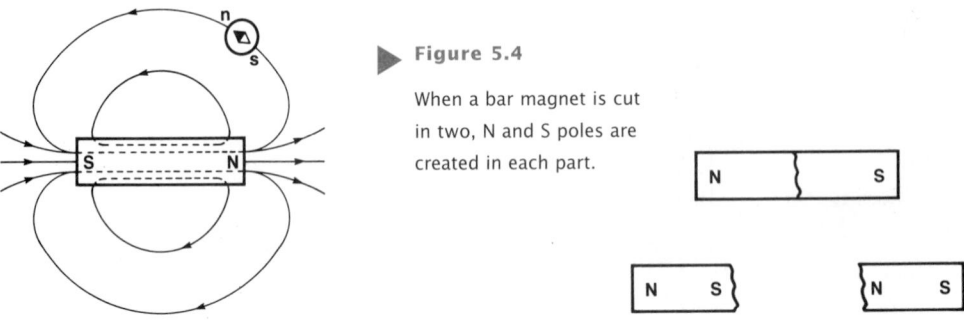

If we cut a bar magnet in two and separate the two parts, we discover that this does not create a single N pole and a single S pole, as we might expect. Instead, each part again has a north and a south pole, as shown in Fig. 5.4. The two poles continue to exist on each part, even if the parts are moved away from each other. This leads us to another important law of magnetism: for every N pole there is always a corresponding S pole.

5.5 Magnetic Domains; Induced and Residual Magnetism

If we could look inside a block of iron, we would discover that it is composed of millions of so-called **magnetic domains**, packed side by side. Each domain is a tiny permanent magnet having one N and one S pole. The domains have irregular shapes and vary in size. However, many are big enough to be seen under an ordinary microscope. Under normal conditions, the N–S poles of the magnetic domains are oriented in every which way. The result is that the magnetic fields cancel each other, and so the block of iron has no external N or S pole.

MAGNETIC DOMAINS

However, if we bring the N pole of a permanent magnet near a block of iron, thousands of magnetic domains will swing around as if they were compass needles. The S poles of these magnetic domains will point toward the N pole of the magnet. This orderly line-up of magnetic domains causes the block of iron to develop an external N and S pole, as shown in Fig. 5.5. Thus, by bringing a permanent magnet near a piece of iron, the iron itself becomes a magnet. In effect, the N pole of the permanent magnet induces a S pole in the iron. Because unlike poles attract, the block of iron will be drawn toward the magnet. This phenomenon is called induced magnetism.

The same effect takes place if we bring the S pole of the bar magnet near the block of iron. The magnetic domains will swing around 180 degrees. Consequently, the induced magnetic poles will reverse, and so the iron will again be attracted to the magnet. That is why a nail is attracted to either the N or S pole of a permanent magnet.

If the magnet is brought very close to the iron block, many more magnetic domains will line up, causing the induced magnetic poles to became stronger. Consequently, the force of attraction will become greater.

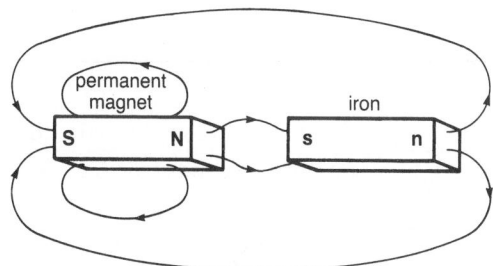

Figure 5.5

A permanent magnet induces N and S poles in a piece of iron.

What happens when the permanent magnet is removed? Ideally, the magnetic domains will return to their random state and the induced magnetic poles will disappear. However, in practice, the magnetic domains do not all swing back to where they were before. As a result, the block of iron will have a weak N and S pole when the magnet is removed. This is known as residual magnetism. In effect, the piece of iron becomes a weak permanent magnet after it has been subjected to a strong magnetic field.

Although we have chosen iron to illustrate the phenomenon of induced and residual magnetism, the same effect takes place when any magnetic material is subjected to an external field.

5.6 Permanent Magnets

Some materials possess magnetic domains that are very hard to turn around. Once they have taken a position, they tend to stay locked in place. If such a material is put in an intense magnetic field, all its magnetic domains will line up, causing all the N-poles to point in the same direction. However, when the external field is removed, the magnetic domains remain frozen in place. Consequently, the material continues to have very strong N and S poles, meaning that it has become a permanent magnet.

Powerful permanent magnets are made of alloys of iron, aluminum, cobalt, platinum, yttrium, oxygen, etc. Alnico V, for example, is a typical permanent magnet alloy made up of 51% iron, 8% aluminum, 14% nickel, 24% cobalt, and 3% copper.

Ceramic magnets form another class of permanent magnets. They are much lighter than metallic magnets and have resistivities as high as those of good insulators. Among other applications, they are used in the manufacture of door-sealing magnetic strips and magnetic tapes.

We sometimes want to demagnetize a permanent magnet. This can be done in three ways:

a)   Heating the magnet until it is red hot.

b)   Subjecting it to a powerful but gradually decreasing ac field.

c)   Striking it repeatedly with sharp blows.

Each of these methods causes the magnetic domains to take a random position.

5.7 Magnetic Field Created by a Current

If we bring a compass close to a current-carrying conductor, the needle always swings to a position at right angles to the conductor (Fig. 5.6). When the current stops flowing, the needle returns to its normal position in the earth's magnetic field. If the current is reversed, the compass needle also reverses, but it still remains at right angles to the conductor. This experiment shows that an electric current produces a magnetic field.

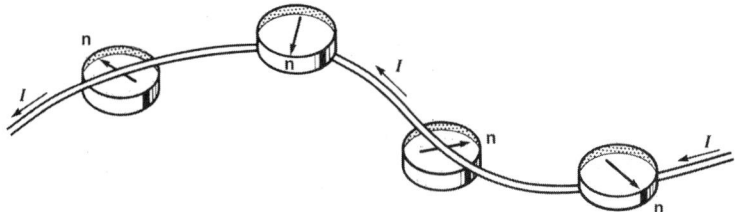

Figure 5.6

A current produces a magnetic field.

Further experiments show that the lines of force exist in circular loops around the conductor (Fig. 5.7). The direction of the lines depends upon the direction of current flow. The so-called left-hand rule gives the relationship between the two:

If the conductor is grasped in the left hand so that the thumb points in the direction of current flow, the fingers indicate the direction of the lines of force (Fig. 5.8).

Referring to Fig. 5.8, you will note that one end of the conductor bears a cross X, while the other bears a dot. The cross shows that current is flowing into the conductor and away from you. The dot indicates that current is flowing out of the conductor and toward you. The dot and cross may be thought of as being the tip and tail of a feathered arrow.

▼ **Figure 5.7**

    The magnetic field around a
    conductor is composed of
    circular loops.

▼ **Figure 5.8**

    The left-hand rule indicates
    the direction of the flux
    lines around a current-
    carrying conductor.

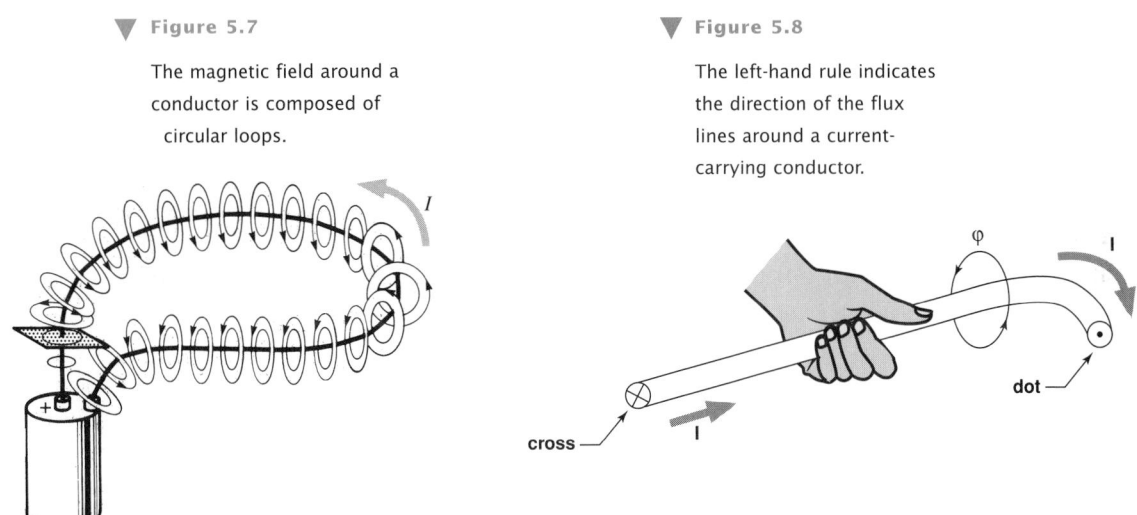

5.8 Magnetic Field Produced by a Short Coil

Fig. 5.9 shows a coil having 100 turns and carrying a current of 5 A. Each turn produces a rather weak magnetic field because the current is small. However, with 100 turns, the field is 100 times stronger, and therefore many flux lines are produced. The magnetic field is similar to that produced by a disc-shaped permanent magnet (Fig. 5.10).

The coil also produces an N pole and an S pole. The N pole is where the flux comes out of the coil and the S pole is where it goes in (Fig. 5.9).

► **Figure 5.9**

A circular coil produces an N
and S pole.

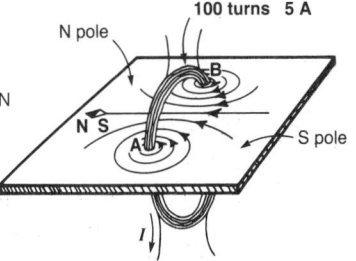

► **Figure 5.9**

A circular coil produces an N
and S pole.

► **Figure 5.10**

The field around a disc-
shaped permanent magnet
is similar to that produced
by the coil in Fig. 5.9.

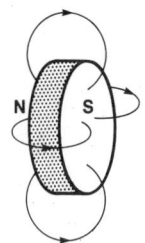

We can increase the strength of the field by raising the current above 5 A. If we double the current, the number of flux lines will double. If we increased the current to
50 A, the number of flux lines would increase ten times. However, a large current
causes the wire to overheat, and the coil may burn out.

5.9 Magnetomotive Force and Flux Density, the Tesla (T)

MAGNETOMOTIVE FORCE

The **magnetomotive force** (mmf) of a coil is equal to the number of turns it has
times the current it carries. Thus, a coil of 50 turns carrying a current of 8 A develops an mmf of (50 × 8) = 400 ampere turns (400 At). The mmf of a coil is the driving force that produces the flux.

FLUX DENSITY

Returning to Fig. 5.9, if the mmf of the coil is increased, the number of lines of force
inside the coil will increase. As a result, the lines inside the coil become more densely
packed. In other words, the number of lines per square centimetre increases. This so-
called **flux density** is a measure of the strength of a magnetic field. For example, in
Fig. 5.2 the field is stronger near the poles because the flux density is greater there. The
SI unit of flux density is the tesla, equal to one weber per square metre. The tesla (symbol T) is equivalent to 10 000 lines per square centimetre.*

5.10 Magnetic Field of a Long Coil, Electromagnets

The long coil, shown in Fig. 5.11, is equivalent to a series of short coils (Fig. 5.9)
stacked side by side. The resulting magnetic field consists of flux lines that pass
through the centre of the coil. Each line forms a separate, closed loop. The direction of the lines inside the coil is easily found by applying the left-hand rule to one
of the turns.

The magnetic field has the same shape as that produced by a bar magnet of equal
size (Fig. 5.12). Furthermore, like a magnet, the coil produces an N pole at one end
and an S pole at the other.

---

* In the centimetre-gram-second system of units, the unit of flux density is the gauss, equal to 1 line per
   square centimetre.

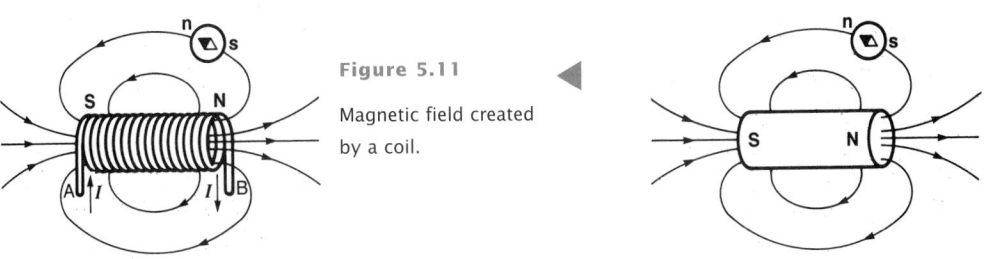

Figure 5.11

Magnetic field created by a coil.

Figure 5.12

The magnetic field around the bar magnet is similar to that produced by the coil of Fig. 5.11.

Unfortunately, the coil produces only a small amount of flux, even when the current is raised to the point at which the coil begins to overheat. But if we introduce a soft iron core inside the coil, the flux increases dramatically. The reason is that the mmf of the coil causes some of the magnetic domains in the iron to line up. The enormous flux produced by the magnetic domains add therefore to the rather weak flux created by the coil alone. The result is a powerful electromagnet. Electromagnets produce a large flux with a moderate mmf.

Electromagnets act in a sense like variable permanent magnets because they enable us to vary the flux by simply varying the current. Furthermore, the magnetic polarity can be reversed by reversing the current flow. Because of this versatility, it is not surprising that electromagnets are found in almost every electric machine and device.

5.11 Typical Applications of Electromagnets

One of the most important uses of electromagnets is to create the field in dc motors and generators. In Fig. 5.13, the coils are wound on iron pole-pieces so as to produce an N and S pole. The flux lines follow the dotted path shown in the diagram. They flow across the two air gaps and return, in closed loops, by way of the iron frame.

Figure 5.14 shows a magnetic brake for an elevator. When the elevator is not moving, a powerful spring causes brake shoes to clamp around a drum. The drum is directly coupled to the elevator motor. As soon as the motor is energized, current

▼ **Figure 5.13**

Magnetic field created by the coils in a dc generator.

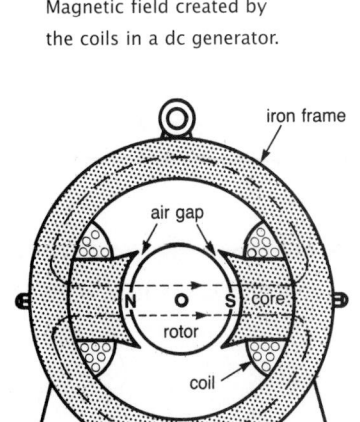

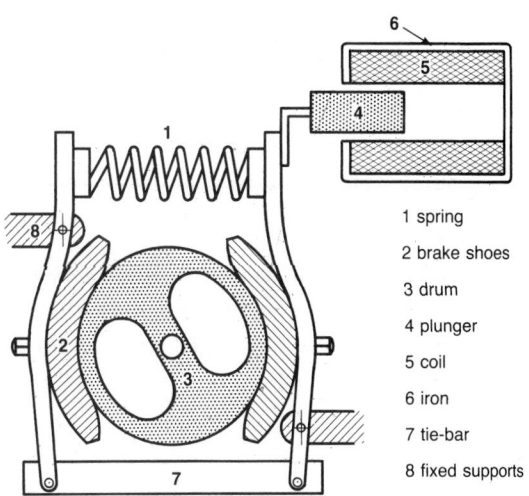

Figure 5.14

Electric brake to prevent an elevator motor from turning when the motor is stopped.

1 spring
2 brake shoes
3 drum
4 plunger
5 coil
6 iron
7 tie-bar
8 fixed supports

Figure 5.15

Relay or contactor contacts can be made to open or close by energizing or de-energizing a coil.

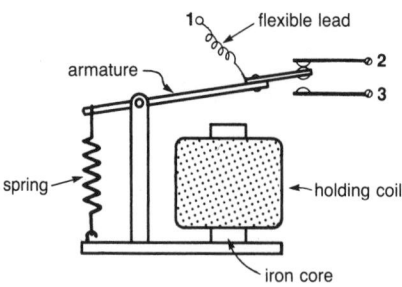

starts flowing in the coil. This attracts the iron plunger, causing it to move inside the coil. This releases the pressure of the brake shoes against the drum, and the elevator motor is free to turn. When the motor stops, the electromagnet is automatically de-energized, which releases the iron plunger. The brake shoes again come into action, clamping the drum and preventing further movement of the elevator.

Figure 5.15 shows a magnetic contactor, which is also called a relay. When no current flows in the holding coil, contact is made between terminals 1 and 2. But when the coil is excited, a flux is produced in the iron core, which attracts the iron armature. This overcomes the tension of the spring, causing contacts 1 and 3 to close. The opening and closing of these contacts enable us to control a device from a distance.

5.12 Properties of Magnetic Circuits

Most electrical machines, such as motors, generators, transformers, and relays, contain coils that produce a magnetic field. The amount of flux produced depends upon the mmf of the coil, the quality of the iron, the length of the air gap, and the particular dimensions of the machine. Calculating the flux in such complicated magnetic circuits is a problem for designers. Nevertheless, we can gain some useful insights by examining the behaviour of a few simple magnetic circuits. In Sections 5.13 to 5.15 we discuss three circuits: a non-magnetic core circuit, a magnetic-core circuit, and a magnetic-core circuit having an air gap.

5.13 Magnetic Circuit with a Non-Magnetic Core

Consider Fig. 5.16, in which a coil of 800 turns is wound on a non-magnetic core, such as wood. The core has a length of 1 m and a cross section of 1 cm^2. A dc source enables us to raise the current gradually from zero to 4 A. A special flux-meter (not shown) indicates the flux produced in the core.

When the current is 1 A, the mmf is 800 ampere-turns and the fluxmeter indicates 10 lines. If the current is doubled, the mmf becomes 1600 At and the flux increases to 20 lines. Finally, with a current of 4 A, the mmf is 3200 At and the fluxmeter indicates 40 lines.

▼ **Figure 5.16**

Coil wound on a non-magnetic core.

▼ **Figure 5.17**

In a non-magnetic material, the flux is directly proportional to the mmf.

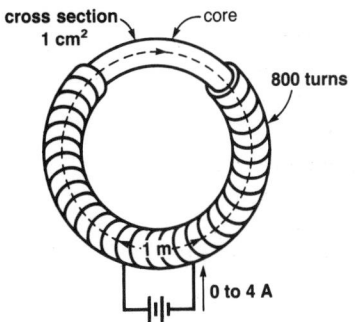

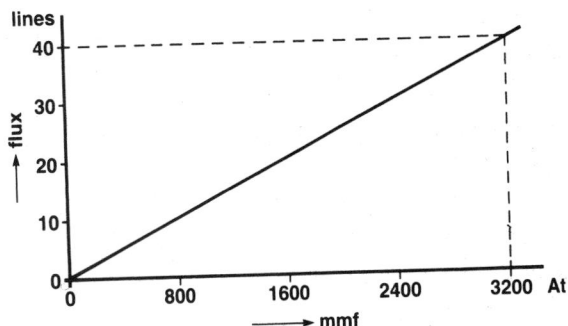

If we plot the number of lines of force versus the mmf of the coil, we obtain a straight line (Fig. 5.17). We conclude that the flux is directly proportional to the mmf when the magnetic circuit is composed of a non-magnetic material, such as wood. The same graph would be obtained if the core were made of air or cement, or even if it were a vacuum. Consequently, non-magnetic materials have the same magnetic properties.

5.14 Magnetic Circuit with a Magnetic Core

Let us replace the wooden core of Fig. 5.16 with an iron core having the same dimensions. We again raise the current from zero to 4 A and observe the corresponding values of flux.

We discover that the same mmf produces much more flux than before. Thus, for a current of 1 A, the mmf is again 800 At, but the flux is 15 000 lines, instead of only 10 lines.

If we double the mmf to 1600 At, the flux rises to 18 000 lines. Finally, for a mmf of 3200 At, the flux is 19 000 lines. These results are plotted in Fig. 5.18. They produce an upward-sloping curve that gradually flattens as the mmf increases.

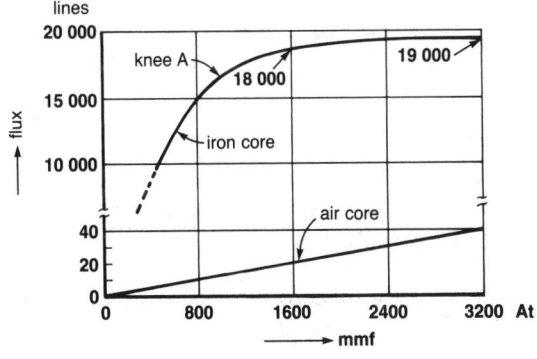

Figure 5.18

Saturation curve obtained when an iron core is used in Fig. 5.16.

This is called a **saturation curve**. More precisely, it is the saturation curve for this particular magnetic circuit.

In analyzing the saturation curve, we note that the flux increases rapidly up to the so-called "knee" of the curve (region A). Beyond the knee the flux increases only slightly, despite large increases in mmf. The reason is that most of the magnetic domains in the iron core line up for rather small values of mmf. They contribute an enormous mount of flux, and so the total flux in the core is high, even though the coil mmf is low. But as we raise the mmf, only a few more magnetic domains remain to be lined up, with the result that the flux cannot increase much more.

Eventually, when the coil mmf is high enough, all the magnetic domains will be lined up. When this point is reached, the iron core cannot produce any additional flux. It is said to be totally saturated. If we increase the mmf beyond this level, the flux will continue to rise, but the increase is then due to the coil alone. In iron, total saturation sets in at a flux density of about 2 T.

5.15 Magnetic Circuit with an Air Gap

As a final experiment, let us cut an opening 1 mm long in the iron core of Fig. 5.16. This small air gap replaces the iron that was there before. Consequently, for a given mmf, we would expect the flux to lie somewhere between the values it had in Fig. 5.17 (non-magnetic core) and Fig. 5.18 (all-magnetic core).

If we repeat the test, we obtain a flux of 13 000 lines at 1600 At, and 18 000 lines at 3200 At. The corresponding saturation curve for this air gap circuit is shown in Fig. 5.19. Note that as the flux increases, the iron begins to saturate, and it takes a progressively larger mmf to increase the flux by a given mount. Thus, the saturation curve flattens off, just as it did when there was no air gap.

We also note that to produce a given flux density, it takes a considerably higher mmf when the circuit contains an air gap. For example, to produce 15 000 lines, it takes 800 At with no air gap, but 2000 At with a 1 mm air gap. Thus, the longer the air gap, the more mmf that is required to produce a given flux.

Figure 5.19

Saturation curve obtained when an iron core having a 1 mm air gap is used in Fig. 5.16.

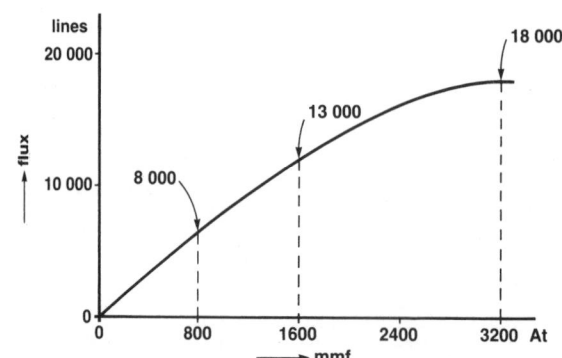

5.16 Reluctance of a Magnetic Circuit

The flux created in a magnetic circuit depends directly upon the mmf of the coil and inversely upon the "magnetic resistance" of the circuit. The lower the magnetic resistance, the higher the flux will be. For example, a closed iron core offers less resistance to the creation of magnetic flux than one having an air gap. The magnetic resistance of a circuit is called its *reluctance.* Circuits that require a large mmf to produce a given flux are said to have a high reluctance.

5.17 Relative Permeability

We have seen that when the coil in Fig. 5.16 is excited, it produces far more flux in an iron core than in a non-magnetic core. The reason for this is sometimes attributed to the **permeability** of the core material. Thus, iron is considered to be much more permeable than air is. Some magnetic materials, such as permalloy, are even more permeable than iron. This means that for a given coil mmf, the flux in a sample of permalloy will exceed that in a similar sample of iron.

PERMEABILITY

The **relative permeability** of a substance is the ratio of the flux produced in the substance to what it would be if the substance were air. The relative permeability is not constant, but varies with the mmf that is applied. We can therefore write:

RELATIVE
PERMEABILITY

$$\frac{\text{relative}}{\text{permeability}} = \frac{\text{flux created in the magnetic substance at a given mmf}}{\text{flux created if the magnetic substance were replaced by air}}$$

EQ. 5.1

Iron that contains very little carbon is said to be soft. Soft iron has a high relative permeability. Cast iron contains considerable carbon and has a lower relative permeability.

EXAMPLE 5.1

Calculate the relative permeability of the iron in Fig. 5.18 at a mmf of 800 At.

SOLUTION:

$$\text{relative permeability} = \frac{\text{flux in iron at 800 At}}{\text{flux in air at 800 At}}$$

EQ. 5.1

$$= \frac{15\ 000 \text{ lines}}{10 \text{ lines}}$$

$$= 1500$$

5.18   Torque Developed by a Magnetic System

Motors and generators are essentially composed of a set of fixed and moveable magnets. The forces and torques developed between them are an important part of the electromechanical conversion process. In this section we examine the nature of these torques for a simple system of magnets.

Consider Fig. 5.20, in which two bar magnets A and B are fixed in space, and a third bar magnet C is free to pivot around its center 0. With C in the position shown, its respective N and S poles are attracted with considerable force to the opposite poles of the fixed magnets. However, the forces pull in opposite directions, and so they tend only to stretch magnet C.

Let us rotate magnet C through an angle of 30° (Fig. 5.21). Because of the magnetic attraction between the S pole of C and the N pole of A, a force F_1 will be produced, acting in the direction shown. A similar force F_2 acts between the N pole of C and the S pole of B. These forces produce a twisting effect on C, tending to bring it back to its original position. Thus, magnet C is subjected to a counterclockwise (ccw) torque. The magnitude of the torque depends upon the angle of rotation. It increases progressively until the angle reaches 90°. Beyond this point (Fig. 5.22), the torque gradually decreases, eventually becoming zero at 180° (Fig. 5.23).

▼ **Figure 5.20**   ▼ **Figure 5.21**   ▼ **Figure 5.22**   ▼ **Figure 5.23**

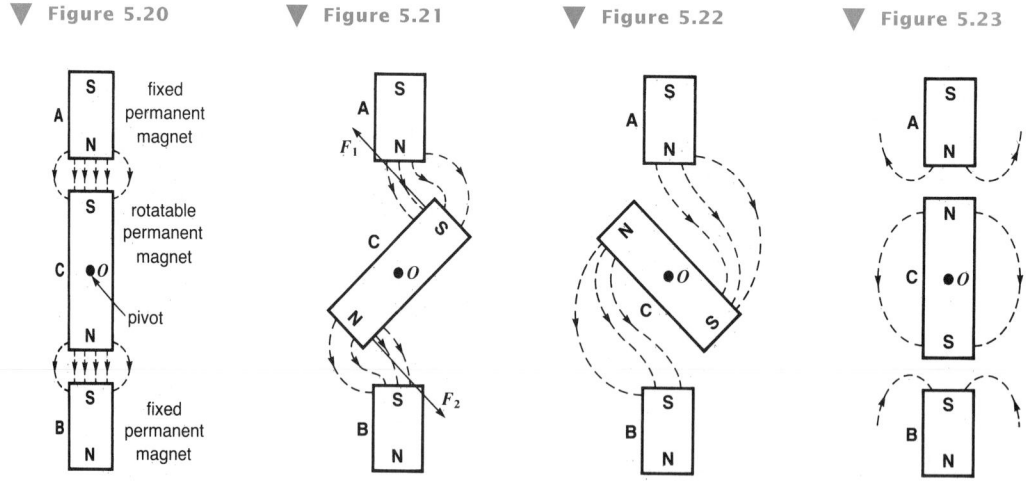

It is interesting to observe how the flux patterns change as the angle moves from zero to 180°. In particular, you will note that the lines never cross each other.

If we rotate C beyond 180°, the torque reverses, becoming clockwise (cw). It rises to a maximum at 270° (Fig. 5.24), and then gradually falls to zero, as we come back to our starting point at 360°.

If we plot the torque versus the angle of rotation, we obtain the curve shown in Fig. 5.25. A positive torque means that the torque acting on C is trying to drive it ccw.

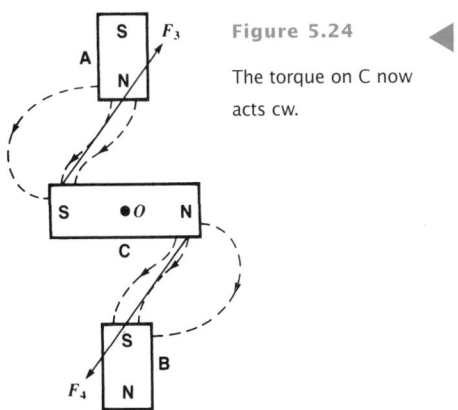

Figure 5.24

The torque on C now acts cw.

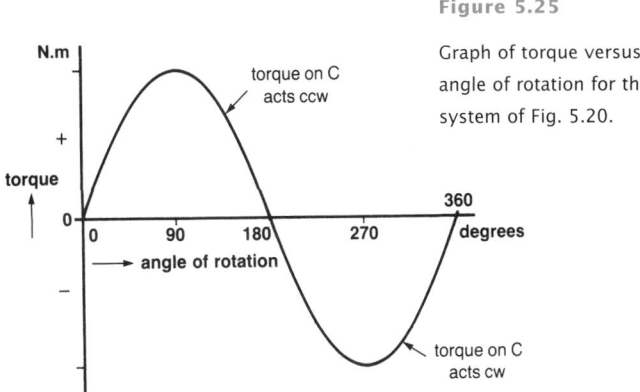

Figure 5.25

Graph of torque versus angle of rotation for the system of Fig. 5.20.

5.19 Reluctance Torque

Let us replace magnet C by a soft iron bar D having exactly the same shape. At an angle of 0°, N and S poles will be induced in D but, although forces are produced, there is no torque (Fig. 5.26). If we rotate D by 30°, N and S poles are again induced, and a torque is developed that acts ccw (Fig. 5.27).

At an angle of 90° (Fig. 5.28), N and S poles are still induced, but they give rise to four equal forces F_2 that act in the directions shown. The net torque on D is therefore zero. If we rotate the bar beyond 90°, the torque reverses, becoming cw (Fig. 5.29).

A torque is exerted on the iron bar because the reluctance of the magnetic path varies with the position of D. Thus, the reluctance is less in Fig. 5.26 than in Fig. 5.27 because the air gaps are shorter. Consequently, the torque is called a *reluctance torque.* It varies with the angle of rotation according to the curve of Fig. 5.30. The torque reaches a maximum at 45°, compared with 90° in the case of the permanent magnet.

Figure 5.26 **Figure 5.27** **Figure 5.28** **Figure 5.29**

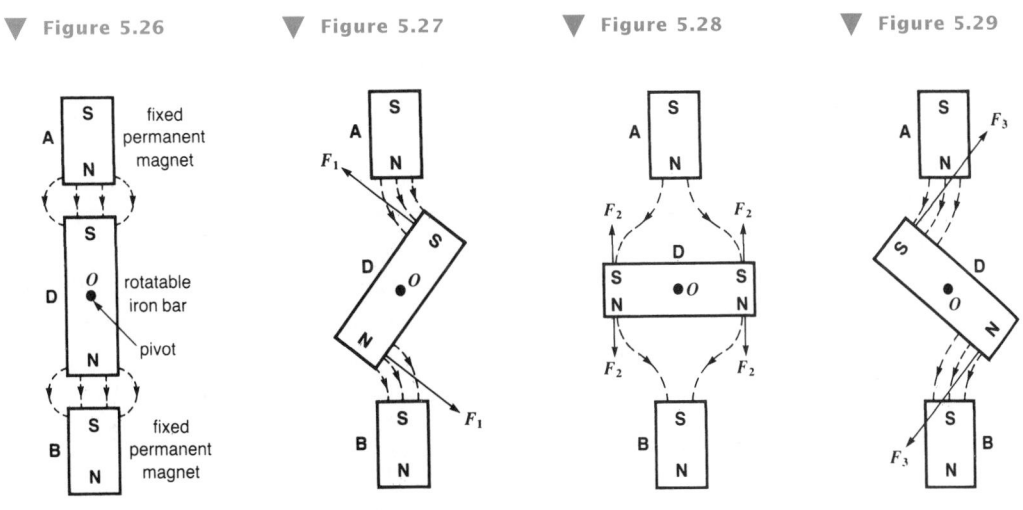

Figure 5.30

Graph of torque versus angle of rotation for the system of Fig. 5.26.

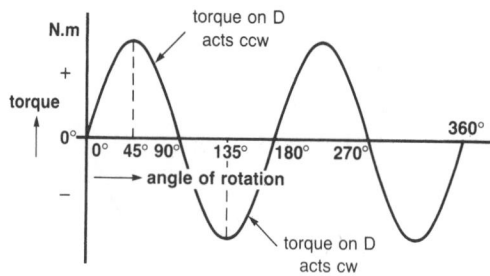

Note that if D were round instead of oblong, the reluctance would be the same for every position because the air gaps would be constant. Consequently, the torque acting on D would always be zero.

5.20 Hysteresis Losses

Consider Fig. 5.31, in which two coils are connected in series to a source of alternating current. Because the current reverses periodically (say, at 60 times a second), the magnetic field ϕ will also reverse periodically. Let us introduce a piece of iron between the coils so that the ac flux passes through it (Fig. 5.32). The magnetic domains will tend to line up with the field, but because the field is alternating, the magnetic domains will also reverse periodically. But we recall that magnetic domains tend to stick in the position they happen to be in. Consequently, when they reverse, frictional effects take place, causing the iron to heat up. In other words, an alternating field produces losses in a magnetic material because of the back-and-forth motion of the magnetic domains. These losses are called **hysteresis losses**. The magnitude of the losses (in watts) depends directly upon the frequency of the ac flux and upon its strength.

HYSTERESIS LOSSES

Figure 5.31

Alternating flux created by alternating current *I*.

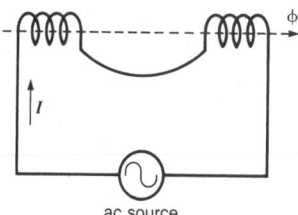

Figure 5.32

Hysteresis losses in the iron bar are produced by the reversal of magnetic domains.

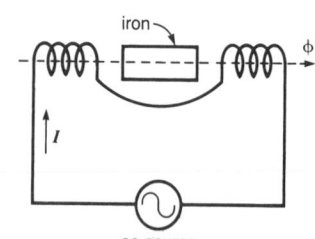

5.21 Hysteresis Losses Due to Rotation

Hysteresis losses also occur when a magnetic material rotates in a stationary magnetic field. Referring to Fig. 5.33, permanent magnets A and B produce a field that passes through a rotor made of iron. The rotor can be rotated by some external means, such as a hand crank. The magnetic field causes the magnetic domains, in the rotor to line up. Note, however, that they are oriented outward in region *x* and inward in region *y*. As we turn the rotor, region *y* will move to the bottom and occupy the position formerly held by region *x*. At the same time, region *x* will move to the top and occupy the position formerly held by *y*. Consequently, the orientation

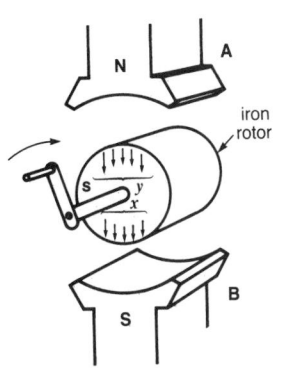

Figure 5.33

Rotation produces hysteresis losses in the rotor.

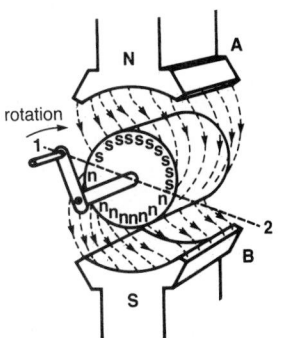

Figure 5.34

The hysteresis losses produce an opposing mechanical torque when the rotor turns.

of the magnetic domains reverses 180° every time the rotor makes half a turn. If we continually rotate the rotor, the magnetic domains will reverse back and forth, just as they did in the case of an ac field. As a result, hysteresis losses will again occur, causing the rotor to heat up. The losses depend upon the speed of rotation and the strength of the magnetic field.

5.22 Torque Produced by Hysteresis

Suppose the rotor in Fig. 5.34 is being turned cw. The stationary N pole continually induces s poles in the rotor, and these s poles will exist until they come under the influence of the stationary S pole. The magnetic domains then reverse, and n poles are induced, as shown. These n poles also continue to exist as the rotor turns until they come under the influence of the stationary N pole. The resulting nn—n and ss—s poles are distributed around the rotor, as shown in Fig. 5.34. They are skewed, or twisted, with respect to the N, S poles of magnets A and B.

As a result, a ccw torque is exerted on the rotor. We must therefore do mechanical work to turn the rotor cw. It is precisely this mechanical work that furnishes the energy needed to reverse the magnetic domains. Thus, hysteresis losses in a rotor always produce a torque, or drag, that tends to oppose the rotation of the rotor.

5.23 Summary

Upon completion of this chapter you should have learned:

• How to describe the properties of permanent magnets.

• That electromagnets are created by current flowing through a conductor and their properties are the same as those of permanent magnets.

• That electromagnets are crucial to the operation of motors, transformers, motor starters, and relays.

• That the type of material, and its dimensions, used in the magnetic circuit affect the flux density of an electromagnet.

• That the interaction between magnetic fields can result in torque. This property is used in motors, starters, and relays.

- That hysteresis losses are similar to frictional losses and result in the heating of the magnetic core.

- That torque resulting from hysteresis opposes the torque applied to a revolving rotor.

Key Terms

FLUX DENSITY: The number of lines of force per square centimetre.

FLUX LINE: Also known as lines of force, these lines flow from the north to the south poles of the magnet.

HYSTERESIS LOSS: These losses are similar to frictional losses in a mechanical system. These losses result from the realignment of the domains when they are subjected to an alternating magnetomotive force.

MAGNETIC DOMAIN: The smallest units within a magnetic material that possess the properties of a magnet. Aligning these domains creates stronger magnets.

MAGNETIC POLE: Lines of force are concentrated in two areas of a magnet; one where the lines enter the magnet (south pole) and

the other where the lines of force exit the magnet (north pole).

MAGNETOMOTIVE FORCE: A measure of the flux-producing capability of a coil. It is the product of the number of turns in a coil and the current flowing through the coil.

PERMEABILITY: A measure of how easily a material allows lines of force to pass. Iron is a commonly used high permeability material, while air is a low permeability material.

RELATIVE PERMEABILITY: A ratio of the flux produced by an electromagnet with a magnetic core compared to the flux produced by the same electromagnet with an air core.

SATURATION CURVE: A graph of magnetic flux versus the magnetomotive force of a coil.

Test Your Knowledge

5.1   The SI unit of magnetic flux is the
    a. maxwell
    b. weber
    c. tesla

5.2   The unit of magnetic flux density is the
    a. Wb/m^2
    b. Tesla (T)
    c. tesla (T)

5.3   The shape of a coil having 60 turns and carrying a current of 17 A has an effect on the mmf it develops.

    true _____   false _____

5.4   Flux lines cannot exist in a vacuum.

    true _____   false _____

5.5   A coil of 5000 turns carrying 1 mA produces an mmf of
    a. 5 At
    b. 5 Wb
    c. 500 At

5.6   In Fig. 5.21, the flux lines within the magnets pass from the N to the S pole.

    true _____   false _____

5.7   A compass needle is made of
   a.   soft iron
   b.   a permanent magnet material
   c.   a permanent magnetic material
         that has been magnetized

5.8   Hysteresis losses can be produced in
       copper.

       true _____   false _____

Questions and Problems

5.9   Name the properties of lines of force.

5.10   How can you determine the magnetic
       polarity of a magnet?

5.11   The earth's magnetic field in the
       province of Ontario is directed
       toward the Arctic Circle. Explain.

5.12   Using the left-hand rule, determine
       the magnetic polarity of end A in the
       electromagnet of Fig. 5.35.

5.13   A coil having 250 turns is connected
       to a 50 V dc source. If the coil resist-
       ance is 10 Ω, calculate the mmf
       developed by the coil.

5.14   A compass needle is oriented toward
       an electromagnet, as shown in
       Fig. 5.36. Determine the direction of
       current flow and the electric polarity
       $(+)$ $(-)$ of terminal 1.

▼ **Figure 5.35**

   See Problems 5.12
   and 5.17.

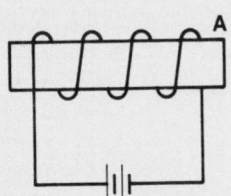

▼ **Figure 5.36**

   See Problem 5.14.

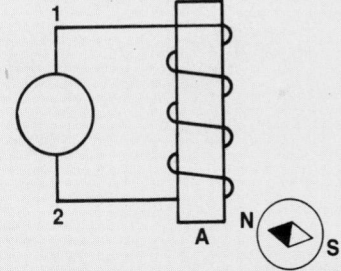

5.15   In Fig. 5.37, an electromagnet having
       an iron core is placed next to a perma-
       nent magnet.
   a.   Will there be attraction or repul-
         sion between them?
   b.   Will there be attraction or repul-
         sion if the terminals of the coil are
         reversed?
   c.   Will there be attraction or repul-
         sion if the coil is disconnected
         from the source?

▼ **Figure 5.37**

   See Problem 5.15.

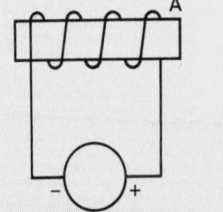

5.16   The electromagnets in Fig. 5.38 are connected to a 600 V source. Coil A has 2000 turns and a resistance of 50 Ω. Coil B has 800 turns and a resistance of 70 Ω.

a. Calculate the mmf produced by each coil.

b. Calculate the power dissipated in each coil.

c. If the coils have the same size, which one will get hotter?

d. Will the magnets attract or repel each other?

e. What happens to the force of attraction (or repulsion) if the battery connections are reversed?

5.17   In Fig. 5.35, why does the mmf of the coil decrease as the coil heats up, even though the battery voltage is fixed?

5.18   A flux of 1.2 mWb exists in a magnet having a cross section of 30 cm². Calculate the flux density.

▶ **Figure 5.38**

See Problem 5.16.

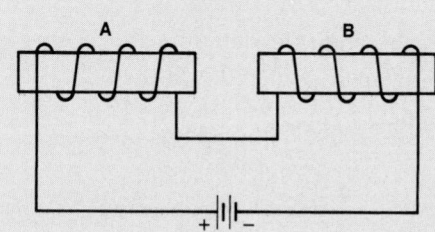

6

Electromagnetic Forces

LEARNING OBJECTIVES

Upon completion of this chapter you will be able to:

- Explain how force is exerted on a conductor in a magnetic field

- Determine the magnitude of the force exerted on a single conductor in a magnetic field

- Describe how force is created between two current-carrying conductors

- Describe the forces acting on a coil

- Describe the operation of blow-out coils

- Determine the torque produced by a rectangular coil in a magnetic field

Chapter Outline

6.1 Force on a Straight Conductor

In Chapter 5 we saw that a current-carrying conductor is surrounded by a magnetic field. If the current flows out of the page, the lines of force appear as shown in Fig. 6.1. We also know the shape of the magnetic field

▼ **Figure 6.1**

Magnetic field around a
conductor when the current
flows out of the page.

▼ **Figure 6.2**

Magnetic field between the
poles of a permanent magnet.

▶ **Figure 6.3**

Superposition of the
magnetic fields.

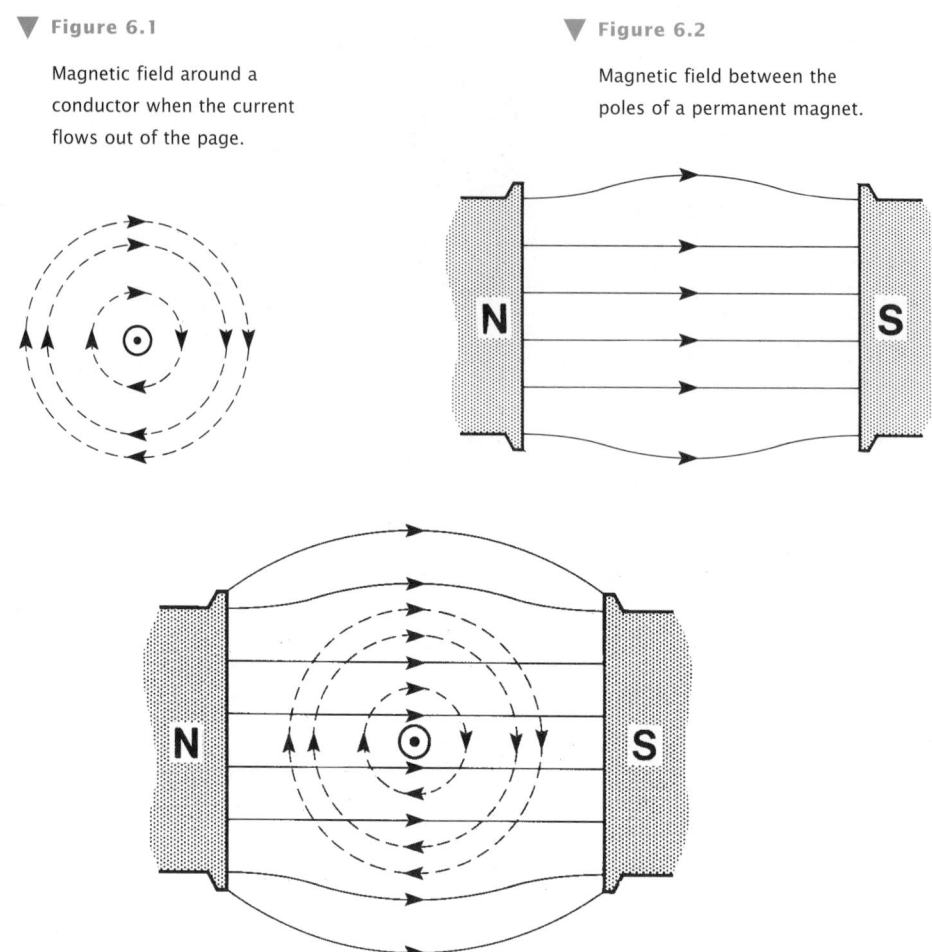

between the N and S poles of two permanent magnets (Fig. 6.2). If the conductor is placed in this magnetic field (Fig. 6.3), we observe that

1. The conductor is subjected to a force that tends to move it downward.

2. If we reverse the direction of current flow, the force acts upward.

To understand how this force is produced, let us examine the resulting magnetic field when the conductor is between the two poles. It cannot have the shape shown in Fig. 6.3 because lines of flux never cross each other. However, in the space above the conductor, we note that the circular flux lines created by the current point in the same direction as the N–S magnetic field. Consequently, the field above the conductor is strengthened. By the same reasoning, the field below the conductor is weakened because the lines of force act in opposite directions. Furthermore, the lines of force produced by the N and S poles must remain the same whether the conductor is there or not. The net result is that the number of lines above the conductor is greater than the number below. The magnetic field must therefore have the shape illustrated in Fig. 6.4.

But we recall that lines of force behave like tight elastic bands that repel each other. When they are concentrated above the conductor, as they are in Fig. 6.4, the force of repulsion between them forces the conductor downward.

This method of determining the direction of the force can be used in other situations. In Fig. 6.5, for example, the force on the conductor acts toward the right.

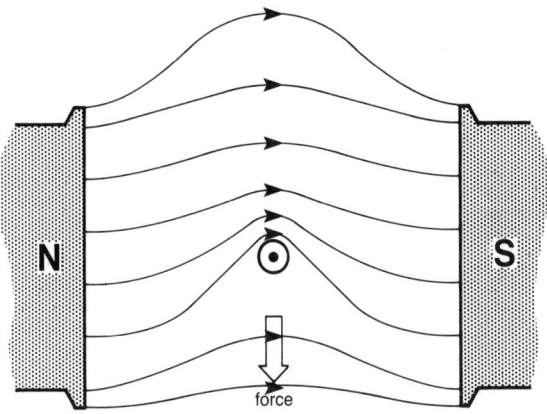

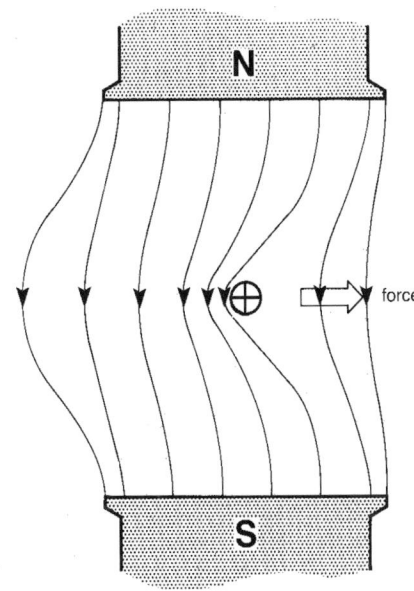

6.2 Magnitude of the Force

The magnitude of the force on a conductor depends upon:

1. the current carried by the conductor. The greater the current, the greater the force.

2. the flux density of the magnetic field in which the conductor is located. The higher the flux density, the greater the force.

3. the length of the conductor that is immersed in the magnetic field. The longer it is, the greater the force.

4. the way the conductor is oriented with respect to the magnetic field. The force is greatest when the conductor is perpendicular to the field (Fig. 6.6). It is zero when the conductor is parallel to the field (Fig. 6.7). Between those two extremes, the force has intermediate values. In practice, the conductors and the magnetic field axe arranged to be perpendicular to each other.

The force on a conductor is
maximum when the conduc-
tor is oriented at right
angles to the magnetic field.

The force on a conductor is
zero when the conductor is
parallel to the magnetic field.

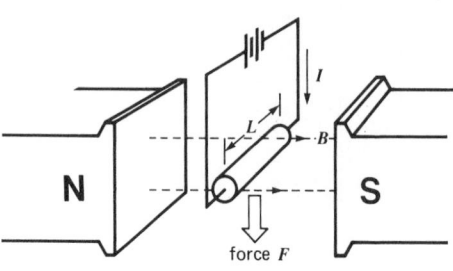

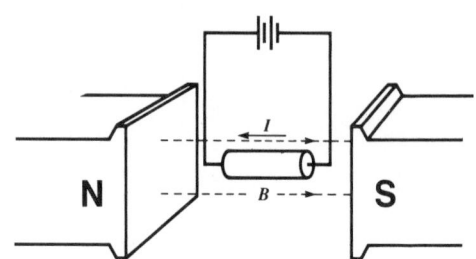

The maximum value of the force is given by the equation:

EQ. 6.1 $F = BLI$

where

F = force, in newtons (N)
B = flux density of the magnetic field, in teslas (T)
L = length of the conductor in the field, in metres (m)
I = current in the conductor, in amperes (A)

EXAMPLE 6.1

A conductor 4 m long has 3 m of its length immersed in a magnetic field. The flux
density of the field is 0.5 T, and the conductor carries a current of 200 A. Calculate
the force acting on the conductor if it is perpendicular to the field, as shown in
Fig. 6.6.

SOLUTION:

EQ. 6.1 $F = BLI$
    $= 0.5 \times 3 \times 200$
    $= 300$ N, or about $300/4.448 = 67$ lbf.

6.3 Force between Two Conductors

When two current-carrying conductors are placed side by side, they either attract
or repel each other. If the currents flow in the same direction, the conductors are
attracted; otherwise, they are repelled. These forces are a direct consequence of the
basic law we have just described.

Consider, for example, Fig. 6.8, in which two parallel conductors, A and B, carry currents that flow in the same direction (out of the page). Conductor B produces its own
circular magnetic field, but it is also immersed in the field created by conductor A.

▼ **Figure 6.8**

Two conductors carrying currents I_1 and I_2 that flow in the same direction.

▼ **Figure 6.9**

Superposition of the magnetic fields created by currents I_1 and I_2.

▼ **Figure 6.10**

Resulting magnetic field when currents flow out of the page. The conductors are attracted.

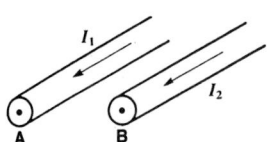

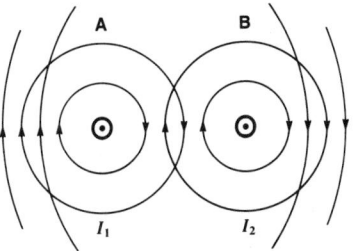

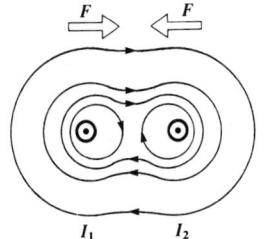

Referring to Fig. 6.9, it is clear that the resulting magnetic field to the right of B is strengthened. On the other hand, the magnetic field to the left is weakened because the fields of A and B are opposed in this region. The increased flux density on the right-hand side of B produces a force that pushes B to the left.

By the same reasoning, a force acts on A, but it is directed toward the right. It follows that conductors A and B are attracted to each other. The complete magnetic field around both conductors is shown in Fig. 6.10.

If the conductors carry currents that flow in opposite directions, as shown in Fig. 6.11, the conductors will repel each other. The corresponding shape of the magnetic field is given in Fig. 6.12.

For a given length and spacing, the force between two parallel conductors depends upon the product of the currents they carry. Under normal conditions, the force is quite small. But if a short-circuit occurs, the line currents may become 100 times larger than usual. This produces a force that is 100×100, or ten thousand, times greater than normal. Heavy copper busbars have been bent by the action of these powerful short-circuit forces, which may reach peaks of several tons. In substations, special bracing is needed to prevent busbars from becoming deformed or being pulled off their supports.

▼ **Figure 6.11**

Two conductors carrying currents I_1 and I_2 that flow in opposite directions, and superposition of the magnetic field created by each.

▼ **Figure 6.12**

Resulting magnetic field when currents flow in opposite directions. The conductors are repelled.

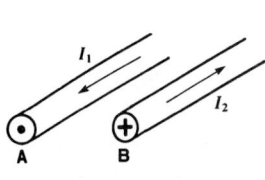

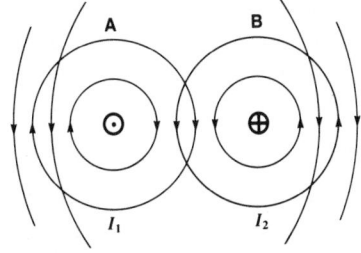

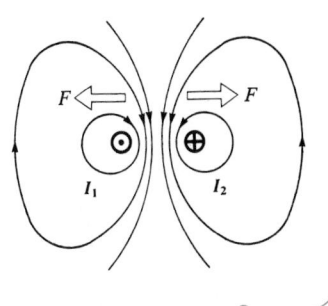

6.4 Forces Acting on a Coil

The turns of a coil can be looked upon as parallel conductors that carry a current flowing in the same direction. As a result, the turns are attracted to each other, and the entire coil tends to become compressed under the action of these forces (Fig. 6.13).

At the same time, each turn tends to balloon outward when it carries a current. To understand why this takes place, let us consider a single turn on the coil (Fig. 6.14). We can imagine the turn consists of short sections, each of which is a short conductor. Sections that are diametrically opposite, such as **a** and **b**, carry currents that flow in opposite directions. Based on Fig. 6.12, these sections repel each other, and so the turn tends to expand.

Normally, the forces tending to compress a coil while causing it to balloon outward are quite small. But in special cases, such as a short-circuit on a big transformer, the forces may become so great that heavy coils are torn apart.

▶ **Figure 6.13**

The turns of a coil are attracted to each other, tending to compress the coil.

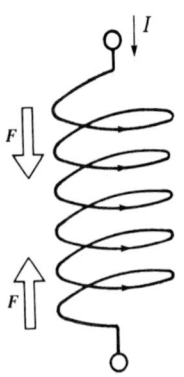

▶ **Figure 6.14**

Opposite segments of a turn repel each other, and so the turn tends to expand.

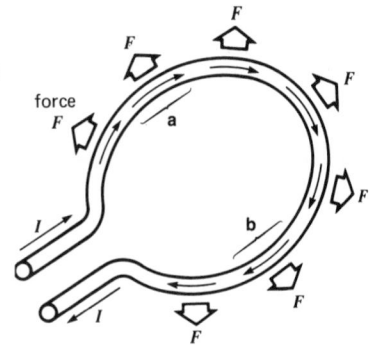

6.5 Blow-Out Coils

Some power circuits carry currents of several hundred amperes. Such circuits are often opened and closed by fast-acting switches called *circuit breakers*. When a circuit breaker opens, an intense arc continues to bridge the opening contacts. To extinguish the arc as quickly as possible, it is driven against a set of insulated plates so as to lengthen it, cool it, and chop it into smaller pieces. A jet of compressed air could do this and effectively blow out the arc. However, a pair of coils placed at right angles to the arc can accomplish the same result (Fig. 6.15). These so-called *blow-out coils* carry the current that flows in the circuit breaker. Furthermore, the magnetic field they create is arranged to intercept the arc. The arc is therefore subjected to a force, and because it has almost negligible mass, the force drives the arc at terrific speed against the insulated plates, thus extinguishing it.

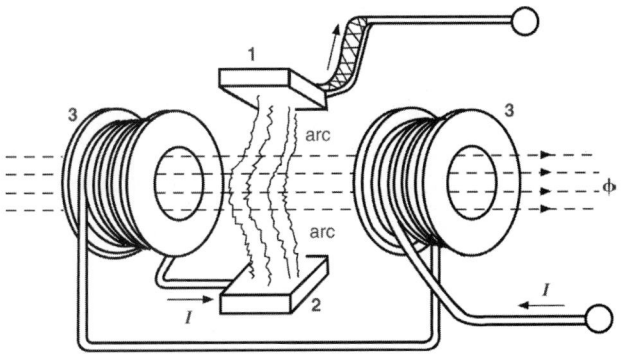

Figure 6.15

Blow-out coils can quickly extinguish an electric arc. As movable contact 1 separates from fixed contact 2, the arc is in the field created by blowout coils 3.

6.6 Torque Produced by a Rectangular Coil

The torque exerted by an electric motor is produced by current-carrying coils that are located in a magnetic field. To show how such a torque is developed, consider a single coil ABCD placed between the poles of a magnet (Fig. 6.16). The coil carries a current, and consequently a force F_1 acts on side AB (Fig. 6.17). An equal force F_2 acts on side CD. No forces act on sides BC and AD because they lie outside the magnetic field.

Forces F_1 and F_2 act in opposite directions because the current flows in opposite directions in the two "active" sides of the coil. Consequently, the coil is subjected to a torque. The magnitude of the torque is given by

$$T = Fd$$

EQ. 6.2

where

T = torque, in newton metres (N.m)
F = force on one coil side, in newtons (N)
d = width of coil, in metres (m)

▼ **Figure 6.16**

A single coil placed in a magnetic field illustrates the basic principle of an electric motor.

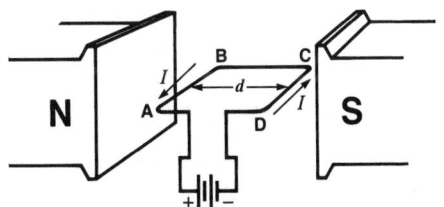

▼ **Figure 6.17**

The forces exerted on the coil produce a torque tending to make the coil rotate.

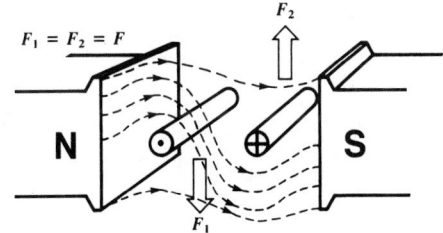

EXAMPLE 6.2

The rectangular coil in Fig. 6.16 has 40 turns and carries a current of 90 A. Coil side AB is 100 cm long and BC is 60 cm long. If the magnetic field created by the magnets has a flux density of 0.5 T, calculate the torque developed by the coil.

SOLUTION:

1. The force exerted on each conductor is

EQ. 6.1
$$F = BLI$$
$$= 0.5 \times 0.1 \times 90$$
$$= 4.5 \text{ newtons} = 4.5 \text{ N}$$

2. The total force acting on side AB is
$$F = 40 \text{ conductors} \times 4.5 \text{ N} = 180 \text{ N}$$

3. The torque produced by the coil is

EQ. 6.2
$$T = Fd = 180 \times 0.6 = 108 \text{ newton metres} = 108 \text{ N.m}$$

6.7 Summary

Upon completion of this chapter you should have learned that:

• When a straight conductor is placed in a magnetic field, the interaction of the magnetic fields will exert a torque on the conductor.

• The magnitude of the force exerted on a single conductor is a function of the strength of the magnetic field, the length of the conductor within the magnetic field, and the current flowing through the conductor.

• For two conductors of a given length and spacing, the force exerted between the two conductors will be determined by the current flowing through the two.

• The magnetic forces acting on a coil will cause the coil to contract lengthwise and the diameter to expand.

• A blow-out coil helps extinguish the arc in a circuit breaker by increasing the distance the arc must travel.

• Torque is produced when a rectangular coil carries current in a magnetic field.

Test Your Knowledge

6.1   If the N and S poles in Fig. 6.4 are interchanged, the force on the conductor will act upward.

true _____   false _____

6.2   The flux density around the conductor of Fig. 6.1 gets weaker as the distance from the conductor increases.

true _____   false _____

6.3 In Fig. 6.8, I_1 is 300 A and I_2 is 400 A, and the force of attraction is 10 N.

If I_1 increases to 1200 A, the force becomes

a. 160 N

b. 40 N

c. 22.86 N

6.4 In Fig. 6.10, if I_1 and I_2 both reverse, the conductor will be attracted, but the flux lines will reverse.

true _____ false _____

6.5 In Fig. 6.13, if current I reverses, the forces F reverse.

true _____ false _____

6.6 In Fig. 6.16, if the battery terminals are reversed, the coil will tend to rotate clockwise.

true _____ false _____

6.7 In Fig. 6.13, if the current increases 20 times, the compression forces F will increase

a. 4.472 times

b. 20 times

c. 400 times

Questions and Problems

6.8 When a long coil carries a large current, the coil tends to get shorter. Explain.

6.9 Draw the resultant field between the magnets of Fig. 6.18 and show the direction of the force on the conductor.

6.10 Determine the magnetic polarity of the poles A and B in Fig. 6.19, knowing that the force on the conductor acts downward.

6.11 In which direction will conductor **ab** in Fig. 6.20 move?

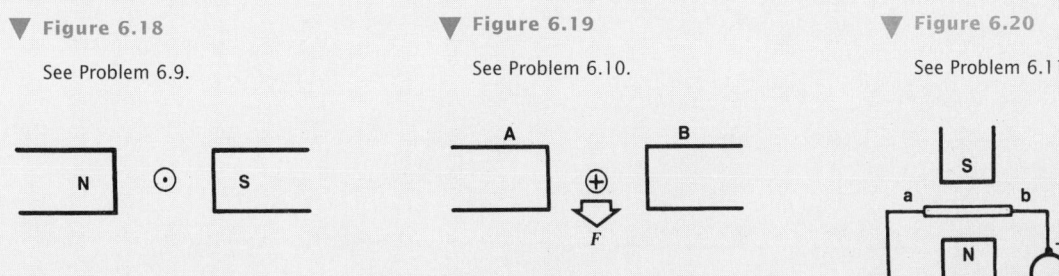

▼ **Figure 6.18**

See Problem 6.9.

▼ **Figure 6.19**

See Problem 6.10.

▼ **Figure 6.20**

See Problem 6.11.

6.12 The electromagnet in Fig. 6.21 is connected to a dry cell having the polarity shown. In which direction does the conductor between the poles tend to move?

6.13 In Fig. 6.22, an electromagnet and rectangular coil are connected in series to a dc source having the polarity shown.

a. Will the coil turn cw or ccw?

b. If the polarity of the source is reversed, in which direction will the coil tend to rotate?

6.14 A conductor carrying 2000 A is placed in a field having a flux density of 0.5 T. Calculate the force exerted per inch of length.

6.15   Figure 6.23 is the schematic diagram of a motor. The rotor contains 80 conductors, each of which carries a current of 50 A. The poles produce a flux density of 1.2 T. Calculate (a) the force on each conductor and (b) the torque developed by the motor in newton metres, and in lbf.ft.

6.16   If the conductor in Fig. 6.3 carries an alternating current having a frequency of 60 Hz, the conductor will not move out of the field. Explain.

▼ Figure 6.21

See Problem 6.12.

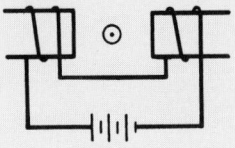

▼ Figure 6.22

See Problem 6.13.

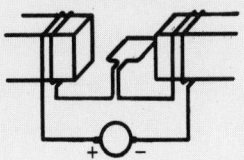

▼ Figure 6.23

See Problem 6.15.

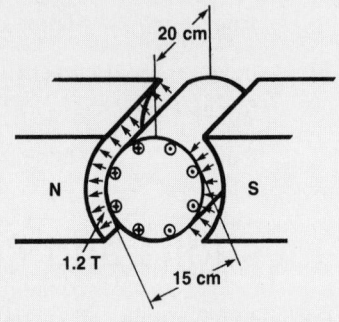

7

Electromagnetic Induction

LEARNING OBJECTIVES

Upon completion of this chapter you will be able to:

- State Faraday's law of induction

- Determine the magnitude and polarity of the induced voltage

- Determine the direction of the induced current

- Apply Fleming's left-hand rule

- Explain how a voltage is induced in single conductors and coils

- Calculate the voltage induced in single conductors and coils

- Explain the nature of eddy currents

7.1 Voltage Induced in a Coil, Faraday's Law of Induction

Consider the coil in Fig. 7.1, wound on a hollow, non-magnetic core and connected to a sensitive voltmeter. The flux from a permanent magnet passes through the interior of the coil. When the coil and magnet are both stationary, no voltage is observed.

When the permanent magnet
is stationary, no voltage
appears across the terminals
of the coil.

When the magnet is moved
downwards, a voltage V_{12} is
induced in the coil. V_{12} is
positive.

When the coil is moved
downwards, a voltage V_{12} is
induced in the coil. V_{12} is
negative.

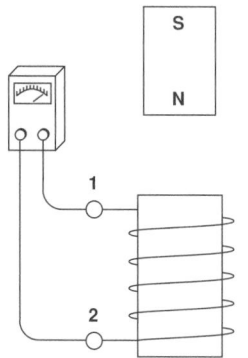
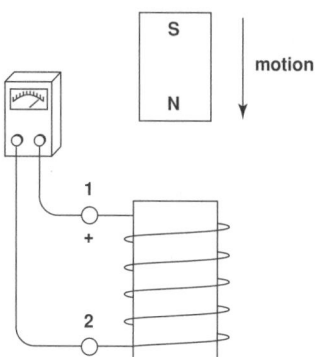
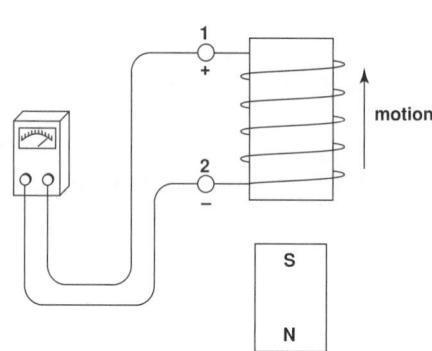

However, if the magnet is suddenly pulled downwards, a voltage appears across the
terminals of the coil. The voltage exists whenever the magnet is moving. But as
soon as the magnet stops, the voltage falls to zero. When the magnet moves downward, the voltage has the polarity shown in Fig. 7.2. If the magnet is moved upward,
a voltage is again produced as long as the magnet is moving. However, its polarity
is the reverse of its previous polarity.

In Fig. 7.3, the permanent magnet remains fixed in place and the coil moves
upward. Again, as long as the coil is moving, a voltage is induced across the terminals of the coil. As soon as the coil stops moving the, the voltage falls to zero.

INDUCED VOLTAGE

The voltage generated by the coil is said to be an **induced voltage**. Furthermore,
the flux that passes through the coil is said to be "linked" with the coil.

ELECTROMAGNETIC
INDUCTION

Michael Faraday showed that the induced voltage is due to the *change* in flux that
passes through the coil. This phenomenon is called **electromagnetic induction**.
The results of his experiments are known as **Faraday's law** of electromagnetic
induction, which states:

FARADAY'S LAW

**Any time there is relative motion between a magnetic field and a coil or
conductor, a voltage will be induced.**

In the above example, we used a moving magnet to change the flux inside the coil.
But Faraday showed that no matter how the flux is produced and no matter what
causes it to vary, a voltage is always induced when the flux linked by a coil varies.

7.2 Magnitude of the Induced Voltage

The magnet in Fig. 7.4 is arranged so that it can move only from position 1 to position 2. This ensures that the initial and final flux inside the coil are always the

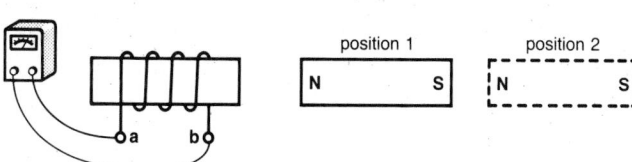

Figure 7.4

The magnitude of the induced voltage depends upon the rate of change of flux inside the coil. See Example 7.1.

same. Thus, whether the magnet moves quickly or slowly, the change of flux inside the coil is constant. As before, a voltmeter indicates the voltage induced in the coil.

If the magnet is moved slowly, we find the induced voltage is only a few millivolts. But if the magnet moves quickly, the induced voltage may be several volts. We conclude that the magnitude of the induced voltage does not depend upon the change in flux, but on the *rate* at which it is changing. According to Faraday's law, the voltage induced in a coil is given by the equation:

$V = N \times$ **rate of change of flux**   EQ. 7.1

which may also be expressed as

$$V = N \frac{\Delta\phi}{\Delta t}$$ EQ. 7.2

where

V = voltage induced in the coil, in volts (V)
N = number of turns on the coil
$\Delta\phi$ = change of flux inside the coil, in webers (Wb)
Δt = duration of the change, in seconds (s)

The rate of change of flux is expressed in webers per second.

EXAMPLE 7.1

A coil having 2000 turns surrounds 50 mWb of flux produced by a large permanent magnet (Fig. 7.4). When the magnet is moved to position 2, the flux inside the coil drops to 10 mWb. Calculate the average voltage induced in the coil if the magnet is moved in 0.1 s.

SOLUTION:

1. The change in flux linking the coil is:
   $\Delta\phi = 50 - 10 = 40$ milliwebers = 40 mWb
2. The interval Δt during which the change takes place = 0.1 s
3. The rate of change of flux is
   $\Delta\phi / \Delta t = 40 \times 10^{-3}/0.1 = 0.4$ webers per second = 0.4 Wb/s
4. From Faraday's law we have:

   $V = N \, \Delta\phi / \Delta t$ EQ. 7.2

   $V = 2000 \times 0.4 = 800$ V

7.3 Induced Current

Let us connect a resistor across the terminals of a coil having N turns (Fig. 7.5). If we bring a magnet near the coil, a voltage is again induced. However, the voltage now causes a current I to flow in the resistor, and therefore in the coil. This current is called an **induced current**.

INDUCED CURRENT

It is important to note that the induced current produces a mmf NI while it is flowing in the coil.

An induced current will also circulate if the terminals of the coil are short-circuited. Although no external voltage can be measured, a voltage is still induced in the coil. The situation is similar to short-circuiting the terminals of a battery. A large current flows because the battery still develops a voltage, despite the fact it cannot be measured externally.

Figure 7.5

A current is induced in the circuit whenever the flux inside the coil is changing.

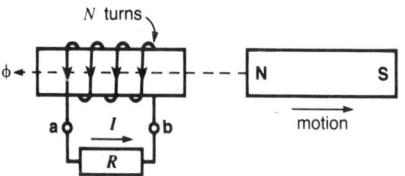

7.4 Direction of the Induced Current

Consider Fig. 7.6, in which a coil is connected to a resistor. A flux produced by an external device (not shown) links with the coil. The flux is directed toward the left. Suppose that the flux increases. A voltage will be induced which, in turn, produces a current. The question is, in what direction will the induced current flow? It has been found that the current always flows in a direction so that the magnetomotive force it creates *opposes* the change of flux inside the coil. If the flux increases, the mmf will tend to oppose the increase. On the other hand, if the flux decreases, the mmf will tend to oppose the decrease.

To illustrate what happens, suppose the flux in Fig. 7.6 increases. To oppose this increase, the mmf of the coil must be directed toward the right (Fig. 7.7). Consequently, the current in the coil must flow in the direction shown.

▼ **Figure 7.6**

The coil tries to oppose any change in the flux which threads through the coil.

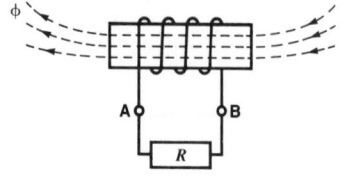

▼ **Figure 7.7**

The external flux is increasing, and the resulting induced current opposes the increase.

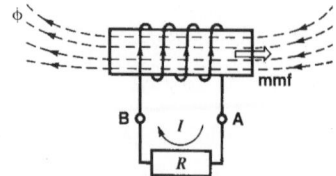

As another example, suppose the flux in Fig. 7.8 is decreasing. To oppose the decrease, the mmf must be directed to the right. Consequently, by applying the left-hand rule, the induced current must flow in the direction shown.

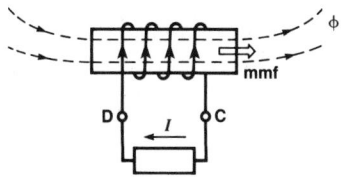

Figure 7.8

The external flux is decreasing and the resulting induced current opposes the decrease.

7.5 Polarity of the Induced Voltage, Lenz's Law

In the previous examples we were able to determine the direction of the induced current. But knowing this, we can determine the polarity of the terminals of the coil because current always flows from (−) to (+) in a resistor. Thus, in Fig. 7.7, terminal A is negative and terminal B is positive. Similarly, in Fig. 7.8, terminal C is negative and D is positive.

The polarity of the terminals is independent of the value of the resistor connected across the coil. Thus, even if the resistance is infinite (meaning that the terminals are an open circuit), the polarities will still be the same.

We therefore have a method of determining the polarity of the terminals. We simply assume a resistor is connected across the terminals and find the resulting direction of current flow, and the problem is solved. This method is known as **Lenz's law**, which may be stated as follows:

LENZ'S LAW

The polarity of the induced voltage across a coil is such that it tends to circulate a current that will oppose the change of flux inside the coil.

7.6 A Single Conductor in a Stationary Magnetic Field

Consider a single conductor having terminals X and Y (Fig. 7.9). Two stationary magnets produce a flux density *B*. The conductor is moving rapidly downward. It is

Figure 7.9

The voltage induced between terminals X and Y can be considered to be due to the conductor cutting the flux lines.

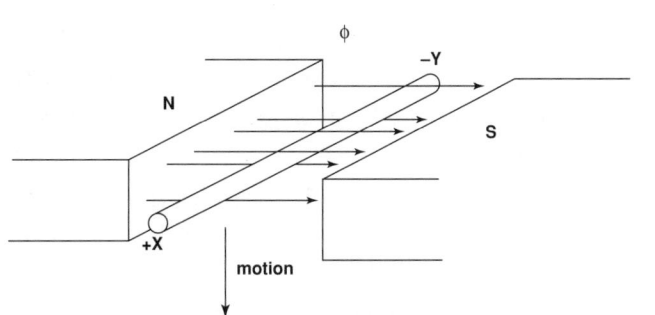

Figure 7.10

The flux-cutting concept means that a voltage is induced in conductor XY.

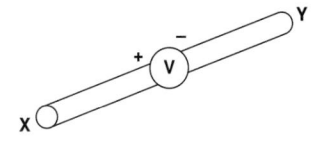

obvious that the flux enclosed by the single conductor is in the process of decreasing. Consequently, an induced voltage appears between terminals X and Y (Fig. 7.10).

It is sometimes convenient to imagine that the voltage is induced because the conductor is "cutting" the lines of force produced by the magnets. The magnitude of the induced voltage is given by the equation:

EQ. 7.3 $V = BLv$

where

V = voltage induced in the conductor, in volts (V)
B = flux density that is being "cut" by the conductor, in teslas (T)
v = speed of the conductor, in metres per second (m/s)
L = length of the conductor that is cutting the flux, in metres (m)

EXAMPLE 7.2

The conductor in Fig. 7.9 has a length of 0.35 m, but only 0.3 m are actually cutting flux lines. The permanent magnets produce a flux density of 0.4 T, and the conductor is moving at 120 km/h. Calculate the voltage induced in the conductor between terminals X and Y.

SOLUTION:

EQ. 7.3 $V = BLv = 0.4 \times 0.3 \times \dfrac{120\ 000}{3600} = 4 \text{ V}$

The voltage induced in the conductor XY is 4 V.

We use this alternative method of calculating the induced voltage because in many practical cases we know the value of the flux density and the speed of the conductor.

In some machines, the coil is stationary and the flux is moving. This does not change the induced voltage because v in Eq. 7.3 is the *relative* speed between the conductor and the magnetic field.

7.7   Polarity of the Induced Voltage in a Straight Conductor

We can predict the polarity of the voltage induced in a straight conductor by means

LEFT-HAND RULE

of a simple rule, called the **left-hand rule**. It works as follows:

1. Extend the thumb, forefinger, and middle finger so they are at right angles to each other.

2. Point the thumb in the direction in which the conductor is moving.

3. Point the forefinger in the direction of the flux.

4. The middle finger then points to the negative end of the conductor.

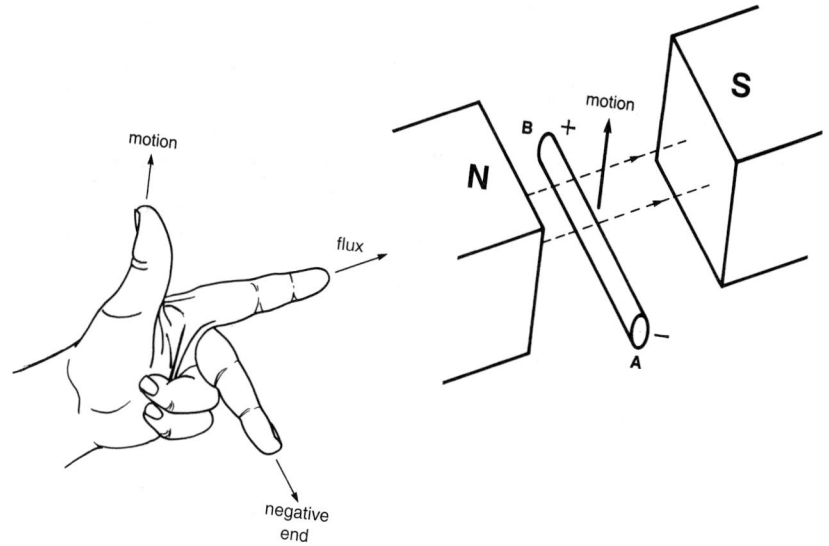

Figure 7.11

The polarity of the induced voltage can be determined using the left-hand rule.

To illustrate the application of this rule, consider Fig. 7.11, in which a conductor is moving upwards, and cutting across the magnetic field produced by two magnets. By extending the fingers according to the above rule, we find that extremity A is (−) and B is therefore (+).

Some students find the left-hand rule awkward to apply, particularly when the flux and motion are directed in ways that require unnatural positions of the hand. Furthermore, the relative motion of the conductor has to be used when the conductor is stationary and the flux is cutting across it. The following alternative rule may be used:

1. Stretch the left hand out flat, with the thumb at right angles to the fingers.

2. Let the fingers point in the direction of the flux.

3. Press the palm of the hand against the conductor to push in the direction of the motion.

4. The thumb then points toward the negative end of the conductor.

Fig. 7.12 illustrates the application of this rule.

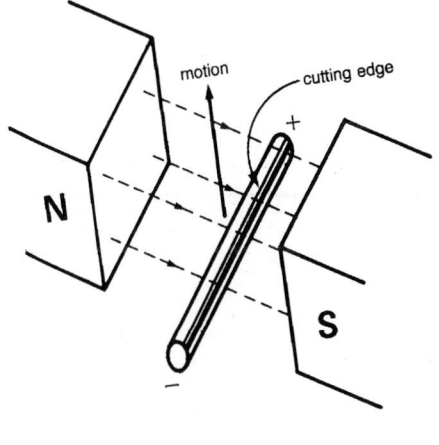

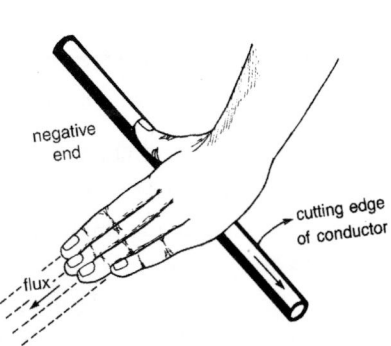

Figure 7.12

The polarity of the induced voltage can also be determined by an alternative method.

7.8 A Coil Revolving in a Stationary Magnetic Field

If we replace the single conductor, described in Section 7.6, with the single turn of wire in Fig. 7.13, we have a very simple electric generator.

Figure 7.13

A practical way to generate a voltage is to revolve a coil in a stationary magnetic field.

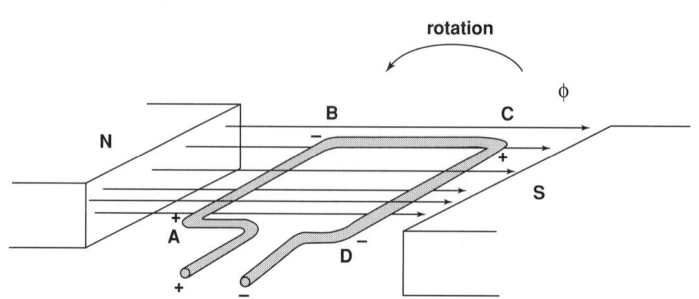

With the coil rotating in a counterclockwise direction, conductor AB will be moving downward across the north magnetic pole (like the single conductor in Fig. 7.9). The opposite side of the coil, conductor CD, will be moving upwards across the face of the south magnetic pole. Applying the left-hand rule separately to conductor AB and CD, we find that while the polarity of each conductor is opposite, the direction of current flow through the entire coil (ABCD) will be the same. Consequently, the voltage generated by the single turn is twice that induced in each conductor.

The magnitude of the induced voltage can be calculated using Equation 7.3, just as it was for a single conductor. If we replace the single conductor in Example 7.2 with a coil of the same dimension, we have doubled the length of the conductor within the magnetic field: 0.3 m for conductor AB plus 0.3 m for conductor CD. The induced voltage will also double, since:

$$V = BLv$$
$$= 0.4 \text{ T} \times 0.6 \text{ m} \times (120\,000/3600)$$
$$= 8 \text{ V}$$

7.9 Eddy Currents

Consider a changing flux ϕ that links a rectangular-shaped conductor (Fig. 7.14). According to Faraday's law, a changing voltage V_{ab} is induced across its terminals.

If the conductor is short-circuited, a large current I_1 will flow, causing the conductor to heat up. If a second conductor is placed inside the first, a smaller voltage is induced because it links a smaller flux. Consequently, the short-circuit current I_2 is less than I_1 and so, too, is the dissipated power. Fig. 7.15 shows four such concentric conductors carrying currents I_1, I_2, I_3, and I_4.

In Figure 7.16, the changing flux passes through a solid metal plate. The plate is equivalent to a set of rectangular conductors that touch each other. Currents swirl back and forth inside the plate, following the paths shown in Fig. 7.16. These so-called **eddy currents** (or Foucault currents) can be very large because of the low resistance of the plate. Consequently, a metal plate penetrated by a varying flux can become very hot.

EDDY CURRENTS

▼ **Figure 7.14**

A changing flux φ induces a varying voltage in the solid conductor.

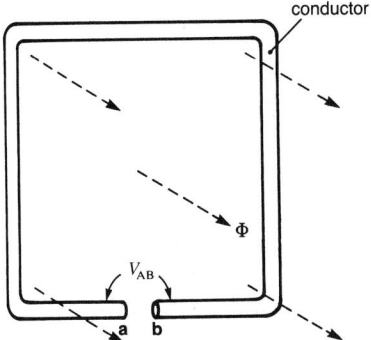

▼ **Figure 7.15**

When the conductors form closed loops, the changing flux induces changing currents.

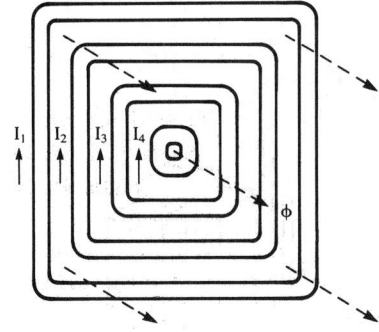

▼ **Figure 7.16**

When a changing flux penetrates a metal plate, the induced currents are called eddy currents.

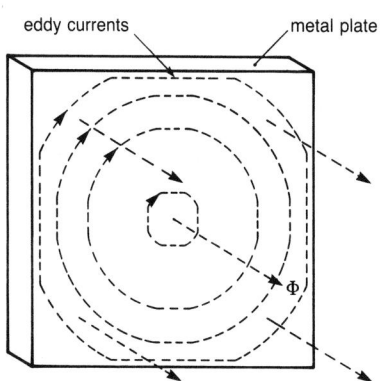

▼ **Figure 7.17**

Eddy currents flowing in an iron core can produce large losses and much heat.

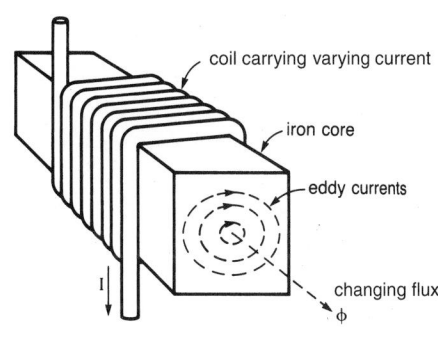

7.10 Eddy Currents in a Stationary Iron Core

The eddy current problem becomes crucially important when iron has to carry a changing flux. Fig. 7.17 shows a coil carrying a changing current that produces a varying flux in a solid iron core. Eddy currents are set up as shown, and they swirl back and forth throughout the length of the core. A large core could eventually become red hot because of the I^2R losses.

We can reduce the losses by splitting the core along its length, taking care to insulate the two sections from each other (Fig. 7.18). The voltage induced in each section is one-half of what it was before, with the result that the eddy currents — and the corresponding losses — are considerably reduced.

▼ Figure 7.18

The losses can be reduced by
subdividing the core into smaller
sections and insulating the
sections from each other.

▼ Figure 7.19

Laminating the iron core can
greatly reduce the core losses.

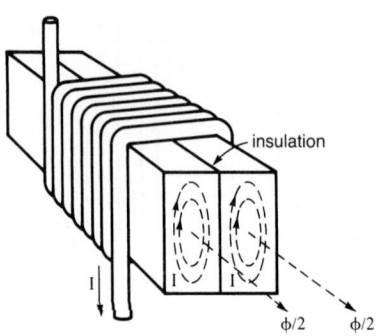

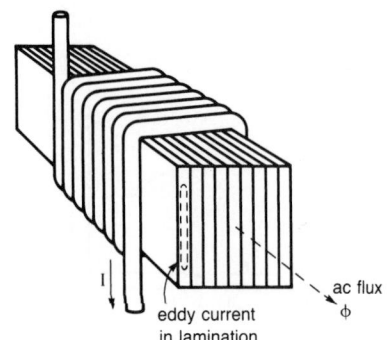

If we continue to subdivide the core, we find that the losses decrease progressively. In practice, the core is composed of stacked laminations, usually a fraction of a
millimetre thick (Fig. 7.19).

The cores of ac motors and generators are always laminated. A thin coating of insulation covers each lamination to prevent electrical contact between the laminations.
They are stacked on top of each other and are held tightly in place by bolts and
end-pieces.

7.11 Eddy Current Losses in a Revolving Core

Eddy currents are also produced when a rotor turns in a constant magnetic flux.
Consider, for example, a solid iron rotor that revolves between the poles of a magnet (Fig. 7.20). As it turns, the rotor cuts flux lines and, according to Faraday's law,
a voltage is induced along its length. Because of this voltage, large eddy currents
flow in the rotor because its resistance is very low. These eddy currents produce
I^2R losses which are immediately converted into heat.

To reduce these losses, we laminate the armature. The laminations are tightly
stacked, with the flat sides running parallel to the flux lines (Fig. 7.21).

▶ Figure 7.20

Eddy currents are induced
when a solid iron rotor turns
in a stationary magnetic
field.

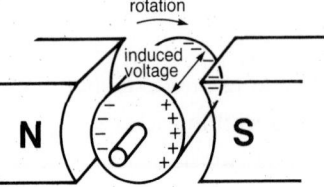

▶ Figure 7.21

Laminating the iron core
reduces the eddy current
losses.

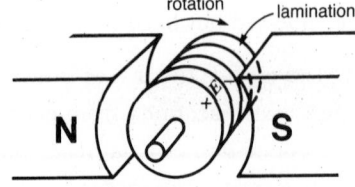

7.12 Summary

Upon completion of this chapter you should have learned that:

• Faraday's law of induction states that any time there is relative motion between a conductor and a magnetic field, a voltage will be induced.

• The magnitude of an induced voltage is determined by the number of turns of wire and the rate at which the magnetic flux is changing.

• The left-hand rule for conductors can be used to determine the direction of the induced current.

• Lenz's law states that the polarity of the induced voltage will cause a current to flow in the direction that opposes a change in the magnetic flux.

• The left-hand rule can be used to determine the polarity of the voltage induced by moving a conductor through a magnetic field.

• A voltage will be induced in single conductors and coils, whenever they are moving in a magnetic field.

• Equation 7.3 can be used to calculate the voltage induced in single conductors and coils.

• Eddy currents are circulating currents induced in conductive materials that are not part of the electrical circuit.

Key Terms

EDDY CURRENTS: Currents induced in the electrically conductive portion of a magnetic core, such as iron. These currents often follow circular paths.

ELECTROMAGNETIC INDUCTION: The voltage created in a coil by a changing magnetic flux.

FARADAY'S LAW: Any time there is relative motion between a magnetic field and a conductor, a voltage will be induced.

INDUCED CURRENT: The current flow in a circuit resulting from an induced voltage.

INDUCED VOLTAGE: The difference in potential (voltage) resulting from electromagnetic induction.

LEFT-HAND RULE: In a generator, if the thumb indicates the direction in which the conductor is moving and the forefinger, held at a right angle to the thumb, indicates the direction of the magnetic field, then the middle finger indicates the negative end of the conductor.

LENZ'S LAW: An induced voltage will have a potential such that it opposes a change in the flux that created it.

Test Your Knowledge

7.1   A coil of 2000 turns surrounds a constant flux of 0.2 Wb. The voltage induced is
   a.   400 V
   b.   zero
   c.   cannot be calculated

7.2   When the flux changes inside a coil that is on open-circuit
   a.   a voltage is induced
   b.   a current is induced
   c.   a voltage and a current are induced

7.3   A voltage of 8 V is induced in a coil when the flux changes from 800 mWb to 600 mWb in 2 s. What is the magnitude of the voltage when the flux changes from 8000 mWb to 8200 mWb in 4 s?
   a.   16 V
   b.   4 V
   c.   40 V

7.4   Eddy currents are always produced when an ac flux passes through a solid metal plate.
   true_____   false_____

7.5   In Fig. 7.14, if the flux ϕ is increasing the voltage is
   a.   positive
   b.   negative
   c.   zero

7.6   In Fig. 7.9, the induced voltage is 6 V when conductor AB moves downward at 2 m/s. Calculate the voltage when it moves vertically upward at 20 m/s.
   a.   60 V
   b.   zero
   c.   –60 V

7.7   In Fig. 7.10, V_{xy} is momentarily
   a.   positive
   b.   zero
   c.   negative

Questions and Problems

7.8   A conductor that is 2 m long moves at 60 km/h across a field whose flux density is 0.6 T. Calculate the magnitude of the induced voltage.

7.9   Refer to Fig. 7.9
   a.   Is the flux in the coil increasing or decreasing?
   b.   What is the polarity of X with respect to Y at this moment?

7.10   A coil having 200 turns is linked by a flux of 3 mWb. If the flux decreases to 1.3 mWb in 12 ms, calculate the average value of the induced voltage.

7.11   Why do the iron cores of ac magnets have to be laminated and those of dc magnets do not?

7.12   A dc voltage can be induced in a coil for only a short time. Explain.

7.13   In Fig. 7.6, the coil has 1000 turns and is linked by a flux of 180 mWb. If the flux decreases to zero at a uniform rate in a period of two hours, calculate the magnitude of the induced voltage and determine its polarity. Is the induced voltage dc or ac?

8
Ac Voltages and Currents

LEARNING OBJECTIVES

Upon completion of this chapter you will be able to:

- List the advantages of alternating current over dc current
- Describe how an ac voltage is generated
- Calculate instantaneous currents and voltages
- Calculate peak and effective values
- Understand double subscript notation
- Represent currents and voltages using phasors
- Explain the difference between electrical and mechanical degrees

8.1 Advantages of Ac

So far, we have used voltages and currents in dc circuits. However, most commercial circuits and machines use alternating current (**ac**).

TRANSFORMERS

Ac has the following advantages over dc:

1. Ac can be stepped-up and stepped-down using **transformers**; therefore ac can be transmitted more efficiently than dc over long distances.

2. Ac machines are mechanically simpler than dc machines. Dc machines require brushes, brush rigging, and a commutator to connect the rotating part of the motor to the current supply. Ac machines are, mostly, induction machines and thus the rotating part of the motor needs no electical connection to the current source. This makes ac machines less expensive to purchase and maintain.

3. Ac machines can be built in larger electrical capacities than dc machines. Because of their need for more complex insulation, dc generators are limited to about 1500 V, while ac alternators commonly generate 13 800 V.

8.2   Generating an Ac Voltage

We saw in Chapter 7 that we could generate a voltage by rotating a coil in a stationary magnetic field. We will now look more closely at that generated voltage.

To simplify this discussion, we will take the three dimensional coil in Fig. 8.1a and view it in two dimensions, as shown in Fig. 8.1b through 8.1h. We begin with the coil in the vertical position (0°) and rotating at a constant speed in the counter-clockwise direction (Fig. 8.1b). For a very brief period of time, the conductor A will be moving parallel to the magnetic lines of force of the fixed magnet. This means that no lines of force are being cut and the generated voltage will be zero.

In Fig. 8.1c, the coil has rotated 30° and A is now cutting across some lines of force, generating a voltage. Since A is moving at a relatively shallow angle, the relative flux density will be low and the induced voltage will be more than zero but less than the maximum. As the coil continues to rotate, it passes through 60° (Fig. 8.1d), cutting more lines of force as the relative flux density increases. This causes the induced voltage to rise. At 90° of rotation (Fig. 8.1e), the coil is moving at right angles to the magnetic field and the relative flux density will be at a maximum. Since the maximum number of lines of force are being cut, the induced voltage will be at its maximum value.

As conductor A passes beyond the face of the magnetic pole, the relative flux density decreases and the induced voltage will decrease. At 120° and 150° (Fig. 8.1f and 8.1g) the conditions will be the same as for 30° and 60° and so the induced voltage will also be the same. In Fig. 8.1h, as conductor A is moving through 180°, it is again moving parallel to the lines of force and the induced voltage is zero.

As conductor A moves beyond 180° toward 360° it will pass through the same sequence described above, except it will now be moving upward with respect to the south pole face of the permanent magnet. If we apply the left-hand rule, we will find that the voltage generated by the two conductors that cut the flux lines has changed polarity. This means that induced voltage from 180° to 360° will have a polarity opposite to the polarity of the induced voltage from 0° to 180°. The relative voltages and the degrees of rotation for the entire sequence are shown in Fig. 8.2. This type of waveform is a sine wave.

(a)

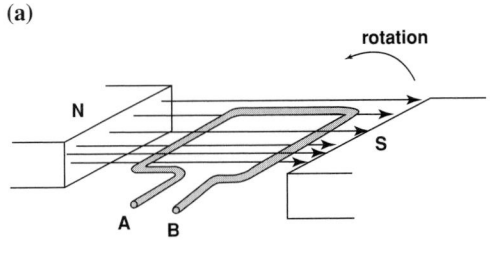

(e)

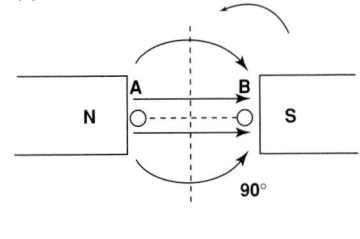

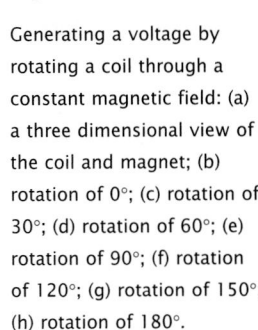

Figure 8.1

Generating a voltage by rotating a coil through a constant magnetic field: (a) a three dimensional view of the coil and magnet; (b) rotation of 0°; (c) rotation of 30°; (d) rotation of 60°; (e) rotation of 90°; (f) rotation of 120°; (g) rotation of 150°; (h) rotation of 180°.

(b)

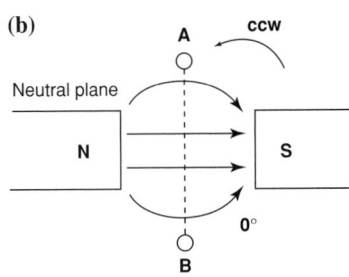

(f)

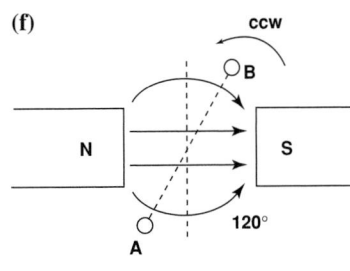

(c)

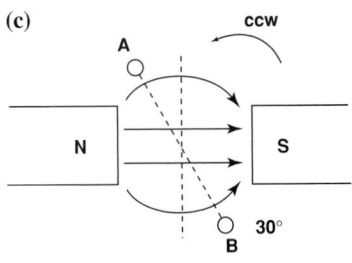

(g)

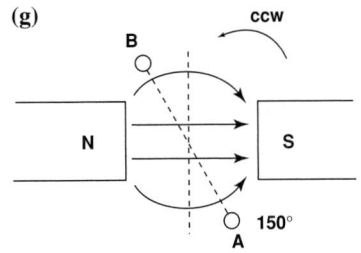

(d)

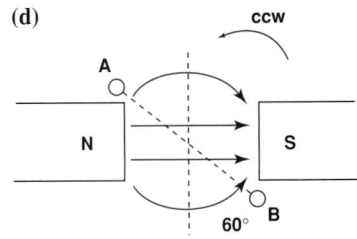

(h)

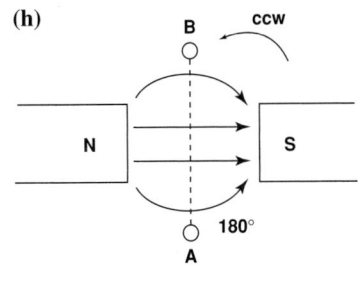

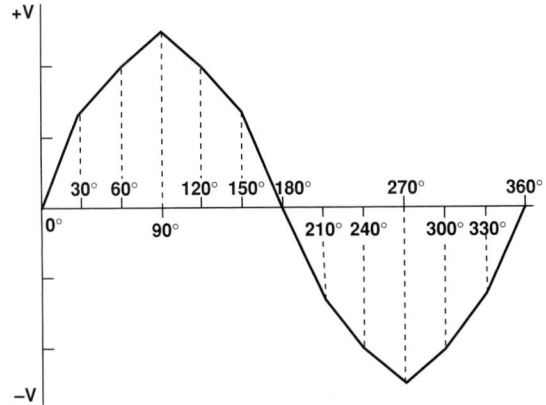

Figure 8.2

Graph of the voltage generated by the machine in Fig. 8.1.

Figure 8.3

A plotted waveform based on 360 points of rotation.

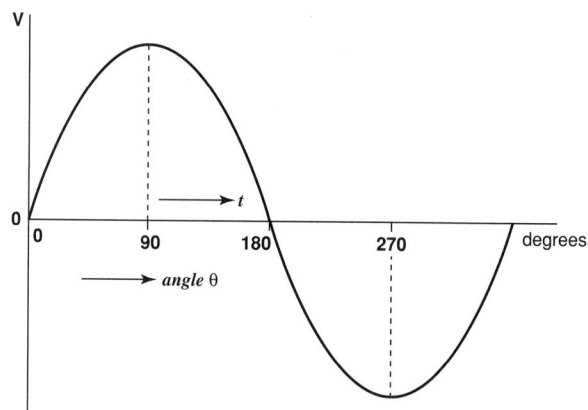

While we have used 13 steps to construct the crude graph in Fig. 8.2, we could have used 360 steps to produce the much smoother, more accurate graph in Fig. 8.3. However, we have shown that the voltage induced in a coil moving at a constant speed through a constant magnetic field is determined by the angle through which the coil is moving at any instant in time. Since the coil is moving at a constant speed, the angle through which it is moving at any instant can be used as a measure of time. Using Equation 7.3, we can calculate the **maximum voltage** induced in the conductor. By combining these two ideas, it is possible to determine the induced voltage at any instant in time:

$$V_{instantaneous} = V_{maximum}\ \sin\theta$$

or

EQ. 8.1

$$V_{inst} = V_{max}\ \sin\theta$$

where

V_{inst} = the induced voltage at any defined instant in time
V_{max} = the maximum induced voltage
$\sin\theta$ = the sine of any defined angle

MAXIMUM VOLTAGE

INSTANTANEOUS VOLTAGE

EXAMPLE 8.1

Calculate the **instantaneous voltage** at 53.2° if the maximum voltage is 155 V.

SOLUTION

$$
\begin{aligned}
V_{inst} &= V_{max}\ \sin\theta \\
&= 155 \times \sin 53.2° \\
&= 155 \times 0.800 \\
&= 124\ V
\end{aligned}
$$

EXAMPLE 8.2

Calculate the maximum voltage if the instantaneous voltage at 45° is 120 V.

SOLUTION:

$V_{max} = V_{inst} / \sin\theta$

$\quad\quad = 120\ V/\sin 45°$

$\quad\quad = 120/0.7071$

$\quad\quad = 170\ V$

In Chapter 2, we discussed power in dc circuits. Since dc values of voltage are constant over time, the power dissipated by a resistive load is simply the product of the voltage and current ($P = VI$). This doesn't work in most ac circuits, since ac varies constantly over time.

If we apply 1 V dc to a 1 Ω resistor, 1 watt of power will be dissipated. If we take the same resistor and connect it to a variable ac source set to 0 V ac, no power is dissipated. If we now increase the ac voltage until 1 watt of power is dissipated by the load, we find the peak output voltage of the source will be 1.414 V, or 1.414 times greater than the dc voltage. Regardless of the voltages, we will always find the same ratio. The ac voltage required to produce the same heating effect as a dc voltage is known as the **effective voltage.**

EFFECTIVE VOLTAGE

The value 1.414 is the square root of two. The inverse of this number ($1/\sqrt{2}$) is 0.7071. This value is commonly used to indicate the relationship between the peak or maximum voltage and the effective voltage of a sine wave:

$V_{effective} = 0.7071 \times V_{pk}$

or

$V_{eff} \quad = 0.7071 \times V_{pk}$

where

$V_{eff} \quad$ = effective voltage for a sine wave

0.7071 = a constant equivalent to $1/\sqrt{2}$

$V_{pk} \quad$ = the positive or negative maximum voltage of a sine wave

EXAMPLE 8.3

A sine wave has a peak value of 310 V. Find the effective value.

SOLUTION:

$V_{eff} = 0.7071 \times V_{pk}$

$\quad\quad = 0.7071 \times 310$

$\quad\quad = 219\ V$

EXAMPLE 8.4

An ac waveform has an effective voltage of 120 V. Find the peak value.

SOLUTION:

$V_{eff} = 0.7071 \times V_{pk}$

$V_{pk} = V_{eff} / 0.7071$

$\phantom{V_{pk}} = 120 / 0.7071$

$\phantom{V_{pk}} = 169.7 \text{ V}$

The effective value is very important when working with ac. All voltages and currents are measured using effective values and all ac meters read effective values.

8.3   Properties of a Sinusoidal Waveshape

Most alternating voltages and currents are sinusoidal—that is, over time they vary according to the properties of a sine wave. Figure 8.4 shows a typical ac current that varies sinusoidally. It flows in a resistor R. The current reaches peak values of +20 A and –20 A at regular intervals of time. The interval between successive positive peaks is called a **cycle**. A cycle is also equal to the interval between any two successive points on the sine wave having the same instantaneous angle. See, for example, instants t_a and t_b. In Fig. 8.4, the duration of one cycle is 1 s.

> **CYCLE**

Figure 8.5 shows a sinusoidal voltage having a peak value of 170 V. It is produced by a source G. As in the case of an alternating current, the interval between any two voltages having the same instantaneous angle is called a cycle. Thus, the voltage completes one cycle between instants t_1 and t_2. However, it is always easier to measure the duration of one cycle by using two successive positive peaks. In this figure, the duration of one cycle is 1/60 s.

> **FREQUENCY**

The **frequency** of an alternating current or voltage is equal to the number of cycles in one second. In Fig. 8.4, the frequency of the current is 1 cycle per second, or 1 hertz (symbol Hz). On the other hand, the frequency of the voltage in Fig. 8.5 is 60 Hz because one cycle is completed every 1/60 of a second.

Figure 8.4

Graph of a sinusoidal ac current having a peak value of 20 A and a frequency of 1 Hz.

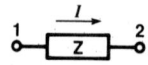

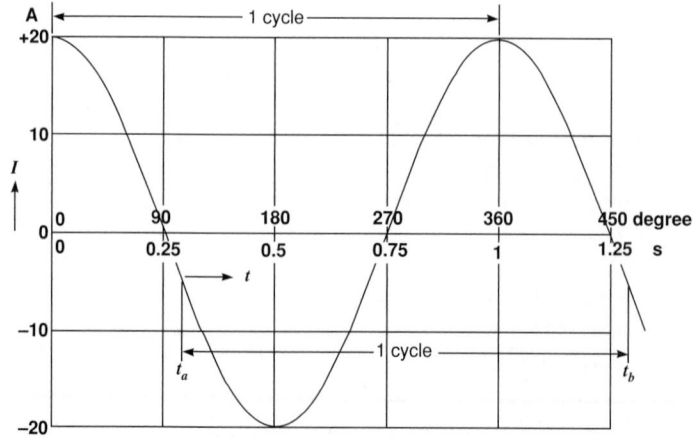

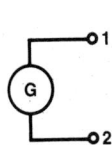

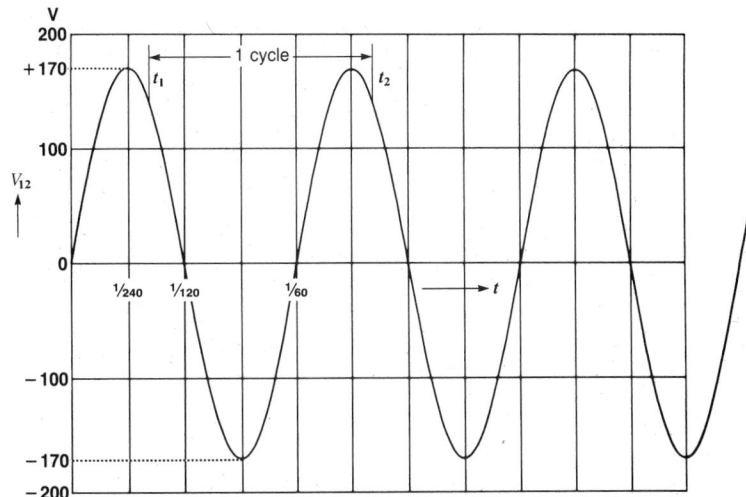

Figure 8.5

Graph of a sinusoidal ac voltage having a peak value of 170 V and a frequency of 60 Hz.

8.4 Positive and Negative Voltages

A voltage has two basic properties: a magnitude and a polarity. We are often inclined to emphasize its magnitude, but the polarity of a voltage is just as important. In this section we give a simple way to indicate both properties.

Consider Fig. 8.6, in which a generator produces 100 V, and terminal A is (+) and terminal B is (−). It is important to understand that the polarity of A is only positive with respect to B. By itself, terminal A has no polarity. Similarly, the polarity of terminal B is only negative with respect to that of terminal A; by itself, terminal B has no polarity. Using these facts, we now describe the generator voltage as either V_{AB} or V_{BA}.

The symbol V_{AB} stands for two things: (1) the magnitude of the voltage between terminals A and B, and (2) the polarity of A with respect to B.

Similarly, the symbol V_{BA} stands for the magnitude of the voltage between terminals A and B, and the polarity of B with respect to A.

Referring to Fig. 8.6, and recognizing that A is positive (+) with respect to B, we can write:

$$V_{AB} = +100 \text{ V}$$

▼ **Figure 8.6**

Terminal A is positive with respect to terminal B. Similarly, terminal B is negative with respect to terminal A.

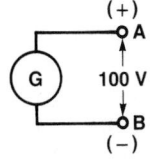

▼ **Figure 8.7**

In reference to this figure, it is known that $V_{21} = -300$ V.

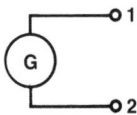

▼ **Figure 8.8**

This figure shows the actual voltage and polarities referred to in Fig. 8.7.

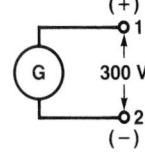

Because B is negative (–) with respect to A, we could equally well write:

$V_{BA} = -100$ V

Thus, $V_{AB} = +100$ V and $V_{BA} = -100$ V convey exactly the same information.

As a further example, suppose that in Fig. 8.7, $V_{21} = -300$ V. This tells us that (1) the voltage between the terminals is 300 V, and (2) terminal 2 is negative with respect to terminal 1. Figure 8.8 shows the actual condition.

DOUBLE SUBSCRIPT NOTATION

This way of designating voltages is known as the **double subscript notation.**

8.5 Positive and Negative Currents

A current, like a voltage, has two basic properties: a magnitude and a direction. We can use positive and negative signs to indicate the direction of current flow. For example, the current in a resistor (Fig. 8.9) may flow from X to Y or from Y to X. If one of these directions is considered to be positive (+), the other is negative (–).

The positive direction is shown arbitrarily by means of an arrow (Fig. 8.10). Thus, if a current of 2 A actually flows from X to Y, it flows in the positive direction and is designated by the symbol +2 A. Conversely, if the current actually flows from X to Y (direction opposite to that of the arrow), it is designated by the symbol –2 A.

A current whose direction is continually changing is called an *alternating current*, or ac current.

▼ **Figure 8.9**

Current may flow from X to Y or from Y to X.

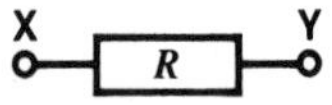

▼ **Figure 8.10**

The arrow shows the direction of current that is arbitrarily considered to be positive.

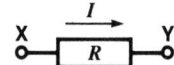

EXAMPLE 8.5

The circuit of Fig. 8.11 shows a current *I* flowing in a resistor *R*. The current varies according to the graph in Fig. 8.12. Interpret the physical meaning of this graph.

SOLUTION:

According to the graph, the current increases from zero to +2 A during the interval from 0 to 1 s. Because the current is positive, it is actually flowing from Y to X in the resistor (direction of the arrow). During the interval from 1 s to 2 s, the current decreases from +2 A to zero, but it still circulates from Y to X in the resistor.

Between 2 s and 3 s, the current increases from zero to –2 A. Because the current is negative, it flows in a direction opposite to the arrow, that is, from X to Y in the resistor.

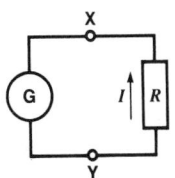

Figure 8.11

See Example 8.5.

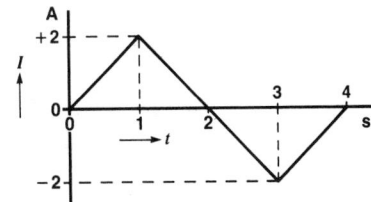

Figure 8.12

See Example 8.5.

This example shows that a graph must always be associated with a corresponding circuit diagram in order to determine the actual direction of current flow.

8.6 Representing Sinusoidal Voltages and Currents by Phasors

The sine waves of Figs. 8.4 and 8.5 are similar to the sine wave generated by the revolving coil of Fig. 8.1. This similarity enables us to represent an ac voltage in a very simple way. In effect, just as a revolving coil can generate a sine wave, we can imagine that a given sine wave is due to a revolving line. In the case of a sinusoidal voltage, the line has a length equal to the peak value of the voltage, and its rate of rotation is equal to the frequency.

The voltage in Fig. 8.5 has a peak value of 170 V and a frequency of 60 Hz. It can therefore be represented by the line OA, having a length of, say, 170 mm and rotating at a speed of 60 revolutions per second (Fig. 8.13). We show the line in three different positions (0A, 0A' and 0A'') to illustrate the correspondence between it and the sine wave. However, we really only need to show its position at time $t = 0$. Thus, the single horizontal line OA represents the sine wave completely. It is standard practice in Canada to show a **phasor** with 0° at the 3 o'clock position and to have the phasor rotate in a counterclockwise direction.

PHASOR

This simplification has far-reaching effects in all ac circuit theory, and we will use it many times.

Because of its importance, this line is called a *phasor*. The phasor is a straight line showing magnitude and direction and is normally shown with an arrowhead at the end opposite to the point of rotation.

Like voltages, alternating currents can also be represented by phasors. The magnitude of the current is shown by the length of the line and the direction of the line

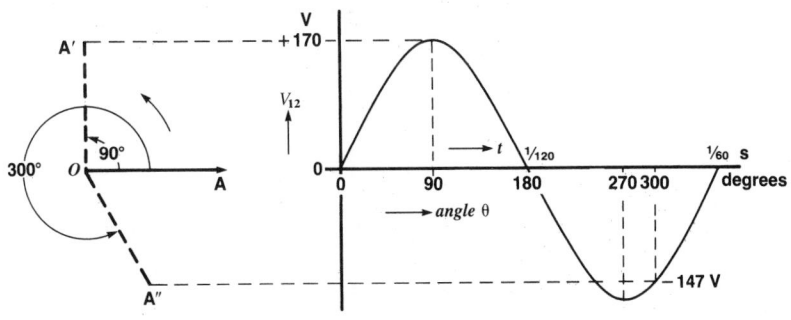

Figure 8.13

Phasor OA revolving at 60 revolutions per second can represent the ac voltage of Fig. 8.5.

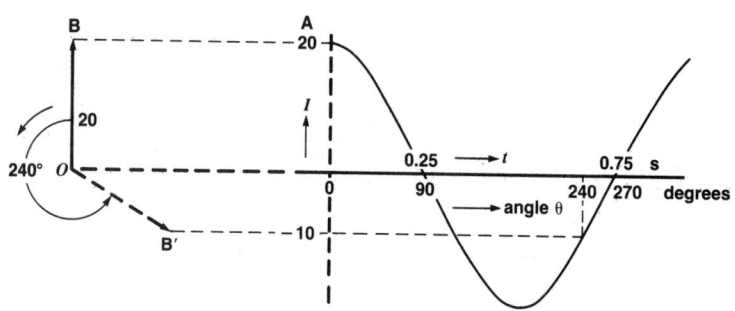

Figure 8.14

Phasor OB revolving at
1 revolution per second can
represent the ac current of
Fig. 8.14.

is indicated by its position relative to 0°. Thus, the sine wave of Fig. 8.4 can be represented by phasor OB (Fig. 8.14). The length of phasor OB may be 20 mm or any other convenient length that represents a current of 20 A.

8.7 Degree Scale Versus Time Scale

Because a sinusoidal voltage or current can be represented by a revolving phasor, it is usually more convenient to draw the sine wave with the horizontal axis calibrated in degrees of rotation rather than in seconds or milliseconds. This angular scale is used in Figs. 8.13 and 8.14. To avoid confusion with **mechanical degrees**, the angles in sine waves and phasor diagrams are called **electrical degrees**. An interval of 360° corresponds to one complete revolution of a phasor, which, in turn, corresponds to the duration of one cycle. We can therefore convert any interval in degrees to an interval of time, and vice versa.

| MECHANICAL DEGREES |
| ELECTRICAL DEGREES |

EXAMPLE 8.6

In Fig. 8.13, calculate the time interval that corresponds to an angle of 30°.

SOLUTION:

1. The duration of one cycle = $1/f$ = 1/60 s = 0.0167 s = 16.67 ms
2. One cycle is equivalent to 360 electrical degrees
3. One electrical degree corresponds therefore to:
    16.67 ms/360 = 0.0463 ms
4. Thirty electrical degrees corresponds to 0.0463 × 30 = 1.389 ms

8.8 Relationship between Two Sinusoidal Waveshapes

In a given ac circuit, the sinusoidal voltages and currents all have the same frequency, but they usually do not reach their peak values at the same instant. Thus,

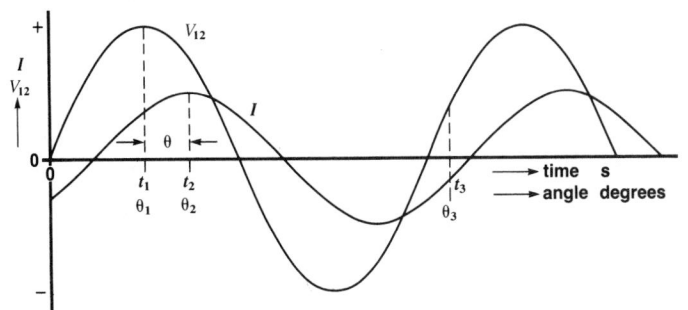

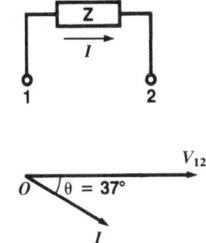

Figure 8.15

Current I lags behind voltage V_{12} by $(t_2 - t_1)$ seconds or $(\theta_2 - \theta_1)$ electrical degrees.

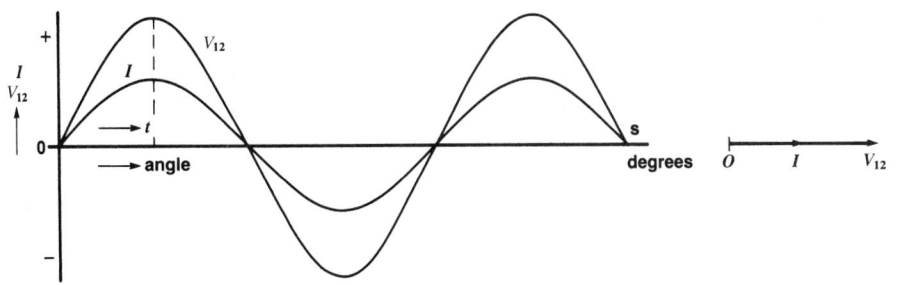

Figure 8.16

Voltage V_{12} and current I are in phase.

in Fig. 8.15, voltage V_{12} and current I in a device Z attain their peak positive values at instants t_1 and t_2, respectively. The corresponding angles are θ_1 and θ_2 degrees. The current peak occurs after the voltage peak, and so the current is said to *lag* behind the voltage. Alternatively, the voltage is said to *lead* the current. The amount of lag (or lead) is expressed as the difference between θ_1 and θ_2. Thus, if $\theta_1 = 90°$ and $\theta_2 = 127°$, current I lags voltage V_{12} by an angle $\theta = (127 - 90) = 37°$.

If the positive peaks of voltage and current occur at the same instant and in the same direction, the voltage and current are said to be in phase. This condition is illustrated in Fig. 8.16. Circuits containing only resistive devices will always be "in-phase." As a result, all the rules and laws you learned for dc circuits can be used.

Whenever we specify the lag or lead of one sine wave with respect to another, the angle must not exceed 180°.

8.9 Typical Phasor Diagrams

The sinusoidal voltages and currents of Figs. 8.15 and 8.16 can be represented by phasors. The so-called phasor diagrams are shown beside the V_{12} and I sine waves. Note how much simpler they are than the corresponding curves.

We shall again encounter phasor diagrams when we study ac circuits. This introduction to phasors and phasor diagrams will then be useful.

8.10 Ac Power

In Chapter 2, we found that we could calculate power using the relationship $P = VI$. With ac resistive circuits, we can use the same relationship because the current and voltage are in-phase (Fig. 8.16):

$$P = V_{\text{eff}} \times I_{\text{eff}}$$

where

P = power in watts

V_{eff} = effective voltage

I_{eff} = effective current

EXAMPLE 8.7

A resistor is connected to a 120 V ac source and draws 8 A; determine the power in watts.

SOLUTION:

$P = V_{\text{eff}} \times I_{\text{eff}}$
$ = 120 \text{ V} \times 8 \text{ A}$
$ = 960 \text{ W}$

8.11 Summary

Upon completion of this chapter you should have learned:

• That alternating current has three advantages over dc current; ac can be stepped up or down, ac machines are simpler in construction and lower in cost than dc machines, and ac machines can be built in larger electrical capacities than dc machines.

• To describe how an ac voltage is generated by revolving a coil in a constant magnetic field.

• That instantaneous currents and voltages can be found using the relationship: $V_{\text{instantaneous}} = V_{\text{maximum}} \sin\theta$ or $I_{\text{instantaneous}} = I_{\text{maximum}} \sin\theta$.

• That peak and effective values can be found using Equation 8.2.

• That double subscript notation is used to describe the polarity of one point with respect to a second point. Thus, V_{AB} indicates the polarity of A with respect to point B.

• How to represent currents and voltages using phasors to plot magnitude and direction.

• That every electrical cycle contains 360 electrical degrees and it is unrelated to the mechanical rotation of an alternator's rotor. Mechanical degrees refer to the physical rotation of an alternator's rotor.

Key Terms

AC: Alternating current.

CYCLE: The interval of time required for a waveform to repeat itself.

DOUBLE SUBSCRIPT NOTATION: A means of indicating relative polarity and magnitude between two specified points in a circuit or system.

EFFECTIVE VOLTAGE: 0.7071 of the peak or maximum voltage of a sine. It is based on a comparison of the heating effect of ac and dc. Unless otherwise specified, all ac values are given in effective values.

ELECTRICAL DEGREES: The number of degrees in one cycle, regardless of the frequency. Electrical degrees are used as a measure of time.

FREQUENCY: The number of cycles per second. The unit is the Hertz (Hz). One cycle per second equals 1 Hz.

INSTANTANEOUS VOLTAGE (OR CURRENT): The voltage value on a sinusoidal waveform at a specified time. See Equation 8.1.

MAXIMUM VOLTAGE (OR PEAK VOLTAGE): The highest magnitude positive and negative voltage found on a sine wave.

MECHANICAL DEGREES: Degrees used to measure the physical rotation in a machine such as a generator.

PHASOR: A graphic means of illustrating the magnitude and direction of currents and voltages.

TRANSFORMER: An electromagnetic device that can be used to change the magnitude of a voltage.

Test Your Knowledge

8.1 The equation $V_{78} = -45$ V means that the voltage is 45 V and
   a. terminal 78 is negative
   b. terminal 8 is positive
   c. terminal 7 is negative with respect to terminal 8

8.2 The equation $I = -2$ A is meaningless unless
   a. we have a graph of the current
   b. we have a circuit diagram showing the positive direction of current flow
   c. both (a) and (b)

8.3 The arrow showing current flow in a circuit is
   a. the direction in which the current is actually flowing
   b. the direction in which the current should flow
   c. the direction in which the current is assumed to flow

8.4 In Fig. 8.2, at 135°, the following is true:
   a. V is positive
   b. V is negative

8.5 In any device having terminals A and B, the sum $V_{AB} + V_{BA}$ is always zero.

   true _____   false _____

8.6 In Fig. 8.13, the instant 1/120 corresponds to
   a. 180° (electrical)
   b. 90°
   c. 180° (mechanical)

8.7   In Fig. 8.13, the interval between 4.16 ms and 12.49 ms corresponds to an electrical angle of
a.   360°
b.   180°
c.   90°

8.8   Fig. 8.15 shows a current leading the voltage.

true _____   false _____

8.9   In Fig. 8.13, 3 ms corresponds to
a.   0.0648°
b.   0.018°
c.   64.8°

8.10   In Fig. 8.13, one second corresponds to
a.   360°
b.   21 600°
c.   43 200°

8.11   An angle of 3476° is equivalent to an angle of
a.   236°
b.   9.655°
c.   0.655°

8.12   An angle of 340° is equivalent to an angle of
a.   680°
b.   160°
c.   −20°

8.13   A positive voltage is more important than a negative voltage.

true _____   false _____

Questions and Problems

8.14   In Fig. 8.12, is there any moment when the rate of change of current is zero? Explain.

8.15   In Fig. 8.12, if $t = 1.5$ s, is V_{XY} positive or negative? Explain.

8.16   Sketch the sine wave of a current having a peak value of 10 A and a frequency of 2 Hz. Assume the current is zero (with positive slope) at $t = 0$.

8.17   Using graph paper scaled off at 30° intervals, draw a sine wave of V_{12} so that the peak value is 200 V and the frequency is 50 Hz. The voltage starts at zero, with a positive slope, and lasts for 30 ms.

8.18   Calculate the instantaneous at 215° if the maximum voltage is 295 V at 60 Hz.

8.19   If the instantaneous voltage at 77° is 317 V, calculate the peak voltage.

8.19   For a peak voltage of 295 V, find the effective value.

8.20   An ac voltmeter reads 360 V. What is the peak voltage?

8.21   Calculate the power consumed by a resistor if the peak voltage is 170 V and the peak current is 25 A.

Inductors and Inductance

LEARNING OBJECTIVES

Upon completion of this chapter you will be able to:

- Explain the difference between mutual and self-inductance

- Determine the amount of energy stored in a coil

- Describe the equivalent circuit of a coil

- Explain how current builds up in a coil

- Describe what happens when a coil circuit is opened

- Explain the effect of ac on an inductance

9.1   Mutual Induction

Consider two coils A and B wound on a common iron core (Fig. 9.1). Coil A and rheostat R are connected in series across the terminals of a battery. By changing the position of the rheostat, current I_a can be varied. This causes the mmf of coil A to vary, and hence the flux ϕ in the core. The magnitude of ϕ will therefore increase and decrease with I_a. But according to Faraday's law, any change in ϕ will induce a voltage in coil B. This means that a change in the current flowing in coil A will induce a voltage V_b in coil B.

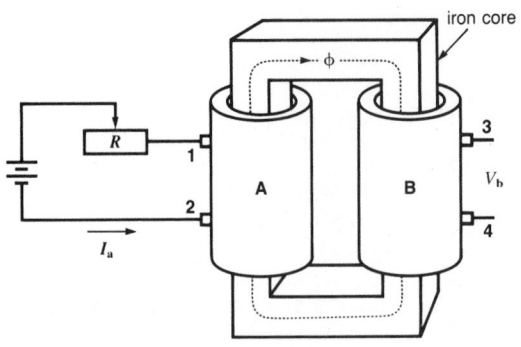

Figure 9.1

A voltage V_b is induced in coil B when current I_a in coil A varies. This is called mutual induction.

The phenomenon by which a change of current in one coil induces a voltage in another is called **mutual induction**.

If a resistor is connected across the terminals of coil B, the induced voltage V_b will cause a current to flow, and so the resistor will heat up. This thermal energy must come from energy that is supplied to coil A. Thus, the mutual induction between two coils enables energy to be transmitted from one coil to another without any physical connection between them. The coils are said to be *coupled* magnetically by the common flux ϕ that links them.

9.2 Mutual Inductance; the Henry (H)

In Fig. 9.1, the magnitude of the induced voltage V_b depends upon the rate at which the flux ϕ is changing. But the rate of change of flux depends upon the rate of change of the mmf developed by coil A. This in turn depends upon the rate at which current I_a is changing. It follows that the induced voltage V_b is proportional to the rate of change of current I_a. We can therefore write

EQ. 9.1 $V_b = M \times$ **rate of change of current** I_a

or

EQ. 9.2 $V_b = M \dfrac{\Delta I_a}{\Delta t}$

where

V_b = voltage induced in coil B, in volts (V)

$\dfrac{\Delta I_a}{\Delta t}$ = rate of change of current in coil A, in amperes per second (A/s)

M = a constant, whose magnitude depends upon the number of turns on the two coils and the coupling between them

The constant M in Eq. 9.1 is called the mutual inductance of the two coils. It is simply a convenient multiplier that relates the rate of change of current in one coil to the voltage induced in the other. The mutual inductance of two coils is a property they share that is just as real as their resistance.

Figure 9.1a

This large inductor, having a rating of 0.5 H and able to carry a dc current of 1800 A, is to smooth the dc current in a 300 kV dc transmission line. Because an inductor opposes any change of current that flows through it, it effectively suppresses the ac currents in the dc line. The coil is immersed in an oil-filled tank and the external radiators are fan-cooled during the summer. The two HV bushings lead the dc current into and out of the inductor.

(Courtesy Manitoba Hydro)

What happens if we interchange the connections in Fig. 9.1 so that coil B carries a variable current I_b and coil A is on open-circuit? A voltage V_a will be induced in coil A, and its value is given by the equation:

$$V_a = M \frac{\Delta I_b}{\Delta t}$$

EQ. 9.3

where M has the same value as in Eq. 9.2. The mutual inductance between two coils is therefore the same, no matter which coil is being excited.

The SI unit of mutual inductance is the **henry** (symbol H). The mutual inductance between two coils is said to be 1 henry when a rate of change of 1 ampere per second in one coil induces 1 volt in the other.

HENRY

EXAMPLE 9.1

The mutual inductance between coils A and B of Fig. 9.1 is 3.7 H. Calculate the voltage induced in coil B if the current in coil A changes from 7 A to 2 A in 2 seconds.

SOLUTION:

1. The change in current is: $\Delta I_a = 7 - 2 = 5$ A
2. The duration of the change is: $\Delta t = 2$ s
3. The rate of change of current is: $\dfrac{\Delta I_a}{\Delta t} = \dfrac{5}{2} = 2.5$ A/s

   $V_b = 3.7 \times 2.5 = 9.25$ V

EQ. 9.2

9.3 Self-Induction and Self-Inductance

Consider Fig. 9.2, in which a coil A and rheostat R are connected in series across a battery. As before, current I_a can be varied by means of the rheostat, and this

Figure 9.2

A voltage V_{12} is induced in coil A when current I_a varies. This is called self-induction.

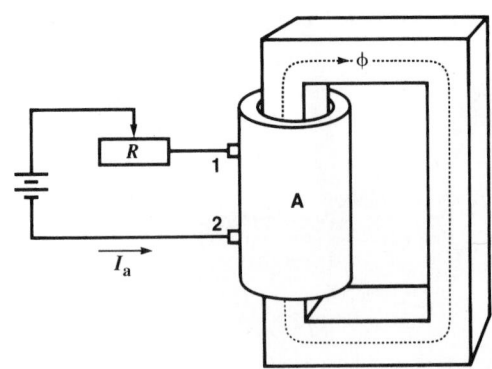

produces a change in flux ϕ. But, by Faraday's law, any change of flux inside a coil induces a voltage across its terminals. Therefore, a change of current in coil A produces a voltage across its own terminals. This phenomenon is called **self-induction**.

SELF-INDUCTION

By analogy with Equation 9.1, the self-induced voltage is given by the equation:

EQ. 9.4 $V_a = L \times$ **rate of change of current** I_a

or

EQ. 9.5 $V_a = L \; \dfrac{\Delta I_a}{\Delta t}$

where

V_a = voltage induced in coil A, in volts (V)

$\dfrac{\Delta I_a}{\Delta t}$ = rate of change of current in coil A, in amperes per second (A/s)

L = a constant whose magnitude depends upon the number of turns on the coil and the reluctance of the magnetic circuit

The constant L is called the self-inductance of the coil. It is simply a convenient multiplier that relates the self-induced voltage to the rate of change of current. Nevertheless, the self-inductance of a coil is one of its basic properties that is just as real as its resistance.

For example, coil A and coil B in Fig. 9.1 each have a certain self-inductance, in addition to their mutual inductance. The self-inductances are usually quite different, depending mainly upon the number of turns. Thus, if coil A has more turns than coil B, its inductance will be greater. (The term "inductance" is often used instead of "self-inductance.")

The SI unit of self-inductance is also the henry. A coil is said to have a self-inductance of 1 H when a rate of change of current of 1 A/s induces 1 V across its own terminals.

EXAMPLE 9.2

A coil having a self-inductance of 2 H is connected across a 3 V battery (Fig. 9.3). The current is 5 A, and it can be interrupted in 0.1 s using switch S. What is the average value of the induced voltage while the current is falling to zero?

▼ **Figure 9.3**

Coil connected to a 3 V battery.

▼ **Figure 9.4**

The induced voltage (100 V) is much higher than the battery voltage when the circuit is interrupted.

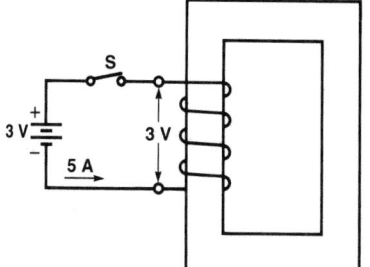

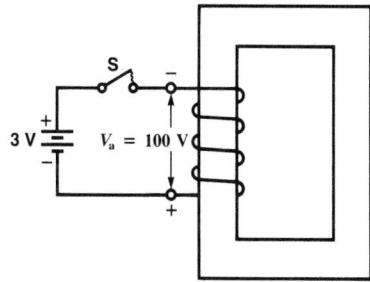

SOLUTION:

$$V_a = L \frac{\Delta I_a}{\Delta t} = 2 \times \frac{5 - 0}{0.1} = 100 \text{ V}$$

EQ. 9.5

Note that the induced voltage (100 V) in Fig. 9.4 is much higher than the battery voltage (3 V) in Fig. 9.3.

9.4 Energy Stored in a Coil

A magnetic field is a form of stored energy. The energy stored in the magnetic field of a coil is given by the equation:

$$W = \frac{1}{2} LI^2$$

EQ. 9.6

where

W = energy stored in the magnetic field, in joules (J)

L = self-inductance of the coil, in henries (H)

I = current in the coil, in amperes (A)

The stored energy increases with the square of the current. Thus, if the current in a coil doubles, the energy increases four times.

EXAMPLE 9.3

A coil having an inductance of 4 H carries a current of 10 A. Calculate the energy stored in its magnetic field. How much energy does the coil release when the current falls from 10 A to 5 A?

SOLUTION:

1. The initial energy in the coil is

$$W = \frac{1}{2} LI^2$$

$$W_1 = \frac{1}{2} \times 4 \times 10^2 = 200 \text{ joules} = 200 \text{ J}$$

2. The final energy in the coil is

$$W = \frac{1}{2} LI^2 = \frac{1}{2} \times 4 \times (5)^2 = 50 \text{ J}$$

3. The energy released by the coil is

$$W = W_1 - W_2 = 200 - 50 = 150 \text{ J}$$

Equation 9.6 tells us that the stored energy increases as the current increases. Thus, if the current in a coil is increasing, the stored energy is increasing. This means that the coil is absorbing energy from the circuit, and the coil therefore acts as a *load*. On the other hand, when the current decreases, the stored energy decreases. During such periods the coil releases energy, and it then acts as a *source*. The coil can therefore be either a load or a source, depending upon whether the current is increasing or decreasing.

Knowing that a coil behaves this way enables us to determine the polarity of the voltage across its terminals. The coil in Fig. 9.5 is part of an electrical circuit (not shown). It carries a current I that flows into terminal 1. The coil is assumed to have negligible resistance. Consequently, the IR drop across its terminals is always zero.

If the current is constant, the flux is not changing, and so the induced voltage is zero. As a result, V_{12} in Fig. 9.5 is zero. But if the current is increasing (Fig. 9.6), the flux is increasing, and so a voltage V_{12} will be induced. Because the coil acts as a load, the polarity of terminal 1 is negative (see Section 2.12).

If the current is decreasing (Fig. 9.7), the energy in the field is dropping and so the coil returns energy to the electrical circuit. Consequently, the coil now acts as a source, and terminal 2 is negative. Note that the polarity is independent of how the coil is wound.

This analysis brings out one of the important properties of an inductance: it tends to oppose the increase or decrease of current in a circuit. For example, in Fig. 9.6, the increasing current causes the coil to generate a voltage V_{12} that attempts to drive a current in the opposite direction to I. Conversely, in Fig. 9.7, the decreasing current causes the coil to generate a voltage that attempts to circulate a current in the same direction as I.

▼ Figure 9.5

The induced voltage is zero because the current is not changing.

▼ Figure 9.6

When the current is increasing, the coil absorbs energy, and so it acts as a load. Therefore terminal 1 is positive.

Figure 9.7

When the current is decreasing, the coil releases energy, and so it acts as a source. Therefore terminal 1 is negative.

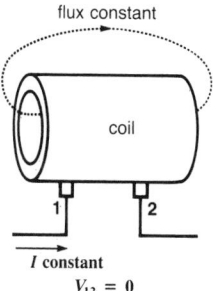

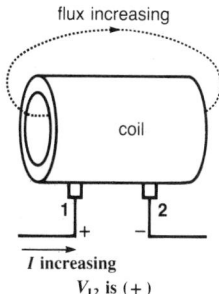

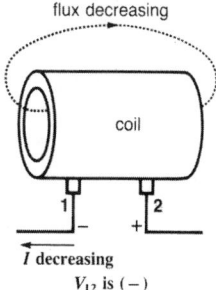

9.5 Equivalent Circuit of a Coil

An inductor is a coil that has zero resistance. It is represented by the wiring diagram symbol shown in Fig. 9.8. If the coil has resistance (as all coils do), the **equivalent circuit** is given by Fig. 9.9. When the coil carries a variable current, the *IR* drop occurs across the coil resistance *R*, and any induced voltage appears across the inductance *L*. The voltage across the terminals of the coil is equal to the vector sum of these two voltages. The terminals are obviously A and B. Point t is not accessible; it exists only in the equivalent circuit. Energy stored in the coil is associated with *L*.

EQUIVALENT CIRCUIT

9.6 Build-Up of Current in a Coil

When a coil is connected across a dc source (Fig. 9.10) the current does not immediately reach its final value because the induced voltage opposes the increase in current. Consequently, the current increases gradually, as shown in Fig. 9.11. When the final value of current is reached, the flux is constant, and so the induced voltage is zero. The current is then limited only by the resistance of the coil.

▼ Figure 9.8

Circuit diagram of a perfect inductor having an inductance *L*.

▼ Figure 9.9

Circuit diagram of an inductor having an inductance *L* and resistance *R*.

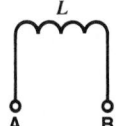

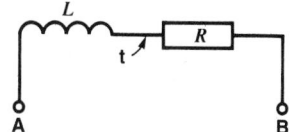

▼ **Figure 9.10**

When a coil is connected to a dc source, the induced voltage opposes the build-up of current I.

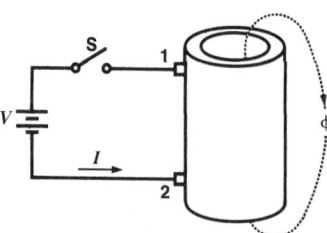

▼ **Figure 9.11**

The current reaches its final value after $5L/R$ seconds.

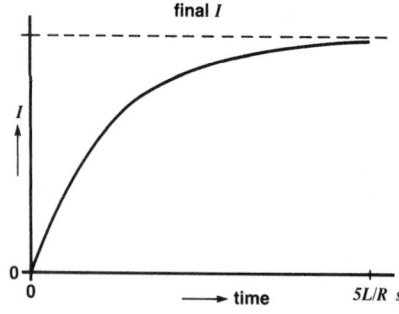

The time to reach this final state depends upon the ratio L/R, which is called the **TIME CONSTANT** **time constant** T of the coil. For all practical purposes, the current reaches its final value about $5L/R$ seconds after the switch is closed.

EXAMPLE 9.4

A coil having an inductance of 4 H and a resistance of 2 Ω is connected across a 20 V dc source. Calculate:
1. The time constant of the coil.
2. The final current in the coil.
3. The time to reach the final current.
4. The energy stored in the coil.

SOLUTION:

1. The time constant of the coil is
    $T = L/R = 4/2 = 2$ s
2. The final current is
    $I = V/R = 20/2 = 10$ A
3. The time to reach 10 A is
    $t = 5L/R = 5 \times 4/2 = 10$ s
4. The energy stored in the coil is
    $W = 1/2\ LI^2 = 1/2 \times 4 \times (10)^2 = 200$ J

• **EQ. 9.6**

9.7 Opening the Circuit of a Coil

Whenever we open the circuit of a coil by means of a switch, several things happen. As soon as the switch opens, the current in the coil is supposed to fall to zero. But if it did, an extremely high voltage V_a would be induced across the coil. The polarity of V_a is shown in Fig. 9.12. The voltage across the switch contacts is therefore

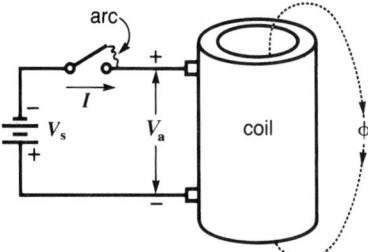

Figure 9.12

When a switch opens, the high induced voltage V_a produces an arc across the switch contacts.

$(V_s + V_a)$, where V_s is the voltage of the source. This very high voltage causes the air between the switch contacts to break down, and an arc is established between them. Thus, although the switch is partly open, the coil is not yet disconnected because the arc completes the circuit.

The high voltage may also break down the coil insulation, causing a short-circuit between turns. Furthermore, it is a shock hazard.

In addition, most of the energy previously stored in the magnetic field is dissipated in the electric arc. The resulting heat may damage and even melt the switch contacts.

The induced voltage can be limited by connecting a resistor across the coil terminals (Fig. 9.13). The resistor also absorbs an important part of the stored magnetic energy, thus reducing the heat at the switch contacts. Unfortunately, the resistor consumes power while the coil is in operation.

Another effective method of suppressing both the high voltage and the arc is to connect a diode across the coil (Fig. 9.14).* The induced voltage across the terminals can never exceed the conduction voltage of the diode (about 2 V), and all the stored energy is dissipated in the coil resistance. The drawback to this method is that the flux decays slowly because current continues to circulate in the coil (and diode) even after the line current I is zero.

The most practical way to limit the high voltage is to use a voltage-sensitive resistor (varistor) in parallel with the coil. A varistor has a high resistance at the normal operating voltage, but when the voltage exceeds a certain level, its resistance automatically becomes much lower.

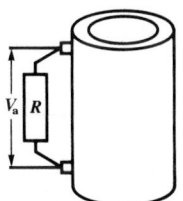

Figure 9.13

The magnitude of the induced voltage can be reduced by connecting a resistor across the coil.

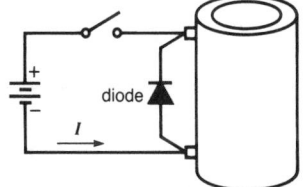

Figure 9.14

The induced voltage appearing across the coil can be reduced to less than 2 V by using a diode.

* The diode must be connected as shown; if it is reversed, it will short-circuit the source.

9.8 Typical Inductance of Coils

Coils that have air cores usually have inductances that are measured in micro-henries or millihenries. On the other hand, if the coil is wound on an iron core, the inductance may be several henries. For example, the coil in Fig. 9.15 has an inductance, by itself, of 80 mH. But if it is mounted on a 12×12 cm soft iron core having an air gap of 1 mm, the inductance increases to about 18 H (Fig. 9.16).

▶ **Figure 9.15**

This coil having an air core has an inductance of 80 mH.

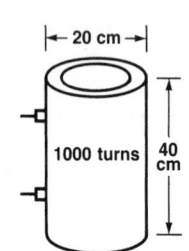

▶ **Figure 9.16**

The same coil mounted on an iron core having an air gap has an inductance of 18 H.

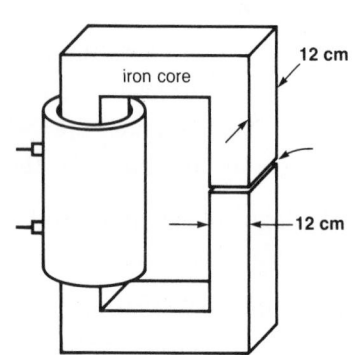

9.9 Inductance of a Transmission Line

In discussing a transmission line, we are usually concerned with its resistance. However, a transmission line also has inductance. When a line carries current, it behaves like a huge, single turn of wire (Fig. 9.17). In effect, the current in the line produces a magnetic field, and so the line behaves like an inductor. The inductance depends upon the length of the line, the spacing between the conductors, and their diameter. For example, a line 10 km long composed of two conductors having a diameter of 25 mm and spaced 3 m apart has an inductance of about 20 mH. If the length of the line were doubled, its inductance would double.

▶ **Figure 9.17**

A two-conductor transmission line has inductance because it acts like a long turn of wire.

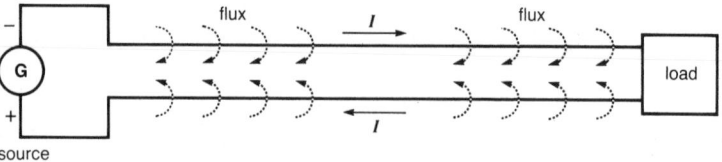

9.10 Inductor Carrying an Ac Current

Alternating current is almost exclusively used on power distribution systems. Accidental short-circuits can occur on such systems, and the resulting currents can be enormous. To limit their magnitude, inductors are sometimes connected in series with the line. Inductors are also used to stabilize the voltage on transmission lines. Because of these practical applications, it is important to understand the voltage–current relationship when an inductor carries a sinusoidal ac current.

Perfect inductor carrying a
sinusoidal ac current.

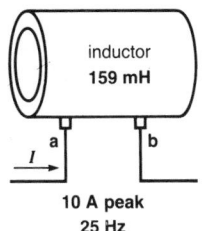

10 A peak
25 Hz

Waveshape of the current
flowing in the inductor of
Fig. 9.18.

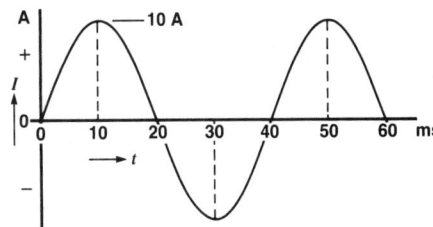

Fig. 9.18 shows a coil having an inductance of 159 mH, connected in series with a 25 Hz ac line. It carries a sinusoidal current I having a peak value of 10 A. The duration of one cycle is 1/25 s, or 40 ms (Fig. 9.19).

A voltage V_{ab} is induced across the terminals of the coil, and its magnitude is given by:

$$V_{ab} = L \frac{\Delta I}{\Delta t}$$

EQ. 9.5

where L is the inductance of the coil.

Let us try to get a general idea of the waveshape of the induced voltage. First, the rate of change of current is zero at instants corresponding to 10, 30, and 50 ms. Consequently, the voltage is zero at these instants.

Second, the current is positive between zero and 10 ms. It is therefore flowing in the direction of the arrow (Fig. 9.18). But because the current is increasing, terminal a is (+), and so V_{ab} is positive during this interval (Fig. 9.20). By the same reasoning, V_{ab} is negative between 10 ms and 20 ms.

We can generalize by stating that V_{ab} is (+) when the slope of I is (+).

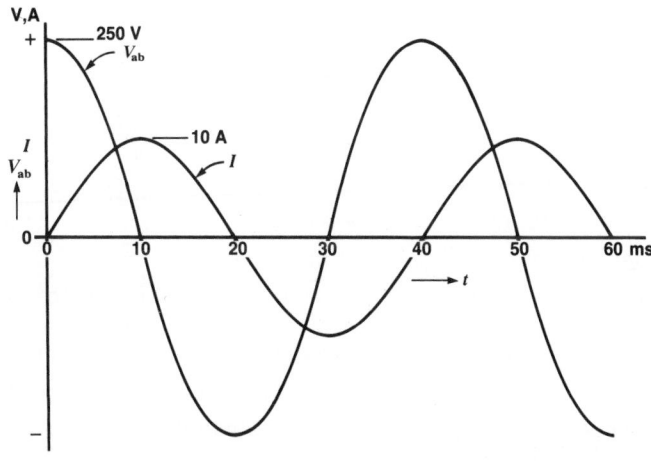

Figure 9.20

Waveshape of the ac voltage
induced across the terminals
of the inductor in Fig. 9.18.

Third, the rate of change of current is greatest at 0, 20, 40, and 60 ms. The induced voltage is therefore greatest at these instants. The maximum rate of change of current is given by the equation:

$$\left(\frac{\Delta I}{\Delta t}\right) = 2\pi f I_m$$

Where: $(\Delta I/\Delta t)$ = maximum rate of change of current in amperes per second

I_m = peak value of the sinusoidal current, in amperes (A)

f = frequency in hertz (Hz)

2π = constant (approximately 6.28)

Therefore, the maximum rate of current change is:

$(\Delta I/\Delta t)_{max} = 2\pi f I_m = 2 \times 3.1416 \times 25 \times 10 = 1570.8$ A/s

The maximum induced voltage is therefore

$$V_{ab} = L\frac{\Delta I}{\Delta t} = 0.159 \times 1570.8 = 250 \text{ V}$$

Based on this line of reasoning, V_{ab} has the waveshape given in Fig. 9.20. It so happens that V_{ab} is also sinusoidal, just as I is. But V_{ab} and I are out of phase because when the one is maximum, the other is zero, and vice versa. Based on the discussion of Section 7.12, the **current lag** is 90° behind the induced voltage. This is one of the fundamental properties of an inductor. We will examine some of its other properties when we reach Chapter 11 on ac circuits.

CURRENT LAG

9.11 Summary

Upon completion of this chapter you should have learned that:

- Mutual inductance is the ability of a coil to induce a voltage in a nearby coil.

- Self-inductance is the ability of a coil to induce a voltage in itself.

- Energy is stored within the magnetic field of a coil.

- The equivalent circuit for a coil contains both resistance and inductance.

- Five time constants are required for the current in a coil to reach its final level.

- Connecting a pure inductance across an AC source causes the current to lag 90° behind the voltage.

Key Terms

CURRENT LAG: The number of degrees that the current is behind the voltage. In a pure inductive circuit, the current lags the voltage by 90°.

EQUIVALENT CIRCUIT: Usually a mathematical circuit model designed to separate characteristics that are actually combined.

HENRY (H): The unit of inductance. One henry of inductance exists when a current changing at the rate 1 A/second induces a voltage of 1 V.

MUTUAL INDUCTANCE: The ability of a coil's changing magnetic flux to induce a voltage in magnetically linked conductive materials.

Usually, mutual induction occurs between linked coils.

SELF-INDUCTION: The ability of a coil's changing magnetic field to induce a voltage within itself.

TIME CONSTANT: For an inductor, the time constant is the ratio of the inductance to the resistance of a coil ($T = L/R$). Five time constants are required for the current to reach a steady state.

Test Your Knowledge

9.1 If we increase the number of turns on a coil, its inductance increases.

true _____ false _____

9.2 In Fig. 9.1, if $V_{34} = -20$ V, there is an induced voltage in coil A.

true _____ false _____

9.3 In Fig. 9.3, the coil has a resistance of 1 Ω. If the switch is closed, the initial current is
a. 0
b. 3 A
c. 1.5 A

9.4 When the current in a coil is constant for 1 minute, the induced voltage in the coil is zero during that period.

true _____ false _____

9.5 When the current in a coil is constant for one-tenth of a microsecond, the induced voltage during that short period is
a. very high
b. zero
c. dependent upon the coil inductance

9.6 The energy stored in a coil is constant during one second. This means that the current in the coil is
a. zero
b. constant
c. increasing

9.7 The current in a coil is momentarily 5 A, and the voltage is 60 V. If the current is increasing and the coil resistance is zero, the coil
a. absorbs 300 J
b. absorbs 300 W
c. delivers 300 W to the circuit

9.8 When an inductor carries a sinusoidal current, the voltage leads the current by 90°.

true _____ false _____

9.9 A coil has a self-inductance of 7 H. If the instantaneous current is 5 A, the induced voltage is
a. unknown
b. 35 V
c. 0 V

9.10 A sinusoidal voltage has a frequency of 400 Hz and a peak value of 200 V. The maximum rate of change is
a. 80 kV/s
b. 502.6 kV/s
c. 160 kV/s

Questions and Problems

9.11 The current in a coil changes from 5 A to 1 A in 0.4 s. If the induced voltage is 40 V, calculate the self-inductance of the coil.

9.12 In Fig. 9.1, $V_b = +40$ V when I_a changes at the rate of 2 A/s. Calculate
   a. the value of V_b when $\Delta I_a \backslash \Delta t = 90$ A/min
   b. the value of the mutual inductance M.

9.13 In Problem 9.12, the connections are interchanged so that coil B is excited and coil A is on open circuit. If I_b changes at the rate of 2 A/s, what is the value of V_a?

9.14 In Fig. 9.1, what is the polarity of terminal 1 if I_a is positive and decreasing?

9.15 A coil having an inductance of 3 H carries a current of 40 A. What is the energy stored in the magnetic field?

9.16 A large inductor used in atomic research has an inductance of 10 mH and a resistance of 4 mΩ. If it carries a constant dc current of 6000 A, calculate (a) the energy stored in the coil, (b) the voltage across the terminals, and (c) the time constant of the coil.

9.17 In Fig. 9.10, the coil has an inductance of 4 H and a resistance of 2 Ω.

The supply voltage is 12 V. When the switch is closed, current I increases gradually from zero to its final value. Knowing that the equivalent circuit of the coil is given by Fig. 9.9, calculate:
   a. the final value of I
   b. the IR drop when $I = 5$ A
   c. the induced voltage when $I = 5$ A
   d. the rate at which the current is changing when $I = 5$ A
   e. the energy stored in the coil when $I = 5$ A

9.18 A 12 V battery is connected to an inductor of 2 H. If the inductor resistance is negligible, what is the current in the coil
   a. after 0.1 s?
   b. after 8 s?
   c. after 1 min?
   d. after 1 h?

9.19 If the coil in Fig. 9.18 carries a current having a peak value of 10 A and a frequency of 50 Hz, what is the peak value of the induced voltage?

9.20 A coil whose inductance is 10 H carries a sinusoidal current having an effective value of 2 A and a frequency of 60 Hz. Calculate the peak value of the induced voltage.

10

Capacitors and Capacitance

LEARNING OBJECTIVES

Upon completion of this chapter you will be able to:

- Explain the basic principles of capacitance

- List the factors that affect capacitance

- Describe how charge is transferred from a source to a capacitor

- Explain the effect of connecting capacitors in series and parallel

- Determine the charging and discharging rates for a capacitor

- Describe the operation of a capacitor connected to an ac source

Chapter Outline

10.1 Free Electrons in a Metal

In Section 2.3, we learned that an enormous number of free electrons exist inside a conductor. It is estimated that in metals there are about 6×10^{19} per cubic millimetre. Because 1 coulomb corresponds to 6.24×10^{18} electrons, the free electron charge is equivalent to 10 coulombs per cubic millimetre.

The electrons are "free" in the sense that they are not attached to any particular atom. However, they cannot escape the block of metal, despite their high speed. The boundaries of the metal act like walls that prevent the electrons from flying out. However, if external electrons touch the metal surface, they are immediately captured and themselves become prisoners inside the "walls."

Normally, the negative charge carried by the free electrons is exactly counterbalanced by the equivalent positive charge on the stationary nuclei of the atoms. Thus, a conductor is normally neutral.

10.2 Transfer of Charge and Potential Difference

Consider two blocks of metal A and B, perfectly insulated from each other and both electrically neutral (Fig. 10.1). Suppose that by some means we are able to remove electrons from block A and deposit them on block B. The resulting lack of electrons on A gives it a positive charge, and the corresponding surplus of electrons on B gives it a negative charge. This difference in charge produces a difference of potential between the two blocks. If we connected a voltmeter between them, we would measure a voltage.

The more electrons we carry from A to B, the greater the voltage becomes. The magnitude of the voltage depends therefore upon the number of coulombs that have been transferred. However, it also depends upon the shape of the bodies, the distance between them, and the kind of dielectric (air, oil, paper, etc.) that separates them.

Only a very small fraction of the free electrons in a body has to be transported to produce a high voltage. For example, suppose the bodies are two identical plates having an area of 1 cm^2 and a thickness of 0.01 mm and separated by a distance of 1 cm (Fig. 10.2). Each plate has a volume of 1 mm^3 and contains about 10 coulombs of free electrons. If we transfer only 0.000 000 001 coulombs from one plate to the other, the resulting voltage between them will reach about 10 000 volts (Fig. 10.3)!

Obviously, in making such transfers, we don't have to worry about running short of available electrons.

Figure 10.1

Transferring electrons from one body to another creates a difference of potential between them.

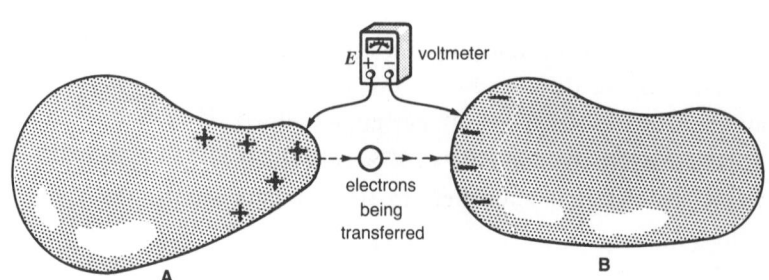

▼ **Figure 10.2**

Each metal plate contains about 10 coulombs of free electrons.

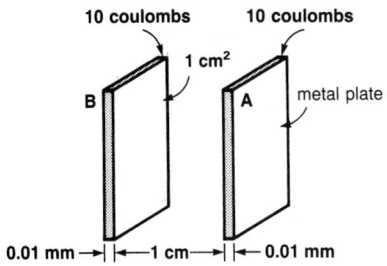

▼ **Figure 10.3**

If only 10^{-9} coulombs are transferred, the resulting voltage is 10 kV.

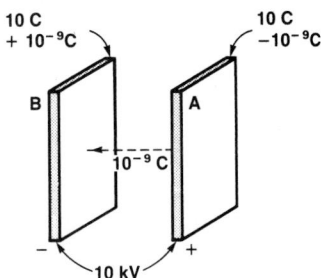

10.3 Energy Stored in an Electric Field

Suppose that a substantial electric charge is transferred from block A to block B in Fig. 10.4, making A strongly positive and B strongly negative. If we now carry an additional negative charge from A to B, it will be repelled by the negative charge on B and attracted by the positive charge on A. Thus, a force will act to the left as we move the charge to the right. Consequently, we have to use energy and do real mechanical work whenever we transfer charges from A to B.

What happens to this energy? It is stored in the so-called **electric field** between the two blocks. Energy can therefore be stored in an electric field just as it can be stored in a magnetic field.

ELECTRIC FIELD

The energy stored in the electric field is given by the equation:

$$W = \frac{1}{2} QV$$

EQ. 10.1

where

W = energy stored, in joules (J)

Q = electric charge transferred between the two bodies, in coulombs (C)

V = voltage between the bodies, in volts (V)

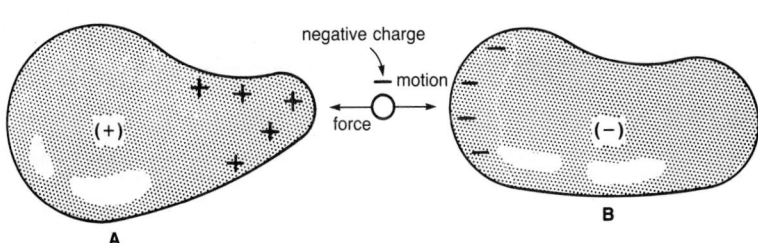

Figure 10.4

Mechanical work is needed to transfer the electric charge. This is converted into electric energy that is stored in the electric field.

10.4 Capacitance; the Farad (F)

Returning to Fig. 10.1, we recall that the voltage V between the charged bodies increases in direct proportion to the charge Q that is transferred. It so happens that for any pair of bodies that are fixed in relation to each other, the ratio Q/V is a constant. This constant is called the **capacitance** of the two bodies. The equation is:

CAPACITANCE

EQ. 10.2
$$C = Q/V$$

where

C = capacitance of the two bodies, in farads (F)

Q = charge transferred, in coulombs (C)

V = voltage between the bodies, in volts (V)

FARAD

The SI unit of capacitance is the **farad** (symbol F). The capacitance of two bodies is equal to 1 farad if the transfer of 1 coulomb between them produces a difference of potential of 1 volt. In practice, the farad is a much larger capacitance than we ordinarily encounter. For this reason, the microfarad, equal to one millionth of a farad, is a more commonly used unit.

The capacitance of two bodies is a basic property they have, which is just as real as their physical size.

EXAMPLE 10.1

In Fig. 10.4, electrons equivalent to 0.2 C are transferred from A to B, and the resulting voltage between the bodies is 2000 V. Calculate:

1. the work done in transferring the electrons.
2. the energy stored in the electric field.
3. the capacitance of the two bodies.

SOLUTION:

1. The work done is

EQ. 10.1
$W = 1/2\ QV$
   $= 1/2 \times 0.2 \times 2000$
   $= 200$ J

2. The energy in the field is equal to the work done in transferring the charges, or 200 J.

3. The capacitance of the two bodies is

EQ. 10.2
$C = Q/V$
   $= 0.2/2000 = 0.0001$ F $= 100$ microfarads $= 100\ \mu$F

10.5 Capacitors

Capacitors are commercial devices that can store an electric charge. They are composed of two metal plates separated by a thin insulator (Fig. 10.5). The insulator (called **dielectric**) may be air, mica, or paper, among other things, and the plates are usually made of thin aluminum foil.

DIELECTRIC

The capacitance of such a parallel-plate capacitor depends on three factors:

1. the area of the plates.

2. the distance between the plates.

3. the type of dielectric between the plates.

The capacitance is given by the equation

$$C = 8.85 \times 10^{-12} \, \frac{kA}{d}$$

EQ. 10.3

where

C = capacitance, in farads (F)

A = area of the plates, in square metres (m²)

d = distance between the plates, in metres (m)

k = dielectric constant of the insulation, a simple number

8.85×10^{-12} = constant to take care of units

The **dielectric constant** of air or a vacuum is equal to 1, and that of oil and paper is about 3. Consequently, for a given capacitor size (A and d), the capacitance is increased by a factor of 3 when paper, instead of air, is used to separate the plates.

DIELECTRIC CONSTANT

According to Equation 10.3, the capacitance doubles when the area of the plates is doubled. But it also doubles if the distance between them is halved. As a result, in manufacturing a capacitor of a given value, we tend to minimize the distance between the plates in order to reduce its size and cost.

The circuit diagram symbol for a capacitor is shown in Fig. 10.6.

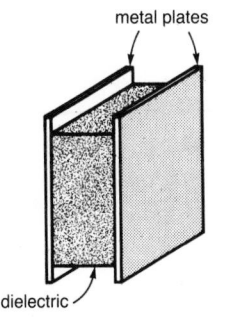

metal plates

dielectric

Figure 10.5

A capacitor consists of two metal plates separated by a dielectric.

Figure 10.6

Circuit diagram symbol for a capacitor.

10.6 Energy Stored in a Capacitor

By combining Eqs. 10.1 and 10.2, we obtain another useful equation for the energy stored in a capacitor:

EQ. 10.4

$$W = \frac{1}{2} CV^2$$

where

W = energy, in joules (J)

C = capacitance, in farads (F)

V = voltage across the capacitor, in volts (V)

It is interesting to recall that the energy stored in a magnetic field is given by a similar equation (Eq. 9.6):

EQ. 9.6

$$W = \frac{1}{2} LI^2$$

EXAMPLE 10.2

Two aluminum plates each having an area of 2 m² are separated by a sheet of paper 0.08 mm thick. The capacitor is charged to 1000 V. If the dielectric constant of paper is 2.5, calculate:

1. the capacitance, in microfarads.
2. the charge on the negative plate, in coulombs.
3. the energy stored in the capacitor, in joules.

SOLUTION:

EQ. 10.3

1. $C = 8.85 \times 10^{-12} \dfrac{kA}{d}$

    $C = 8.85 \times 10^{-12} \times 2.5 \times \dfrac{2}{0.08} \times 10^{-3}$

    $\qquad = 0.000\ 000\ 553$ farads $= 0.553 \times 10^{-6}$ F

    $\qquad = 0.553$ microfarads $= 0.553$ μF

EQ. 10.2

2. $Q = CV$

    $Q = 0.553 \times 10^{-6} \times 1000 = 0.553 \times 10^{-3}$ coulombs

    $\qquad = 553$ microcoulombs $= 553$ μC

EQ. 10.4

3. $W = \dfrac{1}{2} CV^2$

    $\qquad = \dfrac{1}{2} \times 0.553 \times 10^{-6} \times (1000)^2$

    $\qquad = 0.276$ joules $= 0.276$ J

10.7 Using a Source to Transfer a Charge

The simplest way to transfer electrons from one capacitor plate to another is to connect the plates to the terminals of a battery (Fig. 10.7). Electrons are immediately removed from the plate connected to the (+) battery terminal and deposited on the plate connected to the (–) battery terminal. When an electric charge is transferred this way, the voltage between the capacitor plates builds up very quickly. However, as soon as the potential difference between the plates is equal to the battery emf, the transfer of electrons ceases. We can then disconnect the battery, and the voltage across the plates will be maintained forever, at least in theory (Fig. 10.8).

Let us connect a resistor across the capacitor (Fig. 10.9). The difference of potential between the plates will cause electrons to flow from the negative plate, through the resistor, and into the positive plate. Consequently, the capacitor will gradually discharge, and the voltage between the plates will eventually fall to zero. When this happens, the two plates will again be electrically neutral.

▼ **Figure 10.7**

Electrons can be transferred from one plate to another by using a battery.

▼ **Figure 10.8**

A perfect capacitor remains charged forever.

▼ **Figure 10.9**

A capacitor can be discharged by connecting a resistor between the plates.

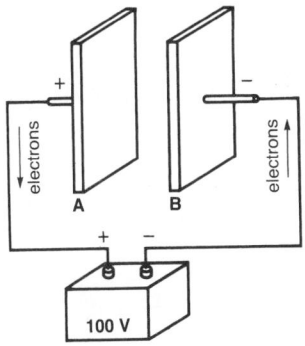

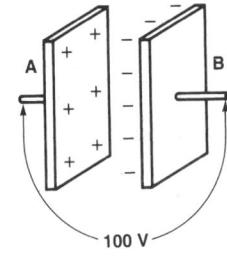

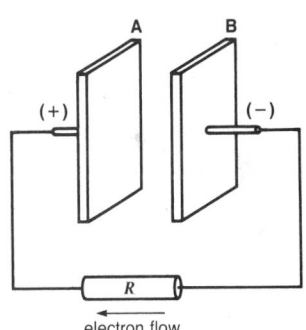

10.8 Capacitor as a Source or Load

Referring again to Fig. 10.7, the battery is a source, delivering energy to the capacitor. This is to be expected because the electric field between the plates is building up. The capacitor is acting as a load because current is flowing into its (–) terminal.

In Fig. 10.9, the capacitor is discharging its energy into a resistor. As a result, conventional current is flowing out of its (–) terminal. Consequently, the capacitor is now acting as a source.

A capacitor can therefore behave either as a source or load, which is similar to the behaviour of a coil.

10.9 Commercial Capacitors

Commercial capacitors are made of two extremely thin sheets of metal separated by equally thin sheets of paper or plastic. The metal and plastic sheets are rolled into a cylinder that is placed inside a protective can (Fig. 10.10). High-voltage capacitors are often impregnated with oil to provide additional security against breakdown. The question of insulation breakdown is important. As we have seen, the capacitance can be increased by reducing the thickness of the dielectric between the plates. But if the dielectric is too thin, it may no longer be able to withstand the voltage between the plates. In this case, an arc will leap between the plates, puncturing and carbonizing the dielectric and putting the capacitor out of service.

A capacitor designed to operate at 1000 V must therefore have a thicker dielectric than one operating at only 100 V. To attain the same capacitance, the plates of a 1000 V capacitor must therefore have a larger area. It follows that a 1000 V capacitor is more bulky than a 100 V capacitor of equal microfarad rating.

The rated voltage of a capacitor is usually indicated on the nameplate. When capacitors of several thousand volts are needed, they are made by connecting lower-voltage units in series. Similarly, when a very large capacitance is required, the practice is to connect several identical capacitors in parallel.

In the interest of safety, large commercial capacitors contain discharge resistors permanently connected across the capacitor terminals. The resistors are usually inside the protective casing of the capacitor. Capacitors rated 600 V and lower are designed to discharge within 1 minute after being disconnected from the line. Capacitors rated above 600 V become discharged after a 5-minute interval. However, it is always good practice to short-circuit the terminals of a capacitor before touching them.

Figure 10.10

Typical construction of a commercial capacitor.

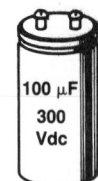

Table 10A   TYPICAL CAPACITOR SIZES

CAPACITANCE (μF)	OPERATING VOLTAGE (V)	APPROXIMATE DIMENSIONS (mm)	APPROXIMATE DIMENSIONS (IN)
40	440 (ac)	140 × 115 × 75	5.5 × 4.5 × 3
5	30 000 (dc)	610 × 360 × 180	24 × 14 × 7
1.3	14 400 (ac)	460 × 340 × 115	18 × 13 × 4.5

10.10 Capacitors in Parallel and in Series

When capacitors are connected in parallel, the total capacitance C_T is equal to the sum of the individual capacitances.

$$C_T = C_1 + C_2 + C_3 + \ldots + C_n$$

EQ. 10.5

When a group of capacitors is connected in series, the total capacitance C_T is given by the equation:

$$\frac{1}{C_T} = \frac{1}{C_1} + \frac{1}{C_2} + \frac{1}{C_3} + \cdots = \frac{1}{C_n}$$

EQ. 10.6

EXAMPLE 10.3

Three capacitors of 8, 42, and 56 microfarads are connected in series. What is the resulting capacitance of the group?

SOLUTION:

EQ. 10.6

$$\frac{1}{C_T} = \frac{1}{8} + \frac{1}{42} + \frac{1}{56}$$

$$= 0.1250 + 0.0238 + 0.0178 = 0.1666$$

$$C_T = \frac{1}{0.1666} = 6 \ \mu F$$

10.11 Charging a Capacitor; Time Constant

When a capacitor charges, how do the voltage and current vary with time? Consider the circuit of Fig. 10.11, in which a capacitor C and resistor R are connected to a battery by means of a switch. The battery produces a voltage V_b. The capacitor is initially discharged, and so the voltage across its terminals is zero. However, as soon as the switch is closed, current begins to flow in the circuit, and the capacitor charges. As a result, voltage V_c across the capacitor increases gradually with time. But as V_c increases, voltage V_R across the resistor decreases because $V_r = V_b - V_c$. A smaller V_r means that current I decreases as the capacitor charges. Eventually, the current becomes zero when $V_c = V_b$.

If we plot the graph of V_c versus time, we get the curve shown in Fig. 10.12. The rate at which the capacitor charges up depends upon the so-called *time constant* of the circuit.

The time constant is given by the equation:

• EQ. 10.7

$$T = RC$$

where

T = time constant, in seconds (s)

R = resistance of the circuit, in ohms (Ω)

C = capacitance, in farads (F)

For all practical purposes, we can assume that the capacitor is completely charged after a period equal to 5 T seconds.

Note that the initial current in the circuit is given by $I = V_b / R$. Thus, if the series resistance is low, the initial charging current is very large. A large initial current (called inrush current) will not harm the capacitor, but it may burn the switch contacts at the moment the switch closes.

▼ **Figure 10.11**

The voltage across a capacitor builds up gradually when the capacitor is charged in series with a resistor.

▼ **Figure 10.12**

The capacitor is fully charged after a period of 5 RC seconds.

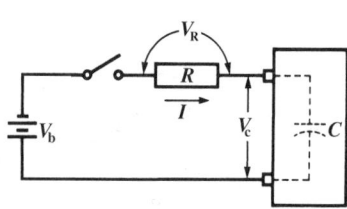

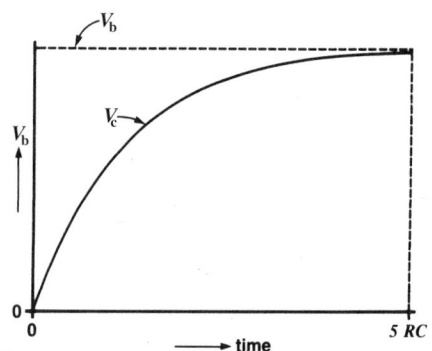

EXAMPLE 10.4

A 100 μF capacitor is connected in series with a 20 Ω resistor to a 128 V dc source. Calculate:

1. the time constant of the circuit.
2. the approximate time to charge the capacitor.
3. the initial current in the circuit.

SOLUTION:

1. The time constant is

• EQ. 10.7

   $$T = RC = 20 \times 100 \times 10^{-6} = 2 \times 10^{-3} = 2 \text{ ms}$$

2. The time to charge the capacitor is

   $$T = 5 RC = 5 \times 2 = 10 \text{ milliseconds} = 10 \text{ ms}$$

3. The initial current is

   $$I = V_b / R = 128/20 = 6.4 \text{ A}$$

10.12 Discharging a Capacitor

We can discharge a capacitor by connecting a resistor across its terminals. If a low resistance is used, the discharge current can be very high. Even a small capacitor can deliver a current of several hundred amperes. This is an important feature of a capacitor: it can deliver very large currents for brief periods.

Fig. 10.13 shows a capacitor that is in the process of discharging. Note that current is flowing out of the (−) terminal, and so the capacitor is acting as a source. The energy dissipated in the resistor is obtained at the expense of the decreasing electric field between the plates. The voltage across the capacitor falls rapidly at first and then much more slowly (Fig. 10.14). We can assume that a capacitor is completely discharged after a period equal to 5 T seconds.

▼ **Figure 10.13**

The voltage across the capacitor decreases with time.

▼ **Figure 10.14**

The capacitor is completely discharged after a period of 5 RC seconds.

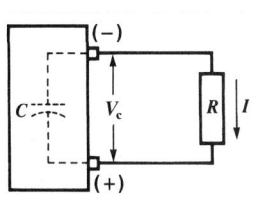

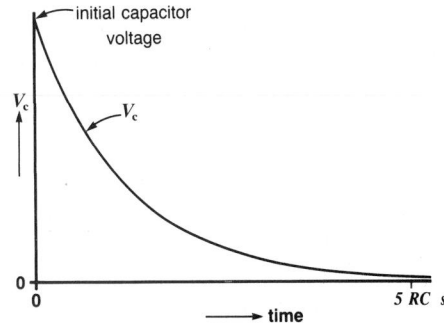

10.13 Capacitance of Transmission Lines

A transmission line has capacitance because the two parallel conductors act like the plates of a capacitor (Fig. 10.15). There is also a capacitance between each line and ground because the ground acts like an enormous flat plate. The total capacitance depends upon the length of the line, the diameter of the conductors, and the spacing between them. For example, a line 10 km long composed of two conductors having a diameter of 25 mm and spaced 3 m apart has a capacitance of about 0.05 μF.

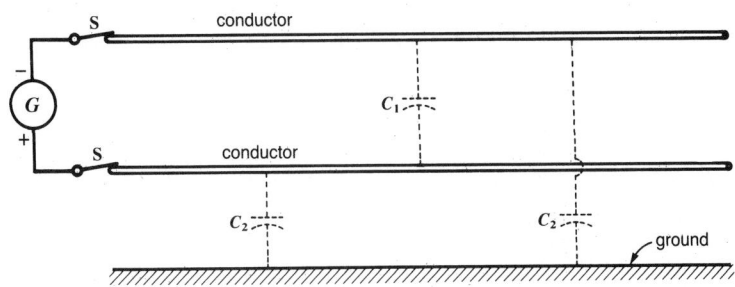

Figure 10.15

The two conductors of a transmission line act like the plates of a capacitor.

The existence of line capacitance raises certain dangers. Suppose the transmission line in Fig. 10.15 is connected to a 69 000 V source, and the switch at the source end is then opened. Although the line is completely disconnected, it will remain charged, and substantial, dangerous voltages will remain between the conductors and ground. If linemen are doing maintenance work, it is essential to short-circuit the lines to ground before beginning repairs, so that the lines are discharged.

10.14 Capacitor Connected to an Ac Voltage

We have already learned that industrial line voltages vary sinusoidally. It is therefore useful to see how the current in a capacitor varies under these ac voltage conditions.

The capacitor in Fig. 10.16 is connected to a 25 Hz ac source that generates a sinusoidal voltage V_{ab} having a peak value of 250 V. The capacitor has a rating of 255 μF. Because the frequency is 25 Hz, the duration of one cycle is 1/25 s, or 40 ms. To determine the waveshape of the current, we reason as follows:

First, the current is zero when the rate of change of voltage is zero. This occurs at 10, 30, and 50 ms because the slope of V_{ab} is zero at these instants (Fig. 10.16).

Second, V_{ab} is positive and increasing between zero and 10 ms. The capacitor is charging, and so it is receiving energy from the source and acting as a load. Because terminal a is (+) during this interval, the actual current must flow in the direction of the arrow. The current is therefore (+) between 0 and 10 ms. By the same reasoning, I is (–) between 10 ms and 20 ms. Thus, I is (+) whenever the slope of V_{ab} is (+).

Third, the current is greatest when the voltage is changing most rapidly. This occurs at 0, 20, 40, and 60 ms. Thus, the current is maximum when the capacitor voltage is zero. This may be surprising, but we must remember that the current in a capacitor does not depend upon the *magnitude* of the voltage across its terminals, but only upon the *rate* at which the voltage is changing.

The maximum rate of change of voltage is given by the equation:

$$\left(\frac{\Delta V}{\Delta t}\right)_{max} = 2\pi f V_{max}$$

Where: $(\Delta V/\Delta t)_{max}$ = maximum rate of change of voltage, in volts per second (V/s)

V_{max} = peak value of sinusoidal voltage, in volts (V)

f = frequency in hertz (Hz)

2π = constant to take care of units (approximate value 6.28)

Therefore, the maximum rate of voltage change is:

$(\Delta V/\Delta t) = 2\pi f V_m$

$= 2 \times 3.1416 \times 25 \times 250 = 39\ 270$ V/s

The peak current is therefore

$I = C\dfrac{\Delta V}{\Delta t} = 225 \times 10^{-6} \times 39\ 270 = 10$ A

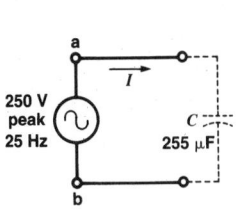

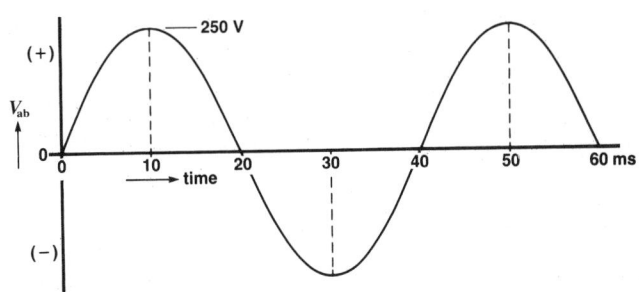

Figure 10.16

A 250 V (peak), 25 Hz
voltage is applied to a
255 μF capacitor.

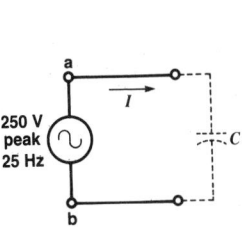

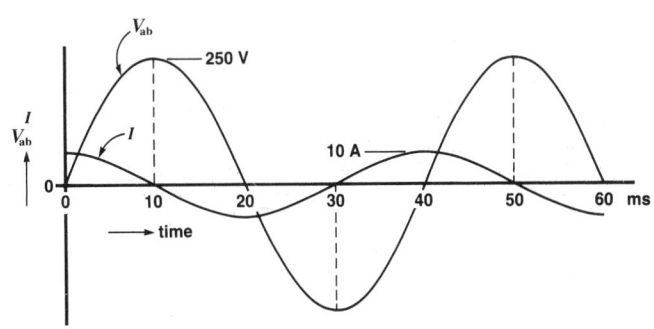

Figure 10.17

The resulting current is
10 A (peak), and it leads
the voltage by 90°.

The waveshape of the current is shown in Fig. 10.17.

It so happens that the current also varies sinusoidally. Clearly, V_{ab} and I are out of phase. The current peaks 90° ahead of the voltage. As shown in Fig. 10.17, the current leads the voltage by 90°. This is one of the important properties of a capacitor when it is connected to an ac source. You will recall that in the case of an inductor, the current lagged 90° *behind* the voltage. Thus, a capacitor and inductor behave somewhat like complementary twins.

10.15 Summary

Upon completion of this chapter you should have learned that:

- A capacitor is a very simple device that can be used to store an electric charge.

- Capacitance is affected by the area of a capacitor's plates, the distance between the plates, and the type of dielectric used.

- Charge will be transferred from a source to a capacitor as long as the potential of the source is greater than the potential across the plates of the capacitor.

- Connecting capacitors in series decreases the total capacitance, while connecting capacitors in parallel increases the total capacitance. This is the opposite of what happens in a resistive circuit.

- The formula $T = RC$ can be used to calculate the charging and discharging constant for a capacitor. A capacitor is considered to be charged or discharged after 5 time constants have elapsed.

- When a capacitor is connected to an AC source, the current will lead the voltage by 90°.

Key Terms

CAPACITANCE: A measure of a capacitor's ability to store a charge.

DIELECTRIC: The insulating material separating the two plates of a capacitor. The type of dielectric will directly affect the amount of charge a capacitor can hold.

DIELECTRIC CONSTANT: A relative measure of the dielectric strength of a material compared to dielectric strength of air.

ELECTRIC FIELD: An area of force between two charged bodies. The force generated may cause attraction or repulsion between the two bodies.

FARAD: The unit of capacitance given the symbol F. The farad is a very large unit and capacitance is normally measured using the microfarad (μF) or nanofarad (nF).

Test Your Knowledge

10.1   In Fig. 10.2, if electrons are transferred from plate B to plate A, the plates will be attracted to each other.

true_____   false _____

10.2   In Fig. 10.2, if a thick sheet of paper is placed between the plates, the capacitance of the plates will
a.   increase
b.   decrease
c.   remain the same

10.3   In Fig. 10.5, the voltage between the plates is 1000 V. If the voltage drops to 200 V, this will affect the capacitance of the plates.

true_____   false _____

10.4   In Fig. 10.11, R = 10 MΩ and C = 30 μF. The time constant of the circuit is:
a.   0.3 s
b.   5 min
c.   3 s

10.5   A capacitor that is initially charged to 600 V is connected across a 5 Ω resistor. The initial discharge current is
a.   120 A
b.   apparently 120 A, but it depends upon the size of the capacitor

10.6   A capacitor that is charged to 600 V stores 100 J of energy. If the voltage increases to 900 V, the stored energy will be:
a.   150 J
b.   225 J
c.   44.4 J

10.7   A 50 μF and a 80 μF capacitor are connected in parallel. The resultant capacitance is
a.   130 μF
b.   30.77 μF
c.   94.34 μF

10.8   When two unequal capacitors are connected in series, the instantaneous current is the same in both.

true_____   false _____

10.9   In Fig. 10.17, if the frequency of the voltage is doubled, the peak current will become
a.   20 A
b.   10 A
c.   40 A

10.10   The current in a capacitor lags 270° behind the voltage.

true_____   false _____

10.11   The voltage in a capacitor lags 90° behind the current.

true_____   false _____

Questions and Problems

10.12   Why are industrial capacitors equipped with discharge resistors?

10.13   A 60 kV, 20 μF capacitor is equipped with a discharge resistor of 3 MΩ.
   a.   How long will it take the capacitor to discharge?
   b.   How much energy is dissipated as heat in the resistor?

10.14   A 100 μF capacitor is connected across a 60 Hz line having a peak voltage of 170 V. Calculate:
   a.   the maximum rate of change of voltage and
   b.   the peak current in the capacitor.

10.15   Twelve 60 μF capacitors are connected in series across a 36 kV dc source. Calculate:
   a.   the voltage across each capacitor,
   b.   the energy stored in each capacitor, and
   c.   the total capacitance of the capacitor bank.

10.16   A special dc source supplies a constant current of 1 mA to a 50 μF capacitor. How long will it take for the voltage to increase from 20 V to 500 V?

10.17   A 100 μF capacitor carries a charge of 0.004 C. Calculate the voltage across the terminals.

10.18   A 10 μF capacitor rated at 600 V is smaller than a 10 μF capacitor rated at 60 kV. Explain.

10.19   We wish to assemble a capacitor bank of 300 μF, rated at 1200 V. A large number of 100 μF capacitors rated at 600 V are available. How many capacitors are needed, and how should they be connected?

10.20   The capacitor shown in Fig. 10.5 is composed of two plates each having an area of 2 m². The dielectric is a piece of plate glass 0.5 mm thick and having a dielectric constant of 7. The dielectric strength of the glass is 80 kV/mm. Calculate:
   a.   the capacitance of the capacitor
   b.   the maximum voltage that can be applied to the plates
   c.   the maximum energy that can be stored without causing the dielectric to break down

10.21   A 12 V car battery can supply a current of 15 A for a period of 2 h.
   a.   How much energy does this represent in joules?
   b.   How much energy is stored in the 5 μF capacitor listed in Table 10A?
   c.   How many such capacitors are needed to store the same amount of energy as that in the car battery?

11

Basic *R, L,* and *C* Circuits

LEARNING OBJECTIVES

Upon completion of this chapter you will be able to:

- Calculate inductive and capacitive reactance

- Determine the current flowing in *R, L,* and *C* circuits

- Calculate the power consumed by *R, L,* and *C* circuits

- Explain the difference between true power and reactive power

11.1 Resistive Circuit

Let us consider a 20 Ω resistor connected across a 60 Hz source V_{ab} (Fig. 11.1). The voltage is sinusoidal and has a peak value of 200 V. One cycle corresponds to 1/60 s and, as we saw in Chapter 8, this period may be represented by an angle of 360° (Fig. 11.2). Because the voltage varies sinusoidally, we can calculate its instantaneous value at any angle. We can therefore calculate the corresponding value of current *I* using Ohm's law.

▼ **Figure 11.1**

Resistor connected to a 60 Hz ac source that generates a peak voltage of 200 V.

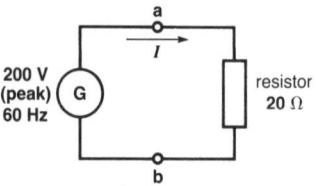

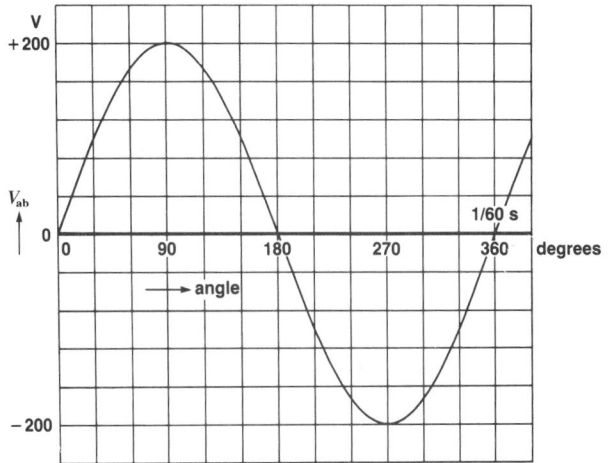

Figure 11.2

The ac source has a peak
voltage of 200 V and a
frequency of 60 Hz.

Thus:

At 30°, voltage V_{ab} = 200 sin 30 = 200 × 0.5 = 100 V;

   current $I = V/R$ = 100/20 = 5 A

At 60°, V_{ab} = 200 sin 60° = 200 × 0.866 = 173 V;

   $I = V/R$ = 173/20 = 8.66 A

At 90°, V_{ab} = 200 sin 90° = 200 × 1.0 = 200 V

   $I = V/R$ = 200/20 = 10 A

At another angle, such as 210°, we find:

V_{ab} = 200 sin 210° = 200 × (−0.5) = −100 V

Consequently, $I = V/R$ = −100/20 = −5 A

If we plot the value of *I*, we obtain a sine wave having a peak value of 10 A
(Fig. 11.3). Note that the peak positive current occurs at the same instant as the
peak positive voltage. The voltage and current are therefore in phase. If we represent the two quantities by phasors, we obtain the diagram of Fig. 11.4.

11.2 Power Dissipated in a Resistive Circuit

The instantaneous power in a circuit is always given by the product of voltage
times current. Thus, in Fig. 11.3, if we multiply the instantaneous values of voltage
and current, we obtain the power from one instant to the next. For example:

At 0°, V_{ab} = 0 V,	I = 0 A:	$P = VI$ = 0 × 0 = W
At 30°, V_{ab} = 100 V,	I = 5 A:	P = 100 × 5 = 500 W
At 60°, V_{ab} = 173 V,	I = 8.66 A:	P = 173 × 8.6 = 1500 W
At 90°, V_{ab} = 200 V,	I = 10 A:	P = 200 × 10 = 2000 W

When the voltage and current are both negative, the power is still positive because
the product of two negative numbers is positive. For example, at 210°, V_{ab} = −100 V,
I = −5 A: $P = (−100) × (−5) = + 500$ W.

▼ Figure 11.3

Instantaneous current and power
in the circuit of Fig. 11.1.

▼ Figure 11.4

This phasor diagram
represents the voltage and
current in Figs. 11.1 and 11.3.

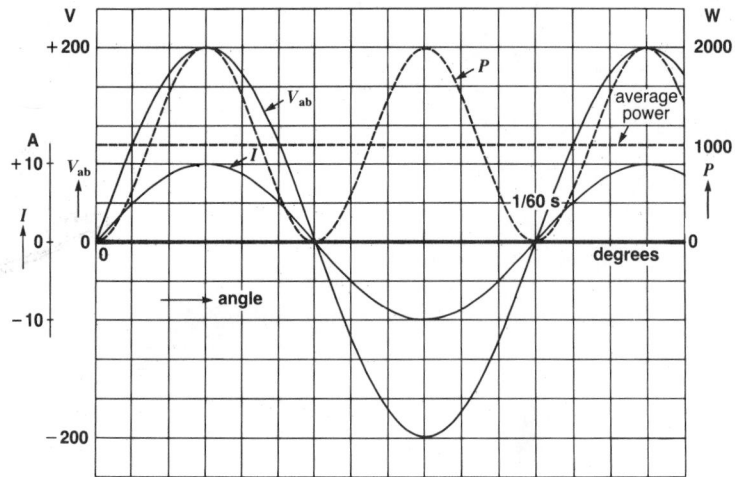

If we plot these instantaneous values of power (Fig. 11.3), we obtain a curve that starts at zero, rises to a maximum of 2000 W, falls to zero, rises again to 2000 W, and so forth. The power dissipated in the resistance varies from instant to instant, but the average power is 1000 W, a value that is found by analyzing the power curve. Consequently, the resistor will reach a temperature corresponding to a continuous heat dissipation of 1000 W.

11.3 Inductive Circuit

In Section 9.10, we learned that when a sinusoidal voltage is applied to an inductor, the resulting current is sinusoidal. Furthermore, the current lags 90° behind the voltage. Knowing this, let us determine the relationship between voltage, current, and power when a peak current of 10 A flows in a coil. The coil has an inductance of 53 mH, and the frequency of the current is 60 Hz (Fig. 11.5). We assume an odd value like 53 mH because we want to relate our findings to the previous case in which we used a 20 Ω resistor.

If a voltmeter and ammeter are connected into the circuit of Fig. 11.5, the voltmeter will read 141.4 V and the ammeter 7.07 A (Fig. 11.7). These readings are the same

▶ Figure 11.5

Inductor connected to a
60 Hz ac source that generates
a peak voltage of 200 V.

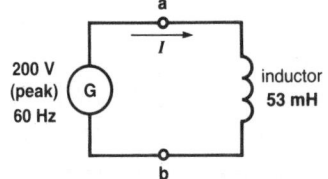

▶ Figure 11.6

Phasor diagram of the voltage
and current in the inductive
circuit of Fig. 11.5.

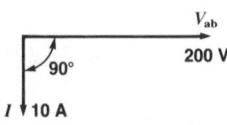

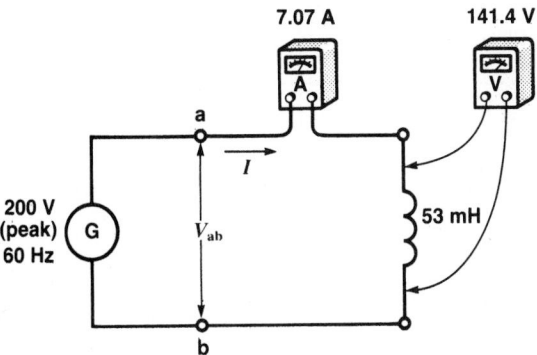

Figure 11.7

Voltmeter and ammeter
readings in the inductive
circuit of Fig. 11.5.

as those in the resistive circuit of Fig. 11.1. It appears therefore that the power in
the inductive circuit is

$P = VI = 141.4 \times 7.07 = 1000$ watts

But we discover that the coil is not warm at all. There is no evidence that it is dis-
sipating 1000 W. What, then, is happening in the circuit?

11.4 Reactive Power in an Inductive Circuit, the Var

Figure 11.8 shows the waveshape of the voltage and current in the inductor, with
the current lagging 90° behind the voltage. According to the explanations given in
Section 7.14, the respective equations are:

$V_{ab} = 200 \sin \theta$

$I = 10 \sin (\theta - 90°)$

Let us multiply the instantaneous values of voltage and current, as we did in the
case of the resistor.

First, the power is zero at 0°, 90°, 180°, and so forth because either the voltage or
current is zero at these moments. But midway between these zero points, the
power reaches a maximum. Thus, it is maximum at 45°, 135°, 225° and so forth.

At 135°, $V_{ab} = 200 \sin 135° = 141.4$ V and $I = \sin (135° - 90°) = 10 \sin 45° = 7.07$
A. Therefore, the maximum power is $P = VI = 141.4 \times 7.07 = 1000$ W. Note that
both V_{ab} and I are positive at this moment, and so P is also positive. Power is flowing into the coil.

The next power maximum occurs at 225°. The current is positive but V_{ab} is negative. Consequently, the power is negative. Power is therefore flowing out of the coil.
Its value is again 1000 W. The resulting positive and negative power swings are
shown in Fig. 11.8.

These cyclic power surges go on indefinitely. The coil absorbs energy during a
quarter cycle and then returns it to the source during the next quarter cycle. The
average power absorbed by the coil is therefore zero, and that is why the coil does

Figure 11.8

Instantaneous current and
power in the inductive
circuit of Fig. 11.5.

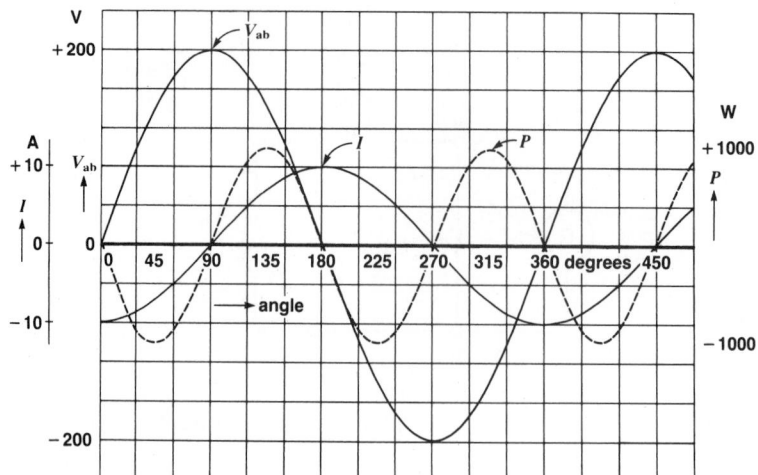

not get hot. In effect, magnetic energy is stored up in the coil for a quarter cycle
and is then released during the next quarter cycle.

REACTIVE POWER

REACTIVE VOLTAMPERES

In an inductor, the product of effective voltage times effective current is called
reactive power. It is designated by the symbol Q. This power is not expressed in
watts, but in **reactive voltamperes**. The unit of reactive voltamperes is the var.
The power absorbed by the coil is therefore 1000 var, and not 1000 W.

For reasons given later, engineers assume that an inductor *absorbs* reactive power.
It is convenient to think that an inductor absorbs reactive power in order to create
its alternating magnetic field.

11.5 Inductive Reactance (X_L)

The voltmeter and ammeter readings in Fig. 11.7 (V = 141.4 V, I = 7.07 A) would
lead us to believe that the "resistance" of the coil is V/I = 141.4 V/7.07 A = 20 Ω.
But a coil does not have the properties of a resistor, and so the ratio V/I is called

INDUCTIVE REACTANCE

the **inductive reactance** of the coil. Inductive reactance (symbol X_L) is expressed
in ohms. Unlike a resistor, the inductive reactance is not constant, but varies with
the frequency. Its value may be calculated by the equation:

EQ. 11.1 $X_L = 2\pi f L$

where

X_L = inductive reactance of the coil, in ohms (Ω)

f = frequency of the source, in hertz (Hz)

L = inductance of the coil, in henries (H)

For example, the inductive reactance of a 53 mH coil at a frequency of 60 Hz is

$X_L = 2\pi f L = 6.28 \times 60 \times 0.053 = 20$ Ω

This calculated value agrees with the value we found previously.

Equation 11.1 shows that the reactance of a coil increases with the inductance and
the frequency of the applied voltage.

EXAMPLE 11.1

A coil having an inductance of 2 H is connected to a 4 kV, 50 Hz source. Calculate:
1.   the inductive reactance X_L of the coil.
2.   the effective current I flowing in the coil.
3.   the reactive power Q absorbed by the coil.

SOLUTION:

1. $X_L = 2\pi f L = 6.28 \times 50 \times 2 = 628 \ \Omega$ **EQ. 11.1**

2.   Because the 4 kV is not stated to be peak or effective, it is *understood* to be the effective value
     $I = V/X_L = 4000/628 = 6.37$ A

3. $Q = VI = 4000 \times 6.37 = 25 \ 480$ var $= 25.48$ kvar

Fig. 11.9 shows a very large reactor used on extra high voltage (EHV) transmission lines.

11.6 Capacitive Circuit, Capacitive Reactance (X_C)

In Section 10.14, we saw that when a sinusoidal voltage is applied to a capacitor, a sinusoidal current is produced. Furthermore, the current leads the voltage by 90°.

The capacitor in Fig. 11.10 has been selected so that a peak current of 10 A flows in the circuit. Thus, the voltage and current have the same magnitude as in the case of the 20 Ω resistor. The only difference is that the current leads the voltage by 90°. The phasor diagram is given in Fig. 11.11.

Figure 11.9

This 10 Mvar, 425 kV 60 Hz reactor is used to prevent over-voltages on long transmission lines. The reactor is immersed in mineral oil and the high insulating bushing enables the reactor to be connected to the EHV line.

(Courtesy Hydro-Québec)

Figure 11.10

Capacitor connected to a
60 Hz ac source having a
peak voltage of 200 V.

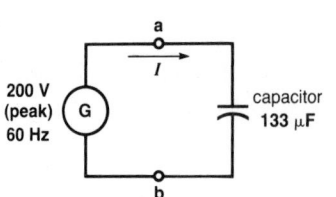

► **Figure 11.11**

Phasor diagram of the
voltage and current in the
circuit of Fig. 11.10.

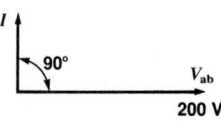

If a voltmeter and ammeter were connected into the circuit, the voltmeter would read 141.4 V and the ammeter 7.07 A (Fig. 11.12). The capacitor appears, therefore, to have a resistance *of V/I* = 141.4/7.07 = 20 Ω. However, because a capacitor is so much different from a resistor, this opposition to current flow is named **capacitive reactance** (symbol X_C).

**CAPACITIVE
REACTANCE**

Figure 11.12

Voltmeter and ammeter
readings in the capacitive
circuit of Fig. 11.10.

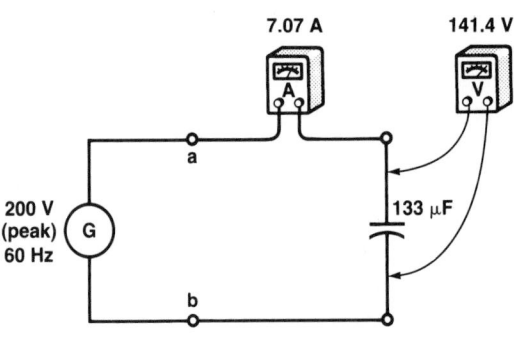

11.7 Reactive Power in a Capacitive Circuit

As in the case of the inductor, we can calculate the instantaneous power in the capacitor by multiplying the voltage by the current. This yields the power curve shown in Fig. 11.13. The power reaches successive positive and negative peaks of 1000 W. The net power absorbed by the capacitor is therefore zero. Consequently, an ideal capacitor does not heat up.

The positive values of power correspond to those intervals when the capacitor is charging and storing electric energy. The negative values occur during the periods when the capacitor is discharging and returning its energy to the source.

Returning to Fig. 11.12, it appears that the power absorbed by the capacitor is

$P = VI = 141.4 \times 7.07 = 1000$ W

But the capacitor does not heat up, and so this capacitive "power" cannot be expressed in watts. As in the case of an inductor, it is called reactive power (symbol Q). The unit of capacitive reactive power is also the var. The reactive power in Fig. 11.12 is therefore 1000 var.

It is convenient to assume that a capacitor *generates* reactive power. On the other hand, as mentioned previously, an inductor is assumed to absorb reactive power.

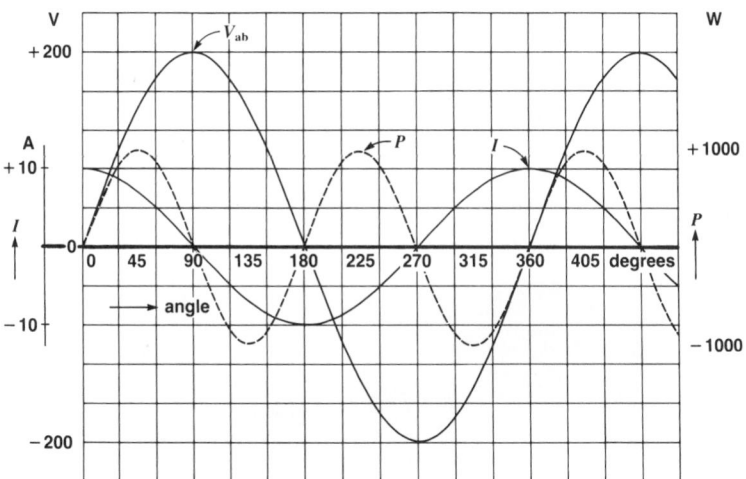

Figure 11.13

Instantaneous current and power in the capacitive circuit of Fig. 11.11.

11.8 Calculation of Capacitive Reactance

We can calculate the capacitive reactance of a capacitor by the equation:

$$X_C = \frac{1}{2\pi fC}$$

EQ. 11.2

where

X_C = capacitive reactance, in ohms (Ω)
f = frequency of the source, in hertz (Hz)
C = capacitance, in farads (F)
2π = constant (approximate value 6.28)

This equation shows that the reactance decreases as the capacitance becomes larger. Furthermore, X_C decreases as the frequency increases.

Applying this equation, we find that the capacitive reactance of the 133 μF capacitor at a frequency of 60 Hz is

$$X_c = \frac{1}{2\pi fC} = \frac{1}{6.28 \times 60 \times 133 \times 10^{-6}} = 20\ \Omega$$

This agrees with the value we found previously.

EXAMPLE 11.2

A 10 μF capacitor is connected to a 120 V, 400 Hz source. Calculate:
1. the capacitive reactance X_C of the capacitor.
2. the peak current I_m in the capacitor.
3. the reactive power Q generated by the capacitor.

SOLUTION:

1. $X_c = \dfrac{1}{2\pi fC} = \dfrac{1}{6.28 \times 400 \times 10 \times 10^{-6}} = 40\ \Omega$

continued

2. The effective value of current $I = V/X_C = 120/40 = 3$ A
    The peak current $I_m = 3/0.707 = 4.24$ A
3. The reactive power produced by the capacitor is
    $Q = VI = 120 \times 3 = 360$ var

Figure 11.14 shows a large capacitor bank.

11.9 True Power and Reactive Power

If we compare the power flow in a resistor with that in an inductor or capacitor, we note some distinctive features. Power in a resistor is always positive (Fig. 11.3). It continually flows from the ac source to the load. On the other hand, power in an inductor surges back and forth between the inductor and the source (Fig. 11.8). The same remarks apply to a capacitor.

In ac circuits we therefore recognize two types of power: **true power** and reactive power.

Power that does real work or produces heat is called *true power (P)*. True power is always expressed in watts. By definition, true power is the product VI of the effective voltage V times the effective current I when V and I are in phase.

Power that oscillates back and forth, such as in an inductor or capacitor, is called *reactive power*. Reactive power is expressed in vars. By definition, reactive power is the product VI of the effective voltage V times the effective current I when V and I are 90° out of phase.

TRUE POWER

▼ **Figure 11.15**

Phasor diagram and power in a resistive circuit.

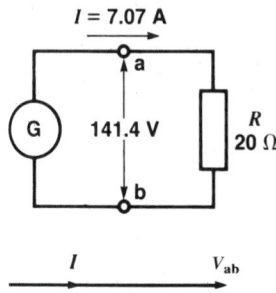

$P = VI = 141.4 \times 7.07$

$P = 1000$ W

resistor absorbs active power *P*

R

▼ **Figure 11.16**

Phasor diagram and power in an inductive circuit.

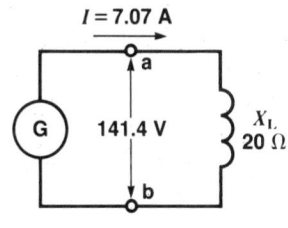

$Q = VI = 141.4 \times 7.07$

$Q = (+) \, 1000$ var

inductor absorbs reactive power *Q*

$X_{L} = 2\pi f L$

▼ **Figure 11.17**

Phasor diagram and power in a capacitive circuit.

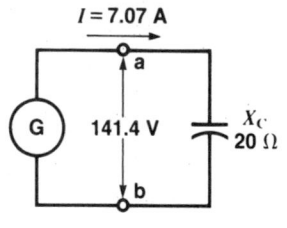

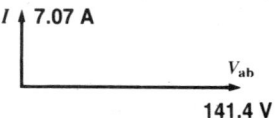

$Q = VI = 141.4 \times 7.07$

$Q = (-) \, 1000$ var

capacitor generates reactive power *Q*

$X_{C} = 1/2\pi f C$

▼ **Figure 11.18**

A resistor absorbs true power.

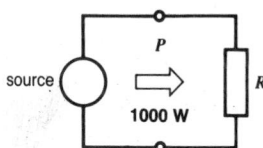

▼ **Figure 11.19**

A reactor absorbs reactive power.

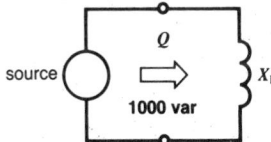

▼ **Figure 11.20**

A capacitor produces reactive power.

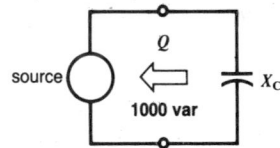

A capacitor is assumed to produce, or generate, reactive power. An inductor is assumed to absorb reactive power. This is somewhat analogous to saying that an ac generator produces true power and a resistor absorbs it.

Because we know that the instantaneous power in an inductor or capacitor merely surges back and forth, it is somewhat surprising to state that an inductor *absorbs* reactive power and a capacitor *generates* reactive power. However, this conventional interpretation of reactive power has been approved by the Standards Committee of the Institute of Electrical and Electronics Engineers and internationally by the Electrotechnical Commission. The reason for assuming that capacitors generate reactive power and inductors absorb it is that it greatly simplifies the treatment of power in ac circuits.

One final important feature of true and reactive power is that one cannot be converted into the other. Each exists in a separate world, so to speak.

11.10 Phasor Diagrams and Effective Values

So far, the phasor diagrams have always shown the peak values of voltage and current. However, because effective values are usually given, we can change the phasor diagrams accordingly. Thus, from now on, and unless indicated otherwise, we show effective values in the phasor diagrams.

11.11 Recapitulation of *R, L, C* Circuits

The relationships found in the *R, L, C* circuits are summarized in Figs. 11.15 to 11.17. You should examine and compare them to ensure that everything is clear. Note that effective values of voltage and current are now used.

Next, to clarify the notion of true and reactive power flow, Figs. 11.18 to 11.20 show how powers *P* and *Q* are assumed to flow over the line. The resistor absorbs true power, and so the true power *P* flows from the source to the load. The inductor absorbs reactive power, and so the reactive power *Q* also flows from the source to the load. On the other hand, the capacitor *delivers* reactive power *Q* to the source to which it is connected.

11.12 Summary

Upon completion of this chapter you should have learned that:

* Inductors and capacitors both have a property that opposes the flow of current in a circuit. This property is called inductive and capacitive reactance.

* The current flowing in an ac circuit can be calculated using Ohm's Law.

* The power consumed by *R, L,* and *C* circuits can be calculated using the relationship *VI*.

* True power is dissipated by a resistance and it is measured using watts. Reactive elements, inductors and capacitors, consume reactive power and reactive power is measured in vars.

Key Terms

CAPACITIVE REACTANCE (X_C): The opposition to the flow of current offered by a capacitor. The unit for X_C is the ohm.

INDUCTIVE REACTANCE (X_L): The opposition to the flow of current offered by an inductor. The unit for X_L is the ohm.

REACTIVE POWER (Q): Non–heat producing power consumed by an inductor or released by a capacitor. It is a measure of the energy associated with the creation of magnetic fields and electric fields.

REACTIVE VOLTAMPERES (VAR): The unit of reactive power. It is the product of the voltage across a reactive element and the current flowing to a reactive element.

TRUE POWER (P): Heat-producing power dissipated by a resistance.

Test Your Knowledge

11.1 An ac ammeter shows a reading of 64 A. The peak value of current is
a. 45.2 A
b. 90.5 A
c. 128 A

11.2 A 5 Ω resistor dissipates 46 kW. The peak ac current in the resistor is
a. 9200 A
b. 95.9 A
c. 135.6 A

11.3 A 60 Hz sinusoidal voltage has an effective value of 240 kV. The maximum rate of change of this voltage occurs when its value is
a. 240 kV
b. 339.4 kV
c. zero

11.4 An inductor has a reactance of 200 Ω at a frequency of 60 Hz. The reactance at 120 Hz is
a. 400 Ω
b. 100 Ω
c. 200 Ω

11.5 An inductor has an inductance of 3 H when used in a 60 Hz line. If it is placed in a circuit in which the frequency is 300 Hz, the inductance is
a. 15 H
b. 600 mH
c. 3 H

11.6 The unit of reactive power is
a. the Var
b. the VAR
c. the var

11.7 The idea that a capacitor generates reactive power is based on a technical convention.

true _____   false _____

11.8 A capacitor connected to a 120 V, 60 Hz source draws a current of 10 A. The capacitance is
a. 12 Ω
b. 31 400 μF
c. 0.000 221 F

11.9 A 60 W, 120 V incandescent lamp draws a peak power of
a. 60 W
b. 120 W
c. 84.85 W

Questions and Problems

11.10 a. Draw the waveshape of a sinusoidal voltage V_{12} having a peak value of 200 V and a frequency of 50 Hz. (The voltage is zero and increasing positively at $t = 0$.)
b. What is the voltage at $t = 5$ ms, and what is the polarity of terminal 2 with respect to terminal 1?

11.11 A sinusoidal voltage of 120 V is applied to a 10 Ω resistor. Calculate:
a. the effective current in the resistor
b. the peak voltage across the resistor

11.12 A capacitor has a rating of 500 kvars, 440 V, 60 Hz. Calculate:
a. the rated effective current
b. the capacitive reactance

c. the capacitance
d. the peak voltage across the capac-
    itor terminals
e. the peak energy stored in the
    capacitor, in joules

11.13 The large reactor* shown in Fig. 11.9
       has a rating of 110 Mvar, 425 kV,
       60 Hz. Calculate:
       a. the rated current of the reactor

b. the inductive reactance of the
    reactor
c. the inductance of the reactor
d. the peak current in the reactor
e. the peak energy stored in the
    magnetic field, in joules

* An inductor that operates on ac is often called a reactor.

Solving Single-Phase Ac Circuits

LEARNING OBJECTIVES

Upon completion of this chapter you will be able to:

- Determine the impedance (Z) of a single-phase circuit
- Solve problems for series *RLC* circuits
- Draw the phasor for a series *RLC* circuit
- Solve problems for parallel *RLC* circuits
- Draw phasors for parallel *RLC* circuits
- Calculate power in single phase ac circuits
- Explain the significance of series resonance in ac circuits
- Explain the significance of power factor in ac circuits

12.1   Impedance of a Circuit

Consider an electric circuit composed of resistors, inductors, and capacitors enclosed in a box. The components are interconnected in any way, but the final circuit has only two terminals, 1 and 2 (Fig. 12.1). Suppose that an ac voltage V applied to the terminals produces a corresponding ac current I.

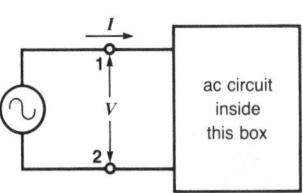

Figure 12.1

Impedance and apparent
power of a single-phase
circuit.

In Chapter 2 we used Ohm's law to calculate the resistance of a circuit using the ratio V/I. In ac circuits we use the same ratio; however, we do not know whether the box in Fig. 12.1 contains R, L, or C components. Therefore, when we apply Ohm's law to the circuit we are not calculating R, we are calculating the total opposition to the flow of current. This ratio is called the **impedance (Z)** and it is measured in ohms.

IMPEDANCE (Z)

For example, if the ac voltage across a circuit is 120 V and the current is 4 A, the impedance of the circuit is $Z = V/I = 120 \text{ V}/4 \text{ A} = 30 \ \Omega$.

In previous chapters we saw that the current flowing through a resistor was in phase with the voltage and we saw that the current through an inductor was 90° behind the voltage. If we use these voltages and currents to calculate the resist-ance and reactance for the circuit, these too will be 90° out of phase. With this information, we can construct the right-angle triangle in Fig. 12.2. In a series circuit, impedance will always be the hypotenuse, resistance will always be the adjacent side, and the reactance will always be the side opposite. This triangle is known as the **impedance triangle**.

IMPEDANCE TRIANGLE

If we apply Pythagoras' theorem to the sides of the triangle, we find:

$$Z^2 = R^{2} + X_L^2.$$

Solving for Z yields:

EQ. 12.1

$$Z = \sqrt{R^2 + X_L^2}$$

If the circuit in Fig. 12.1 contained capacitive reactance, the impedance triangle would have the same shape, except the side opposite would be drawn downward as in Fig. 12.3. If the circuit contained both inductive and capacitive reactance, we would draw X_L upward and X_C downward. Since the reactive values are 180° apart, the side opposite of the impedance triangle would be the difference between X_L and X_C (Fig. 12.4).

▼ **Figure 12.2**

Impedance triangle for a
series *R-L* circuit.

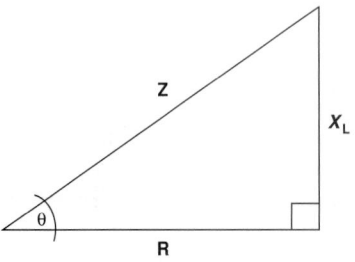

▼ **Figure 12.3**

Impedance triangle for a
series *R-C* circuit.

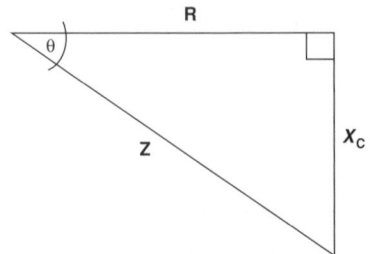

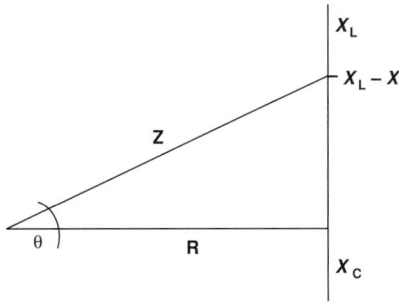

Figure 12.4

Impedance triangle for a
series *RLC* circuit.

In each of these triangles, the angle θ (theta) tells how far out-of-phase the circuit impedance is relative to the resistance (which is always in-phase). This angle is referred to as the **phase angle.**

PHASE ANGLE

EXAMPLE 12.1

A 100 Ω resistor and a 0.5 H coil are connected to a 60 Hz, 120 V supply. Calculate the current flowing in the circuit and sketch the impedance triangle.

SOLUTION:

a) $X_L = 2\pi fL$
    $ = 6.28 \times 60 \times 0.5$
    $ = 188.4\ \Omega$

b) $Z = \sqrt{R^2 + X_L^2}$
    $ = \sqrt{100^2 + 188.4^2}$
    $ = 213.3\ \Omega$

c) $I = V/Z$
    $ = 120/213.3$
    $ = 0.56$ A

The impedance triangle is shown in Figure 12.5.

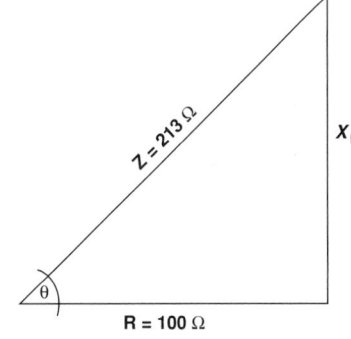

Figure 12.5

The impedance triangle
for Example 12.1.

12.2 The Series *RLC* Circuit

In Chapter 2, we discussed Kirchhoff's current and voltage laws. These laws also apply to series *RLC* circuits connected to an ac source. Since the current is the same throughout a series circuit, we can determine the voltage across any circuit component as the product of the current and the component impedance. Thus:

$V_R = I_R\ R$

$V_X = I_R\ X$

and

$V_T = I_R\ Z$

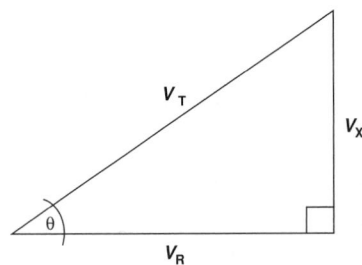

Figure 12.6

Voltage triangle for a series
R-L circuit.

VOLTAGE TRIANGLE

Graphically, we can represent these values in a **voltage triangle** (Fig. 12.6). The
voltage triangle will have the same mathematical proportions as the impedance triangle, but each of its sides will be larger by a factor of *I*. Because the voltage triangle is a right-angle triangle, we can apply Pythagoras' theorem. This will give us:

$$V_T^2 = V_R^2 + V_X^2$$

Solving for V_T yields

EQ. 12.2 $$V_T = \sqrt{V_R^2 + V_X^2}$$

EXAMPLE 12.2

Using the values from Example 12.1, draw the voltage triangle for the circuit.

1. $V_R = I R$
     $= 0.56 \times 100$
     $= 56$ V

2. $V_X = I X_L$
     $= 0.56 \times 188.4$
     $= 105.5$ V

3. $V_T = \sqrt{V_R^2 + V_{XL}^2}$
     $= \sqrt{56^2 + 105.5^2}$
     $= 119.4$ V

SOLUTION:

The completed voltage triangle is shown in Figure 12.7.

Figure 12.7

The voltage triangle for
Example 12.2.

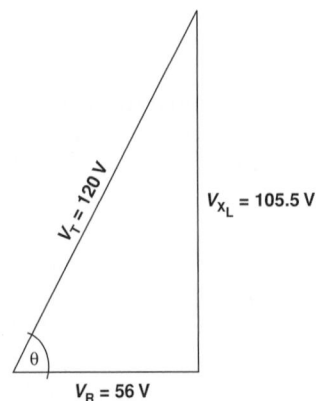

12.3 Phasors for Series *RLC* Circuits

While the voltage triangle illustrates the magnitude and direction of all the voltages in a series *RLC* circuit, it does not show the circuit current and it does not use a common reference for all the values. In order to show these characteristics, we use a phasor diagram.

To construct a phasor diagram, begin by showing the circuit current at 0° (Fig. 12.8). Since the current is the same through all the components of a series circuit, it will become the reference against which all the voltages are shown. Next, draw the voltage across the resistive portion of the circuit. Since the voltage and current for a resistor are in-phase, the voltage across the resistor will be at 0°. The current through an inductor lags the voltage by 90°, so we draw that voltage at +90°. Since the current through a capacitor leads the voltage by 90°, the capacitive voltage is drawn at –90°. The total reactive voltage will be the difference between the inductive and capacitive voltage. Depending on the individual circuit characteristics, the reactive voltage may be either positive or negative. The total voltage for the circuit will be drawn at the intersection of the resistive voltage and the reactive voltage. This will be the same as the value calculated using Equation 12.2.

EXAMPLE 12.3

Using the values from Example 12.1 and 12.2, draw the circuit phasor.

SOLUTION:

The solution is shown in Figure 12.9.

▼ **Figure 12.8**

A phasor diagram for a
series R-L circuit.

▼ **Figure 12.9**

Phasor diagram for
Example 12.3.

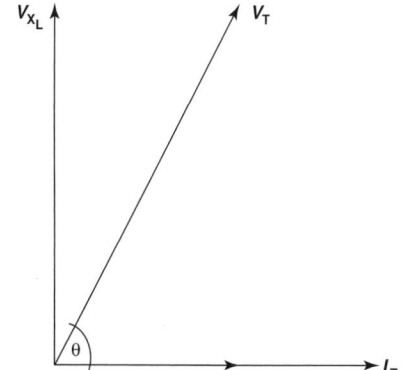

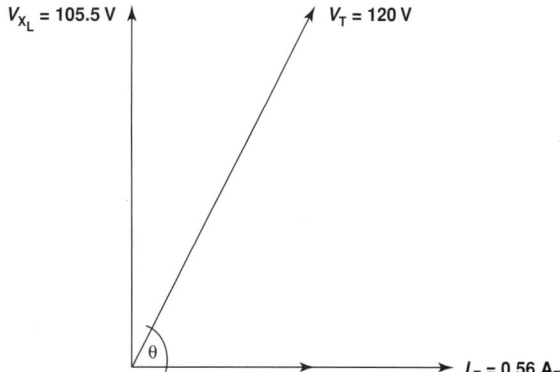

EXAMPLE 12.4

Draw the phasor for the circuit shown in Fig. 12.10.

SOLUTION:

a) Find X_L and X_C:
$$X_L = 2\pi fL$$
$$= 6.28 \times 60 \times 1.0$$
$$= 377\ \Omega$$
$$X_C = 1/(2\pi fC)$$
$$= 1/(6.28 \times 60 \times 20\ \mu F)$$
$$= 132.6\ \Omega$$

b) Find Z for the circuit:
$$Z = \sqrt{R^2 + X^2}$$
$$= \sqrt{150^2 + (377 - 132.6)^2}$$
$$= 286.7\ \Omega$$

c) Find the circuit current:
$$I = V/Z$$
$$= 220/286.7$$
$$= 0.767\ A$$

d) Find the voltage across each of the circuit components:
$$V_R = IR$$
$$= 0.767 \times 150$$
$$= 115\ V$$
$$V_{XL} = I\,X_L$$
$$= 0.767 \times 377$$
$$= 289\ V$$
$$V_{XC} = I\,X_C$$
$$= 0.767 \times 132.6$$
$$= 101\ V$$

The completed phasor is shown in Fig 12.11.

Figure 12.10

Circuit diagram for Example 12.4.

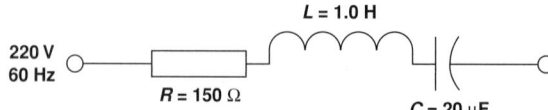

In each of the phasors, it is apparent that the supply voltage and the circuit current are out-of-phase. How far out-of-phase they are is shown by the angle between total voltage and the voltage across the resistive portion of the circuit. The cosine of this angle is known as the **power factor (pf)**.

POWER FACTOR (PF)

$$pf = \cos\theta$$

If the circuit is mostly inductive, the power factor will be lagging; if it is mostly a capacitive circuit, the power factor will be leading. Circuits with leading power factors are seldom seen.

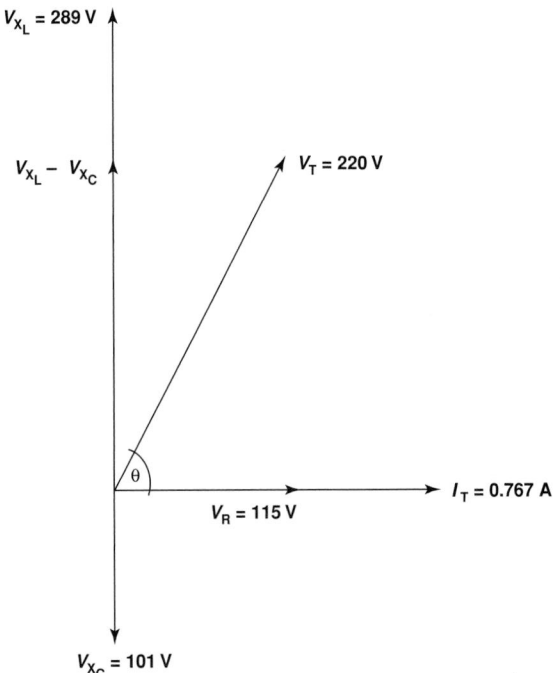

Figure 12.11

Phasor diagram for
Example 12.4.

12.4 Parallel *RLC* Circuits

We cannot use the impedance triangle for parallel *RLC* circuits, for the triangle will
not close. However, we know from Kirchhoff's current law that the sum of the currents flowing into the various branches must equal the total circuit current. Since
the current flowing through the resistive branch is 90° out-of-phase with both the
inductive and capacitive currents, we can use Pythagoras' theorem to construct a
current triangle (Fig. 12.12).

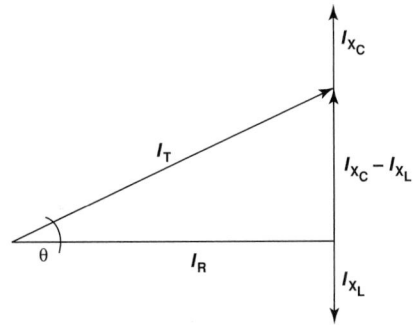

Figure 12.12

Current triangle for a series
RLC circuit.

EXAMPLE 12.5

A 100 Ω, 0.1 H coil and a 20 µF capacitor are connected in parallel to a 120 V, 60
Hz supply. Draw the current triangle for this circuit.

continued

SOLUTION:

a) Calculate the impedance components:

$X_L = 2\pi fL$

$= 6.28 \times 60 \times 0.1$

$= 37.68 \ \Omega$

$X_C = 1/(2\pi fC)$

$= 1/(6.28 \times 60 \times 20 \ \mu F)$

$= 132.6 \ \Omega$

b) Calculate the branch currents:

$I_R = V/R$

$= 120/100$

$= 1.2 \ A$

$I_L = V/X_L$

$= 120/37.68$

$= 3.18 \ A$

$I_C = V/X_C$

$= 120/132.6$

$= 0.90 \ A$

c) Find the total current:

$I_T = \sqrt{I_R^2 + I_X^2}$

$= \sqrt{1.2^2 + (3.18 - 0.90)^2}$

$= 2.57 \ A$

The completed current triangle is shown in Fig. 12.13.

Figure 12.13

Current triangle for
Example 12.5.

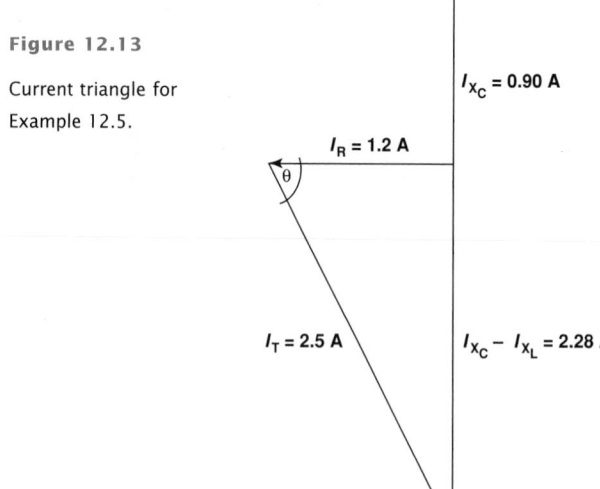

$I_{X_C} = 0.90 \ A$

$I_R = 1.2 \ A$

θ

$I_T = 2.5 \ A$

$I_{X_C} - I_{X_L} = 2.28 \ A$

$I_{X_L} = 3.18 \ A$

12.5 Phasors for Parallel *RLC* Circuits

As in the series circuit, we show the circuit values for a parallel *RLC* circuit in a phasor. In a parallel circuit, the voltage is the same across each of the branches; therefore, in the phasor for a parallel circuit the voltage becomes the reference and the various currents are plotted against this reference. Since the inductive current is 90° behind the voltage, the inductive current is drawn in the negative direction, while the capacitive current, which is 90° ahead of the voltage, is drawn in the positive direction.

EXAMPLE 12.6

Draw the phasor diagram for the circuit in Example 12.5.

SOLUTION:

See Figure 12.14.

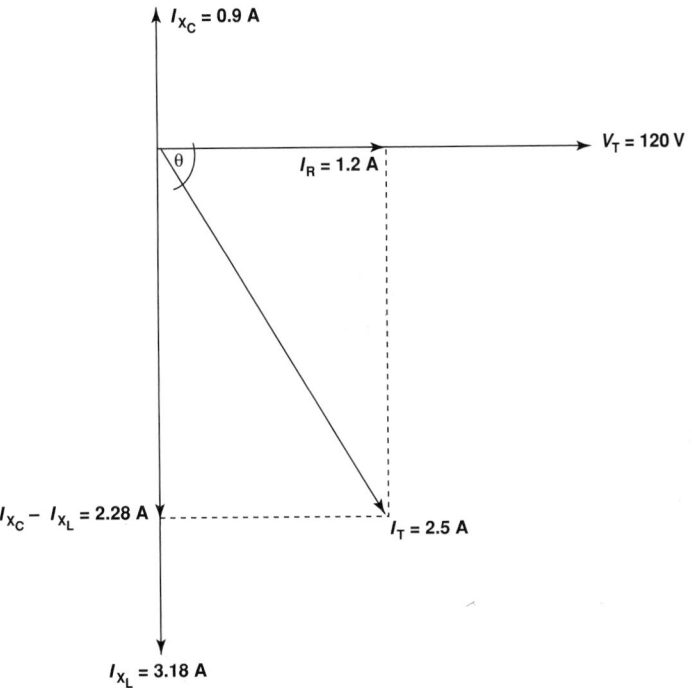

Figure 12.14

Phasor diagram for Example 12.6.

12.6 Power in *RLC* Circuits

In Section 12.2 we developed a voltage triangle from the impedance triangle. We can also develop a **power triangle** from either of the other triangles. We know from previous chapters that true power is the product of the current through a resistor and the voltage across it. Likewise, reactive power (vars) equals the current through a reactive component times the voltage across the component. It stands to reason, then, that if we multiply the total voltage by the circuit current, we will calculate the total power. Not quite.

POWER TRIANGLE

Figure 12.15

Power triangle for a series
R-L circuit.

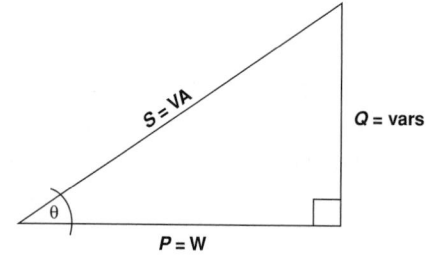

We saw in the previous section that the total voltage and current are out-of-phase and we know, from previous chapters, that true power is only consumed by a resistance. If we multiply total current by the supply voltage, it appears to give us total power. We call the result **apparent power (S)**. The unit for apparent power is the voltampere (VA).

APPARENT POWER (S)

Apparent power is an important component of electrical power. Power utilities must size their generating equipment in VA in order to supply their customer loads. All transformers are rated in VA, KVA (thousands of VA), or MVA (millions of VA).

We can derive these values from the voltage triangle in Fig 12.6 by multiplying each of the voltages by the circuit current. This will result in the power triangle shown in Fig. 12.15. We could also develop the power triangle from the impedance triangle by multiplying each of the impedance components by I^2. Because the power triangle is derived from either of the other two triangles, the mathematical proportions will be the same even though the triangle will be a different size.

EXAMPLE 12.7

Draw the power triangle for the circuit in Example 12.4.

SOLUTION:

Calculate the power components for the circuit.

$P = I^2 R$

$\quad = 0.767^2 \times 150$

$\quad = 88.24$ W

$Q_L = I^2 X_L$

$\quad = 0.767^2 \times 377$

$\quad = 221.8$ vars

$Q_C = I^2 X_C$

$\quad = 0.767^2 \times 132.6$

$\quad = 78$ vars

$SA = I^2 Z$

$\quad = 0.767^2 \times 286.7$

$\quad = 168.7$ VA

The completed power triangle is shown in Fig 12.16.

▼ **Figure 12.16**

Power triangle for
Example 12.7.

$Q_L = 221.8$ vars

$S = 168.7$ VA

$Q_L - Q_C = 143$ vars

$P = 88.24$ W

$Q_C = 78$ vars

12.7 Series Resonance

A circuit composed of an inductor in series with a capacitor can also produce **series resonance**. Series resonance occurs when $X_L = X_C$. The current in a series resonant circuit is limited only by the circuit resistance. Very high voltages can then appear across both the inductor and capacitor, compared with the voltage of the source.

EXAMPLE 12.8

A coil having a resistance of 10 Ω and a reactance of 100 Ω is connected in series with a capacitor whose capacitive reactance is 100 Ω (Fig. 12.17). Calculate the voltage across the coil and the capacitor when the circuit is connected to a 120 V source.

SOLUTION:

1. The impedance of the circuit is

$$Z_{ab} = \sqrt{R^2 + (X_L - X_C)^2} = \sqrt{10^2 + (100 - 100)^2} = 10 \ \Omega$$

2. $I = V/Z = 120/10 = 12$ A. The current is in phase with the voltage because the circuit is effectively resistive.

3. The voltage V_c across the capacitor lags 90° behind I.

4. $V_c = IX_C = 12 \times 100 = 1200$ V

5. The impedance of the coil is $Z_c = \sqrt{R^2 + X_L^2} = \sqrt{10^2 + 100^2} = 100.5 \ \Omega$

6. Voltage across the coil is $V = IZ_c = 12 \times 100.5 = 1206$ V

The phasor diagram is shown in Fig. 12.18.

▼ **Figure 12.17**

See Example 12.8.

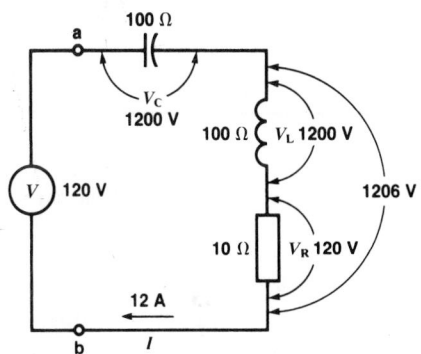

▼ **Figure 12.18**

See Example 12.8.

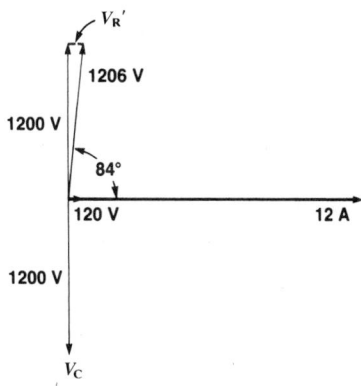

Any series circuit containing capacitive and inductive reactance will resonate at some frequency. We can calculate the frequency of resonance f_r since X_L equals X_C:

$$X_L = X_C$$

$$2\pi fL = 1/(2\pi fC)$$

$$f = 1/(4\pi^2 fLC)$$

$$f^2 = 1/(4\pi^2 LC)$$

Taking the square root of both sides of the equation yields:

EQ. 12.3 $$f = 1/(2\pi\sqrt{LC})$$

EXAMPLE 12.9

Calculate the resonant frequency for the circuit in Example 12.5.

SOLUTION:

$$f = 1/(2\pi\sqrt{LC})$$

$$= 1/(2\pi\sqrt{0.1\text{H} \times 20\ \mu\text{F}})$$

$$= 1/(8.836 \times 10^{-3})$$

$$= 112.54 \text{ Hz}$$

We can also calculate the values L and C required to cause a circuit to resonate at a particular frequency. This is, again, based upon X_L being equal to X_C at the resonant frequency. The value of C can be calculated thus:

$$X_L = X_C$$

$$2\pi fL = 1/(2\pi fC)$$

$$4\pi^2 f^2 L = 1/C$$

EQ. 12.4 $$C = 1/(4^2\pi^2 f^2 L)$$

Or L may be calculated:

$$X_L = X_C$$

$$2\pi fL = 1/(2\pi fC)$$

EQ. 12.5 $$L = 1/(4\pi^2 f^2 C)$$

12.8 Power Factor

In power circuits, we are mainly interested in the true power P absorbed by the load. This is the power that does work or produces heat. However, the apparent power S supplied to the load is usually greater than P. By definition, the ratio of true power to apparent power is called the *power factor* of the load.

EQ. 12.6   **power factor = P/S**

The power factor can never be greater than 1 and it may be expressed as a decimal, such as 0.83, or as a percentage, such as 83%.

Referring to Fig. 12.17, we recall that $P = VI_R$ and $S = VI$. Consequently:

$$\text{power factor} = P/S = \frac{VI_p}{VI} = \frac{I_p}{I} = \cos \theta \qquad \qquad \textbf{EQ. 12.7}$$

and

$$P = S \cos \theta = VI \cos \theta \qquad \qquad \textbf{EQ. 12.8}$$

The power factor of a circuit is therefore equal to the cosine of the angle between the line voltage V and the line current I. This important result holds true for any single-phase ac circuit.

The power factor is said to be *lagging* when the current lags behind the voltage. The power factor is said to be *leading* when the current leads the voltage.

EXAMPLE 12.10

A motor connected to a 120 V line draws a current of 20 A. A wattmeter indicates 1800 W (Fig. 12.19). Calculate:

1. the apparent power S consumed by the motor.
2. the power factor of the motor.
3. the phase angle between the voltage and current.

SOLUTION:

1. $S = VI = 120 \times 20 = 2400$ VA
2. power factor $= P/S = 1800/2400 = 0.75$, or 75%   **EQ. 12.7**
3. $\cos \theta = 0.75$; therefore, $\theta = \cos^{-1} 0.75 = 41.4°$ behind the voltage because the motor absorbs reactive power

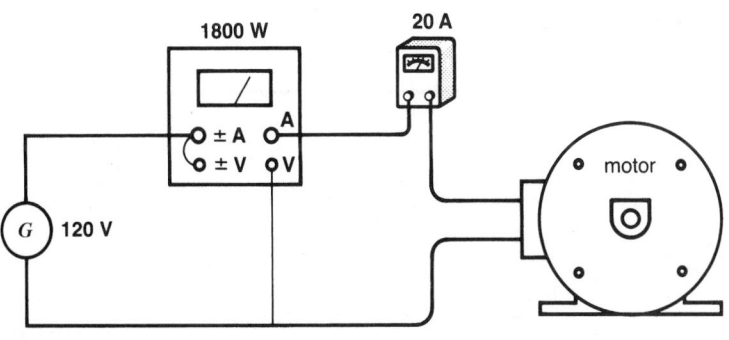

Figure 12.19

See Example 12.10.

EXAMPLE 12.11

An industrial load (Fig. 12.20) consists of several motors, a capacitor, and some incandescent lighting. The motors draw a total of 100 kW at a power factor of 80%. The capacitor has a rating of 30 kvar, and the lighting load is 20 kW. The incoming feeder voltage is 600 V. Calculate:

1. the active, reactive, and apparent power absorbed by the plant.
2. the overall power factor of the plant.
3. the current in the feeder line.

SOLUTION:

1. In all such problems we have to find (1) the total active power and (2) the total reactive power absorbed by the load. The units kVA, kW, and kvar tell us whether the stated power is apparent, active, or reactive, and so we must watch them carefully.

    a) Apparent power drawn by the motors is
    $$S = P/\cos \theta = 100/0.8 = 125 \text{ kVA}$$

    b) Reactive power absorbed by the motors is
    $$Q = \sqrt{S^2 - P^2} = \sqrt{125^2 - 100^2} = 75 \text{ kvar}$$

    c) Total active power absorbed by the plant is
    $$P = P_{\text{motor}} + P_{\text{capacitor}} + P_{\text{lighting}}$$
    $$P = 100 + 0 + 20 = 120 \text{ kW}$$

    d) Total reactive power absorbed by the plant is
    $$Q = Q_{\text{motor}} + Q_{\text{capacitor}} + Q_{\text{lighting}}$$
    $$Q = 75 - 30 + 0 = 45 \text{ kvars}$$

    e) The apparent power drawn by the plant is
    $$S = \sqrt{P^2 + Q^2} = \sqrt{120^2 + 45^2} = \sqrt{16\,425} = 128.2 \text{ kVA}$$

2. The overall power factor is
   power factor $= P/S = 120/128.2 = 0.936$, or 93.6%

3. The current in the feeder line is
   $$I = S/V = 128\,200/600 = 213.7 \text{ A}$$

Figure 12.20

See Example 12.11.

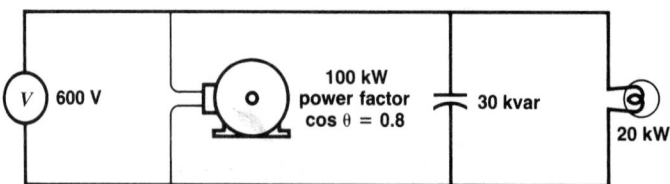

12.9 Power Factor Correction

Industrial power loads often contain a large inductive component resulting from motors and fluorescent lighting, with a relatively small resistive component made up of incandescent lighting and heating loads. This would mean that the power utility would have to supply a large apparent power component in order to supply, and bill for, a relatively small true power component. It also means that a disproportionate amount of the utility's generating capacity must be devoted to a single load. In order to avoid these conditions, the power utility will probably require that the power be corrected to some minimum value. Many utilities use 0.9 lagging as the minimum acceptable power factor. The industrial user would be required to pay a heavy financial penalty for the poor power factor or required to correct the power factor to an acceptable level.

From Section 11.7, we know that a capacitive reactance generates reactive power while an inductive reactance absorbs it. By adding capacitance, in parallel with a highly inductive load, we alter the overall power factor of a circuit. We can use this principle to adjust the load power factor to a value acceptable to the power utility. Normally, the power factor would not be corrected to a value of 1.0 because turning off some of the resistive load or turning on additional capacitive load would result in a leading power factor, and power utilities do not encourage customers to run a leading power factor. Usually the power factor is corrected to a minimum of 0.9 lagging. The specific power factor value is determined through agreement with the power utility.

EXAMPLE 12.12

Determine the capacitance needed to correct a 100 kVA load with a power factor of 0.656 (49°) lagging to a power factor of 0.85 (31.8°) lagging.

SOLUTION:

For the original load at 0.656 lagging power factor:

Q = kVA sinθ
    = 100 kVA × sin 49°
    = 100 kVA × 0.755
    = 75.5 kvars

For the load with the power factor corrected to 0.85 lagging:

Since kW remains constant:

P = kVA × cos θ
   = 100 × 0.656
   = 65.6 kW

At the corrected power-factor:

S = P/cos θ
   = 65.6 kW/0.85
   = 77.18 kVA

and

Q = S × sin θ
   = 77.18 kVA × sin 31.8°
   = 77.18 kVA × 0.527
   = 40.67 kvars

continued

Enough capitance must be connected in parallel with the load to offset the two values of Q (the difference between the kvars of the original load, 75.5 kvars, and the kvars at the corrected power, 40.67 kvars, is 34.8 kvars). Power factor correction capacitors are sold in kvar ratings, so it is not necessary to calculate the capacitor's farad rating. In the example, the utility customers would likely install a 35 kvar capacitor at their own expense.

12.10 Summary

Upon completion of this chapter you should have learned that:

- The impedance (Z) of a single-phase circuit represents the total opposition to the flow of current. It can be found using Ohm's law.

- The relationship between the current and all the voltages in series RLC circuits can be drawn on a phasor diagram. Since the current through a series circuit is constant, it is the reference against which all the circuit voltages are plotted.

- Ac circuits are supplied with apparent power (VA), but only true power produces heat and performs work.

- Series resonance occurs in ac circuits when the inductive and capacitive reactances are equal. Current is limited only by the circuit resistance.

- The power factor in ac circuits is the ratio of the true power (W) to the apparent power (S). Power factor is the cosine of the angle between the voltage and the current.

Key Terms

APPARENT POWER (S): The product of total voltage and total current in an ac circuit.

IMPEDANCE (Z): The total opposition to the flow of current. Impedance is measured in ohms and includes both resistance and reactance.

IMPEDANCE TRIANGLE: A graphic means of illustrating circuit impedance characteristics.

PHASE ANGLE: The angle between the supply voltage and line current in an ac circuit.

POWER FACTOR (pf): Cosine of the angle between the apparent power and true power in an ac circuit.

POWER TRIANGLE: A graphical means of illustrating apparent power, true power and reactive power components in an ac circuit.

SERIES RESONANCE: A circuit in which the inductive and capacitive reactance are equal. As a result, current is limited only by the circuit resistance.

VOLTAGE TRIANGLE: A graphical means of illustrating all voltages in an ac circuit and the relationships between them.

Test Your Knowledge

12.1 A resistor and capacitor are connected in series to an ac source. The currents in the two elements are
a. different
b. in phase
c. 90° out-of-phase

12.2 An inductor and a capacitor are connected in parallel to an ac source. The respective currents are 30 A and 40 A. The total current drawn from the source is
a. 70 A
b. 50 A
c. 10 A

12.3 The X component of a voltage is 30 V and the Y component is 60 V. The magnitude and phase angle of V is
a. 90 V, 63.4°
b. 67.08 V, 63.4°
c. 67.08 V, 26.5°

12.4 The unit of apparent power is
a. the VA
b. the va
c. the watt

12.5 A load draws 60 kW and 120 kvar from a line. The power factor of the load is
a. 50%
b. 44.7%
c. 33.3%

12.6 A coil has a resistance of 20 Ω and an inductance of 15 H. If it is connected to a 12 V battery, the final current is
a. 0.6 A
b. 0.48 A
c. zero

12.7 An ac line carries simultaneously 120 kW and 70 kvar. If a varmeter is connected into the line, it will read
a. 50 kvar
b. 70 kvar
c. 138.9 kvar

12.8 A motor draws 7 kW from a 240 V, 60 Hz line. If the line current is 36 A, the reactive power absorbed by the motor is
a. 1640 va
b. 5.06 kvar
c. 11.1 kvar

12.9 A capacitor connected to an ac line has a power factor that is
a. leading and zero
b. lagging and zero
c. 100 percent

12.10 A baseboard heater in a home has a power factor of
a. 1
b. zero
c. 0.707

Questions and Problems

12.11 The current in a single-phase motor lags 50° behind the voltage. What is the power factor of the motor?

12.12 A large motor absorbs 600 kW at a power factor of 88%. Calculate (a) the apparent power and (b) the reactive power absorbed by the machine.

12.13 A 200 μF capacitor is connected to a 240 V, 60 Hz source. Calculate the reactive power it generates.

12.14 In Example 12.1, what value of capacitive reactance must be connected in series with the inductive reactance for the circuit to become resonant?

12.15   In Fig. 12.21, calculate:
   a.   the current in each element
   b.   the current delivered by the source
   c.   the power factor of the circuit
   d.   the impedance of the circuit

   Draw the complete phasor diagram.

12.16   Repeat Problem 12.15 for the circuit of Fig. 12.22.

12.17   Repeat Problem 12.15 for the circuit of Fig. 12.23.

▼ Figure 12.21

See Problem 12.15.

▼ Figure 12.22

See Problem 12.16.

▼ Figure 12.23

See Problem 12.17.

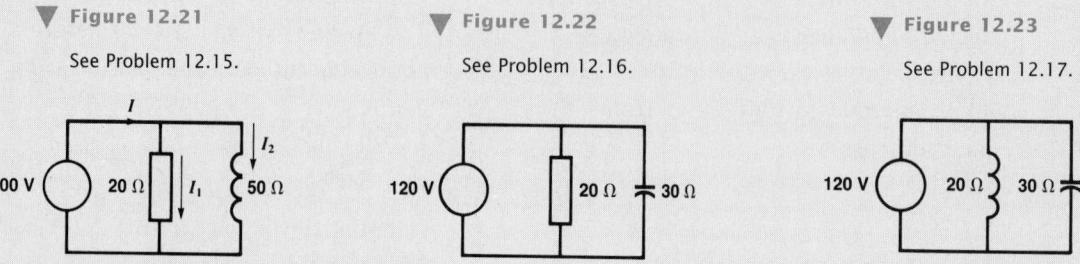

12.18   In Fig. 12.24, calculate:
   a.   the impedance of the circuit
   b.   the voltage across each element
   c.   the active power supplied by the source

   Draw the complete phasor diagram.

12.19   Repeat Problem 12.18 for the circuit of Fig. 12.25.

12.20   Repeat Problem 12.18 for the circuit of Fig. 12.26.

12.21   In Fig. 12.27, calculate in the following order:
   a.   the current in the reactor

   b.   the current in the 30 Ω resistor
   c.   the current in the 40 Ω resistor
   d.   the total active power absorbed by the circuit
   e.   the total reactive power absorbed by the circuit
   f.   the apparent power absorbed by the circuit
   g.   the current supplied to the circuit
   h.   the voltage of the source
   i.   the power factor of the circuit
   j.   the phase angle between V_1 and I

▼ Figure 12.24

See Problem 12.18.

▼ Figure 12.25

See Problem 12.19.

▼ Figure 12.26

See Problem 12.20.

▼ Figure 12.27

See Problem 12.21.

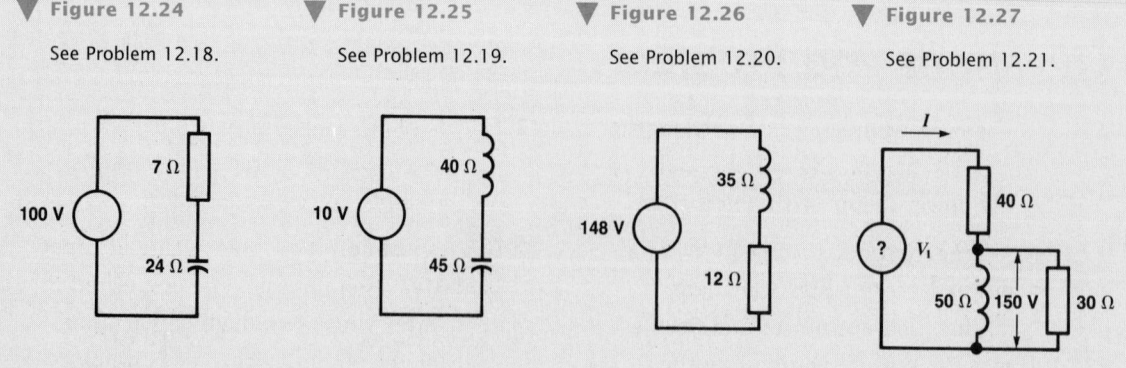

12.22 In Fig. 12.27, calculate the current flowing in the capacitor if the frequency of the source is doubled, while keeping V_2 constant.

▶ **Figure 12.28**

See Problem 12.22.

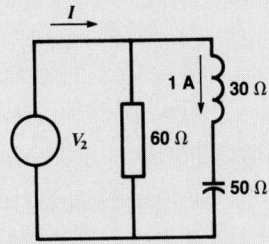

12.23 In Fig. 12.28, calculate in the following order:

a. the impedance of the circuit

b. the voltage across the inductor

c. the voltage across the capacitor

d. the supply voltage V_2

e. the current in the resistor

f. the active power consumed in the circuit

g. the reactive power absorbed by the inductor

h. the reactive power generated by the capacitor

i. the reactive power delivered to the source V_2

j. the apparent power of the source

k. the power factor of the source

l. the phase angle between V_2 and I

13

Three-Phase Circuits

LEARNING OBJECTIVES

Upon completion of this chapter you will be able to:

- Describe how a three-phase voltage is generated

- Describe how current flows in a three-phase line

- Recognize wye and delta connections

- Explain the relationship between current and voltage in wye and delta connections

- Determine the power factor in a three-phase system

- Measure power in a three-phase system using the 2-wattmeter and 3-wattmeter methods

- Explain the significance of phase sequence

13.1   Polyphase Systems

We can gain a preliminary understanding of **polyphase systems** by referring to the common gasoline engine. A single-cylinder engine having one piston is comparable to a single-phase machine. A two-cylinder engine is comparable to a two-phase machine, and the more common six-cylinder engine could be called a six-phase

POLYPHASE SYSTEMS

machine. In a six-cylinder engine, identical pistons move up and down inside identical cylinders, but they do not move in unison. They are staggered in such a way as to deliver power to the shaft in successive pulses rather than at the same time. This produces a smoother-running engine and a smoother output torque.

Similarly, in a three-phase electrical system, the three phases are identical, and deliver power at different times. As a result, the total instantaneous power flow from the three phases is constant. Furthermore, because the phases are identical, one phase* may be used to represent the behaviour of all three.

Although we must be careful not to carry analogies too far, the above description reveals that a three-phase system is basically composed of three single-phase systems which operate in sequence. Once this is understood, any mystery surrounding three-phase systems disappears.

13.2 Generating a Three-Phase Voltage

We have already seen that a single coil revolving between the N and S poles of a permanent magnet produces an ac voltage (see Section 8.2). If we place three identical coils on the armature, symmetrically spaced at 120° to each other (Fig. 13.1), the voltage generated by each coil will have the same effective value. However, the

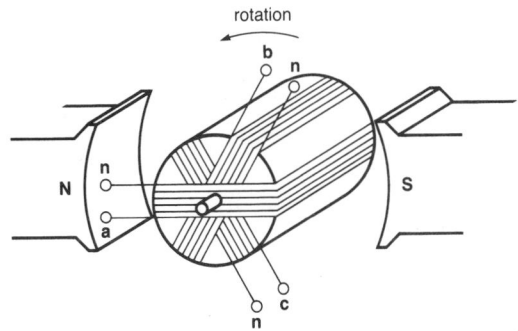

Figure 13.1

A simple three-phase generator.

---

* The term "phase" is used to designate different things; consequently, it has to be read in context to be understood. The following examples show some of the ways in which "phase" is used:

1. the current is out of phase with the voltage (refers to phasor diagram);

2. the three phases of a transmission line (meaning the three conductors of the line);

3. the phase-to-phase voltage (meaning line voltage);

4. the phase sequence (the order in which the phasors follow each other);

5. the burned-out phase (the burned-out winding of a 3-phase machine);

6. the three-phase voltage (the line voltage of a 3-phase system);

7. the 3-phase currents are unbalanced (the currents in a 3-phase line or machine are unequal and not displaced at 120°);

8. phase-shift transformer (a device which can change the phase angle of the output voltage with respect to the input voltage);

9. phase-to-phase fault (a short-circuit between two line conductors;

10. phase-to-ground short-circuit (a short-circuit between one line conductor and ground);

11. the phases are unbalanced (the line voltages or the line currents are unequal or not displaced at 120° to each other).

Figure 13.2

The generated voltages are displaced 120° from each other.

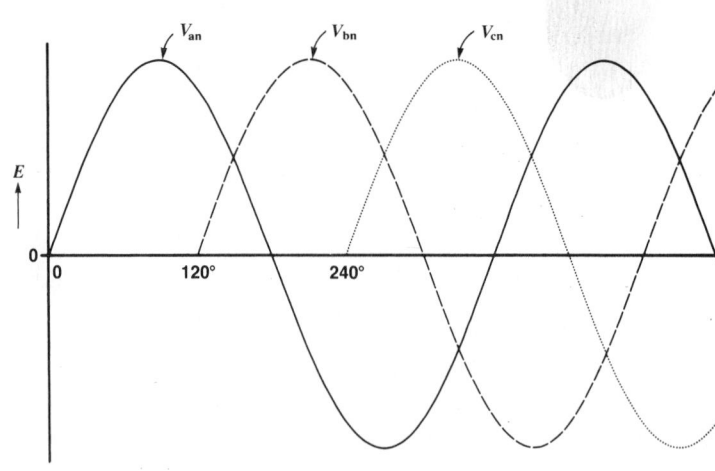

Figure 13.3

Phasor diagram representing the generated voltages.

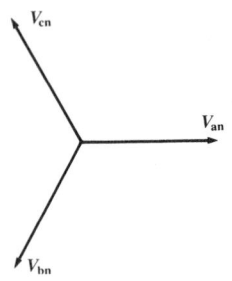

peak positive values will not occur at the same time, but will be displaced at 120° to each other. If the terminals of the coils are labelled an, bn, and cn, the corresponding voltages can be represented by the sine waves of Fig. 13.2. The peak value of each voltage is V_m, but V_{bn} lags 120° behind V_{an}, while V_{cn} lags 240° behind V_{an}. The three voltages can be represented more simply by the phasors of Fig. 13.3.

Each winding generates a single-phase voltage between its terminals. Thus, voltages V_{an}, V_{bn}, and V_{cn} are single-phase voltages, but together they make up a **three-phase system**. The coil ends n are usually connected to create a neutral terminal **n**. Consequently, voltages will appear between terminals a, b, and c as well as between terminals an, bn, and cn (Fig. 13.4).

The line voltages V_{ab}, V_{bc}, and V_{ca} between terminals a, b, and c are also equal and displaced at 120° to each other. Their magnitude and phase angle can be determined from phasors V_{an}, V_{bn}, and V_{cn} and the circuit diagram of Fig. 13.4.

For example, by looking at Fig. 13.4, we see that $V_{ab} = V_{an} + V_{nb}$. The phasor sum V_{ab} is constructed as shown in Fig. 13.5. (Phasor V_{nb} is equal and opposite to phasor V_{bn}.) It shows that V_{ab}, is larger than V_{an} and that it is 30° ahead of V_{an}. Phasors V_{bc} and V_{ca} are similarly found from the phasor sums $V_{bc} = V_{bn} + V_{nc}$ and $V_{ca} = V_{cn} + V_{na}$.

There is a definite relationship between the magnitude of the line voltages (such as V_{ab}) and the line-to-neutral voltages (such as V_{an}). Referring to Fig. 13.5 and from the discussion in Section 1.20, we have $V_{ab} = V_{ab} = \sqrt{3}\, V_{an}$.

Figure 13.4

The generator windings are connected to form a common neutral.

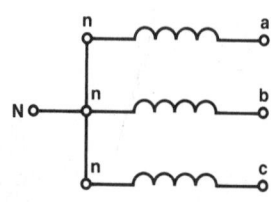

Figure 13.5

The voltages between the terminals are found by phasor addition.

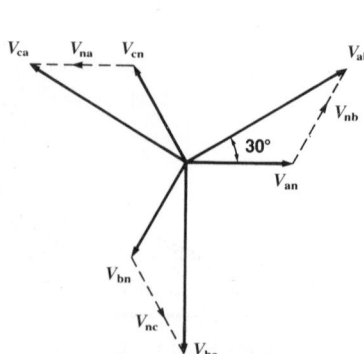

We can therefore write:

$$V = \sqrt{3}\ V_{LN}$$

EQ. 13.1

where

V = line voltage, in volts (V)

V_{LN} = line-to-neutral voltage, in volts (V)

$\sqrt{3}$ = 1.732...

In order to appreciate the meaning of these three-phase relationships, Fig. 13.6 shows the voltages indicated by voltmeters connected across the terminals of a three-phase, 440 V generator. Note that the line-to-neutral voltages are indeed $440/\sqrt{3}$ = 254 V. Furthermore, the three line voltages have the same values, as do the three line-to-neutral voltages.

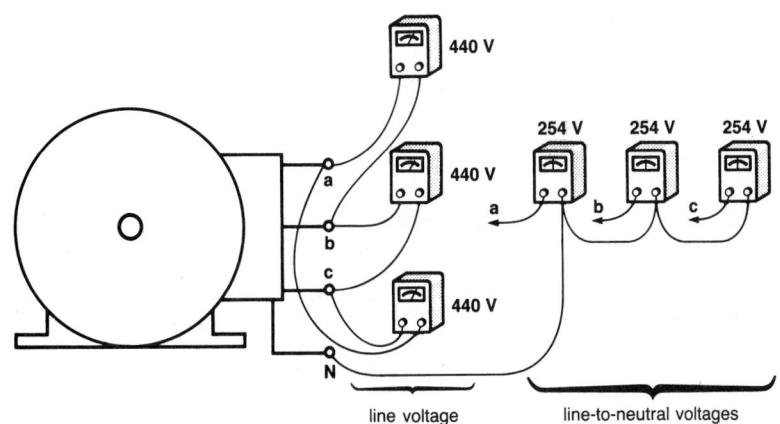

Figure 13.6

Voltages generated by a 3-phase, 440 V ac generator.

13.3 Three-Phase Currents

When a three-phase source is connected to a three-phase load, only the line termi-nals a, b, and c need to be connected. The neutral terminal is left open (Fig. 13.7). The currents I_a, I_b, and I_c in the three lines will have the same values, but they, too, are out of phase with each other by 120° (Fig. 13.8). If the effective line current is 106 A and ammeters are connected in each line, they will all indicate a current of 106 A. The peak current in each line is therefore 106/0.707 = 150 A.

▼ **Figure 13.7**

A balanced three-phase load causes three-phase currents to flow in the generator, line, and load.

▼ **Figure 13.8**

Phasor diagram of the three-phase currents in Fig. 13.7. Each phasor cor-responds to a peak current of 150 A.

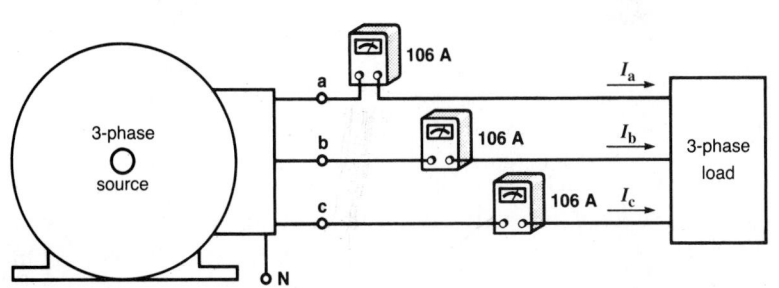

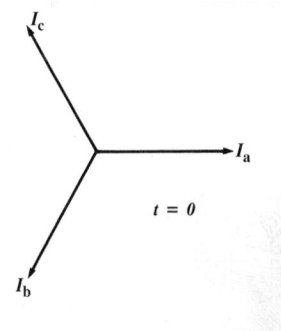

Figure 13.9

The magnitude and direction of the currents in the three lines change continually. The magnitudes of the instantaneous currents can be visualized by assuming that the rotating phasors are projected on a screen at the right. The magnitudes are given at three instants, separated by intervals of 30°.

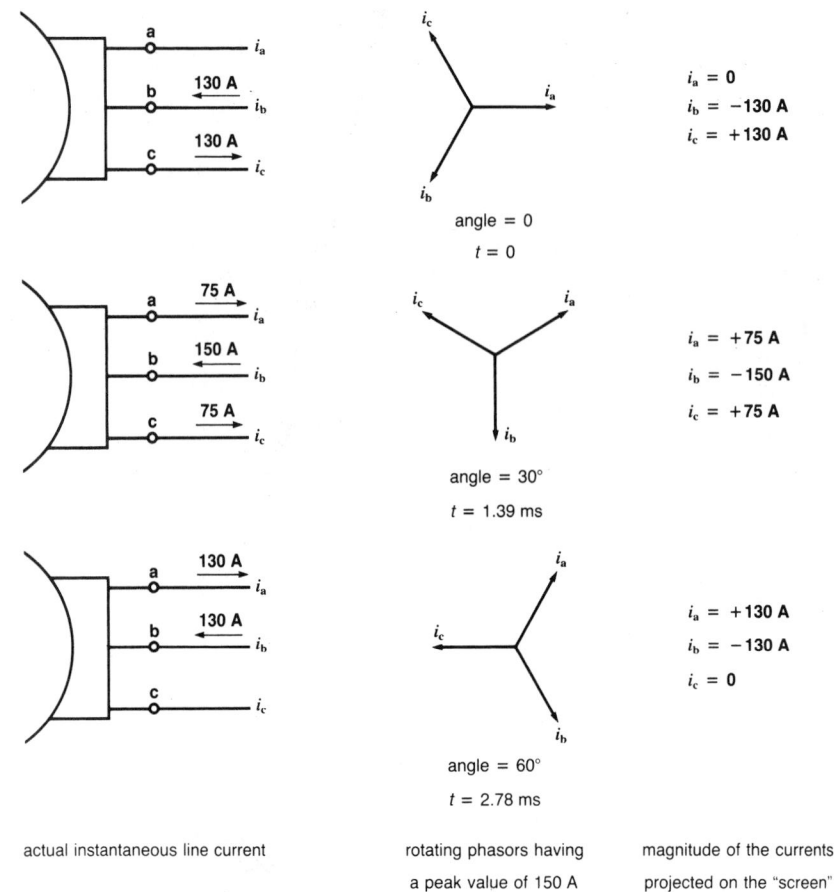

actual instantaneous line current

rotating phasors having a peak value of 150 A

magnitude of the currents projected on the "screen"

In order to understand the nature of this three-phase current flow, Fig. 13.9 shows the instantaneous currents i_a, i_b, and i_c at successive intervals of 30°. On a 60 Hz line, 30° corresponds to an interval of 1.39 ms. The instantaneous line currents at three successive moments are shown. Note that the revolving phasors enable us to visualize the relative magnitudes and signs of the currents.

However, we can also calculate the instantaneous currents from the equations:

$$i_a = 150 \sin \theta$$
$$i_b = 150 \sin (\theta - 120)$$
$$i_c = 150 \sin (\theta - 240)$$

These equations are obtained from the sine waves represented by the three phasors of Fig. 13.8.

When the line currents are equal and displaced at 120°, and the line voltages are equal and displaced at 120°, the three-phase system is said to be *balanced*. We always try to maintain a balanced condition.

13.4 Wye and Delta Connections

A balanced three-phase load is actually composed of three identical single-phase loads. The loads are connected symmetrically, and there are two basic ways of accomplishing this. The single-phase loads are connected either in **wye** or in **delta** (Figs. 13.10 and 13.11). These schematic drawings try to capture the phase

WYE

DELTA

▼ **Figure 13.10**

Three single-phase loads
connected in wye.

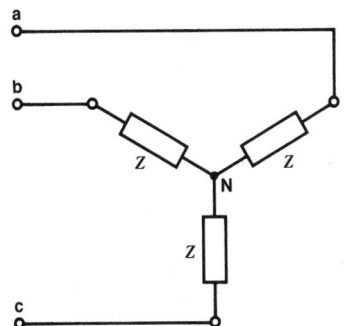

▼ **Figure 13.11**

Three single-phase loads
connected in delta.

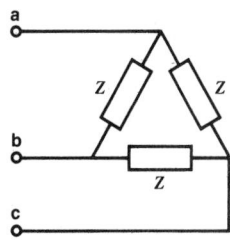

▼ **Figure 13.12**

Alternative method of showing a wye connection.

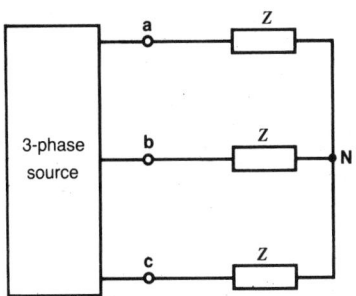

▼ **Figure 13.13**

Alternative method of showing a delta connection.

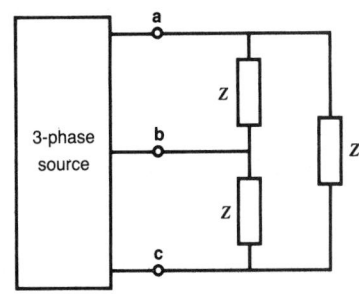

relationship between the line and line-to-neutral voltages by drawing the loads at
120° angles. However, the circuit diagrams can also be drawn as shown in Figs. 13.12
and 13.13. This, of course, does not alter the voltages or currents.

13.5 Currents and Voltages in a Wye Connection

Figure 13.14 shows the line voltages and line-to-neutral voltages when a wye-connected
load is powered by a 208 V, 3-phase source. The voltages across the loads are equal in
magnitude, and so we show only one voltmeter reading. The line-to-neutral voltage (120
V) is less than the line voltage (208 V). The ratio between the two is again $\sqrt{3}$.

The current I_L in each load is obviously equal to the line current I, which is assumed
to have a value of 45 A.

These results are generalized in Fig. 13.15. Two simple rules apply to a wye connection: if the line voltage is V and the line current is I,

1. the current in each load is equal to I
2. the voltage across each load is equal to $V/1.732$.

▼ Figure 13.14

Currents and voltages in a
208 V, 3-phase line and a
wye-connected load.

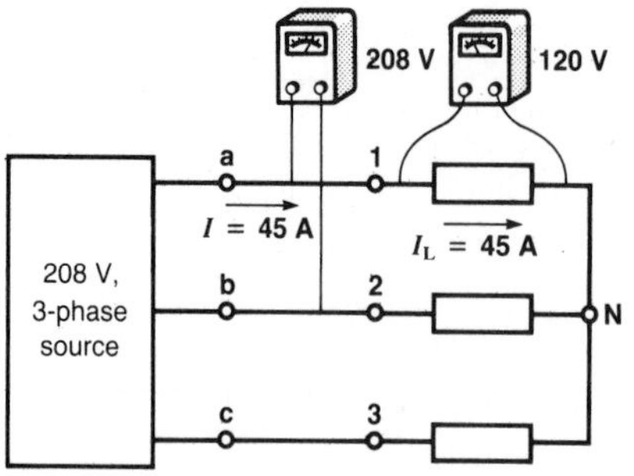

▼ Figure 13.15

General current and voltage
relationships in a balanced
wye-connected load.

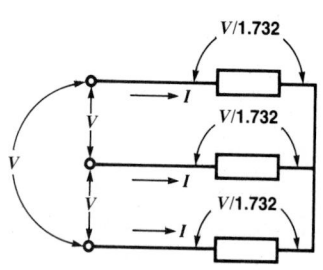

13.6 Currents and Voltages in a Delta Connection

Figure 13.16 shows the line currents and load currents when a delta-connected load is fed by a 440 V, 3-phase source. The currents in the loads are all equal and so we show only one ammeter reading. The load current (26 A) is less than the line current (45 A). The ratio between the two is $\sqrt{3}$ or 1.732.

The voltage across each load is obviously equal to the line voltage.

These results are generalized in Fig. 13.17. Two simple roles apply to a delta connection: if the line voltage is V and the line current is I,

1.   the voltage across each load is equal to V

2.   the current in each load is equal to $I/1.732$.

▼ Figure 13.16

Currents and voltages in a
440 V, 3-phase line and
delta-connected load.

▼ Figure 13.17

General current and voltage
relationships in a balanced
delta-connected load.

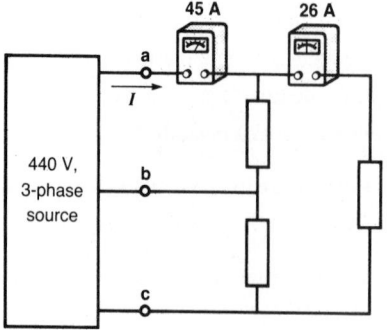

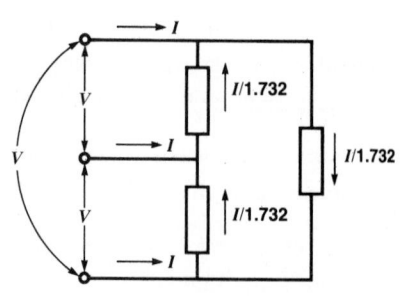

13.7 Power and Power Factor in a Three-Phase Line

In discussing wye and delta connections, we did not specify the nature of the single-phase loads. We only said they were identical. Consequently, they may be resistors, inductors, capacitors, motors, or any other devices. However, the active power P_L absorbed by each of the three single-phase loads is the same. The apparent powers S_L are also the same. The power factor (cos θ) of each single-phase load is therefore $\cos \theta = P_L/S_L$.

The 3-phase line is delivering $P = 3P_L$ watts to the three loads. It is also supplying $S = 3S_L$ voltamperes. It follows that the power factor of the three-phase line is $3P_L/3S_L = P_L/S_L$, which is the same as the power factor of the individual single-phase loads. Thus, the power factor of a balanced three-phase line is given by

$$\cos \theta = \frac{\text{active power of the line}}{\text{apparent power of the line}} = \frac{P}{S}$$ EQ. 13.2

What is the apparent power S supplied by a three-phase line? To answer this question, let us return to Fig. 13.17. It shows a three-phase load connected to a line in which the line current is I and the line voltage is V. The current in each single-phase branch is $I/\sqrt{3}$ and the voltage across it is V. The apparent power of each branch is therefore $VI/\sqrt{3}$ voltamperes. For the three loads, the apparent power is three times as great, so we have:

$$S = 3\,VI/\sqrt{3} = VI\sqrt{3}$$

and so

$$S = 1.732\,VI \qquad S = \sqrt{3}\,V_{LL}\,I_{Lme}.$$ EQ. 13.3

where

S = apparent power of a three-phase line or load, in voltamperes (VA)

V = line voltage, in volts (V)

I = line current, in amperes (A)

Equations 13.2 and 13.3 can be applied to any three-phase balanced load or line. The load may be connected in any way as long as it is balanced.

13.8 Solving Three-Phase Circuits

The secret to solving a three-phase circuit is to consider only one phase. Because we know how to solve single-phase circuits, it is advantageous to reduce a three-phase circuit to a single-phase equivalent. Another important technique is to draw a sketch of the three-phase circuit, listing the important values. The following examples illustrate the procedure.

EXAMPLE 13.1

Three resistors are connected in wye across a 440 V, 3-phase line. If they dissipate a total of 6000 W, calculate:

1. the current in each line
2. the value of each resistor

SOLUTION:

1. First, we make a sketch of the circuit (Fig. 13.18).

Figure 13.18

See Example 13.1.

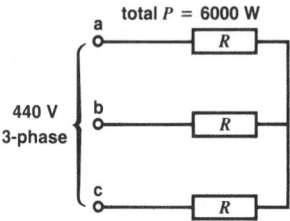

2. Next, we make a list of everything we know about the single-phase load:
    a) the power dissipated by one resistor is $P = 6000/3 = 2000$ W
    b) the voltage across the resistor is $V = 440/1.732 = 254$ V
    c) the current in the resistor is $I = P/V = 2000/254 = 7.87$ A
    d) the line current $= 7.87$ A
    e) the resistance of the resistor is $R = V/I = 254/7.87 = 32.3$ Ω

EXAMPLE 13.2

A 4 kV, 3-phase line carries a line current of 90 A. The power factor is 0.85 lagging, and the load is connected in delta. Calculate:

1. the impedance of the load, per phase
2. the reactive power, per phase

SOLUTION:

1. We first make a sketch of the delta-connected load (Fig. 13.19).

Figure 13.19

See Example 13.2.

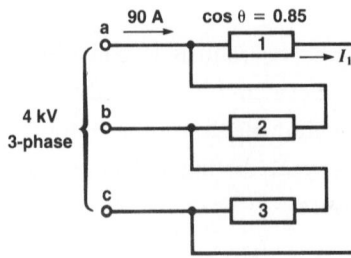

continued

2. Next, we make a list of everything we know about the single-phase loads, taking load 1 as a sample:

    a) the current in load 1 is I_1 = 90/1.732 = 52 A

    b) the voltage across load 1 is V = 4000 V

    c) impedance of load 1 is Z = V/I = 4000/52 = 76.9 Ω

    d) apparent power of load 1 is
        $S = VI = 4000 \times 52 = 208\ 000 = 208$ kVA

    e) active power of load 1 is
        $P = S \cos \theta = 208 \times 0.85 = 176.8$ kW

    f) reactive power is $Q = \sqrt{S^2 - P^2} = \sqrt{208^2 - 176.8^2} = 109.6$ kvar

EQ. 13.2

13.9 Measuring Three-Phase Power

The active power P flowing in a 3-phase, 3-wire line can be measured by using two single-phase wattmeters. The instruments are connected as shown in Fig. 13.20. The total active power consumed by the three phases is equal to the sum of the two wattmeter readings. When the power factor is less than 50 percent, one of the instruments will give a negative reading. To measure it, we must reverse the leads connected to the voltage terminals of the instrument. The total power is then equal to the difference of the two readings.

Note that this so-called 2-wattmeter method of measuring power yields the correct value even if the three-phase system is unbalanced.

In some three-phase installations, the neutral wire is also used. For example, in a 208 V/120 V system, motor loads are connected between lines, while lighting loads and service outlets are connected between the lines and neutral. This is called a 3-phase, 4-wire system. We need three wattmeters to measure the active power in such a system. They are connected as shown in Fig. 13.21. The total power is equal to the sum of the three wattmeter readings. This method also gives correct results even if the loads are unbalanced.

Reactive power can be measured by means of varmeters. The varmeter connections for 3-wire and 4-wire systems are the same as for wattmeters. However, varmeters give meaningful readings only when the loads are balanced.

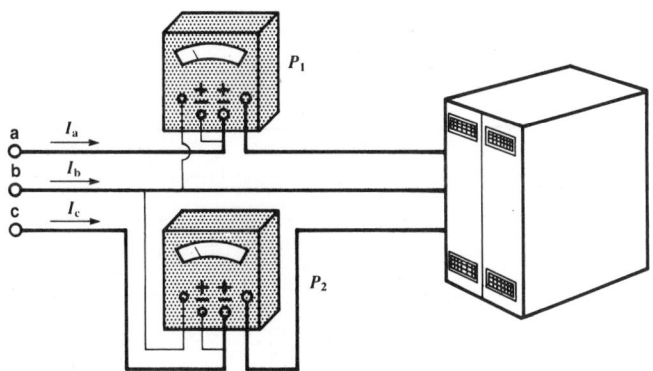

Figure 13.20

Measuring the active power in a 3-phase, 3-wire line.

Figure 13.21

Measuring the active power
in a 3-phase, 4-wire line.

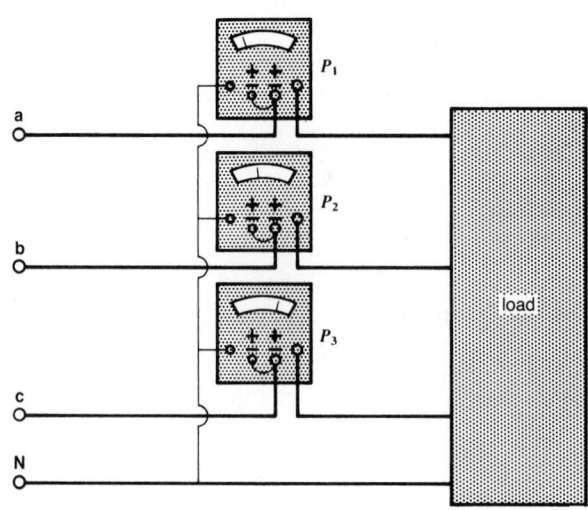

Figure 13.21

Measuring the active power
in a 3-phase, 4-wire line.

EXAMPLE 13.3

A test on a three-phase motor running at light load on a 440 V line gives wattmeter readings $P_1 = +2300$ W and $P_2 = -500$ W. We assume the motor is connected in wye. If the line current is 10 A, calculate the power factor of the motor and its line-to-neutral impedance.

SOLUTION:

1. We first draw a diagram of the problem, showing all the given information (Fig. 13.22).

Figure 13.22

Example 13.3.

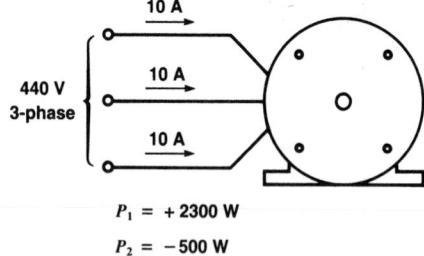

$P_1 = +2300$ W

$P_2 = -500$ W

2. Next, we make a list of everything we know about one phase of the motor:
    a) voltage from line-to-neutral is $V = 440/1.732 = 254$ V (the neutral connection is made inside the motor)
    b) current in one phase is $I = 10$ A because of the wye connection
    c) impedance per phase is $Z = V/I = 254/10 = 25.4\ \Omega$
    d) apparent power per phase is $S = VI = 254 \times 10 = 2540$ VA
    e) total 3-phase active power is $P = P_1 + P_2 = 2300 - 500 = 1800$ W
    f) active power in one phase is $P = 1800/3 = 600$ W
    g) $\cos \theta$ of one phase $= P/S = 600/2540 = 0.236$ or 23.6 percent
    h) power factor of the three-phase motor is 23.6 percent

In many three-phase loads, the three individual phases are placed in a single enclosure, and so it is impossible to tell whether they are connected in wye or in delta. In such cases we *assume* a wye connection because it is a slightly simpler arrangement than the delta connection.

13.10 Phase Sequence

An important property of a three-phase system is its **phase sequence**. This is the order in which the line voltages become positive. Suppose that the voltages between the lines a, b, and c of Fig. 13.23 can be represented by the phasor diagram shown. Based upon our knowledge of revolving phasors (Section 8.6), the peak positive values of voltage occur in the sequence V_{ab}, V_{ca}, V_{bc}. The phase sequence is then said to be a - c - b - a - c - b . . . or simply acb.

PHASE SEQUENCE

When a load having terminals 1, 2, and 3 is connected to lines a, b, and c as shown, the phase sequence for the load is obviously in the order 1 - 3 - 2. However, as far as the load is concerned, we can change the phase sequence by interchanging any two leads, as shown in Fig. 13.24. The line phase sequence a - c - b now produces a load phase sequence 1 - 2 - 3. Thus, we can change the phase sequence of a three-phase line by interchanging any two lines.

Phase sequence is important because it determines the direction of rotation of three-phase motors. It is also important whenever three-phase generators or transformers have to be connected in parallel.

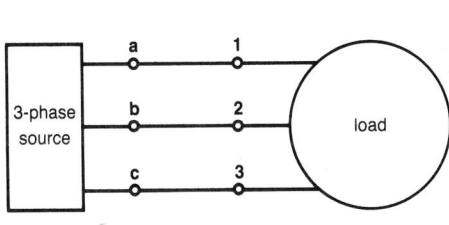

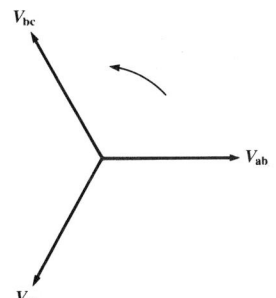

Figure 13.23

Load terminals 1, 2, 3 have the same phase sequence as line terminals a, b, c.

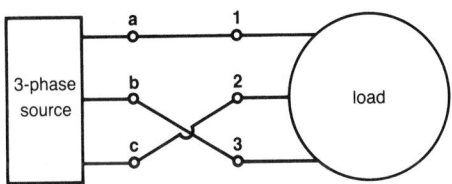

Figure 13.24

Load terminals 1, 2, 3 have the reverse phase sequence of line terminals a, b, c.

13.11 Summary

Upon completion of this chapter you should have learned that:

• Three-phase voltages are generated 120° apart by rotating three coils, mechanically separated by 120°, in a stationary magnetic field.

- There are two possible three-phase connections: wye and delta. These connections are shown in Figs. 13.10 and 13.11.

- In the wye connection, the line current and phase current are equal, while the line voltage is 1.73 larger than the phase voltage. In the delta connection, the line voltage equals the phase voltage, while the line current is 1.73 larger than the phase current.

- As in single-phase systems, the power factor in a three-phase system can be calculated using apparent power and true power ($\cos \theta = P/S$).

- Total power in a three-phase system can be measured using either the 2-wattmeter or 3-wattmeter method. In each of these methods, the total power will be the sum of the wattmeter readings.

- The phase sequence of a - b - c can be changed to an a - c - b by interchanging any two phases of the a - c - b system.

Key Terms

DELTA CONNECTION: A three-phase connection resembling the Greek letter delta. In a delta connection, the line voltage equals the phase voltage and the line current is $\sqrt{3}$ larger than the phase current.

PHASE SEQUENCE: In a polyphase system, the phase sequence is the order in which the phases occur. In a three-phase system, the phase sequence can be a - b - c or a - c - b.

POLYPHASE SYSTEMS: Any system with more than one phase. Although two-phase, six-phase, and twelve-phase systems can be found, the three-phase system is by far the most common polyphase system.

THREE-PHASE SYSTEM: A polyphase system in which three equal voltages are separated by 120°.

WYE CONNECTION: A three-phase connection resembling the letter Y. In a wye connection, the line current equals the phase current and the line voltage is $\sqrt{3}$ larger than the phase voltage.

Test Your Knowledge

13.1 The rotor in Fig. 13.1 turns at 1500 r/ min. The time V_{an} to complete one cycle is
a. 25 s
b. 40 ms
c. 251.2 ms

13.2 The frequency of the voltages in Fig. 13.2 is 400 Hz. The time interval between the positive peaks of V_{an} and V_{bn} is
a. 7.5 ms
b. 2.5 ms
c. 833.3 s

13.3 In Fig. 13.2, V_{bn} lags behind V_{an} but leads V_{cn} by 120°.

true_____ false_____

13.4 In Fig. 13.4, if V_{ab} = 380 V, then V_{bn} is
a. 219 V
b. 657 V
c. 190 V

13.5 In Fig. 13.6, the peak voltage between terminals b and n is
a. 440 V
b. 359 V
c. 254 V

13.6 In Fig. 13.9, when t = 5.56 ms, the value of i_a is
a. 150 A
b. −130 A
c. +130 A

13.7 A 69 kV, 3-phase transmission line carries 350 A per conductor. The apparent power carried by the line is
a. 24.15 MVA
b. 41.8 MW
c. 41.8 MVA

13.8 The load in Fig. 13.16 has a power factor of 82 percent, lagging. It consumes an active power of
a. 28.1 kW
b. 28.1 kVA
c. 16.2 kW

13.9 The phase sequence of the currents in Fig. 13.8 is I_a - I_c - I_b.

true_____ false_____

Questions and Problems

13.10 The line voltage in Fig. 13.10 is 620 V, and the load is resistive.
a. What is the voltage across each resistor?
b. If each resistor has a value of 15 Ω, what is the current in each line?
c. Calculate the power supplied by the source.

13.11 Three resistors are connected in delta. If the line voltage is 13.2 kV and the line current is 1202 A, calculate:
a. the current in each resistor
b. the voltage across each resistor
c. the power supplied to each resistor
d. the power factor of the load

13.12 Three 120 V, 60 W lamps are connected in wye across a 160 V, 3-phase line. Will the lamps be dim or bright?

13.13 A resistance of 18 Ω is measured between any two terminals of the three-phase resistor bank shown in

Fig. 13.12. If the load is connected to a 460 V, 3-phase line, calculate the total power that is dissipated.

13.14 The windings of a 3-phase motor are connected in delta. If the resistance between any two terminals is 0.6 Ω, what is the resistance of each winding?

13.15 In Fig. 13.2, the peak voltage is 340 V. Express the three voltages in trigonometric form.

13.16 A three-phase motor connected to a 440 V line draws a current of 136 A. Two wattmeters connected into the line as shown in Fig. 13.20 give readings of 59.5 kW and 23.8 kW. Calculate:
a. the apparent power absorbed by the motor
b. the power factor of the motor
c. the reactive power absorbed by the motor

14

Transformers

LEARNING OBJECTIVES

Upon completion of this chapter you will be able to:

- Explain the operation of a simple transformer under no-load and full-load conditions

- Explain transformer polarity and the test method used to determine polarity

- Explain the use of transformer taps

- Describe how transformers can be connected in parallel

- Describe several methods for cooling transformers

- Explain the importance of transformer impedance

- Describe the operation and application of current and voltage transformers

- Recognize various three-phase transformer connections

14.1   The Transformer and Power Transmission

You will recall that the power delivered by a transmission line is equal to the product of the line voltage times the line current: $P = VI$. This means that for a give amount of power, the line current becomes smaller as the line voltage is increased. A smaller current reduces the required conductor size, as well as the I^2R losses.

For example, suppose we need to transmit 1000 kW over a distance of 30 km. If we decide to use a line voltage of 1000 V, the line current is 1000 A, and this would require a large conductor. On the other hand, if we use 10 000 V, the current will be only 100 A. We can therefore use a much smaller conductor, producing considerable savings. That is why voltages as high as 14 400 V, 345 000 V, and even 765 000 V are used to carry large blocks of energy over great distances.

Figure 14.1 shows a simple transmission system composed of a generating station, a transmission line, and a power consumer. At the generating station, a transformer T_1 raises the voltage from 4160 V to 69 kV to reduce the transmission line current and corresponding line losses. At the other end of the line, a second transformer T_2 reduces the voltage from 69 kV to a more usable, practical value, such as 480 V.

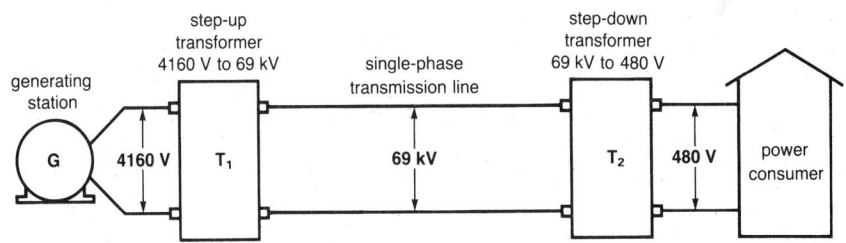

Figure 14.1

Transformers enable the economical transmission of power over a large distance.

14.2 Simple Transformer

A transformer in its simplest form is composed of two coils that are mounted on a laminated iron core (Fig. 14.2). The coils are carefully insulated from each other and from the core.

One of the coils is connected to the ac source. It is called the **primary winding**, or simply primary. The other coil, connected to the load, is called the **secondary winding**, or simply secondary. Power therefore flows from the primary to the secondary winding.

> PRIMARY WINDING
>
> SECONDARY WINDING

Note that the power flow through a transformer is reversible: the primary can become a secondary, and vice versa. Thus, in Fig. 14.2, if terminals 1 and 2 are connected to a source, the secondary winding automatically becomes a primary winding. Furthermore, because terminals a and b are now connected to a load, the primary winding becomes the secondary winding.

Figure 14.3 shows how the HV (high voltage) coils of a large transformer are pre-formed on a slowly rotating drum.

14.3 No-Load Operation

At no-load the secondary is on open-circuit and so the primary behaves like a simple inductor as far as the source is concerned (Fig. 14.2). Therefore, the current I_m drawn

Figure 14.2

Construction of a simple transformer.

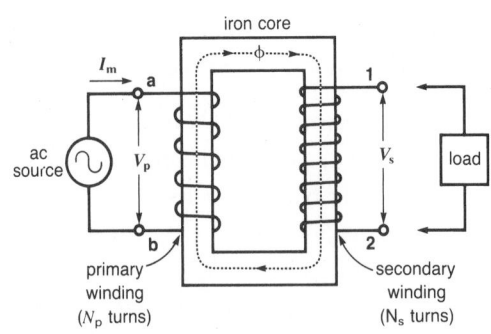

Figure 14.3

Winding the HV coil of a large transformer.

(Courtesy ABB)

MAGNETIZING CURRENT

from the source lags 90° behind voltage V_p. This so-called **magnetizing current** produces an ac flux ϕ in the core. The flux, in turn, induces a small ac voltage v in each turn of the primary.

If the primary has N_p turns, the voltage induced across its terminals is equal to the sum of the voltages induced in all the turns, namely $v \times N_p$ volts. We therefore can write:

EQ. 14.1 $V_p = v \times N_p$ **volts**

The secondary links the same ac flux; therefore the voltage v induced in each turn must be the same as that induced in a primary turn. If the secondary has N_s turns, the voltage V_s induced across its terminals is given by

EQ. 14.2 $V_s = v \times N_s$

From these results we obtain an important ratio, called the **transformer ratio**.

TRANSFORMER RATIO

$$\frac{V_p}{V_s} = \frac{v \times N_p}{v \times N_s} = \frac{N_p}{N_s}$$

thus

$$\frac{V_p}{V_s} = \frac{N_p}{N_s}$$

EQ. 14.3

where

V_p = voltage applied to the primary winding, in volts (V)

V_s = voltage induced in the secondary winding, in volts (V)

N_p = number of primary turns

N_s = number of secondary turns

Equation 14.3 means that the ratio of the primary voltage to secondary voltage is the same as the ratio of the number of turns. Furthermore, because the primary and secondary voltages are produced by the same ac flux, they must be in phase. Thus, when the primary voltage is zero, the secondary voltage is zero. Similarly, when V_p is maximum positive, the secondary voltage V_s is maximum positive.

The relationship between V_p, V_s, and I_m is shown in the phasor diagram of Fig. 14.4. Phasor V_s is longer than phasor V_p because the secondary winding is assumed to have more turns than the primary. Note that the flux ϕ in the core is necessarily in phase with the magnetizing current I_m.

▼ Figure 14.4

Phasor diagram of the voltages and current when the transformer is operating at no-load.

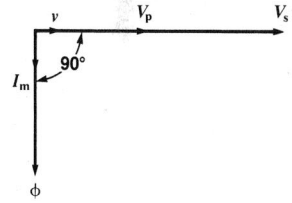

EXAMPLE 14.1

A source of 4160 V is connected to a step-down transformer whose primary has 2600 turns, while the secondary has 300 turns. Calculate:

1. the voltage V_s induced in the secondary.
2. the volts per turn.
3. the transformer ratio.

SOLUTION:

1. $V_s = \dfrac{N_s}{N_p} \times V_p = \dfrac{300}{2600} \times 4160 = 480 \text{ V}$

EQ. 14.3

2. The volts per turn is $v = V_p/N_p = 4160/2600 = 1.6$ V.
3. The transformer ratio can be expressed either as 4160 V/480 V = 8.666 or 480 V/ 4160 V = 0.1154. We recommend using the ratio that gives a number greater than 1.

14.4 Transformer Under Load

If a *resistive* load is connected across the secondary winding of a transformer (Fig. 14.5), the secondary load current I_s will be in phase with V_s. The power delivered to the load is $V_s I_s$ watts. Because this power must come from the ac

▼ **Figure 14.5**

Transformer connected to a
resistive load.

▼ **Figure 14.6**

Phasor diagram of a transformer feeding a resistive
load. The magnetizing current is assumed to be zero.

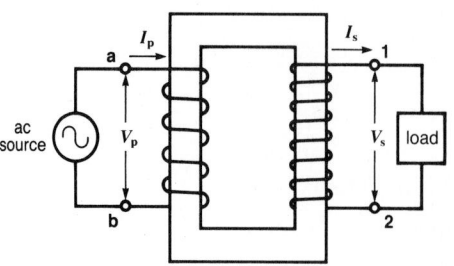

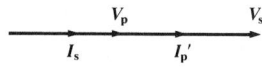

▼ **Figure 14.7**

Phasor diagram of a transformer feeding a resistive
load. The magnetizing current is I_m.

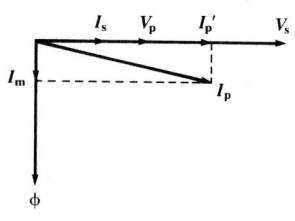

source, the source must deliver a current I_p' *so* that $V_p \times I_p' = V_s I_s$ watts. This expresses the fact that the power received by the transformer must be equal to the power it delivers. Current I_p' must also be in phase with V_p because the load is resistive (Fig. 14.6).

But we have just learned that the source must supply a current I_m to produce the flux in the core. This current lags 90° behind V_p. The total current I_p supplied by the source is therefore equal to the phasor sum of I_p' and I_m (Fig. 14.7).

Fortunately, the value of I_m is negligible compared with the rated value of I_p.

Consequently, at full-load I_p is very nearly equal to I_p', and so we can write the approximate equation:

$$V_p \times I_p = V_s \times I_s$$

or

EQ. 14.4
$$\frac{I_p}{I_s} = \frac{V_s}{V_p}$$

Equation 14.4 states that the ratio of currents is the inverse of the ratio of voltages. The current in a coil is large when its voltage is small, and vice versa. In effect, what we gain in voltage, we lose in current.

Knowing that $V_p/V_s = N_p/N_s$, we obtain another useful equation:

$$\frac{I_p}{I_s} = \frac{N_s}{N_p}$$

or

EQ. 14.5
$$I_p N_p = I_s N_s$$

This equation states that the ratio of primary to secondary current is inversely proportional to the ratio of the number of turns. It also states that the mmf of the primary is equal to the mmf of the secondary.

14.5 Losses, Efficiency, and Rating of a Transformer

Like any electrical machine, a transformer has losses. They are composed of

1. I_2R losses in the windings (commonly called the copper losses).

2. Hysteresis and eddy current losses in the core (commonly called the iron losses).

The losses appear in the form of heat and produce an increase in temperature and a drop in efficiency. Under normal operating conditions, the efficiency of transformers is very high, usually above 98 percent.

The heat produced by the iron losses depends upon the flux in the core, which, in turn, depends upon the applied voltage. On the other hand, the heat dissipated in the windings depends upon the current they carry. Consequently, to keep the temperature of the transformer at an acceptable level, we must set limits to both the applied voltage and the current drawn by the load. These two limits determine the **rated voltage** and **rated current** of the transformer.

The power rating of a transformer is equal to the product of the rated voltage times rated current. The product is the same for either the primary or the secondary side. However, the power rating is not expressed in watts, as we would expect, because the phase angle between the voltage and current may have any value, depending upon the nature of the load. Consequently, the power-handling capacity of a transformer is expressed in terms of apparent power, with units in voltamperes (VA). The rating of large transformers is given in kilovoltamperes (kVA), or in megavoltamperes (MVA), depending upon the size of the transformer.

RATED VOLTAGE

RATED CURRENT

Figure 14.8a

Three-phase transformer for an electric arc furnace rated 36 MVA, 13.8 kV/160 V to 320 V, 60 HZ. The primary and secondary coils are mounted on a three-legged core. The secondary voltage is adjustable from 160 V to 320 V by means of 32 taps on each primary winding. The taps from the three phases can be seen in the foreground. The secondary consists of three large busbars, each of which can deliver 65 000 A. The busbars can be seen protruding from behind the transformer.

(Courtesy Ferranti-Packard)

Figure 14.8b

This photograph shows the same transformer ready for delivery. It is mounted on a depressed flatcar in order to obtain maximum overpass clearance.

(Courtesy Ferranti-Packard)

The temperature rise of a transformer is directly related to the apparent power that flows through it. This means that a 500 kVA transformer will get just as hot feeding a 500 kvar inductive load as a 500 kW resistive load.

The rated kVA, frequency, and voltages are indicated on the nameplate. In large transformers, the corresponding rated currents are also shown. Figure 14.8 (a and b) shows the construction of a large transformer.

EXAMPLE 14.2

The nameplate of a distribution transformer shows the rating to be 250 kVA, 60 Hz, primary 4160 V, secondary 480 V.

1. Calculate the rated value of the primary and secondary currents.
2. If we apply 2000 V to the 4160 V primary, can we still draw 250 kVA from the transformer?

SOLUTION:

1. Rated current of the 4160 V winding is:

$$I_p = \frac{\text{rated apparent power } S}{\text{rated primary voltage } V_p} = \frac{250 \times 1000}{4160} = 60 \text{ A}$$

Rated current of the 480 V winding is:

$$I_p = \frac{\text{rated apparent power } S}{\text{rated secondary voltage } V_s} = \frac{250 \times 1000}{480} = 521 \text{ A}$$

2. By applying 2000 V to the primary (instead of 4160 V), the flux and the iron losses will be lower than normal, and the core will be cooler. However, the load current should not exceed its rated value; otherwise, the windings will overheat. Consequently, the maximum power output using this lower voltage is:

$$S = 2000 \text{ V} \times 60 \text{ A} = 120 \text{ kVA}$$

14.6 Rated Voltage of a Transformer

Most transformers are designed so that the peak flux density in the iron core is slightly above the "knee" of the saturation curve when rated voltage is applied to the primary winding.

If we apply a voltage below the rated value, the core becomes less saturated, and so the iron losses and the magnetizing current become smaller.

On the other hand, if the applied voltage exceeds its rated value, the flux density increases, and the core becomes more saturated. This abnormal situation increases the iron losses slightly, but produces a very large increase in the magnetizing current. For example, if we apply twice the rated voltage to a winding, the magnetizing current can easily exceed the rated full-load current. As a general rule, we should not apply a voltage greater than 110 percent of the rated value.

14.7 Polarity of a Transformer

Referring to Fig. 14.9, we recall that the primary and secondary voltages V_p and V_s attain their peak values at the same instant. Suppose that during one of these peak moments primary terminal a is positive with respect to primary terminal b, and secondary terminal c is positive with respect to secondary terminal d. Terminals a and c are then said to possess the same polarity because they are "positive" at the same instant. This "sameness" can be shown by placing a dot beside primary terminal a and secondary terminal c. The dots are called **polarity marks**.

POLARITY MARK

The polarity marks in Fig. 14.9 could equally well be placed next to terminals b and d because, as the voltage alternates, they, too, become simultaneously positive. Thus, the polarity marks could be placed beside terminals a and c *or* beside terminals b and d.

This dot-type marking is used on instrument transformers. On power transformers, however, the terminals are designated by the symbols H_1 and H_2 for the high-voltage (HV) winding and by X_1 and X_2 for the low-voltage (LV) winding. By convention, H_1 and X_1 have the same polarity.

Although the polarity is known when the symbols H_1, H_2, X_1, and X_2 are given, it is common practice to mount the four terminals in a standard way so that the transformer has either **additive** or **subtractive polarity**. A transformer is said to have additive polarity when terminal H_1 is diagonally opposite to terminal X_1. A transformer has subtractive polarity when terminal H_1 is adjacent to terminal X_1 (Fig. 14.10).

ADDITIVE
POLARITY

SUBTRACTIVE
POLARITY

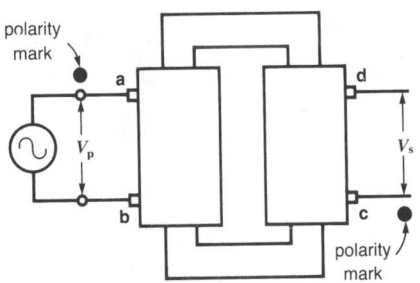

Figure 14.9

Polarity marks of a transformer.

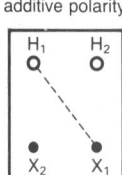
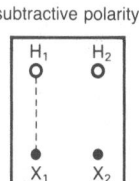

additive polarity   subtractive polarity

Figure 14.10

Definition of additive and
subtractive polarity.

Subtractive polarity is standard for all single-phase transformers above 200 kVA, provided the high-voltage winding is rated above 8660 V. All other transformers have additive polarity.

14.8 Polarity Tests

Figure 14.11

Determining the polarity of
a transformer.

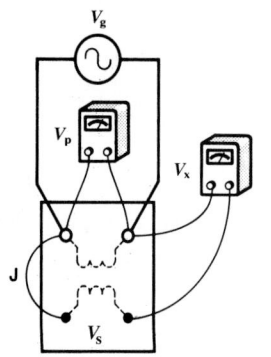

Suppose the terminals of a transformer are not marked in any way. To determine whether it has additive or subtractive polarity, we connect the high-voltage winding to a low voltage ac source V_g (Fig. 14.11). A jumper J is connected between any two adjacent HV and LV terminals, and a voltmeter V_x is connected across the remaining HV and LV terminals. Another voltmeter V_p is connected across the HV winding.

If V_x gives a higher reading than V_p, the polarity is additive. This means that the terminals diagonally opposite to each other must be marked H_1 and X_1, On the other hand, if V_x gives a lower reading than V_p, the polarity is subtractive and terminals H_1 and X_1 are adjacent.

In this polarity test, jumper J effectively connects the secondary voltage V_s in series with the primary voltage V_p. Consequently, V_s either adds to or subtracts from V_p. In other words, $V_x = V_p + V_s$ or $V_x = V_p - V_s$, depending on the polarity. That is how the terms additive and subtractive originated.

In making the polarity test, an ordinary 120 V, 60 Hz source can be connected to the HV winding even if its voltage rating is several hundred kilovolts.

EXAMPLE 14.3

During a polarity test on a 150 kVA, 69 kV/600 V transformer (Fig. 14.11), the following readings are obtained: $V_p = 118$ V, $V_x = 119$ V. Determine the polarity markings of the terminals.

SOLUTION:

The polarity is additive because V_x is greater than V_p. Consequently, the HV and LV terminals connected by the jumper must respectively be labelled H_1 and X_2. (However, they could also be labelled H_2 and X_1.)

14.9 Transformer Taps

It often happens that the voltage at an electric utility load centre is below normal. For example, a utility transformer having a ratio of 2400 V to 120 V may be connected to a transmission line whose voltage is never higher than 2000 V. Under these conditions, the voltage across the secondary is considerably less than 120 V. Incandescent lamps glow dimly, electric stoves take longer to cook food, and motors may stall as soon as they are slightly overloaded.

To correct this problem, taps are provided on the primary windings of distribution transformers (Fig. 14.12). Taps enable us to change the transformer ratio so as to raise the secondary voltage. We can therefore maintain a satisfactory secondary voltage, even though the primary voltage may be below normal. For example, suppose the 2400 V/120 V transformer of Fig. 14.12 is connected to a line whose voltage is only 2076 V. We can still obtain 120 V on the secondary, side if the HV line is connected to taps 1 and 5.

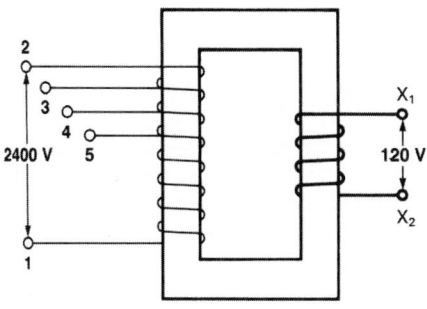

Figure 14.12

A transformer with taps permits various primary to secondary voltage ratios.

high-voltage terminals	percent tap	primary voltage	secondary voltage
1 - 2	0	2400 V	120 V
1 - 3	$4^1/_2$	2292 V	120 V
1 - 4	9	2184 V	120 V
1 - 5	$13^1/_2$	2076 V	120 V

Some transformers are designed to change taps automatically whenever the secondary voltage is above or below a preset level. Such tap-changing transformers can maintain the secondary voltage within ± 2 percent of its rated value, even though the primary voltage may fluctuate by as much as ± 10%.

Figure 14.13 shows the high-voltage taps of a three-phase transformer.

14.10 Transformers in Parallel

When a growing load eventually exceeds the power rating of an installed transformer, we sometimes connect a second transformer in parallel with it. The voltage rating of the two transformers must be the same. Furthermore, only those terminals having the same polarity marks shall be connected (Fig. 14.14).

Polarity marks are then of crucial importance because a wrong connection produces the same effect as a short-circuited winding on both transformers.

Figure 14.14

Two transformers connected in parallel.

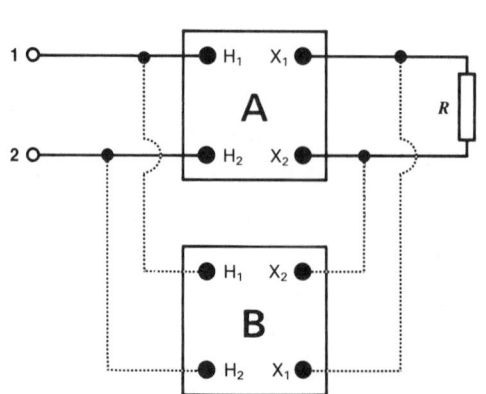

14.11 Cooling Methods

To prevent rapid deterioration of the insulation inside a transformer, the windings and core must be adequately cooled.

Low-power transformers below 50 kVA can be cooled by the natural circulation of air. The metal housing is fitted with ventilating louvers so that convection currents can flow over the windings and around the core (Fig. 14.15). Larger transformers are built the same way, but forced circulation of clean air must be used. Such dry-type transformers are used inside buildings, where the air is clean.

Transformers above 200 kVA are usually immersed in mineral oil and enclosed in a steel tank. Oil carries the heat from the transformer to the tank, where it is dissipated by radiation and convection to the outside air. Oil is a much better insulator than air is; consequently, it is always used in high-voltage transformers.

As the power rating increases, we add external radiators to increase the cooling surface of the oil-filled tank (Fig. 14.16). For still higher ratings, cooling fans blow air over the radiators.

▼ **Figure 14.15**

Single-phase transformer rated 15 kVA for indoor use.

(Courtesy Hammond Manufacturing Company)

▼ **Figure 14.16**

Two single-phase oil-filled transformers rated 75 KVA, 14.4 kV/240 V, 60 Hz. The radiators at the side increase the effective cooling area.

Some large transformers are designed to have a triple power rating, depending on the method of cooling used. Thus, a transformer may have a rating of 18/24/32 MVA depending on whether it is cooled by

1. the natural circulation of air (18 MVA),

2. forced-air cooling using fans (24 MVA), or

3. the forced circulation of oil accompanied by forced-air cooling (32 MVA).

These elaborate cooling systems are used because they permit a greater output from a transformer of given size (Fig. 14.17).

Figure 14.17

Three-phase transformer
rated 36/48/60 MVA,
depending upon the type of
cooling used.

14.12 Transformer Impedance

Figure 14.18 shows an *ideal* transformer having a rated secondary voltage V_s and delivering rated current I_s to a load Z_L. The rated load impedance Z_L is defined as

EQ. 14.6 $Z_L = V_s/I_s$

In an ideal transformer, V_s remains constant from no-load to full-load, as long as V_p is fixed.

Unfortunately, transformers are not perfect, and so the secondary voltage at full-load is different from what it is at no-load. The reason is that the windings have a certain amount of resistance and reactance. The resulting transformer impedance Z_T produces an internal voltage drop when the transformer is under load. A practical transformer can therefore be represented by the equivalent circuit shown in Fig. 14.19. It consists of an ideal transformer and an internal impedance Z_L. The internal impedance is due to both the primary and secondary windings. However, it may be considered to be concentrated in the secondary winding alone. That is why it is shown in series with the secondary in Fig. 14.19. The actual terminals of the transformer are labelled A, B, C, and D.

▼ **Figure 14.18**

In an ideal transformer, the secondary voltage remains the same from no-load to full-load.

▼ **Figure 14.19**

In a practical transformer, the secondary voltage varies slightly from no-load to full-load because of the internal impedance Z_L.

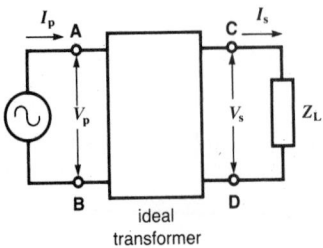

ideal
transformer

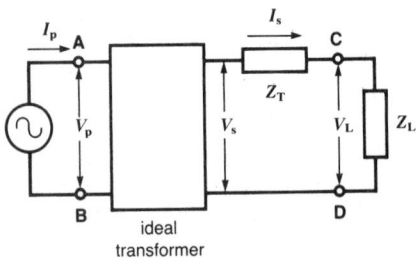

ideal
transformer

The voltage V_L across the load is different from the ideal secondary voltage V_s. However, because Z_T is small compared with the rated load impedance Z_L, voltage V_L is nearly equal to V_s.

The relative magnitude of Z_T may be expressed as a percentage of the rated load impedance Z_L. This percentage value is called the **percent impedance** of the transformer. By definition, the percent impedance is given by the equation:

PERCENT IMPEDANCE

$$\text{percent } Z_T = \frac{Z_T}{Z_L} \times 100 \qquad \textbf{EQ. 14.7}$$

where

percent Z_T = impedance of the transformer, in percent (%)

$\quad\quad Z_T$ = impedance of the transformer, in ohms (Ω)

$\quad\quad Z_L$ = rated load impedance, in ohms (Ω)

We can measure Z_T by short-circuiting the primary winding, and applying a low voltage v_s to the secondary (Fig. 14.20). Voltage v_s must be low enough so that the resulting current i_s does not exceed the rated value of the secondary current. Z_T is then given by

$$Z_T = v_s/i_s \qquad \textbf{EQ. 14.8}$$

Knowing Z_T, we can calculate percent Z_T by using Eqs. 14.6 and 14.7.

EXAMPLE 14.4

An impedance test is made on a transformer rated at 500 kVA, 69 kV/4160 V, 60 Hz. The primary terminals are short-circuited, and the secondary is connected to a source v_s, as shown in Fig. 14.20. When v_s = 75 V, the resulting current i_s = 35 A. Calculate:

1. The rated impedance of the load, referred to the secondary.
2. The transformer impedance Z_T, referred to the secondary.
3. The percent impedance of the transformer.

SOLUTION:

1. a. The rated secondary current is

$$I_s = \frac{S}{V_s} = \frac{500\ 000}{4160} = 120.2 \text{ A}$$

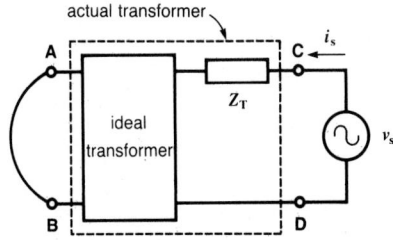

Figure 14.20

See Example 14.4.

continued

b.   The rated load impedance referred to the secondary is
$$Z_L = V_s/I_s = 4160/120.2 = 34.6 \ \Omega$$

According to the test, $Z_T = v_s/i_s = 75/35 = 2.14 \ \Omega$

The percent impedance is

EQ. 14.6 $$\text{percent } Z_T = \frac{Z_T}{Z_L} \times 100 = \frac{2.14}{34.6} \times 100 = 6.18 \ \%$$

14.13 Distribution Transformers

Transformers that supply electric power to residential areas generally have two secondary windings, each rated at 120 V. When the two windings are connected in series, the voltage between the lines is 240 V and that between the lines and the middle conductor is 120 V (Fig. 14.21). The middle conductor, called neutral, is always connected to ground.

These so-called distribution transformers are often mounted on the poles of the electric utility company (Fig. 14.22). They may supply power to as many as twenty consumers.

▼ **Figure 14.21**

Schematic diagram of a distribution transformer.

▼ **Figure 14.22**

Single-phase pole-mounted distribution transformer rated 25 kVA, 14.4 kV/120-240 V, 60 Hz. It is connected between one line and neutral of a 24 940/14 400 V, 60 Hz 3-phase transmission line.

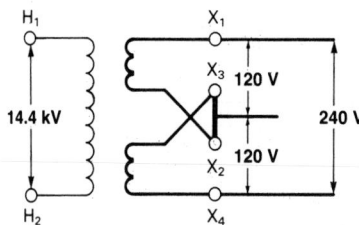

The load on distribution transformers varies greatly throughout the day, depending upon customer demand. In residential districts, one peak occurs in the morning and another in the late afternoon. The power peaks seldom last for more than one or two hours, and so the transformers operate far below their rating most of the time. Because thousands of such units are connected to the electric utility system, they are specially designed to keep the no-load losses small. Towards this end, core steels are used that have particularly low hysteresis and eddy-current losses.

14.14 Voltage Transformers

Voltage transformers (formerly called potential transformers) are high-precision transformers that are used to measure or monitor the voltage on transmission lines, and to isolate the metering equipment from these lines (Fig. 14.23). In these transformers, the ratio of primary voltage to secondary voltage is a known constant that changes very little with load.* The rated secondary voltage is usually 115 V, which permits standard instruments and relays to be used.

One terminal of the secondary winding is always connected to ground to reduce the danger of shock when touching one of the secondary leads. Although the secondary *appears* to be isolated from the primary, the distributed capacitance between the two windings makes an invisible connection that can produce a dangerously high voltage between the secondary winding and ground (Fig. 14.23). By grounding one of the secondary terminals, the highest voltage between the secondary lines and ground is limited to 115 V.

The construction of voltage transformers (VTs) is similar to that of conventional transformers. However, their power rating is usually less than 500 VA. Figure 14.24 shows a 7000 VA, 80.5 kV/115 V/115 V transformer. It has a tall ceramic bushing to isolate the HV line from the grounded case. The case houses the actual transformer. The insulation between the primary and secondary windings must be sufficient to withstand the full line voltage, as well as lightning and switching surges.

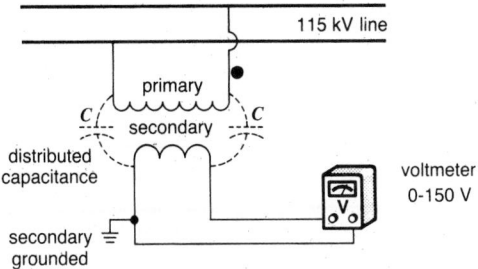

VOLTAGE
TRANSFORMER

Figure 14.23

Voltage transformer installed on a 115 kV line. Note the distributed capacitance between the windings.

* In the case of voltage transformers and current transformers, the load is called "burden."

▶ Figure 14.24a

Voltage transformer installed on a 230 kV line in a substation.

▶ Figure 14.24b

Voltage transformer rated at 7000 VA, 80.5 kV/115 V/115 V, 50/60 Hz, accuracy 0.3 %. The primary terminal at the top of the porcelain bushing is connected to the HV line, and the other primary terminal is connected to ground. The transformer has a height of 2565 mm and weighs 740 kg.

(Courtesy Ferranti-Packard)

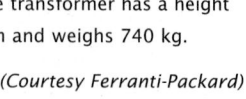
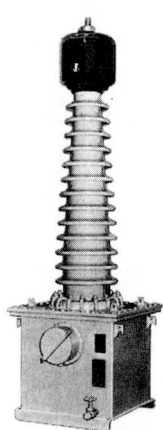

14.15 Current Transformers

CURRENT TRANSFORMER

Current transformers are high-precision transformers in which the ratio of primary to secondary current is a known constant that changes very little with the burden.

Current transformers are used to measure or monitor the current in a line while isolating the metering and relay equipment from it. The primary winding is connected in series with the line, as shown in Fig. 14.25. The rated secondary current is usually 5 A, irrespective of the primary current rating.

Because current transformers (CTs) are used only for measurement and protection, their power rating is small — generally between 15 and 200 VA. As in the case of conventional transformers, the current ratio is inversely proportional to the number of turns on the primary and secondary windings. A current transformer having a ratio of 150 A/5 A therefore has 30 times more turns on the secondary than on the primary.

For safety reasons, current transformers must be used when measuring currents in HV transmission lines. The insulation between the primary and secondary windings must be sufficient to withstand the full line-to-neutral voltage. The maximum voltage that the CT can withstand is stamped on the nameplate.

▶ Figure 14.25

Current transformer installed on a 115 kV line, Note the polarity marks indicated by the dots.

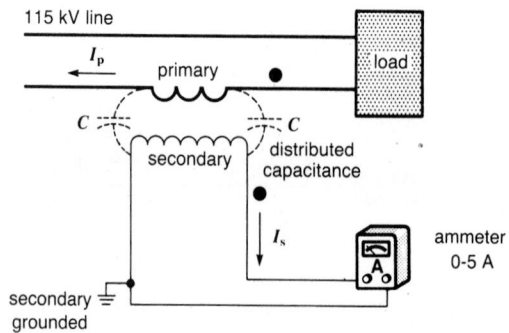

Figure 14.26b

Current transformer in series
with one phase of a 230 kV
line inside a substation.

As in the case of voltage transformers (and for the same safety reasons), one of the
secondary terminals is always connected to ground. Another important precaution
is never to open the secondary circuit of a current transformer. The reason is that
a dangerous high voltage will then appear across the secondary. The precision of
the transformer may also be affected.

Figure 14.26b shows a 500 VA, 1000 A/5 A current transformer designed for a
230 kV line. The large bushing permits the line current to flow into and out of
the primary winding. The CT is housed in the steel case at the lower end of the
bushing.

At lower voltages and when the line current exceeds 100 A, we can sometimes
use a toroidal current transformer. It consists of a ring-shaped core which carries the secondary winding. The primary is the line conductor that simply passes through the ring (Fig. 14.27). The conductor produces the same effect as a single primary turn. If the secondary possesses N turns, the ratio of transformation
is N. Thus, a toroidal CT having a ratio of 300 A/5 A must have 60 turns on the
secondary winding.

Toroidal CTs are simple and inexpensive and are widely used in LV (low voltage)
and MV (medium voltage) indoor installations. They are also used internally in circuit breakers to monitor the current flowing through them.

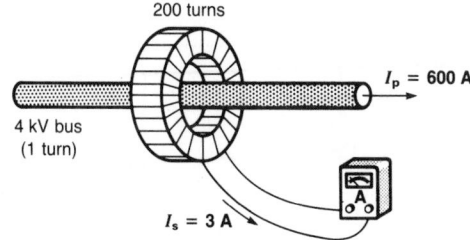

200 turns

4 kV bus
(1 turn)

I_p = 600 A

I_s = 3 A

Figure 14.27

Toroidal CT having a ratio
of 600 A/3 A, connected
to indicate the current in a
4 kV line.

EXAMPLE 14.5

A voltage transformer rated 14 400 V / 115 V and a current transformer of 75 A/5 A are used to measure the voltage and current in a transmission line. If the voltmeter indicates 112 V and the ammeter reads 3.5 A, what are the voltage and current in the line?

SOLUTION:

1. Voltage on the line is:
   $V = 112 \times (14\ 400/115) = 14\ 024$ V
2. Current in the line is:
   $I = 3.5 \times (75/5) = 52.5$ A

14.16 Autotransformers

AUTOTRANSFORMER

An **autotransformer** consists basically of a single winding mounted on an iron core. The "high" voltage is obtained across the entire winding and the "low" voltage appears between one end of the winding and an intermediate tap. For a given power output, an autotransformer is smaller and cheaper than a standard two-winding transformer. The cost and weight advantage is particularly important when the transformer ratio is close to 1. However, the absence of electrical isolation between primary and secondary is sometimes a serious drawback.

Autotransformers are used in reduced-voltage motor starters, and to increase or decrease transmission-line voltages by fixed amounts.

Consider an autotransformer (Fig. 14.28) having a tap T located at 80 percent of the winding (commonly called an 80 percent tap). If we apply a voltage $V_p = 300$ V to terminals A and B, the voltage V_s between terminals T and B will be 80 percent of 300 V, or 240 V. The transformer ratio is therefore 300/240 = 1.25.

If a 12 Ω resistive load is connected across the secondary terminals, it will draw a current of $I_s = V/R = 240/12 = 20$ A. The corresponding power is

$P = V_s I_s = 240 \times 20 = 4800$ W

But this load power must come from the 300 V source, and so the source must deliver a current I_p given by

$I_p = P/V_p = 4800/300 = 16$ A

Figure 14.28

Construction and method of connecting an autotransformer to the source and load.

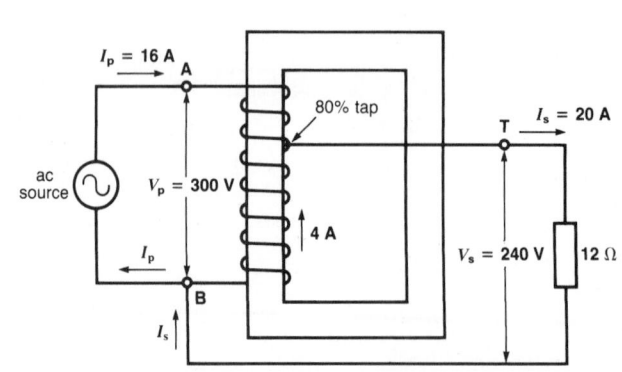

Applying Kirchhoff's current law to point B, we discover that the current flowing in winding TB is equal to the *difference* between I_p and I_s. Its value is $(20 - 16) = 4$ A. This current is one-fourth of that flowing in portion TA of the winding. Consequently, the conductor in portion TB need be only one-quarter the size of that in portion TA.

14.17 Connecting a Standard Transformer as an Autotransformer

A conventional two-winding transformer can be made into an autotransformer by connecting the windings in series. Depending upon the connection used, the secondary voltage will either add to or subtract from the primary voltage.

Consider, for example, the standard transformer of Fig. 14.29, which has a ratio of 600 V to 120 V. If terminals having the same polarity marks (H_1 and X_1, or H_2 and X_2) are connected, the low voltage subtracts from the high voltage. The resulting secondary voltage is therefore 600 V − 120 V = 480 V (Fig. 14.30). On the other hand, if terminals having opposite polarity marks (H_1 and X_2, or H_2 and X_1) are connected, the two voltages add. The resulting secondary voltage is 600 V + 120 V = 720 V (Fig. 14.31).

▼ **Figure 14.29**

Conventional transformer having a ratio of 600 V/120 V.

▼ **Figure 14.30**

Conventional transformer connected as an auto-transformer so that the secondary voltage subtracts from the primary voltage.

▼ **Figure 14.31**

Conventional transformer connected as an auto-transformer so that the secondary voltage adds to the primary voltage.

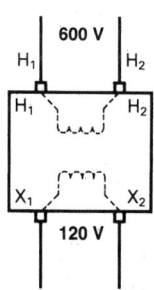

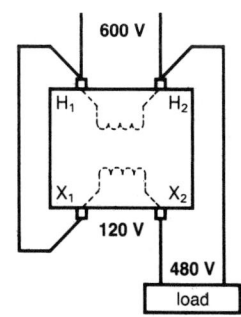

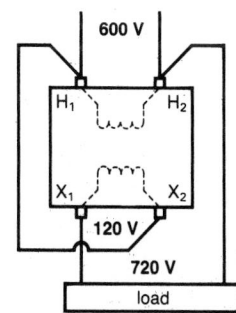

EXAMPLE 14.6

A standard single-phase transformer has a rating of 30 kVA, 600 V/120 V, 60 Hz. We want to reconnect it as an autotransformer to give a ratio of 600 V/480 V. Calculate the maximum load it can carry.

SOLUTION:

1. Rated current of the 600 V winding is
    $I_1 = S/V_1 = 30\ 000/600 = 50$ A

continued

▼ **Figure 14.32**

See Example 14.6.

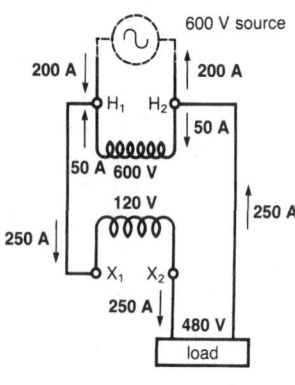

2. Rated current of the 120 V winding is

   $I_2 = S/V_2 = 30\ 000/120 = 250$ A

3. To obtain 480 V, the low voltage (120 V) must subtract from the high voltage (600 V). Consequently, terminals having the same polarity are connected, as shown in Fig. 14.30. The corresponding schematic diagram is shown in Fig. 14.32.

4. Note that the 120 V winding is in series with the load. Because this winding can carry 250 A, the load can also draw 250 A. The power rating of the load can therefore be

   $S = VI = 480 \times 250 = 120$ kVA

   This load rating is four times the transformer rating, and yet the transformer is not overloaded.

5. The currents flowing in the circuit at full load are shown in Fig. 14.32.

Example 14.6 shows that when a conventional transformer is used as an autotransformer, it can sometimes carry a load that is far greater than the rated capacity of the transformer. In such cases, an autotransformer is the most economical way to make the voltage transformation.

14.18 Variable Autotransformers

A variable autotransformer is often used when we wish to obtain a variable ac voltage from a fixed ac source. It is composed of a single-layer winding on a toroidal iron core (Fig. 14.33). A movable carbon brush in contact with the winding serves as a variable tap. The brush can be set in any position between zero and 330°.

▼ **Figure 14.33a**

Variable autotransformer whose position can be set manually by means of a knob. The tap on the winding is seen on the left.

(Courtesy American Superior Electric)

▼ **Figure 14.33b**

Cutaway view of a 0-140 V, 15 A variable autotransformer showing (1) the laminated toroidal core; (2) the single-layer winding; and (3) the movable brush.

(Courtesy American Superior Electric)

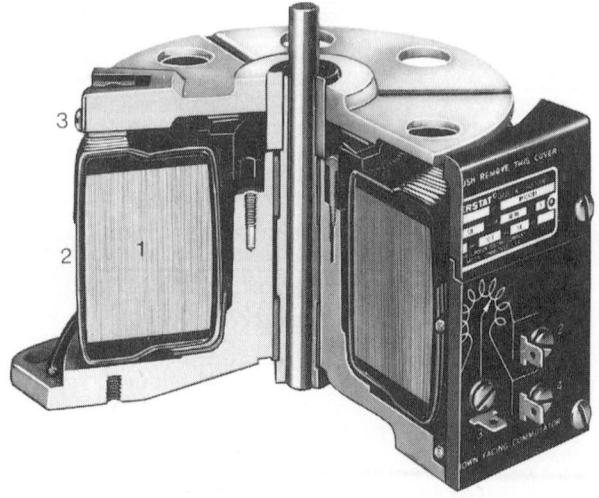

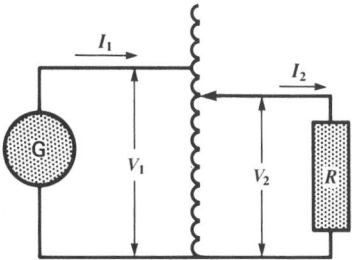

Figure 14.34

Schematic diagram of a variable autotransformer having a fixed 90% tap.

As the brush slides over the bared portion of the windings, the secondary voltage V_2 increases in proportion to the number of turns swept out (Fig. 14.34). The input voltage V_1 is usually connected to a fixed 90 percent tap on the winding. This enables us to vary V_2 from zero to 110 percent of the input voltage.

Variable autotransformers are far more efficient than rheostats are, and they give much better voltage regulation under variable loads. The secondary line should always be protected by a fuse or circuit breaker so that the output current I_2 never exceeds the normal current rating of the autotransformer.

To raise or lower the voltage of a three-phase transmission line, we use transformers, as in the case of single-phase lines. The transformers may be three-phase, having three primary windings and three secondary windings mounted on a common core, as we saw in Fig. 14.13. Alternatively, they may be three single-phase transformers connected together to form a so-called three-phase transformer bank.

When single-phase transformers are used to transform a three-phase voltage, the windings can be connected in several ways. Thus, the primaries may be connected in delta and the secondaries in wye, or vice versa. As a result, the ratio of the input *line* voltage to the output *line* voltage depends not only upon the turns ratio of the transformers, but also upon how they are connected.

In making connections, it is important to observe transformer polarities. An error in polarity produces either a short-circuit or unbalanced line voltages.

14.19 Delta-Delta Connection

The three single-phase transformers P, Q, and R of Fig. 14.35 are connected in *delta-delta.* The figure shows the actual physical layout of the transformers; the corresponding schematic diagram is given in Fig. 14.36. Note the symmetrical way the connections between H_1 and H_2 and X_1 and X_2 are made.

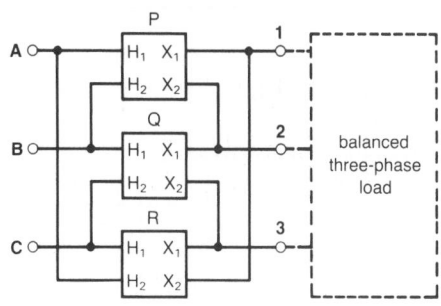

Figure 14.35

Three-phase transformer bank connected in delta-delta.

Figure 14.36

Schematic diagram of the delta-delta connection shown in Fig. 14.35. Primary and secondary windings that are drawn parallel to each other have voltages that are in phase.

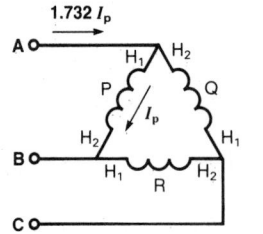
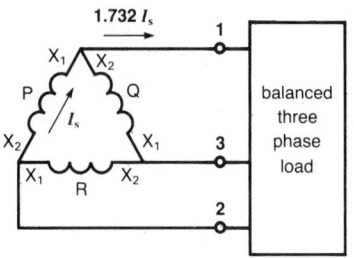

The schematic diagram is drawn so that each secondary winding is parallel to the corresponding primary winding to which it is coupled. Because the primary and secondary voltages of a given transformer are in phase, $V_{H_1H_2}$ of transformer P is in phase with $V_{X_1X_2}$ of the same transformer. Similarly $V_{H_1H_2}$ of transformer Q is in phase with $V_{X_1X_2}$ of transformer Q.

Figure 14.36 shows that the incoming *lines* A, B, and C are directly connected to the primaries of the transformers. Furthermore, the voltages between outgoing lines 1, 2, and 3 are equal to the voltages induced in the respective secondary windings. If a balanced three-phase load is connected across lines 1, 2, and 3, the line currents on both the primary and secondary side of the transformer bank will be balanced.

As in any delta connection, the line currents are 1.732 times greater than the currents flowing in the respective windings.

14.20 Delta-Wye Connection

In a *delta-wye* connection, the primary windings of the three transformers are connected the same way as in Fig. 14.36. However, the secondary windings are connected with the X_2 terminals joined, to create a common neutral N (Fig. 14.37). In such a delta-wye connection, the primary voltage across each transformer is equal to the incoming line voltage. However, the outgoing line voltage is 1.732 times the secondary voltage across each transformer. The relative values of the corresponding currents in the transformer windings and transmission lines are given in Fig. 14.38. For example, the line currents in phases A, B, and C are 1.732 times the currents in the primary windings.

Figure 14.37

Three-phase transformer bank connected in delta-wye.

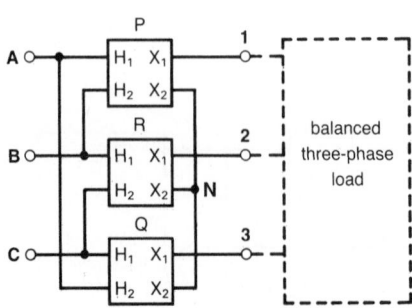

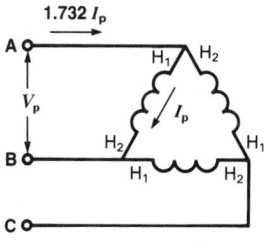

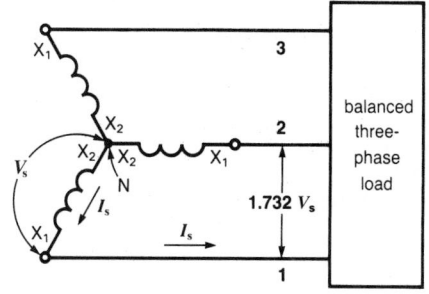

Figure 14.38

Schematic diagram of the
transformer connections in
Fig. 14.37.

One of the important advantages of the wye connection is that it reduces the insulation requirements of the transformer. In effect, the HV windings have to be insulated for only 1/1.732, or 57.7 percent of the line voltage.

14.21 Wye-Delta Connection

The currents and voltages in a *wye-delta* connection are identical to those in the delta-wye connection of Section 14.20. The primary and secondary connections are simply interchanged. In other words, the H_2 terminals are connected to create a neutral, and the X_1, X_2 terminals are connected in delta.

14.22 Wye-Wye Connection

The wye-wye connection is used only when the neutral N_1 of the primary can be solidly connected to the neutral N_g of the source, usually by way of the ground (Fig. 14.39). When the neutrals are not joined, the line-to-neutral voltages become distorted (nonsinusoidal).

A wye-wye connection can be used without joining the neutrals N_1 and N_g, provided that each transformer carries a third winding, called *tertiary winding.* The tertiary windings of the transformers must be connected in delta (Fig. 14.40). The tertiary windings eliminate voltage distortion, and maintain balanced line-to-neutral voltages even when the load is unbalanced. In addition, the tertiary windings often provide the substation service voltage where the transformers are installed.

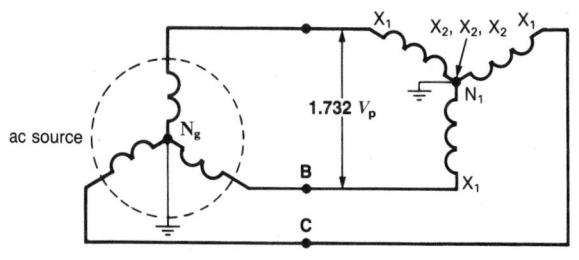

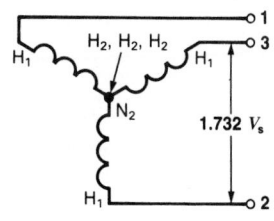

Figure 14.39

In a wye-wye connection,
the neutral of the trans-
former bank is connected to
the neutral of the source.

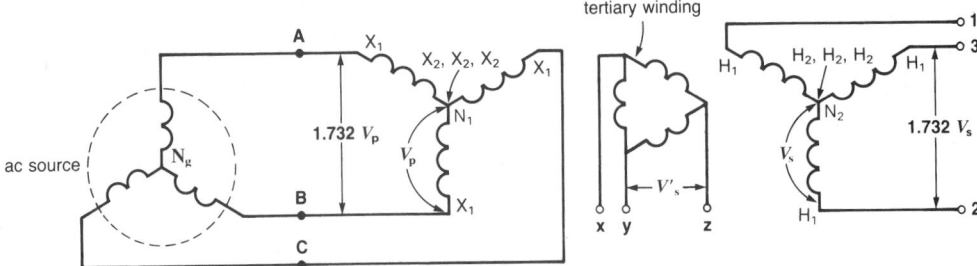

14.23 Open-Delta Connection

We can transform the voltage of a three-phase line by using only two transformers connected in *open-delta. The* open-delta connection is identical to a delta-delta connection, but with one fewer transformer (Fig. 14.41). This is one of the advantages of a delta-delta connection, because two transformers can continue to feed the load if one of them should become defective.

In medium- and high-power installations, the open-delta connection is always temporary because the load capacity of the transformer bank is only 86.6 percent of the installed transformer capacity. For example, if the transformers in Fig 14.41 are each rated at 100 kVA, the maximum possible load is not 200 kVA (as we might expect), but only $86.6\% \times 200 = 173$ kVA.

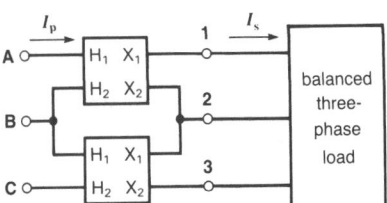

14.24 Three-Phase Transformers

A transformer bank composed of three single-phase transformers may be replaced by a three-phase transformer. The magnetic core of such a transformer has three legs, which carry the primary and secondary windings of each phase (Fig. 14.13). The windings are connected internally, either in wye or in delta (Fig. 14.37). Consequently, only six terminals have to be brought outside the tank. Figure 14.42 shows the three HV bushing of a large transformer.

For a given capacity, a three-phase transformer is always smaller and cheaper than three single-phase transformers. Nevertheless, single-phase transformers are sometimes preferred, particularly when an emergency standby unit is essential. For example, suppose a manufacturing plant absorbs 5000 kVA. To guarantee continued service, we can install a three-phase 5000 kVA transformer and keep a second one as a spare. Alternatively, we can install three single-phase transformers, each rated 1667 kVA, and one spare. The three-phase transformer option is more expensive (total capacity 10 000 kVA) than the single-phase option (total capacity 6667 kVA).

Figure 14.42

Three-phase transformer rated 330 MVA, 735 kV/16 kV, 60 Hz. It serves to connect a 300 MVA synchronous capacitor to a 735 kV line.

(Courtesy Hydro-Québec)

14.25 Summary

Upon completion of this chapter you should have learned that:

- A simple transformer operates on the principle of mutual induction. The primary winding of the transformer induces a voltage in a secondary winding. At no-load only a magnetizing current flows in the transformer primary. The magnetizing current supplies the internal transformer losses. At full-load the magnetizing current plus the load current flow in the transformer primary winding while only the load current flows through the secondary winding.

- All transformers have a polarity that is either additive or subtractive. When the H_1 and X_1 terminals of a transformer are mounted diagonally opposite, a transformer is said to be additive in polarity. When H_1 and X_1 are directly opposite, the transformer is subtractive. All transformers above 200 kVA are subtractive in polarity; all other transformers have a polarity mark.

- Transformer taps can be used to raise or lower the secondary voltage by adjusting the transformer turns ratio. Adjusting the output voltage using a transformer tap can be done to compensate for line drop in a distribution system. A tap changer works by changing the transformer ratio.

- In order to connect transformers in parallel to increase system capacity, they must be the same voltage, and they must be the same polarity.

- Heat builds-up in transformers due to fixed core losses (eddy current and hysteresis losses) and variable copper losses (I^2R losses of the windings). As the transformer is loaded, these losses cause a build-up of heat that results in decreased transformer efficiency. When convective air or mineral oil circulate through the transformer they absorb internal heat and carry it to the transformer surface, where it can be dissipated to the surrounding air.

- The internal transformer impedance is reflected to the secondary side of a transformer and causes a small difference between the secondary terminal voltage at no-load and at full-load. The ratio of the internal transformer impedance and the load impedance is known as the percent impedance of the transformer.

- Current and voltage transformers are used to meter line current and voltage. The secondary current of a current transformer is 5 A and the secondary voltage of a voltage transformer is 120 V. The secondary value of these transformers must be multiplied by the transformer ratio in order to determine the primary value.

- Four possible three-phase transformer configurations are possible: wye-wye, wye-delta, delta-delta, and delta-wye.

Key Terms

ADDITIVE POLARITY: A transformer is said to have additive polarity when the H_1 and X_1 terminals are diagonally opposite. Transformers rated at less than 200 kVA and with a high voltage winding rated at less than 8660 V are additive polarity transformers.

AUTOTRANSFORMER: A transformer in which the primary and secondary windings are connected electrically.

CURRENT TRANSFORMER: A metering transformer used to monitor line currents. The primary winding is rated for the load current and the secondary current is usually limited to 5 A.

MAGNETIZING CURRENT: The current flowing in the primary winding that is responsible for producing the magnetizing flux in the transformer core.

PERCENT IMPEDANCE: Ratio of the internal impedance of a transformer to the rated impedance of the load. This ratio is expressed as a percentage.

POLARITY MARK: An indicator on transformer terminals used to indicate which terminals are positive at the same instant in time.

PRIMARY WINDING: The winding of a transformer that is connected to a voltage supply.

RATED CURRENT: The maximum current that a transformer is designed to supply on a continuous basis. Rated current does not normally appear on the nameplate.

RATED VOLTAGE: The nameplate voltage for a given transformer.

SECONDARY WINDING: The winding of a transformer that is connected to a load.

SUBTRACTIVE POLARITY: A transformer is said to have subtractive polarity when the H_1 and X_1 terminals are adjacant. Transformers rated at more than 200 kVA and with a high voltage winding rated at more than 8660 V are subtractive polarity transformers.

TRANSFORMER RATIO: (turns ratio): A simple ratio of the primary voltage to the secondary voltage of a transformer. This ratio is the same for the number of turns in the primary and secondary windings of the transformer.

VOLTAGE TRANSFORMER (potential transformer): A special transformer used in metering. The primary voltage will equal the line voltage; the secondary voltage is usually limited to 120 V.

Test Your Knowledge

14.1 A single-phase transmission line delivers 120 A at a voltage of 14.4 kV. The apparent power it delivers is
a. 728 kW
b. 120 W
c. 1728 kVA

14.2 The consumer in Fig. 14.1 absorbs 10.35 MVA of power. The current in the 69 kV single-phase line is
a. 15 A
b. 150 A
c. 21 562.5 A

14.3 The transformer ratio of T_1 in Fig. 14.1 is
a. 60.29
b. 16.586 V
c. 16.586

14.4 The primary winding of a transformer is *always* the winding that is connected to the source.

true_____   false_____

14.5 In Fig. 14.2, V_p = 480 V and V_s = 7200. If the primary has 600 turns, the secondary has
a. 5760 turns
b. 40 turns
c. 9000 turns

14.6 In Fig. 14.5, suppose V_p = 480 V, V_s = 7200 V, and the load absorbs 180 kW. The value of I_p is
a. 375 A
b. 25 A
c. 180 kVA

14.7 In Fig. 14.9, if V_p = 12 470 V and V_s = 240 V, the peak value of V_s is
a. 480 V
b. 415.69
c. 339.4 V

14.8 A distribution transformer has a rating of 100 kVA, 14.4 kV to 480 V. If we apply a voltage of 7.2 kV to the primary side, the transformer will be able to deliver a maximum of
a. 50 kVA
b. 100 kVA
c. 100 kvar

14.9 If we know that a transformer has additive polarity, we don't need polarity marks to indicate where the respective H_1 and X_1 terminals are.

true_____   false_____

14.10 In Fig. 14.12, if we apply 2400 V between terminals 4 and 1, the voltage between X_1 and X_2 will be
a. 120 V
b. 131.87 V
c. 109.2 V

14.11 A transformer has a rating of 15 kVA, 600 V/240 V, 60 Hz. What is the rated current on the 240 V side?
a. 16 A
b. 62.5 A
c. 625 A

What is the rated load impedance on the 240 V side?
d. 15 000 W
e. 15 Ω
f. 3.84 Ω

14.12 The transformer in Problem 14.11 has an impedance of 5 percent. What is the transformer impedance, in ohms, on the 240 V side?
a. 0.192 Ω
b. 76.8 Ω
c. 5.208 Ω

14.13   The secondary side of a VT or CT must *always* be grounded in order to
  a. get an accurate reading
  b. eliminate the capacitance between the primary and secondary windings
  c. reduce the danger of shock

14.14   A toroidal CT has a current rating of 1600 A/5 A. How many turns does it have on the primary?
  a. 1 turn
  b. 320 turns
  c. none

14.15   In Fig. 14.36, if I_p = 600 A, what is the value of the line current in phase C, assuming the system is balanced?
  a. 1200 A
  b. zero
  c. 1039 A

14.16   In Fig. 14.37, the primary to secondary voltage rating of each transformer is 24 940 V/120 V. If the line voltage between phases A, B, and C is 24 000 V, the line voltage between phases 1, 2, and 3 is
  a. 200 V
  b. 115.48 V
  c. 163.3 V

14.17   Each transformer in Fig. 14.41 has a rating of 4000 kVA. The maximum load they can carry is
  a. 8000 kVA
  b. 6928 kVA
  c. 8000 kvar

Questions and Problems

14.18   Name the principal components of a transformer.

14.19   What purpose does the no-load current of a transformer serve?

14.20   Explain how a voltage is induced in the secondary winding of a transformer.

14.21   The secondary winding of a transformer has twice as many turns as the primary. Is the secondary voltage higher or lower than the primary voltage?

14.22   State the voltage and current relationships between the primary and secondary windings of a transformer under load. The primary and secondary windings have N_1 and N_2 turns, respectively.

14.23   Name the losses produced in a transformer.

14.24   Which winding is connected to the load: the primary or secondary?

14.25   What conditions must be met in order to connect two transformers in parallel?

14.26   What is the purpose of taps on a transformer?

14.27   What is the difference between an autotransformer and a conventional transformer?

14.28   What is the purpose of a potential transformer? Of a current transformer?

14.29   Why must we never open the secondary of a current transformer?

14.30   The primary of a transformer is connected to a 600 V, 60 Hz source. If the primary has 1200 turns and the secondary has 240, calculate the secondary voltage.

14.31   The windings of a transformer respectively have 300 and 7500 turns. If the LV winding is excited by a 2400 V source, calculate the voltage across the HV winding.

14.32   A 6.9 kV transmission line is connected to a transformer having 1500 turns on the primary and 24 turns on the secondary. If the load across the secondary has an impedance of 5 Ω, calculate (a) the secondary voltage and (b) the primary and secondary currents.

14.33   The primary of a transformer has twice as many turns as the secondary. The primary voltage is 220 V and a 5 Ω resistor is connected across the secondary. Calculate:
   a.   the power delivered by the transformer.
   b.   the primary and secondary currents.

14.34   A 3000 kVA transformer has a ratio of 60 kV to 2.4 kV. Calculate the rated current of each winding.

14.35   In Fig. 14.10, when 600 V is applied to terminals H_1 and H_2, 80 V is measured across terminals X_1 and X_2.
   a.   What is the voltage between terminals H_1 and X_2?
   b.   If terminals H_1X_1 are connected, calculate the voltage across terminals H_2X_2.

14.36   a.   Referring to Fig. 14.14, what would happen if we reversed terminals H_1 and H_2 of transformer B?
   b.   Would the operation of the transformer bank be affected if terminals H_1H_2 *and* X_1X_2 of transformer B were reversed? Explain.

14.37   What is meant by (a) transformer impedance and (b) percent impedance of a transformer?

14.38   A 2300 V line is connected to terminals 1 and 4 in Fig. 14.12. Calculate:
   a.   the voltage between terminals X_1 and X_2
   b.   the current in each winding if a 12 kVA load is connected across the secondary

14.39   A 66.7 MVA transformer has an efficiency of 99.3% when it delivers full power to a load having a power factor of 100%.
   a.   Calculate the losses in the transformer under these conditions.
   b.   Calculate the losses and efficiency when the transformer delivers 66.7 MVA to a load having a power factor of 80%. (*Hint*: efficiency is always calculated on the basis of active power in and active power out.)

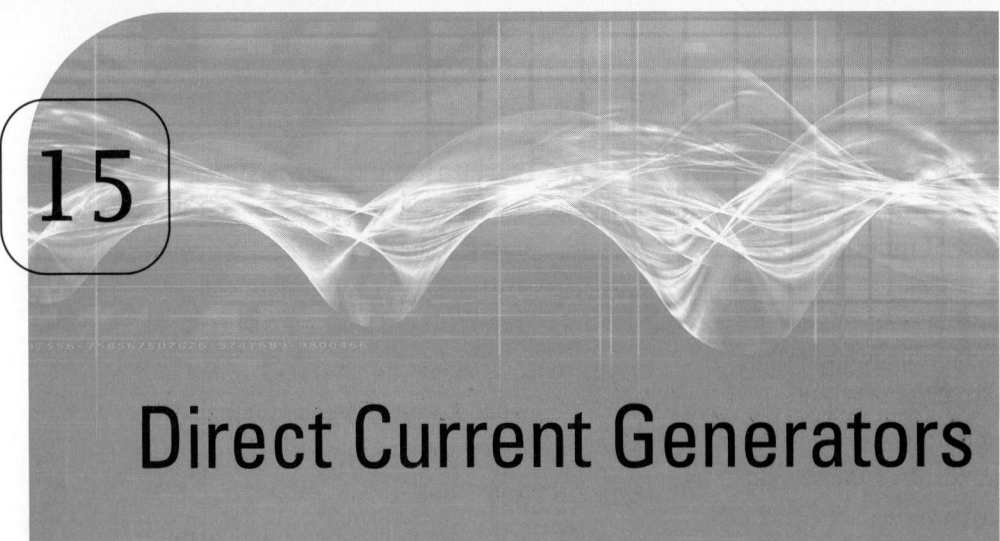

15

Direct Current Generators

LEARNING OBJECTIVES

Upon completion of this chapter you will be able to:

- Explain how a dc voltage is generated
- Describe the construction of various dc generators
- Describe the no-load operation of a shunt and a self-excited generator
- Calculate the voltage induced in a dc generator
- Describe the operation of a separately excited generator under load
- Describe the operation of a compound dc generator
- Calculate the percent voltage regulation of a dc generator
- Describe armature reaction and the use of commutating poles

15.1 Generating a Dc Voltage

In Section 7.8, we saw that an ac voltage is induced in a coil when it rotates between the poles of a permanent magnet. This simple generator is again shown in Fig. 15.1. However, we have added slip rings and brushes so that the

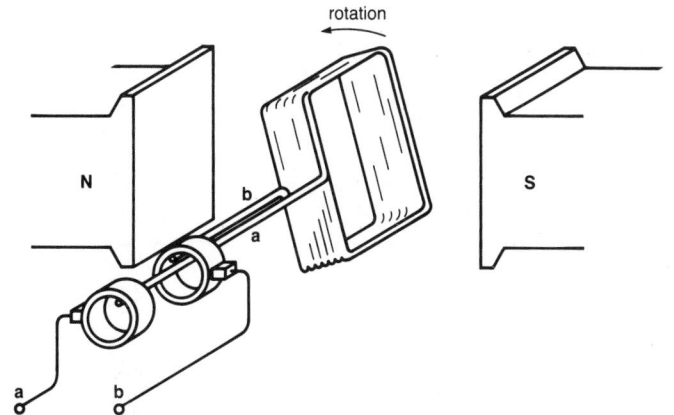

Figure 15.1

Simple ac generator producing an output voltage between terminals a and b.

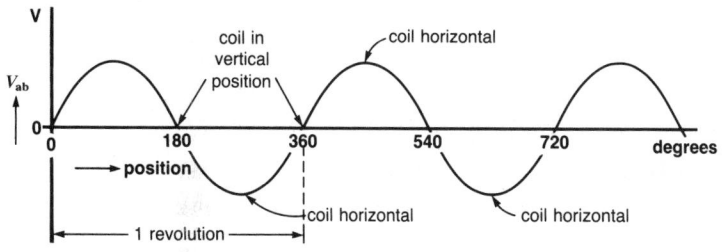

Figure 15.2

Waveshape of the ac output voltage and corresponding position of the coil in Fig. 15.1.

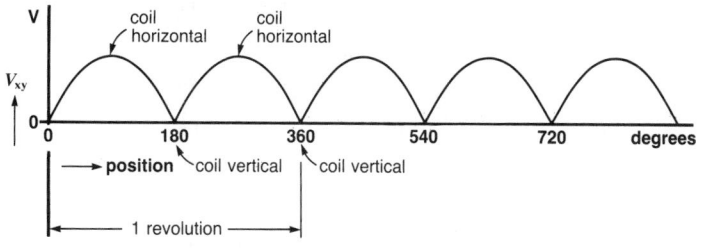

Figure 15.3

Waveshape of V_{ab} in Fig 15.2 after rectification.

ac voltage is available between the stationary terminals a and b. The output voltage V_{ab} has the general shape given in Fig. 15.2.

In order to obtain a dc output, the negative half of the ac voltage must be rectified. Thus, when V_{ab} is rectified, we obtain the pulsating voltage V_{xy} shown in Fig. 15.3. We could attain this result by connecting a reversing switch to terminals a and b (Fig. 15.4). When V_{ab} is positive, terminal x is connected to a, and terminal y to b. But as soon as the polarity reverses, the switch is transferred so that terminal x is connected to b and terminal y to a. Because the polarity of V_{ab} changes every time the coil is in the vertical position, the switching action must be synchronized with the position of the coil.

A simpler way to **rectify** the voltage is to use a ring that is cut in half, so as to form two segments. The split ring is mounted on the shaft but insulated from it. The segments are directly connected to the two ends of the coil, as shown in Fig. 15.5. Two brushes enable us to bring the voltage to stationary, terminals x and y. The combination of the split ring and brushes is equivalent to the previous reversing switch. Note that the split ring is mounted in such a way that the switching action takes place when the coil is in the vertical position. The split ring is called a **commutator**.

| RECTIFY |
| COMMUTATOR |

Figure 15.4

A manual reversing switch could rectify the ac output voltage in Fig. 15.1.

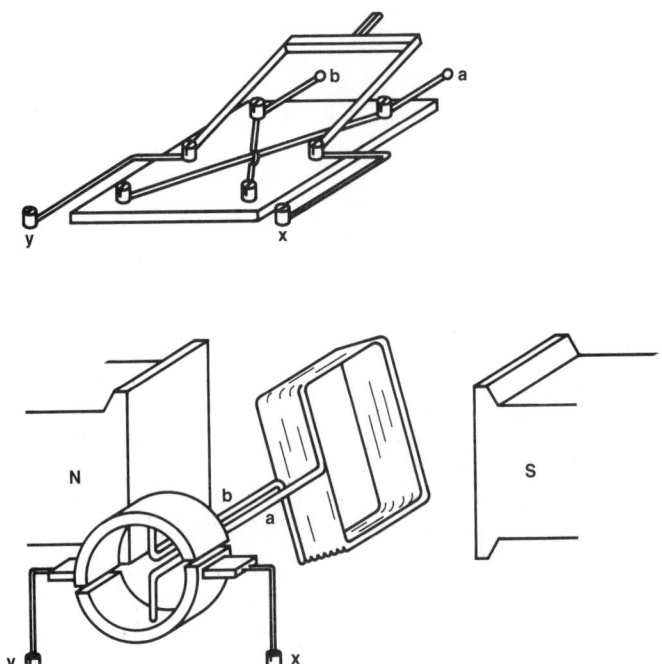

Figure 15.5

A split ring commutator acts as a reversing switch to rectify the ac voltage induced in the coil.

15.2 Armature of a Dc Generator

We can obtain a higher dc voltage, and one that is much smoother, by increasing the number of coils and the number of segments on the commutator. The coils are identical and evenly spaced around a cylindrical iron core (Fig. 15.6). They are embedded in slots and insulated from the core by appropriate slot insulation. The coils are then connected to adjacent segments, so there are as many segments as there are coils. A detailed explanation of the coil and commutator connections is given in Section 15.13.

ARMATURE

The assembly composed of the commutator, coils, and iron core is called the **armature**. The core is made of thin laminations stacked together to form a single block (Fig. 15.7). The laminated core reduces the eddy current losses when the armature rotates, as was explained in Section 7.11.

Figure 15.6

Components and construction of a dc armature.

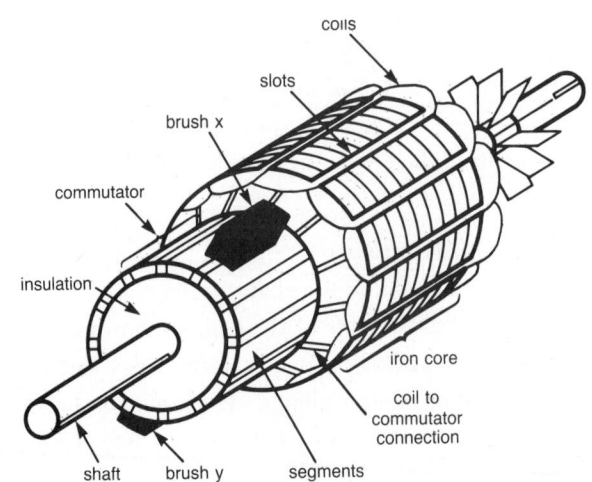

▼ **Figure 15.7**

The armature core is made of stacked laminations insulated from each other.

▼ **Figure 15.8**

The dc output voltage of a multisegment commutator contains only a small ripple.

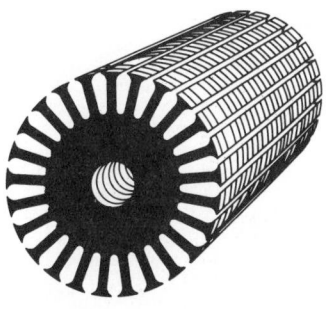

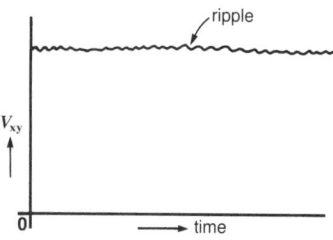

The dc output voltage is obtained by means of carbon brushes that ride on the commutator surface. In two-pole generators, the brushes are spaced 180° apart.

To summarize, when the armature of Fig. 15.6 rotates, the armature coils cut across the flux lines created by two stationary magnets (not shown). This action induces an ac voltage in each coil. The sum of the ac voltages induced in the coils is rectified by means of a commutator. The resulting dc voltage is picked off by means of two brushes riding on the commutator. The output voltage fluctuates slightly (Fig. 15.8); therefore, it is not as steady as the voltage produced by a battery. However, this so-called "commutator ripple" is unimportant in most industrial applications.

Figures 15.9 and 15.10 show the armature of a commercial dc generator. The much larger armature of a 500 kW generator is shown in Fig. 15.11.

▼ **Figure 15.9**

Armature of a commercial dc generator showing coils, commutator, iron core, cooling fan, and bearings.

(Courtesy General Electric Company, USA)

▼ **Figure 15.10**

Closeup of the armature in Fig. 15.9, showing slot insulation, laminated core and wedges that hold the coils in the slots. The steel band on the right firmly holds the coils against the centrifuge forces.

(Courtesy General Electric Company, USA)

Figure 15.11

Armature of an 1150 kW, 750 V, 1000 r/min dc generator.

(Courtesy General Electric Company, USA)

15.3 Field of a Dc Generator

The magnetic flux in a generator is created by its "field." Here, the term field means all the components needed to create the flux in the machine. Figure 15.12 shows the typical construction of the field of a two-pole dc generator. A circular cast-steel frame supports the **salient poles** and also provides a low-reluctance path for the magnetic flux. Mounting feet and lifting lugs are usually welded to the frame.

Two identical pre-wound coils are slipped over the poles and are then connected in series. These so-called **shunt coils** usually have many turns of small wire, and produce the mmf that creates the flux in the machine. The two field leads are brought out to terminals F1 and F2 (Fig. 15.13).

SALIENT POLES

SHUNT COILS

▼ **Figure 15.12**

Field structure of a two-pole dc generator.

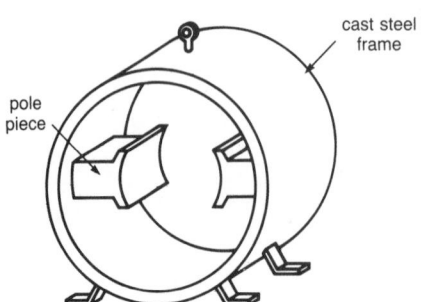

▼ **Figure 15.13**

Shunt field coils are mounted on the pole-pieces and connected in series.

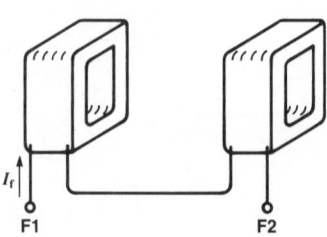

15.4 Assembly of a Dc Generator

Figures 15.14 and 15.15 show cutaway views of a dc generator when it is assembled. The armature fits between the salient poles, leaving two small air gaps. The field flux flows across the air gaps and armature and then divides in two parts as it returns by way of the cast-steel frame. Because the armature core is made of iron, the reluctance of the magnetic circuit is reduced. Consequently, the flux is much greater than it otherwise would be.

The armature shaft is supported by bearings that are mounted inside the two end-bells. The end-bells and frame usually have openings for the intake and exhaust of cooling air. A fan mounted on the armature shaft provides the required ventilation.

When the machine is being assembled, it is important to adjust the position of the brushes. They can be shifted as a unit, usually as much as 45° (Fig. 15.16). They are locked in the so-called *neutral* position, which corresponds to the spot where the dc output voltage at no-load is maximum.

Another way to locate the neutral position is to connect the armature terminals x and y to a 60 Hz ac source. An ac voltmeter is connected across the field terminals F1, F2 and the brushes are shifted, as a unit, until the voltmeter reads zero. The

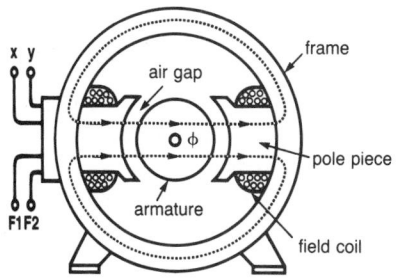

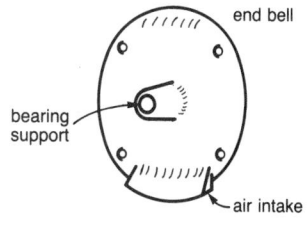

Figure 15.14

Cross section of a dc generator showing the flux path, field terminals F1 and F2, and armature terminals x and y.

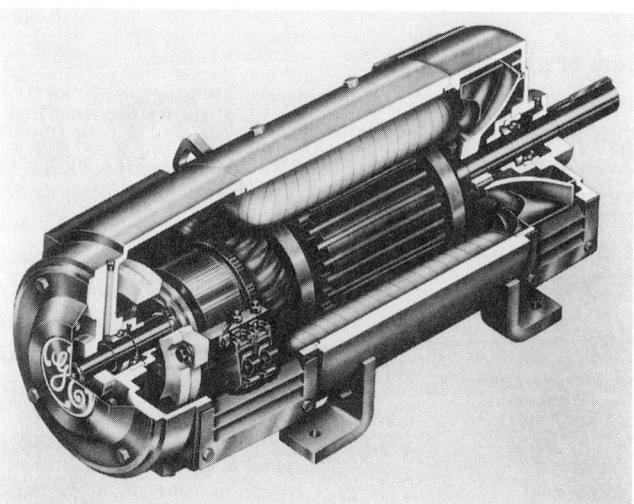

Figure 15.15

Cutaway view of a two-pole dc generator.

(Courtesy General Electric Company, USA)

Figure 15.16

Brush assembly of a four-pole dc generator. The brushes are spring-loaded so they press uniformly against the commutator.

(Courtesy General Electric Company, USA)

brush yoke is then locked in this position. This method of finding the neutral position is based upon the principle of mutual induction discussed in Section 9.1. In effect, when the brushes are in the neutral position, the mutual inductance between the armature coils and field coils is zero.

15.5 Schematic Diagram of a Dc Generator

A schematic diagram of the generator is given in Fig. 15.17. It shows the field flux ϕ created by field current I_f. Only one pole is shown, but it is understood that it represents both poles. The circles inside the armature represent the conductors that are lodged in the slots. The diagram can be further simplified to that shown in Fig. 15.18.

15.6 Current in the Armature; Armature Reaction

Before studying the generator, let us see what happens when the armature carries a current. Referring back to Fig. 15.6, when current flows into brush y and out of brush x, it flows in all the armature coils. The armature then behaves like an elec-

Figure 15.17

Schematic diagram of a dc generator. The single pole represents two or more poles.

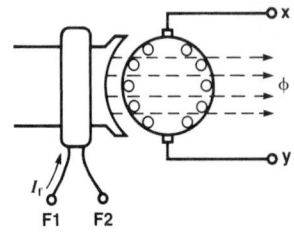

Figure 15.18

Schematic diagram of a separately excited dc generator using graphic symbols recommended by the Institute of Electrical and Electronic Engineers.

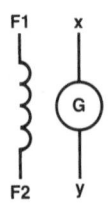

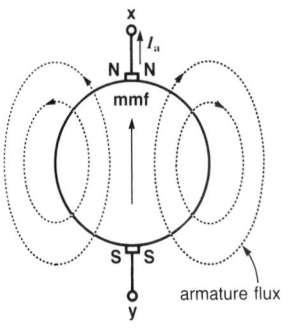

Figure 15.19

The armature produces a substantial mmf and flux when it carries its rated current. In this figure, the mmf acts along the axis of the brushes.

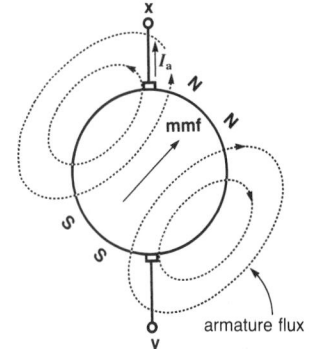

Figure 15.20

In some dc machines the armature acts at an angle to the brush axis.

tromagnet producing an mmf and corresponding N and S poles (Fig. 15.19). The armature mmf is almost as strong as the field mmf when the armature is carrying its rated current.

The direction of the armature mmf depends upon the position of the brushes. If the brushes are shifted 30°, the mmf shifts 30°. We are assuming that the mmf acts along the axis of the brushes (Fig. 15.19). In practice, it could be at any angle to the brush axis, as shown in Fig. 15.20. The direction of the mmf with respect to the brushes depends upon how the armature coils are connected to the commutator segments.

What happens to the mmf when the armature begins to rotate? It remains unchanged as long as the armature current I_a is the same. Thus, the mmf remains fixed in space whether or not the armature is turning. However, if the armature current reverses, the mmf reverses, as well as the N, S poles of the armature.

When the armature is mounted inside the generator, its mmf will have important magnetic effects. These effects are grouped under the general term **armature reaction**.

ARMATURE REACTION

In Fig. 15.21, for example, the field mmf acts from left to right, but the direction of the armature mmf depends upon the brush setting. It so happens that when the brushes are in the neutral position, the armature mmf in a two-pole machine *always* acts at right angles to the field mmf. In a multi-pole machine the axis of the armature mmf is midway between adjacent poles.

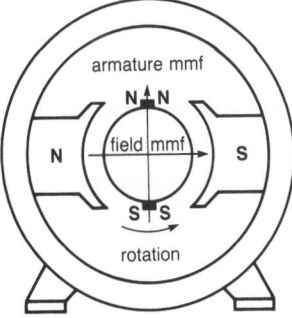

Figure 15.21

Direction of the armature and field mmfs when the brushes are in the neutral position and the armature is turning ccw.

15.7 Separately Excited Dc Generator; No-Load Saturation Curve

The flux in a dc machine is created by the field current I_f. When this current is supplied by an independent dc source, such as a battery, the generator is said to be **separately excited**. Figure 15.22 shows the schematic diagram of such a machine. The field current can be varied from zero to maximum by moving the potentiometer wiper from point A to point B. We assume the armature is driven by an internal combustion engine or electric motor.

Figure 15.22

Separately excited generator using a potentiometer in order to vary the field current from zero to maximum.

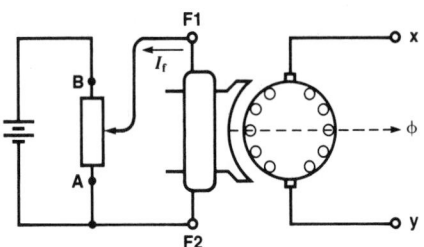

When such a generator operates at no-load — with the armature terminals x and y on open circuit — the armature voltage V_{xy} depends upon the speed of rotation and the field current I_f.

If the speed of the driving motor is increased, the armature voltage increases in direct proportion to the armature speed. In effect, the armature conductors cut the flux lines more quickly, which raises the induced voltage (V_i) in every conductor, according to the equation $v_i = BLv$. At no-load, the total induced voltage V_o appears as V_{xy} across the armature terminals.

On the other hand, if we increase the field current while keeping the speed constant, the flux ϕ will increase. The increase in flux will produce a proportional increase in the flux density B, and hence in the induced voltage V_o. However, as we continue to raise I_f, the iron in the magnetic circuit begins to saturate. This means that for a large increase in I_f, the flux will increase only slightly. Consequently, the induced voltage V_o and the corresponding output voltage V_{xy} will tend to flatten with increasing I_f.

If we plot V_{xy} versus I_f, we obtain a curve such as the one shown in Fig. 15.23. For low values of I_f, V_{xy} increases linearly with I_f. The reason is that the reluctance of the magnetic circuit is then mainly due to the air gaps. In Section 5.15, we saw that the flux in air is directly proportional to the mmf. But, as I_f is increased and the iron begins to saturate, the corresponding increase in flux is small, causing the curve to

level off. This is called the no-load **saturation curve** of the generator.

If we reverse the direction of I_f, the flux will reverse, and this will reverse the polarity of V_{xy}.

Finally, if we reverse the direction of rotation, the polarity of V_{xy} will reverse.

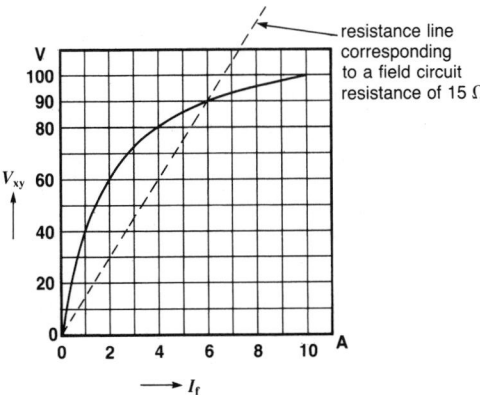

resistance line
corresponding
to a field circuit
resistance of 15 Ω

Figure 15.23

No-load saturation curve
of a separately excited dc
generator.

15.8 Value of the Induced Voltage

The voltage induced in a dc generator is given by the equation

$$V_o = Kn\phi$$

EQ. 15.1

where

V_0 = dc voltage induced in the armature, in volts (V)

n = speed of rotation, in revolutions per minute (r/min)

ϕ = flux per pole, in webers (Wb)

K = a constant that depends upon the winding on the armature

The flux ϕ is that produced by the field coils. However, when the generator is under load, the value of ϕ can also be affected by the presence of the armature mmf.

At no-load, the magnitude of V_0 can be measured by connecting a voltmeter across the armature terminals x and y.

EXAMPLE 15.1

The armature of a six-pole dc generator produces a voltage of 240 V when it turns at 800 r/min. The flux per pole is 0.04 Wb. Calculate the value of K for this machine.

SOLUTION:

From $V_0 = Kn\phi$

EQ. 15.1

we have $240 = K \times 800 \times 0.04$

therefore $K = 7.5$

15.9 Shunt Generator at No-Load

A **self-excited** shunt generator is one that provides its own field excitation. The shunt field is connected to the armature terminals, usually in series with a field rheostat R (Fig. 15.24). By varying the position of the rheostat, current I_f varies, which varies flux ϕ and the output voltage V_{xy}.

Once the generator is in operation and generating a voltage, there is no problem in maintaining the field excitation. The question is, what happens when the generator is initially at rest and then put into service? If the flux from the poles is initially zero, V_{xy} will also be zero, no matter what the speed is. And if V_{xy} is zero, current I_f is zero, and so there is no excitation.

Fortunately, residual magnetism comes to the rescue. If the field poles are excited only once (such as by being connected to a battery), some residual magnetism will remain. Consequently, when the generator runs at rated speed, a low voltage will be induced between terminals x and y. This will cause a weak current I_f to flow in the windings (Fig. 15.24). This increases the flux slightly above its residual value, which in turn increases V_{xy}, which increases I_f, which increases ϕ, which increases V_{xy}, and so forth. Voltage V_{xy} will build up, and it seems it will become greater and greater without limit.

However, V_{xy} reaches a final value that depends upon the no-load saturation curve and the total resistance R_f of the shunt field circuit. If we draw a straight line corresponding to R_f and superimpose it on the no-load saturation curve, the point of intersection gives the limiting value of V_{xy}. For example, given the saturation curve of Fig. 15.23, if $R_f = 15\ \Omega$, the resistance line intersects the curve at $V_{xy} = 90$ V. Because of the inductance of the field coils, it may take several seconds for the voltage to reach this final value (see Section 9.6).

If the resistance of the field rheostat is increased, the resistance line becomes steeper and a lower V_{xy} is obtained. If the resistance is too high, the resistance line will no longer intersect the saturation curve, and the armature voltage will not build up.

Note that the armature voltage cannot build up if we reverse the direction of rotation. The reason is that the polarity of V_{xy} will reverse, causing the initial I_f to reverse, thus *reducing* the flux below its residual value. To remedy the situation, we must interchange the field connections F1, F2.

Figure 15.24

Build-up of a self-excited shunt generator.

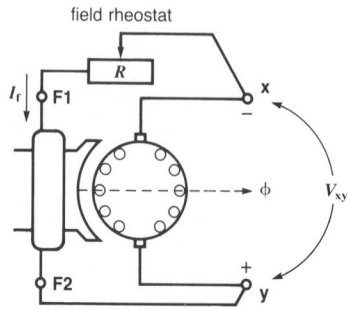

15.10 Separately Excited Generator Under Load

When a dc generator delivers power to a load (Fig. 15.25), several factors must be considered.

1. The flux ϕ induces a voltage V_o in the armature.

2. The armature has a low, but not negligible, resistance R_a. It causes an internal voltage drop $I_a R_a$, similar to that in a battery. Consequently, the voltage V_{xy} across the generator terminals is less than the induced voltage V_o.

3. The armature current I_a produces an armature mmf that acts at right angles to the field mmf. The resultant mmf is therefore inclined at an angle, as shown in Fig. 15.26. This causes the flux to move diagonally across the armature. Unfortunately, this increases the flux density in pole tips a and b, and so they become saturated. This, in turn, reduces the total flux ϕ that crosses the armature. As a result, the induced voltage V_o is less at full-load than at no-load.

The overall effect of armature resistance and armature reaction is that the armature voltage V_{xy} decreases with increasing load current, as shown in Fig. 15.27.

▼ **Figure 15.25**

Separately excited dc generator under load.

▼ **Figure 15.26**

The flux crossing the armature becomes distorted and smaller because of armature reaction.

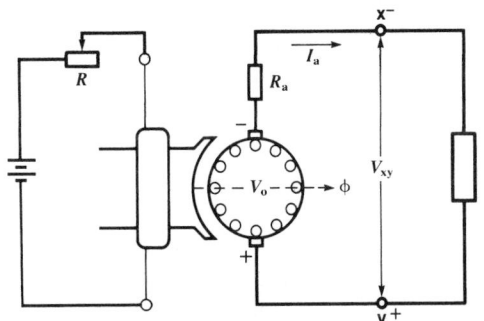

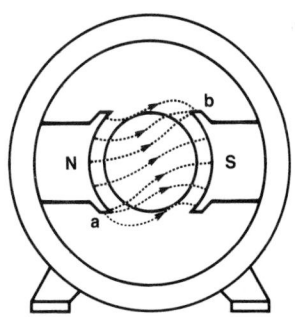

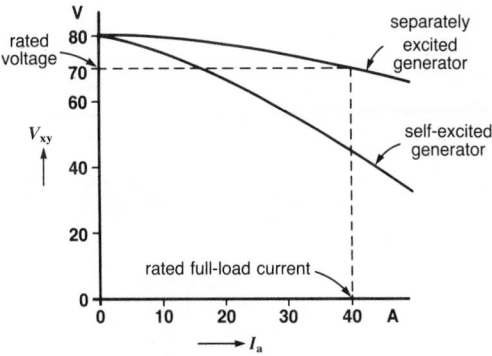

Figure 15.27

Voltage-regulation curves of separately excited and self-excited dc generator starting from the same no-load voltages. To obtain rated voltage at rated current, the no-load excitation of the self-excited generator must be raised.

The same voltage drop takes place in a self-excited shunt generator, but is accentuated. The reason is that as the armature voltage decreases (due to the effects just mentioned), there is a corresponding drop in field current. Therefore, the flux ϕ decreases even more with increasing load than it did before. Thus, the voltage regulation curve of a self-excited generator drops more steeply than that of a separately excited generator (Fig. 15.27).

15.11 Compound Generator

COMPOUND
GENERATOR

One way to avoid the drop in armature voltage is to increase the field flux as the load increases. This can be accomplished by placing an extra winding around each field pole (Fig. 15.28). The winding carries the load current, and the mmf it produces adds to that of the shunt field. When this so-called *series* winding is added, we obtain a **compound generator**. Figures 15.29 and 15.30 show the construction of a four-pole compound generator.

The series winding is composed of a few turns of heavy wire to carry the armature current. Depending upon the number of turns, the terminal voltage under load can be made equal to, or greater than, the no-load voltage.

Figure 15.28

Compound dc generator under load.

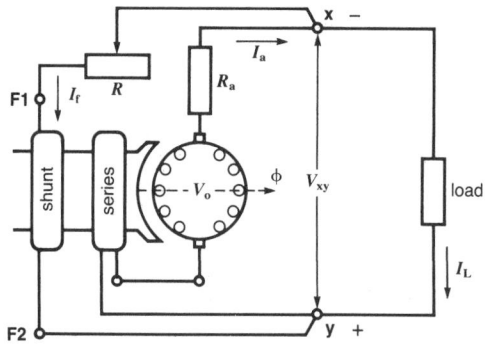

Figure 15.29

Construction of a four-pole compound generator showing the main poles and four intermediate commutating poles.

(Courtesy General Electric Company, USA)

Figure 15.30

Construction of the field winding of the generator in Fig. 15.29. The two heavy terminals are the series field and the two small wires are the shunt field.

(Courtesy General Electric Company, USA)

Typical voltage-regulation curves are shown in Fig. 15.31. The **flat-compound** generator has zero voltage regulation because the no-load voltage is equal to the full-load voltage. The **overcompound** generator has negative voltage regulation because the no-load voltage is less than the full-load voltage.

FLAT-COMPOUND

OVERCOMPOUND

How much mechanical power is needed to drive the compound generator of Fig. 15.28? First, all the electric power that is consumed by the load, the shunt field, the series field, the armature resistance, and the shunt field rheostat must be equal to the total generated power, which is equal to $V_o I_a$. Second, this generated power is entirely produced by the "internal" mechanical power P_{mi} that is needed to drive the armature. Thus, we can write

$$P_{mi} = V_o I_a$$

EQ. 15.2

where

P_{mi} = mechanical power needed to produce the electrical output, in watts (W)

V_o = induced voltage, in volts (V)

I_a = armature current, in amperes (A)

It takes slightly more mechanical power than P_{mi} to drive the generator because of the windage and friction losses, and the hysteresis and eddy-current losses in the armature core. Note that Equation 15.2 applies to any dc generator — compound, shunt, or series.

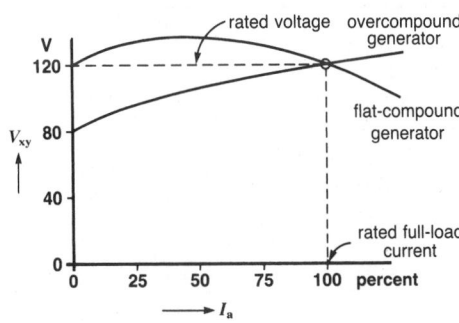

Figure 15.31

Voltage-regulation curves of a flat-compound and an overcompound dc generator.

EXAMPLE 15.2

The following information is given for the two-pole compound generator shown in Fig. 15.32.

shunt field resistance = 40 Ω   load current I_L = 90 A

series field resistance = 0.04 Ω   windage and friction losses = 200 W

armature resistance = 0.16 Ω   iron losses in the armature = 300 W

field rheostat resistance = 10 Ω   turns on the shunt field = 240

terminal voltage V_{xy} = 250 V   turns on the series field = 4

Calculate:
1. the shunt field current I_f.
2. the voltage across the shunt field coils.
3. the power loss in the series field.
4. the value of the induced voltage V_o.
5. the mechanical power needed to drive the generator.
6. the total mmf of the shunt and series windings, per pole.

SOLUTION:

1. a) The total resistance R_t of the shunt field circuit is equal to the sum of the shunt field resistance (40 Ω) and the rheostat resistance (10 Ω):
   $R_t = 40 + 10 = 50$ Ω
   b) The shunt field current is:
   $I_f = V_{xy}/R_t = 250/50 = 5$ A
2. The voltage across the shunt field is:
   $V = IR = 5 \times 40 = 200$ V
3. a) The current I_a in the armature circuit is:
   $I_a = I_L + I_F = 90 + 5 = 95$ A
   b) The loss in the series field is:
   $P = I_a^2 R_s = 95^2 \times 0.04 = 361$ W
4. a) The voltage drop in the armature resistance is:
   $v_a = I_a R_a = 95 \times 0.16 = 15.2$ V
   b) The voltage drop across the series field is:
   $v_s = I_a R_s = 95 \times 0.04 = 3.8$ V

Figure 15.32

See Example 15.2.

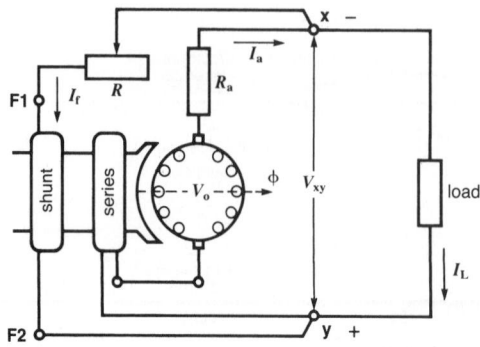

continued

c) The total voltage drop in the armature circuit is:
$V_t = 15.2 + 3.8 = 19$ V

d) The induced voltage is:
$V_o = V_{xy} + 19 = 250 + 19 = 269$ V

5. a) The mechanical power to generate the electricity is:
$P_{mi} = V_o I_a = 269 \times 95 = 25\ 555$ W

b) The mechanical power needed to overcome the windage, friction, and iron losses is:
$P_f = 200 + 300 = 500$W

c) Total mechanical power needed to drive the generator is:
$P_{mi} + P_f = 25\ 555 + 500 = 26\ 055$ W

6. a) The mmf of the shunt field is $NI_f = 240 \times 5 = 1200$ At

b) The mmf of the series field is $NI_a = 4 \times 95 = 380$ At

c) The total mmf per pole is $NI_f + NI_a = 1200 + 380 = 1580$ At

15.12 Rating and Voltage Regulation of a Dc Generator

A dc generator is designed to produce a definite power output at a given terminal voltage and speed. These three quantities, together with the temperature rise, make up what is called the *rating* of the generator. For example, a generator may be rated at 120 kW, 240 V, 1750 rpm, with a 50°C temperature rise. The corresponding rated current is:

$I = P/V = 120\ 000/240 = 500$ A

Another important characteristic of a generator is its **voltage regulation**, expressed in percent. It can be determined in the following way:

1. The generator is driven at rated speed and loaded up so that it delivers rated current.

2. The field excitation is adjusted so that the generator produces its rated voltage V_{FL}.

3. Without touching the field rheostat or changing the speed, the load is disconnected, and the no-load armature voltage V_{NL} is measured.

4. The percent regulation is given by the equation

% regulation $= 100 \times \dfrac{V_{NL} - V_{FL}}{V_{FL}}$

EQ. 15.3

VOLTAGE REGULATION

where V_{FL} and V_{NL} have the meaning given above.

For example, in Fig. 15.27, the rated voltage of the separately excited generator is 70 V and the rated armature current is 40 A. The voltage regulation is therefore:

% regulation $= 100 \times \dfrac{V_{NL} - V_{FL}}{V_{FL}}$

$= 100 \times \dfrac{80 - 70}{70} = 14.3\%$

15.13 Actual Construction of a Dc Armature

To understand some of the special aspects of a dc machine, it is useful to know how the armature is actually constructed. Consider Fig. 15.33, in which a single coil revolves ccw between the poles of a permanent magnet. Let us begin with the coil in the vertical position. Voltage V_{ab} is zero because conductors 1, 2 and 3, 4 are moving parallel to the flux lines. However, when the coil has moved through 90° (Fig. 15.34), the conductors are cutting across the flux lines and V_{ab} is maximum. By applying the left-hand rule, we can show that V_{ab} is positive. Let us suppose it is +10 V.

After another 90° (Fig. 15.34), the coil will again be vertical and $V_{ab} = 0$. This means that between zero and 180°, V_{ab} is always positive. But if we go beyond 180° V_{ab} is negative and remains so until the coil has reached 360°. For example, at an angle of (180 + 45) or 225°, $V_{ab} = -7$ V (Fig. 15.36).

We show these successive positions of the coil and the corresponding voltages and polarities in Fig. 15.37. (To simplify the drawing, we show a narrow coil.) The voltages depend upon the position of the coil. For example, whenever the coil is at the 225° position, the voltage between its terminals is 7 V, and b is (+) with respect to a.

▼ **Figure 15.33**

At 0°, the induced voltage V_{ab} is zero and increasing positively.

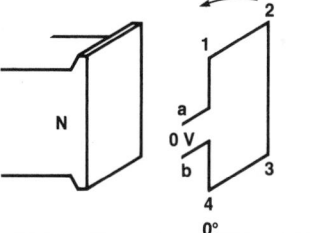
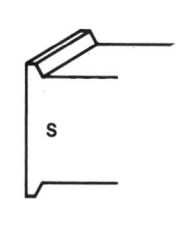

▼ **Figure 15.34**

At 90°, the induced voltage V_{ab} is maximum positive.

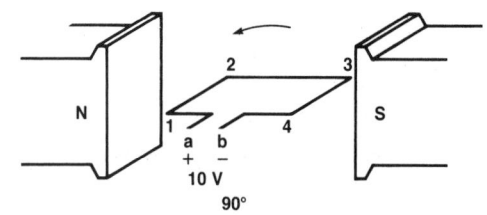

▼ **Figure 15.35**

At 180°, the induced voltage V_{ab} is zero and increasing negatively.

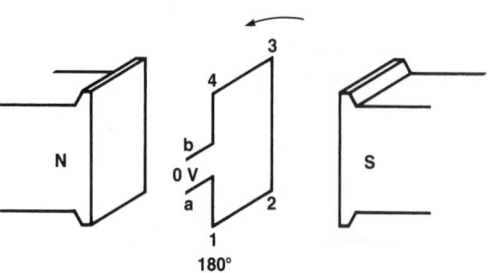

▼ **Figure 15.36**

At 225°, the induced voltage V_{ab} is –7 V, and increasing negatively.

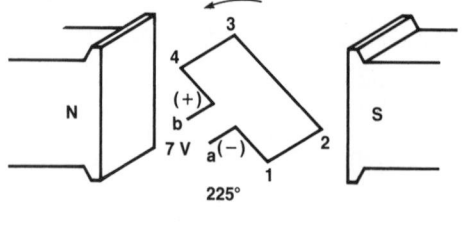

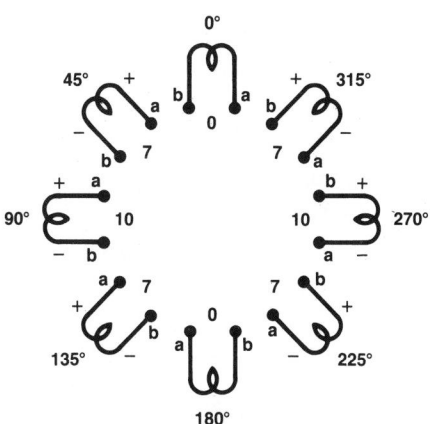

Figure 15.37

Voltages induced in the coil at eight different positions.

Suppose we build a special armature having *eight* coils identical to the coil in Fig. 15.33. The coils are uniformly distributed in a circle, at 45° to each other (Fig. 15.38). They are numbered 1 to 8 so that we can readily identify them.

Let us rotate this assembly of eight coils ccw at the same speed as before. Each coil will generate a voltage and polarity corresponding to its position. These voltages are the same as those induced in the single coil of Fig. 15.37. If we freeze the action when coil 1 is at 0°, the voltages in the coils will instantaneously be as shown in Fig. 15.38. A moment later, when the entire assembly has moved through 45° the voltage in coil 1 will be +7 V, that in coil 2 will be zero, that in coil 3 will be −7 V, and so forth around the circle.

So far, the coils are isolated from one another, but we can connect them in series to form a closed loop, as shown in Fig 15.39. No current will flow in the loop because the algebraic sum of the voltages around the loop is zero. In other words, the voltage rises are equal to the voltage drops. The coil voltages in Fig. 15.39 are therefore the same as in Fig. 15.38.

The next step is to connect the coils to the commutator. These connections are shown by the dotted lines in Fig. 15.40. The voltages between the segments are obviously equal to the corresponding coil voltages.

▼ **Figure 15.38**

Snapshot of the voltages induced in an eight-coil armature.

▼ **Figure 15.39**

The coils of Fig. 15.37 can be connected in a closed loop without causing a current to flow.

▼ **Figure 15.40**

The coils are connected to a commutator and the brushes are placed to obtain the highest dc voltage.

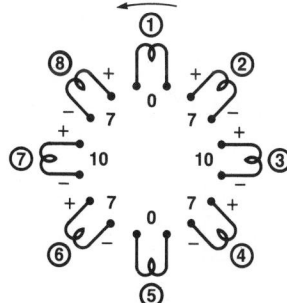

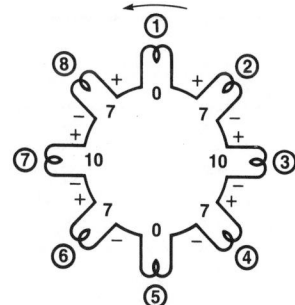

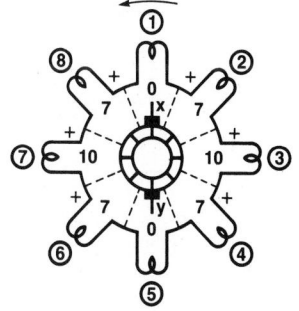

Let us now place brushes x and y in the position indicated in Fig. 15.40. The voltage between the brushes is equal to the sum of the voltages between the segments, which at this moment is 7 + 10 + 7 = 24 V. Thus, V_{xy} = +24 V. When the armature rotates 45° from its original position, the induced voltages are the same except they are generated by a different set of coils. Consequently, the voltage between the brushes remains fixed at 24 V, and brush x is always positive with respect to brush y. V_{xy} is therefore a dc voltage. Note, however, that when the armature has turned 22.5°, there will be four coils between the brushes, and the sum of their voltages will be slightly different from 24 V. That is why the dc voltage fluctuates, giving rise to commutator ripple.

Brush x touches two commutator segments in Fig. 15.40, thus placing a momentary short-circuit on coil 1. In the same way, brush y short-circuits coil 5. But because the voltage in these coils is zero, no harm will result. However, if the brushes were shifted cw by 45°, they would short-circuit coils 2 and 6. The 7 V induced in these coils would produce a large current in the brushes, and sparking could result. When brushes spark, the commutation is said to be poor.

15.14 Commutation of Current

Figure 15.41 shows the current in the armature coils when the load draws 100 A. The current flows through the armature in two parallel paths, with 50 A flowing in each coil.

However, the currents in coils 2, 3, and 4 flow in the opposite direction to those in coils 6, 7, and 8. This means that when the armature rotates, the current in each coil reverses periodically. This current reversal is called *commutation*.

The problem is that the current must change from +50 A to –50 A in a very short time. The time is equal to that needed for the commutator to move the width of one brush. It is therefore only a fraction of a millisecond long. The coils possess inductance, and such a rapid change of current produces a self-induced voltage V_L, given by $V_L = L\Delta I / \Delta t$. This voltage opposes the change in the current and the result is sparking at the brushes. In Fig. 15.41, the current in coil 1 in the process of changing from +50 A. That in coil 5 is changing from –50 A to +50 A.

Figure 15.41

The load current is carried equally by the armature coils. The current in coil 1 is in the process of reversing from +50 A to –50 A.

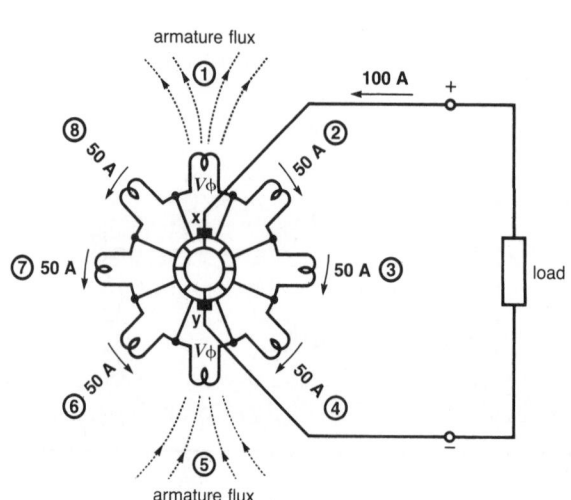

armature flux

100 A

load

armature flux

EXAMPLE 15.3

The individual coils in Fig. 15.41 have a self-inductance of 40 μH. The diameter of the commutator is 100 mm, and the width of the brushes is 8 mm. If the armature turns at 1800 r/min, calculate the average value of the induced voltage V_L.

SOLUTION:

1. The commutator makes one turn in 60/1800 = 1/30 s
2. The circumference of the commutator is πd = π × 100 = 314 mm
3. The commutator therefore moves at a surface speed of
    314 × 30 = 9420 mm/s
4. The time to move a distance of 8 mm (the width of a brush) is
    Δt = 8/9420 = 8.49 × 10^{-4} s
5. The change in current is ΔI = 50 − (−50) = 100 A
6. The induced voltage is
    $V_L = L \, \Delta I/\Delta t$
        = 40 × 10^{-6} × 100/(8.49 × 10^{-4})
        = 4.7 V

15.15 Armature Reaction and Commutation

We recall that when current flows in the armature, an armature flux is created. This flux is strongest in the region of coils 1 and 5 (Fig. 15.41). A voltage $V\phi$ is therefore induced in these coils as they cut the armature flux. Because they are short-circuited by the brushes, a large current can result. This again contributes to poor commutation under load.

15.16 Commutating Poles

We can improve the commutation by placing **commutating poles** *between the main* poles of the generator. They are connected in series with the armature in order to produce an mmf equal and opposite to the armature mmf. Consequently, they eliminate the armature flux that induced the undesired voltage $V\phi$ in coils 1 and 5 (Fig. 15.41).

In practice, the mmf of the commutating poles is made slightly greater than the armature mmf. This produces a small net flux whose direction is *opposite* to that shown in Fig. 15.41. The resulting induced voltage opposes the voltage V_L due to self-induction, and so the total voltage induced in coils 1 and 5 is practically zero. As a result, the commutation is much improved.

Figure 15.42 shows the commutating poles in a two-pole generator. The total mmf ($2M_C$) created by the two commutating poles is slightly greater than the mmf (M_A) created by the armature. The mmf (M_F) of the shunt field is constant, but M_A and M_C vary in direct proportion to the load current. Fig. 15.29 shows the commutating poles in a 4-pole generator.

COMMUTATING POLES

Figure 15.42

Commutating poles reduce
sparking at the brushes.

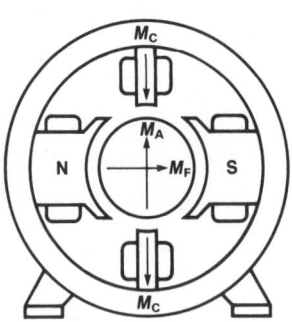

15.17 Multipolar Machines

Direct current machines rated below 1 kW usually have two poles. Larger machines
have four, six, eight, or more poles. The main reason for increasing the number of
poles is to reduce weight and cost, and to improve machine performance. Nevertheless, the basic properties of multipolar machines are identical to those of the
two-pole generators we have discussed here.

15.18 Summary

Upon completion of this chapter you should have learned how to:

• Explain that a conductor rotating in a magnetic field will have a voltage induced
in the conductor. The magnitude of the induced voltage is determined by the
strength of the magnetic field, the speed of rotation, the angle at which the lines
of force are cut, and the length of the conductor within the field.

• Describe the construction of the armature and field of a dc generator, and explain
how they can be connected to create a series-wound, a shunt-wound, and a compound-wound dc generator.

• Describe how the no-load curve for a shunt generator and self-excited generator
relates to the mechanical operation of the generator. As the level of excitation
increases, the open circuit voltage will increase in direct proportion until the
magnetic circuit is saturated. A further increase in excitation will not result in a
proportional increase in the terminal voltage.

• Calculate the voltage induced in a dc generator using Equation 15.1.

• Describe how the losses in a separately excited generator under load require that
the field voltage be set to a level that will allow the generator to produce rated
voltage. This means that at no-load, voltage of the generator will be higher than
the full-load voltage.

• Describe the construction of a compound dc generator with both a series winding and a shunt winding. Depending on the excitation provided, a compound generator can operate as an overcompound or flat-compound generator.

• Describe the percentage voltage regulation, which represents the change in a
generator's terminal voltage between no-load and full-load, expressed as a percentage of the full-load voltage.

Key Terms

ARMATURE: The rotating portion of a dc generator.

ARMATURE REACTION: A distortion of the magnetic fields in a generator resulting from the mmf produced by the current flowing in the armature.

COMMUTATING POLES: Magnetic poles used to counteract the effect of armature reaction. Commutating poles are connected in series with the armature.

COMMUTATOR: A mechanical rectifier composed of a number of metal segments. Each segment is connected to one end of an armature coil. Brushes ride on the surface of the commutator segments.

COMPOUND GENERATOR: A generator configuration with both a shunt field and a series field.

FLAT-COMPOUND: A generator configuration that causes the output voltage at no-load and full-load to be almost the same value.

OVER-COMPOUND: A generator configuration that causes the output voltage to increase as the generator is loaded.

RECTIFY: The term used to describe the conversion of an ac current to a dc current.

SALIENT POLES: Field coils that are attached to the inside of a generator frame. In large generators these coils may be bolted in place.

SATURATION CURVE: A graph showing the relationship between the generator output voltage and the field current.

SELF-EXCITED: A generator configuration that uses the generated voltage to supply the field current. There is no external field connection. Initial field current is supplied by residual magnetism.

SEPARATELY EXCITED: A generator configuration in which the field coils are connected to an external power source.

SHUNT COILS: Generator field coils that are connected in parallel with the armature.

VOLTAGE REGULATION: The change between no-load and full-load output voltage expressed as a percentage of the full-load output voltage.

Test Your Knowledge

15.1   A commutator and its brushes together form a mechanical rectifier.

true_____   false_____

15.2   If the armature core in Fig. 15.11 were made of plastic instead of iron, the armature voltage would
a.   remain the same
b.   diminish greatly
c.   become zero

15.3   When the brushes of a two-pole dc generator are in the neutral position, the angle between the armature mmf and the field mmf
a.   is usually 90°

b.   is always 90°
c.   depends upon how the armature is wound

15.4   In Fig. 15.25, if the battery terminals are reversed,
a. I_a will reverse
b. I_a will become zero
c. I_a will remain unchanged

15.5   In Fig. 15.40, if the armature turns 90°, the voltage in coil 8 will be
a.   zero
b.   7 V
c.   10 V

15.6   In Fig. 15.41, the instantaneous power delivered by coil 4 is
   a.   350 W
   b.   2400 W
   c.   350 J

15.7   In Fig. 15.42, the armature mmf is 6000 At. The interpoles should each develop an mmf of
   a.   6000 At
   b.   3000 At
   c.   slightly more than 3000 At

Questions and Problems

15.8   Why should we always place the brushes of a dc generator in the neutral position?

15.9   What effect does an increase in the field current have on a dc generator?

15.10   Why does the terminal voltage of a separately excited dc generator decrease with increasing load?

15.11   A separately excited dc generator develops an induced voltage of 127 V when the armature turns at 1400 r/min.

   (a) If the armature resistance is 2 Ω, what is the armature terminal voltage when the armature current is 12 A?

   (b) How much heat is lost in the armature?

15.12   A separately excited generator produces an open-circuit voltage of 115 V. Explain in detail what will happen if

   a.   the speed is increased 20 percent?

   b.   the direction of rotation is reversed?

   c.   the field current is increased 20 percent?

   d.   the polarity of the shunt field is reversed?

15.13   A flat-compound generator rated at 100 kW, 250 V has a shunt field of 2000 turns, and a series field of 7 turns. The shunt field has a resistance of 100 Ω and is connected across the armature terminals in series with a rheostat of 25 Ω, as shown in Fig. 15.28. Calculate the mmf per pole when the machine operates (a) at no-load and (b) at full-load.

15.14   The coils in Fig. 15.41 carry an ac current, but the output current is dc. Explain.

15.15   The voltage in the coils of Fig. 15.41 is ac, but the output voltage is dc. Explain.

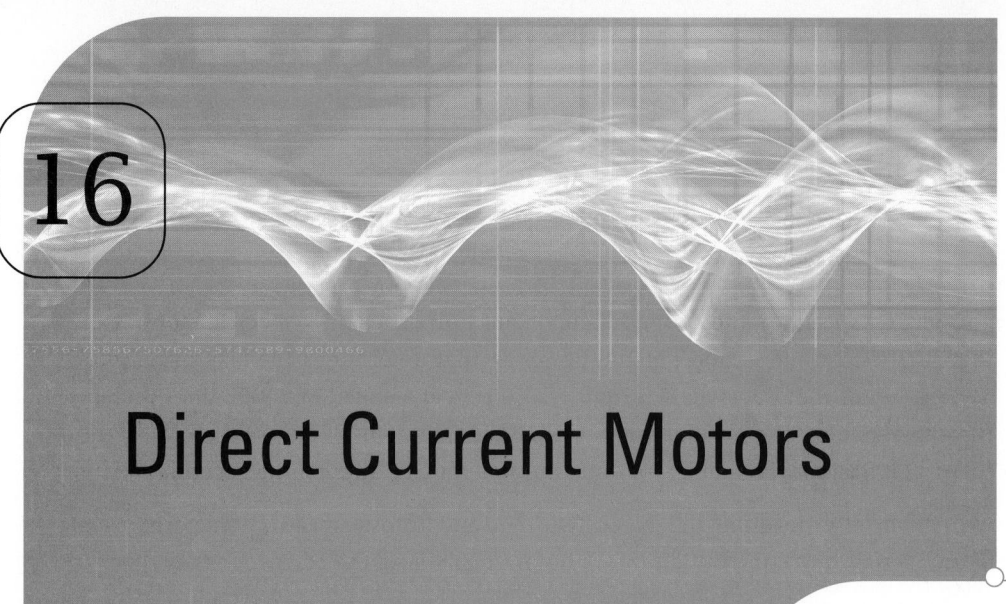

16

Direct Current Motors

LEARNING OBJECTIVES

Upon completion of this chapter you will be able to:

- Describe the construction of dc motors

- Explain the theory of operation for dc motors

- Describe the losses associated with dc motors and calculate the efficiency

- Explain how a dc motor is started

- Calculate the torque developed by a dc motor

- Describe the operation of a dc motor as it accelerates

- Describe the torque-speed characteristics of series, shunt, and compound dc motors

- Explain how the speed of a dc motor can be controlled

- Describe how a dc motor can be stopped using dynamic braking and plugging

- Describe the operation of manual dc motor starter

16.1 Construction and Torque-Speed Characteristics of Dc Motors

Torque and speed are the two most important properties of an electric motor. Note that it is the torque — and not the power — that determines the size of a motor. Thus, a motor that develops a torque of 160 N.m at a speed of 2000 r/min is about the same size as one developing 160 N.m at 500 r/min. But from a power standpoint, the first machine delivers four times as much power as the second.

We will briefly describe the basic features and torque-speed characteristics of shunt, series, and compound motors before explaining the corresponding theory.

SHUNT MOTOR

The **shunt motor** has a shunt field and an armature, both of which are connected to the dc source V_s (Fig. 16.1). The figure shows only one pole, but it represents the two, four, six, or more poles that are on the actual machine. The motor usually has commutating poles, but they are considered to be part of the armature circuit and are not shown. Consequently, R_a is the sum of the armature resistance and the resistance of the commutating poles.

The torque-speed curve for this motor is shown in Fig. 16.2. The rated torque is T_o and the rated speed is n_o. The no-load speed is slightly higher than the rated speed.

▼ **Figure 16.1**

Shunt motor connected to the dc source.

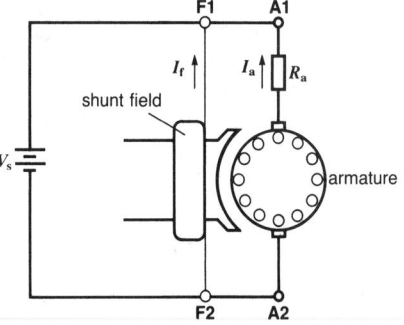

▼ **Figure 16.2**

Torque-speed characteristic of a shunt motor.

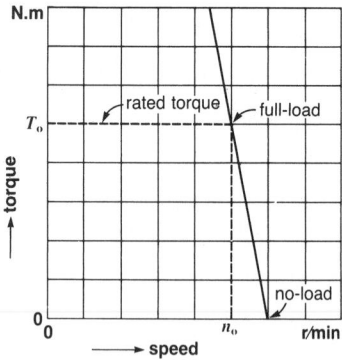

▶ **Figure 16.3**

Four-pole stator of a 40 hp, 1750 r/min, 600 V dc stabilized-shunt motor, showing main poles and cummutating poles.

(Courtesy Gould)

▼ Figure 16.4

Series motor connected to
the dc source.

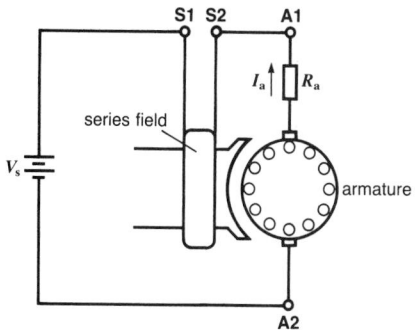

▼ Figure 16.5

Torque-speed characteristic
of a series motor.

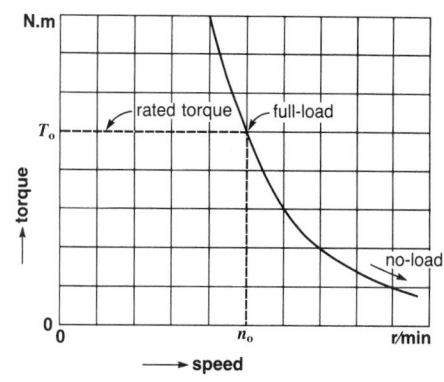

The **series motor** has a series field and an armature, connected to the dc source V_s,
as shown in Fig. 16.4. Because the series field carries the armature current, it is
made of large wire. The field has relatively few turns because the large current does
not require many turns to produce a substantial field mmf. The motor also has commutating poles, connected in series with the armature. Consequently, R_a represents
the sum of the resistances of the armature, commutating poles, and series field.

The torque-speed curve of a series motor is shown in Fig. 16.5. The rated torque
and speed are again T_o and n_o. The no-load speed is dangerously high, and so this
motor should never be disconnected from its load. Compared with a shunt motor,
the speed falls sharply with increasing torque.

The **compound motor** has both a series field and a shunt field, connected as shown
in Fig. 16.6. The series mmf adds to the shunt mmf, and so the resultant field flux
increases with increasing load. This motor also has commutating poles, and so R_a is
again the sum of armature, series field, and commutating pole resistances.

The torque-speed curve for this motor is shown in Fig. 16.7. It is similar to that of
a shunt motor, but because of the series field, the speed falls more rapidly with

SERIES MOTOR

COMPOUND MOTOR

▼ Figure 16.6

Compound motor connected
to the dc source.

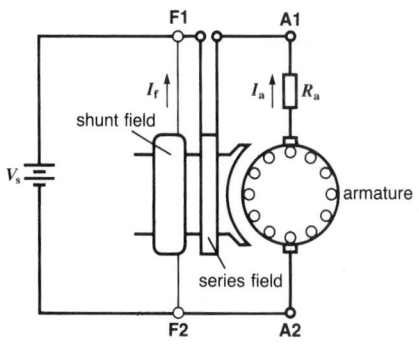

▼ Figure 16.7

Torque-speed characteristic
of a compound motor.

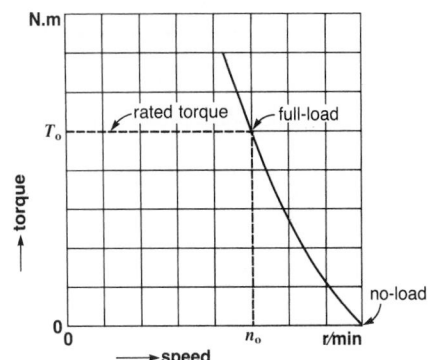

increasing torque. However, it does not fall as steeply as the curve for a series motor. The no-load speed is typically 30 percent higher than the rated speed n_o.

In comparing these motors, it is important to remember that if they have the same rated torque, they will be the same size. In other words, the size of any dc motor — shunt, compound, or series — depends on its rated torque.

16.2 Motor Losses and Efficiency

The dc motor converts electrical energy into mechanical energy, and it therefore has losses (see Section 1.9). Figure 16.8 schematically shows the power flow and losses in the machine.

The total electrical input P_e provides power P_f to the shunt field and power P_a to armature. Power P_r is dissipated as heat in the field coils and field rheostat. Power P_a supplies the I^2R losses of the series field, commutating poles, and armature. When these losses are subtracted from P_a, we obtain the electrical power that is converted into "internal" mechanical power P_{mi}. A part of this mechanical power is used up in brush friction, bearing friction, and windage losses. The windage losses are due to the fan and air turbulence around the armature. Another part of P_{mi} is used up in the hysteresis and eddy-current losses in the armature. Although these iron losses are electrical in nature, they show up as a mechanical drag on the armature. The resulting mechanical power P_m available at the shaft is therefore less than the internal mechanical power P_{mi}. The total losses in the motor are equal to $P_e - P_m$, and they appear as heat.

Some of the losses in Fig. 16.8 depend upon the mechanical load, while others do not. Thus, as the load increases, the armature current I_a increases. This causes the $I_a^2R_a$ losses to increase. However, the other losses remain essentially fixed. For example, the brush friction loss decreases when the speed drops by a few percent, but the change is not significant. Thus, the graph of motor losses versus power output has the typical shape given in Fig. 16.9.

The losses cause the motor to heat up, and adequate cooling means are needed to keep its temperature from becoming too high (Fig. 16.10).

Figure 16.8

Input power and losses in a dc motor.

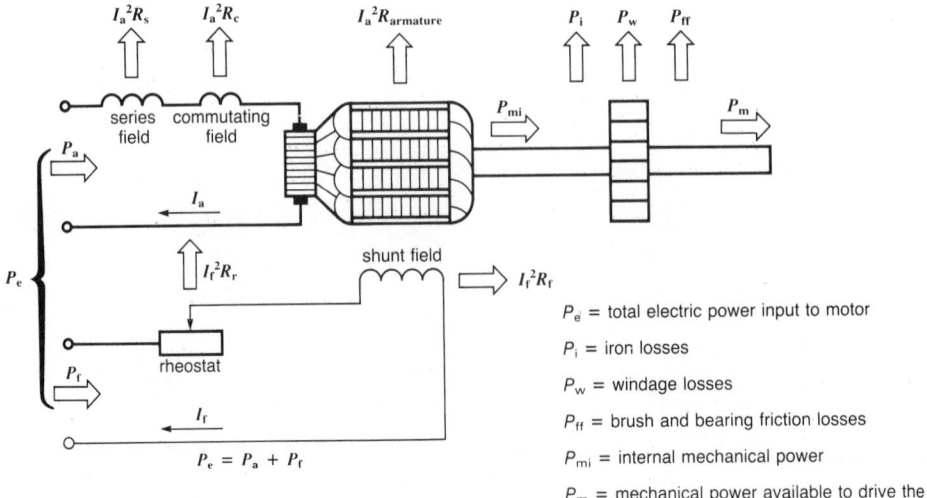

$$P_e = P_a + P_f$$

P_e = total electric power input to motor

P_i = iron losses

P_w = windage losses

P_{ff} = brush and bearing friction losses

P_{mi} = internal mechanical power

P_m = mechanical power available to drive the load

▼ **Figure 16.9**

Typical losses versus power output of a 10 hp dc motor.

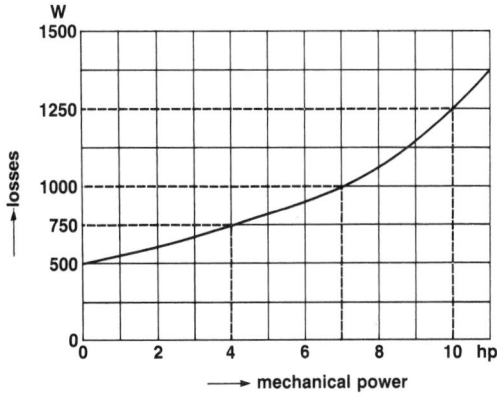

▼ **Figure 16.10**

Totally enclosed 2000 hp dc motor cooled with an air-to-water heat exchanger. Hot air from the motor circulates in the piping from the upper, commutator end, down through the heat exchanger on the left, and the cooled air reenters the motor at the lower fan end. This motor is used to position the platform over the hole in offshore oil/gas well drilling.

(Courtesy General Electric Company, USA)

EXAMPLE 16.1

A 10 hp motor has the loss curve given in Fig. 16.9. Calculate the efficiency of the motor when it delivers an output of 7 hp.

SOLUTION:

1. 7 hp output corresponds to $P_m = 7 \times 746 = 5222$ W
2. The corresponding losses are 1000 W, taken from the graph
3. The power input to the motor is
   $P_e = 5222 + 1000 = 6222$ W
4. $eff = 100 \times \dfrac{5222}{6222} = 83.9\%$

EQ. 1.11

16.3 Starting a Dc Motor

When a dc motor is running, the armature is connected across the dc source. But if we attempt to start the motor this way, the line fuses will blow. The reason is that when the armature is not turning, the only opposition to current flow is the armature resistance. It is so low that the **locked-rotor current** may be as much as 50 times the rated current. (The term locked-rotor means that the armature is not turning.)

LOCKED-ROTOR CURRENT

We must therefore place a resistor R_s in series with the armature during start-up.

Figure 16.11

Circuit to start a dc motor.
The shunt field is connected
across the source.

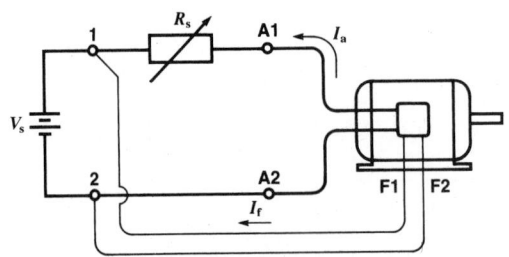

The shunt field is fully excited during this time to produce maximum flux and maximum starting torque. A simple starting circuit is shown in Fig. 16.11a. To get a particularly smooth start, resistor R_s should be gradually reduced to zero as the motor speed increases. However, we usually design the circuit so that R_s drops to zero in one or more steps. This may be done manually or automatically by using a dc starter.

EXAMPLE 16.2

A 15 hp, 225 V, 950 r/min dc shunt motor has a rated armature current of 60 A. The armature resistance is 0.15 Ω, and the shunt field resistance is 50 Ω. Calculate (1) the initial starting current if the motor is directly connected across the 225 V line and (2) the value of the starting resistance R_s needed to limit the locked-rotor current to 90 A.

SOLUTION:

1. Without a current-limiting resistor, the locked-rotor current would be
    $I_a = V/R_a = 225/0.15 = 1500$ A (25 times the rated current)
2. a) To limit I_a to 90 A requires a total resistance in the armature circuit of
        $R = V/I_a = 225/90 = 2.5$ Ω
    b) Because the armature already contributes 0.15 Ω, the external resistance
        $R_s = 2.5 - 0.15 = 2.35$ Ω

16.4 Theory of the Dc Motor

Now that we have a general idea of the properties of dc motors, we can study the underlying theory. Fig. 16.12 is the schematic diagram of a separately excited shunt-wound motor that is connected to a dc source V_s. The motor draws a current I_a, and the armature is turning ccw at a speed of n turns per minute. The shunt field current I_f produces a flux ϕ, which is cut by the rotating armature conductors. As a result, a voltage V_o is induced in the armature. This voltage is *identical* to the voltage that would be induced if the machine were operating as a generator. Finally, the armature resistance R_a produces a small voltage drop $I_a R_a$. It follows that the induced voltage V_o is only slightly less than the applied voltage V_o.

Figure 16.11b

A hot-strip rolling mill compresses a steel slab to the desired thickness. The stand is driven by large dc motors, one of which is seen on the platform at the right. The white-hot strip is carried along on rollers driven by dozens of 3 hp dc motors mounted side by side.

(Courtesy. General Electric)

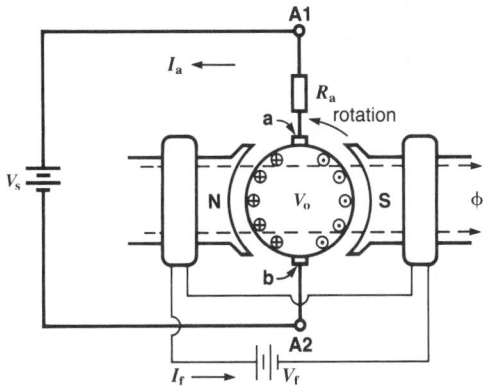

Figure 16.12

Circuit enabling the development of the basic equations of a dc motor.

We now can develop some of the basic equations and relationships of a dc motor.

1. Armature current I_a must flow out of the (−) terminal of the source because the source is supplying power to the motor. The power absorbed by the armature is

$$P_a = V_s I_a$$

EQ. 16.1

2. The armature resistance produces losses equal to $I_a^2 R_a$. *The* net power supplied to the armature is therefore

$$P_{mi} = V_s I_a - I_a^2 R_a$$

EQ. 16.2

This electric power is entirely converted into the "internal" mechanical power mentioned previously.

Equation 16.2 can be simplified as follows:

$$P_{mi} = (V_s - I_a R_a) I_a$$

from which

$$P_{mi} = V_o I_a$$

EQ. 16.3

Thus, the internal mechanical power is equal to the product of the induced voltage V_o times the armature current I_a. This same result was obtained for a dc generator (see Section 15.11).

3. What is the polarity of V_o? Point a must be (+) with respect to b because the armature winding absorbs electric power. The induced voltage V_o is sometimes called the **counter emf (cemf)** of the motor. The reason is that its polarity tends to produce a current in the armature circuit opposite (counter) to the direction of I_a.

COUNTER EMF (CEMF)

4. The current in the armature conductors flows in the direction given by the crosses and dots of Fig. 16.12. We come to this conclusion because the force ($F = BLI$) on the conductors next to the N pole must act downward in order to produce the ccw rotation. Similarly, the force on the conductors facing the S pole acts upward.

5. The current flowing in the armature conductors produces an armature mmf M_a that acts downward, as shown in Fig. 16.13. As a result, the flux crossing the armature is distorted and pole tips c and d tend to saturate. Thus, as in the case of a generator, the armature reaction tends to reduce the flux ϕ at the same time as it tends to cause sparking at the brushes.

Figure 16.13

Armature reaction in a dc motor distorts the field flux and saturates pole tips c and d.

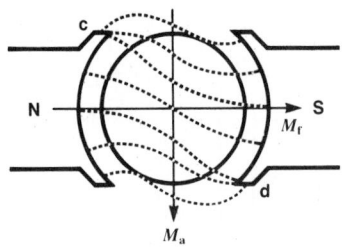

16.5 Torque of a Dc Motor

Returning to Fig. 16.12, we see each armature conductor is subjected to a force given by $F = BLI$. Furthermore, the flux density B is directly proportional to the flux ϕ. Consequently, the torque produced by the motor depends on both ϕ and I_a. We can establish the exact relationship as follows:

According to Equation 1.9, the torque T is given by

EQ. 16.4

$$T = \frac{9.55\ P}{n} = \frac{9.55\ P_{mi}}{n}$$

Substituting Equation 16.3 in Equation 16.4, we obtain

EQ. 16.5

$$T = 9.55\ \frac{V_o I_a}{n}$$

But the induced voltage V_o is a generator voltage, which is given by Equation 15.1:

EQ. 15.1

$$V_o = Kn\phi$$

If we substitute Equation 15.1 in Equation 16.5, we obtain the torque equation

EQ. 16.6

$$T = 9.55\ K\phi I_a$$

where

T = torque, in newton metres (N.m)

ϕ = flux per pole, in webers (Wb)

I_a = armature current, in amperes (A)

K = a constant that depends upon the winding on the armature

9.55 = a constant to take care of units

Although we used the shunt-wound motor of Fig. 16.12 to arrive at this torque equation, it applies to any type of dc motor. For example, the flux ϕ may be produced by the combined effect of a series and shunt field. Equation 16.6 also tells us that the torque depends only upon the value of ϕ and I_a; the speed of the motor does not matter. However, the speed *does* affect the value of I_a and sometimes even the flux ϕ. Consequently, the speed has an indirect effect upon the torque, and this creates the various torque-speed curves we saw in Figs. 16.2, 16.5, and 16.7.

16.6 Speed of a Dc Motor

Referring again to Fig. 16.12, we see the induced voltage V_o is given by:

$$V_o = V_s - I_aR_a$$ EQ. 16.7

When the motor runs between no-load and full-load, the I_aR_a drop is always small compared with the source voltage V_s. Consequently, V_o is nearly equal to V_s. Using Equation 15.1, we can therefore write

$$n = \frac{V_o}{K\phi} = \frac{V_s - I_aR_a}{K\phi} \text{ (exactly)}$$ EQ. 16.8

from which we get

$$n = \frac{V_s}{K\phi} \text{ (approximately)}$$ EQ. 16.9

where

n = speed of rotation, in revolutions per minute (r/min)

V_s = voltage across the armature, in volts (V)

ϕ = flux per pole, in webers (Wb)

K = constant that depends upon the winding on the armature

To interpret the meaning of Equation 16.9, suppose that ϕ is held constant. The speed will then vary directly with the voltage V_s applied to the armature. This means that we can vary the motor speed from zero to maximum simply by varying V_s. This is one of the important features of a dc motor.

Next, suppose V_s is fixed and we vary ϕ. If the flux decreases, the denominator in Equation 16.9 decreases, causing speed n to increase. Conversely, if ϕ increases, the speed will drop. This means that we can vary the speed by varying the field current I_f. This is another important feature of a dc motor.

16.7 Acceleration of a Shunt Motor

Consider Fig. 16.14, in which a shunt motor having an armature resistance R_a is about to be connected to a source V_s by means of switch S. An external resistor R_s is used to limit the starting current to about 1.5 times its rated value. The total resistance of the armature circuit is $R_t = R_a + R_s$. The shunt field is excited and produces flux ϕ. At the instant the switch closes, a current I_a will flow in the armature. Because the armature is not yet turning, the current is given by

$$I_a = V_s/R_t$$

The current will produce a strong starting torque, causing the motor to accelerate. As it picks up speed, the conductors cut across the flux lines, inducing a voltage V_o (Fig. 16.15). The greater the speed, the greater this cemf will become. The net voltage acting on the circuit is $V_s - V_o$. The resulting current I_a is therefore

EQ. 16.10 $$I_a = (V_s - V_o)/R_t$$

Equation 16.10 shows that the current will decrease as V_o increases. This means that I_a will decrease with increasing speed. Is there a limit to the speed? Yes, for suppose the speed rises to a level at which $V_o = V_s$. Then, according to Equation 16.10, current I_a will be zero. As a result, the torque will also be zero, and the motor will cease to accelerate.

In practice, the speed will not quite rise to the point at which $V_o = V_s$ because the motor has to develop *some* torque to keep running. A relatively small torque is needed to balance the opposing torque due to windage, friction, and iron losses.

▼ **Figure 16.14**

Shunt motor with the armature at rest.

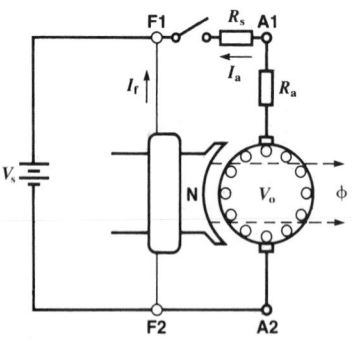

▼ **Figure 16.15**

A counter emf V_o is generated in the armature when the motor turns.

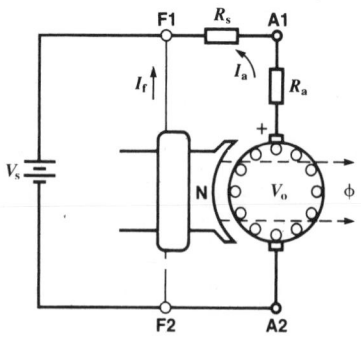

EXAMPLE 16.3

A permanent-magnet dc generator (Fig. 16.16) produces 60 V when it is rotated at 500 r/min. The armature resistance is 2 Ω. If this machine operates as a motor connected to a 200 V source, calculate:

1. the locked-rotor current
2. the induced voltage (counter-emf) when the motor turns at 1200 r/min
3. the armature current at 1200 r/min

4. the "internal" mechanical power at 1200 r/min
5. the "internal" torque developed at 1200 r/min
6. the approximate final speed of the motor

SOLUTION:

1. The motor circuit at the moment of start-up is shown in Fig. 16.17. The induced voltage is zero because the armature is not yet turning. Consequently

$I_a = V_s/R_a = 200/2 = 100$ A

2. When the motor turns at 1200 r/min (Fig. 16.18), the induced voltage, or cemf, is

$V_o = \dfrac{1200}{500} \times 60 = 144$ V

▼ **Figure 16.16**

See Example 16.3. Machine operating as a generator.

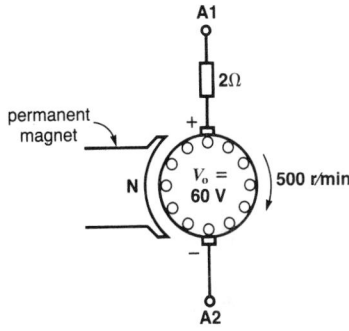

▼ **Figure 16.17**

See Example 16.3. Machine operating as a motor, but not yet turning.

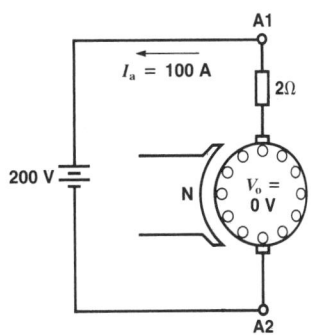

▼ **Figure 16.18**

See Example 16.3. Machine operating as a motor, at 1200 r/min.

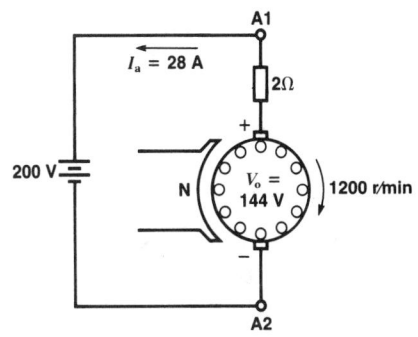

3. The voltage across R_a = (200 − 144) = 56 V
   The armature current $I_a = V/R_a = 56/2 = 28$ A

4. The mechanical power $P_{mi} = V_o I_a = 144 \times 28 = 4032$ W
   which, in horsepower = 4032/746 = 5.4 hp

5. $T = 9.55\ P/n$ **EQ. 1.9**
   $= 9.55 \times 4032/1200 = 32.09$ N.m

6. If the friction losses were negligible, the motor speed would rise until $V_o = 200$ V. Because we know that $V_o = 60$ V corresponds to a generator speed of 500 r/min, it follows that $V_o = 200$ V corresponds to 500 × (200/60) = 1667 r/min. Thus, the motor will turn at a final speed slightly below 1667 r/min.

16.8 Torque and Speed Characteristics of a Shunt Motor

Equations 16.1 to 16.10 enable us to determine the torque and speed of a dc motor when we know its basic properties. We thus can determine the torque and speed of a shunt motor between no-load and full-load. Using a numerical example, we assume the motor has the following ratings:

V_s = 250 V   rated I_a = 500 A

R_a = 0.02 K = 3   rated n = 800 r/min

From Equation 16.8, the flux ϕ is

$$\phi = \frac{V_0}{Kn} = \frac{250 - 500 \times 0.02}{3 \times 800} = \frac{240}{2400} = 0.1 \text{ Wb}$$

From Eq. 16.6, the full-load torque is

$$T = 9.55\ K\phi I_a = 9.55 \times 3 \times 0.1 \times 500 = 1432.5 \text{ N.m}$$

In a shunt motor, the flux ϕ remains constant. It follows from Equation 16.6 that the torque T is directly proportional to I_a. This straight-line relationship is shown in Fig. 16.19. We have also plotted the value of V_0; it slopes downward because of the $I_a R_a$ drop. Knowing V_0 and using Equation 16.8, we can find the speed n for any load I_a.

For example, at no-load, $V_0 = V_s = 250$ V and $I_a = 0$, which gives us

EQ. 16.8 $$n = \frac{V_0}{K\phi} = \frac{250}{3 \times 0.1} = 833.3 \text{ r/min}$$

At full-load, $V_0 = V_s - I_a R_a = 250 - 500 \times 0.02 = 240$ V

Therefore $n = \dfrac{V_0}{K\phi} = \dfrac{240}{3 \times 0.1} = 800$ r/min

The speed curve is a straight line ranging from $n = 833$ r/min at $I_a = 0$ to $n = 800$ r/min when $I_a = 500$ A.

The torque and speed can be replotted as a torque-speed curve, and this will yield a curve similar to that shown in Fig. 16.2.

In Section 16.4 we mentioned that due to armature reaction, the field flux decreases when the motor is under load. This becomes a serious problem in large shunt motors because it causes them to run faster as the load increases. To obtain a drooping speed characteristic, a weak series field is added. Such machines are called *stabilized shunt* motors (see Fig. 16.3).

Figure 16.19

Torque and speed versus armature current of a shunt motor.

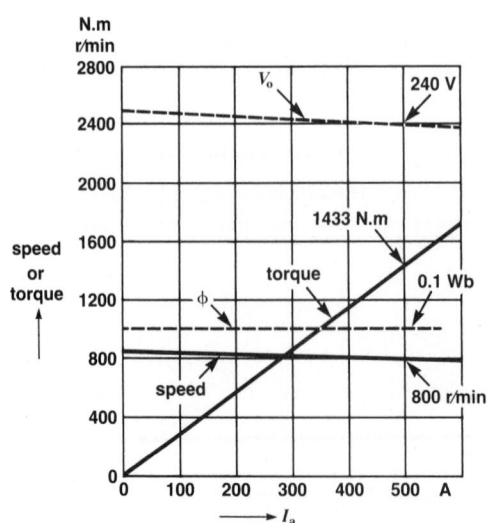

16.9 Torque and Speed Characteristics of a Series Motor

We shall now determine the torque and speed of a series motor from no-load to full-load. We assume the motor has the same full-load rating as the shunt motor studied in the previous section. Thus, the full-load flux is again 0.1 Wb. However, in a series motor, the flux decreases as the current decreases, and the assumed relationship between the two is shown in Fig. 16.20. It is not a straight line because we assume the iron begins to saturate as the current in the series winding increases.

Using the same technique as for a shunt motor, we can calculate the torque and speed of the series motor for any load I_a. For example, when $I_a = 200$ A, $\phi = 0.06$ Wb (read from the graph), and so

$$n = \frac{V_o}{K\phi} = \frac{250 - 200 \times 0.02}{3 \times 0.06} = \frac{246}{0.18} = 1367 \text{ r/min}$$

and

$$T = 9.55 \, K\phi I = 9.55 \times 3 \times 0.06 \times 200 = 344 \text{ N.m}$$

The solid curves in Fig. 16.20 show the torque and speed.

It is obvious that the no-load speed of a series motor can rise to dangerous levels.

If we replot the torque and speed on a torque-speed curve, we obtain the general result shown in Fig. 16.5.

Series motors are used to drive large exhaust fans on ships, and electric trains and buses (Fig. 16.21).

▼ **Figure 16.20**

Torque and speed versus armature current of a series motor.

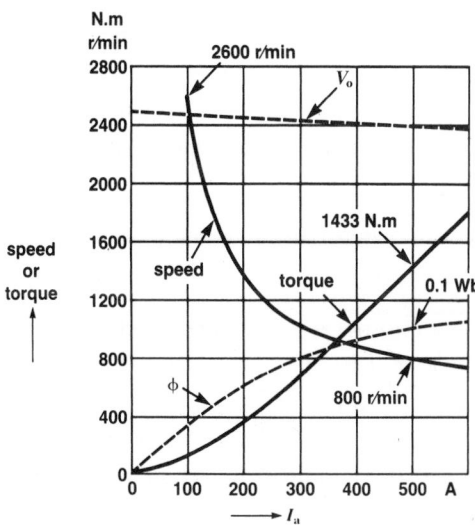

▼ **Figure 16.21**

This metro train is driven by two 153 hp, 360 V series motors having a speed range from zero to 2160 r/min. Each motor weighs 625 kg and is insulated with 155°C insulation.

16.10 Torque and Speed Characteristics of a Compound Motor

Figure 16.22 shows the torque and speed of a compound motor. We assume this machine has the same full-load rating as the shunt motor studied in Section 16.8. However, the flux is assumed to increase from 0.06 Wb at no-load to 0.1 Wb at full-load.

The torque and speed in different load currents are calculated the same way as before.

Figure 16.22

Torque and speed versus armature current of a compound motor.

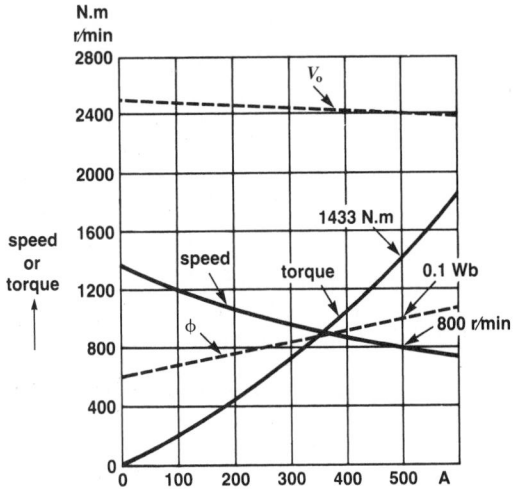

16.11 Speed Control of a Dc Motor

The speed of a shunt motor can be varied over a wide range by changing the field current with a rheostat. When the speed is varied this way, the armature current and armature voltage can retain their rated values. It follows that the motor can deliver its rated horsepower for all values of I_f.

On the other hand, if the field current is kept at its rated value, the same motor can operate below rated (base) speed if we apply a lower-than-rated voltage V_s to the armature. However, the armature current can retain its rated value. Consequently, the motor can develop its full rated torque for any value of armature voltage.

Thus, as far as rating is concerned, a shunt motor is a constant-torque machine when it operates below base speed and a constant-horsepower machine when it operates above base speed.

In some cases, the load has to be accelerated and decelerated very quickly. Field control is usually not feasible because the field current cannot change quickly enough because of the field inductance. Thus, if we want fast response, we have to vary the armature voltage. Acceleration is obtained by increasing V_s. We also can obtain *forced* deceleration by decreasing V_s. For example, suppose the motor in

▼ Figure 16.23

Dc motor running normally at
a speed of 1200 r/min with a
supply voltage at 120 V.

▼ Figure 16.24

Reducing the supply voltage
to 106 V causes the armature
current and torque to reverse.

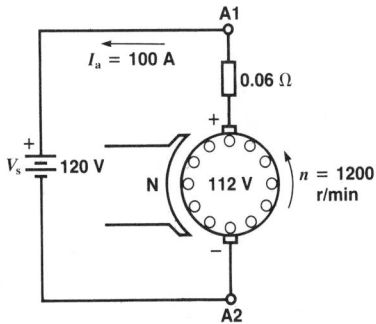

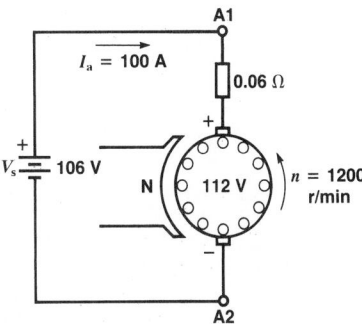

Fig. 16.23 is running at constant speed and exerting rated torque. It is connected
to a source V_s of 120 V, and its cemf is 112 V. The net voltage acting on the armature circuit is $(V_s - V_o) = (120 - 112) = 6$ V, and so $I_a = V/R_a = 6/0.06 = 100$ A.
Current flows in the direction shown because V_s exceeds V_o.

If we suddenly reduce V_s to 106 V, we obtain the condition shown in Fig. 16.24. V_o
is now greater than V_s and so the current I_a reverses. As a result, a strong *braking*
torque is exerted on the motor, causing its speed to drop rapidly. In Fig. 16.24, the
motor is actually operating as a generator, delivering power to the 106 V "source,"
which is now acting as a load.

Such fast speed control is obtained by the so-called **Ward-Leonard system** (Fig. 16.25).
A dc generator G produces a variable voltage V_s that is applied to the armature of the
motor we want to control. The motor field is fixed. The generator is driven by a motor
M_d connected to the ac power line in the plant. By varying the field excitation I_f of the
generator, voltage V_s varies, which in turn controls the motor speed. The speed can be
reversed by reversing the polarity of V_f.

WARD-LEONARD
SYSTEM

Rapid speed changes and reversals are needed in the operation of mine hoists and
rolling mills in the steel industry. Figure 16.26 shows two 7000 hp motors that
operate in tandem to drive a slabbing mill.

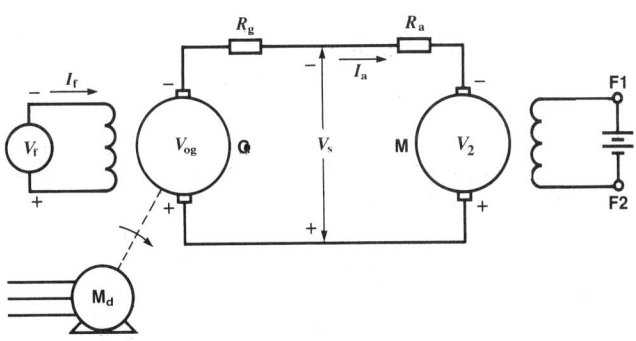

Figure 16.25

Ward-Leonard speed control
system.

Figure 16.26

Two 7000 hp, 30 r/min dc
motors operate together to
drive a metal rolling mill.
The motor on the left is
complete with its 24-pole
stator. The partly assembled
motor on the right shows
the armature with its adult-
size commutator.

*(Courtesy General Electric
Company, USA)*

16.12 Dynamic Braking and Plugging

DYNAMIC BRAKING

Whenever a motor has to be brought to a rapid stop, a method called **dynamic braking** may be used. It consists of connecting a resistor R_d across the armature terminals immediately after the armature has been disconnected from the line (Fig. 16.27). The motor, now acting as a generator, dissipates its kinetic energy in the resistor until it comes to rest.

PLUGGING

If emergency stopping is needed, dynamic braking may not be quick enough. In such cases, we use a method called **plugging**. It consists of reversing the polarity of the supply voltage V_s across the terminals of the armature (Fig. 16.28). The net voltage acting in the armature circuit suddenly changes from $(V_s - V_o)$ to $(-V_s - V_o)$. To limit the very high braking current I_a that would otherwise result, a resistor R_p is connected in series with the armature while the motor is stopping.

When the motor has come to rest and is about to reverse, a switch S opens automatically, disconnecting the armature from the line.

▼ **Figure 16.27**

A motor can be stopped quickly
by using dynamic braking.

▼ **Figure 16.28**

A dc motor can be stopped
even faster by plugging.

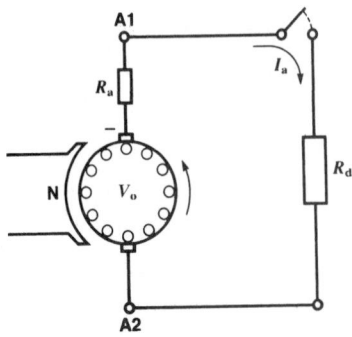

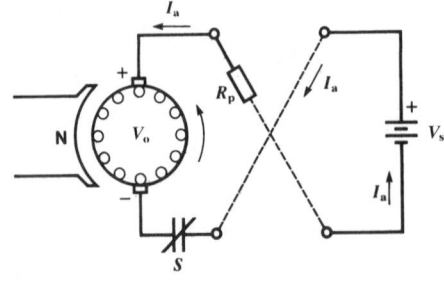

16.13 Starters for Dc Motors

Many types of starters are available to bring dc motors up to speed. We will limit our study to one type of manual starter and then cover the general principles of automatic starters. Figure 16.29 shows the schematic diagram of a manual face-plate starter for a shunt motor. Bare copper contacts are connected to resistors R_1, R_2, R_3, and R_4. Conducting arm 1 sweeps across the contacts when it is pulled to the right by means of insulated handle 2. In the position shown, the arm touches dead copper contact M and the motor circuit is open. As we draw the handle to the right, the conducting arm first touches fixed contact N.

The supply voltage V_s immediately causes full field current I_f to flow, but the armature current I is limited by the four resistors in the starter box. The motor begins to turn and, as the cemf builds up, the armature current gradually falls. When the motor speed ceases to rise any more, we pull the arm to the next contact, thereby removing resistor R_1 from the armature circuit. The current immediately jumps to a higher value and the motor quickly accelerates to the next higher speed. When the speed is again stable, we move to the next contact until the arm finally touches the last contact. The arm is magnetically held in this position by a small electromagnet (4), which is in series with the shunt field.

If the supply voltage is suddenly interrupted or if the field excitation should accidentally be cut, the electromagnet releases the arm, allowing it to return to its dead position, under the pull of spring 3. This safety feature prevents the motor from starting by itself when the supply voltage is re-established.

Automatic starters perform the same function as manual starters. The only difference is that the current-limiting resistors are short-circuited, in succession, by a set of magnetic contactors. The timing is effected by slow-action pneumatic or electronic relays whose contacts close several seconds after their holding coils are energized.

Automatic starters will be more fully discussed in Chapter 22 because they involve symbols and principles better covered in a separate chapter.

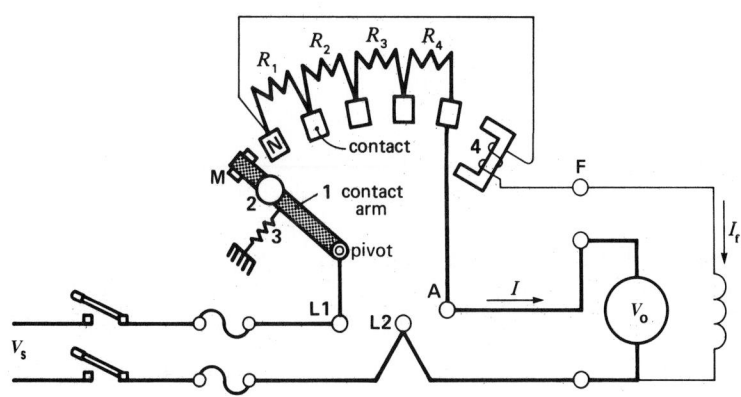

Figure 16.29

Manual face-plate starter for a dc motor.

16.14 Summary

Upon completion of this chapter you should be able to:

- Recognize that the construction of dc motors is the same as the construction of a dc generator.

- Explain the theory of operation for dc motors.

- List the losses associated with dc motors and calculate the motor efficiency using Equation 16.11.

- Explain how a dc motor is started by using a series resistor to limit the armature current.

- Calculate the torque developed by a dc motor using Equation 16.6.

- Explain that as a dc motor accelerates, the cemf increases, causing the net voltage to decrease. This results in a decrease in the motor current as the motor speed increases.

- Describe the torque-speed characteristics of series, shunt and compound dc motors as shown in Figs. 16.19, 16.20, and 16.22.

- Explain how the speed of a dc motor can be controlled by varying the terminal voltage. The Ward-Leonard system is used where rapid changes in motor speed are required.

- Describe how a dc motor can be stopped using dynamic braking and plugging.

- Describe how a dc motor can be started by manually varying a resistor connected in series with the armature, as shown in Fig. 16.29.

Key Terms

COMPOUND MOTOR: A dc motor with both a series and shunt-wound coil.

COUNTER EMF (CEMF): The voltage generated by the armature as it rotates through the magnetic field produced by the field coils. The cemf has a polarity opposite to the source voltage.

DYNAMIC BRAKING: A means of slowing a dc motor using an external resistor. As the supply voltage is disconnected from the motor, a resistor is connected across the motor terminals.

The resistor provides an electrical load that dissipates the energy generated by the decelerating motor. This slows the motor by converting mechanical energy to heat.

LOCKED ROTOR CURRENT: The current flowing in a motor armature when the armature is not rotating. The locked rotor current may be up to 50 times the rated motor current.

PLUGGING: A braking method for dc motors that is accomplished by reversing the motor's armature voltage. The armature current is limited by inserting a resistance in series with the armature circuit (see Figs. 16.27 and 16.28).

SERIES MOTOR: A dc motor in which the field coils are connected in series with the armature. Series motors are used in application requiring high starting torques, such as fans and electric vehicles.

SHUNT MOTOR: A dc motor in which the field windings are connected to an external power source.

WARD-LEONARD SYSTEM: A dc motor speed control system in which the motor armature voltage is supplied by a generator. By varying the generator output voltage, the dc motor speed can be varied or reversed quite rapidly.

Test Your Knowledge

16.1   The shunt field of a motor is connected
   a.   in parallel with the source
   b.   in series with the armature

16.2   Referring to Fig. 16.5, the rated torque (T_o) is 250 N.m and speed (n_o) is 1500 r/min. The rated power of the dc motor is:
   a.   375 hp
   b.   52.6 hp
   c.   502.7 hp

16.3   Figure 16.1 represents a four-pole shunt motor. The resistance of each field coil is 60 Ω, and V_s = 300 V. The field current I_f is
   a.   1.25 A
   b.   20 A
   c.   5 A

16.4   Figure 16.6 represents a four-pole compound motor. The armature resistance is 0.2 Ω, and each series field coil has a resistance of 0.05 Ω. If each interpole has a resistance of 0.02 Ω, the value of R_a is
   a.   480 Ω
   b.   0.27 Ω
   c.   480 mΩ

16.5   The iron losses in a dc motor are due to
   a.   the heat released by the field coils
   b.   hysteresis and eddy currents in the armature

   c.   hysteresis and eddy currents in the armature and frame

16.6   A 450 hp dc motor has total losses of 26 kW. The efficiency is
   a.   91.6%
   b.   94.5%
   c.   92.8%

16.7   In Fig. 16.12, armature reaction is due to
   a. I_a
   b. I_f
   c. I_a and I_f

16.8   A compound motor running at 600 r/min has a field flux of 150 mWb. If the flux is reduced to 120 mWb, the speed will
   a.   rise to 750 r/min
   b.   rise to 937.5 r/min
   c.   fall to 480 r/min

16.9   A four-pole, compound-wound motor connected to a 250 V source draws an armature current of 600 A. The induced voltage V_o is 240 V. The total mechanical power developed is
   a.   144 kW
   b.   150 kW
   c.   201 hp

16.10   When a shunt-wound motor suddenly acts as a generator,
   a.   the armature current reverses
   b.   it develops a greater torque
   c.   its speed may run away

Questions and Problems

16.11   Name three types of motors, and make a sketch of their armature and field-coil connections.

16.12   What determines the magnitude of the counter emf of a given dc motor?

16.13   What determines the polarity of the cemf of a dc motor?

16.14   The cemf of a dc motor is always slightly less than the applied armature voltage. Explain.

16.15   Name two ways to vary the speed of a dc motor.

16.16   Why is it dangerous to start a dc motor without a starting resistance?

16.17   In Fig. 16.11, if the shunt field is connected to terminals Al and A2 during the starting period, the motor will probably not be able to bring the load up to speed. Explain.

16.18   In Fig. 16.11, if F1 and F2 are interchanged, what will happen?

16.19   In Fig. 16.I I, if A1 and A2 are interchanged, what will happen?

16.20   A 500 V shunt-wound motor has a rated armature current of 1200 A. If the total resistance of the armature circuit is 0.008 Ω, calculate
a.   the cemf at full-load
b.   the total "internal" mechanical power developed by the motor, in horsepower
c.   the armature circuit heat loss

16.21   In Problem 16.20, calculate the locked-rotor current if the armature were directly connected to the line.

16.22   The motor of Fig. 16.6 has 1200 turns on the shunt winding and 4 turns on the series winding, per pole. The shunt field has a total resistance of 500 Ω, and the rated armature current I_a is 50 A. If the motor is fed by a 250 V line, calculate
a.   the mmf per pole at no-load
b.   the mmf per pole at full-load

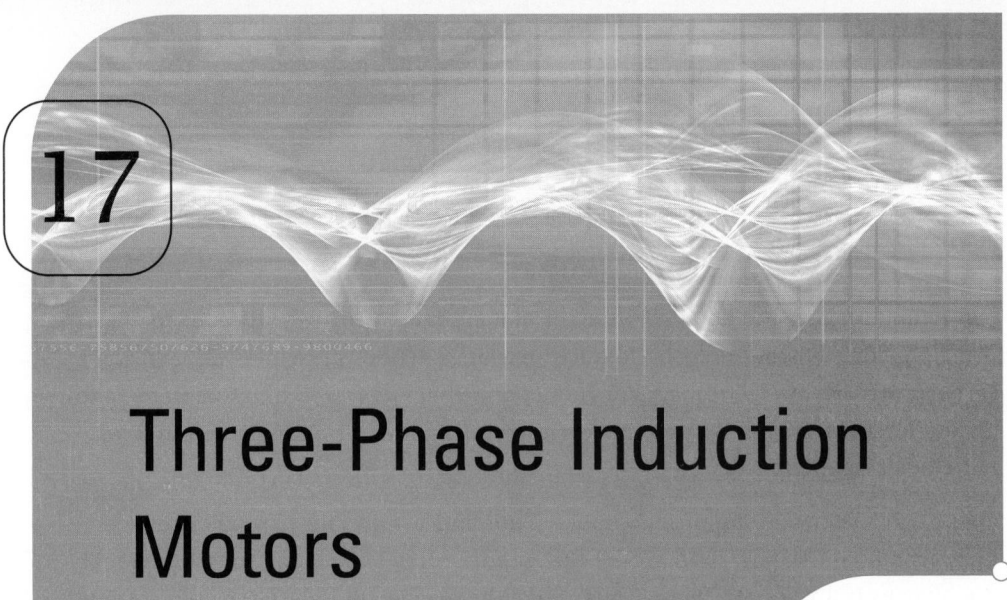

17

Three-Phase Induction Motors

LEARNING OBJECTIVES

Upon completion of this chapter you will be able to:

- Explain the operation of a three-phase rotating magnetic field

- Describe the construction of a three-phase squirrel cage induction motor

- Describe the operation of a three-phase squirrel cage induction motor under no-load, load and overload conditions

- Explain the effect of the number of poles on motor speed

- Explain the effect of rotor resistance on motor performance

- Describe the operation of a sector motor and a linear induction motor

Chapter Outline

17.1 Forces Produced by a Moving Magnetic Field

Before undertaking the detailed study of induction motors, we will cover the basic principles that enable us to build such machines. These principles depend upon (1) Faraday's law of electromagnetic induction, which we covered in Chapter 7, and (2) the force developed when a current-carrying conductor is immersed in a magnetic field, covered in Chapter 6.

Figure 17.1 shows a stationary copper plate and a movable permanent magnet. Copper is non-magnetic, and so the flux produced by the magnet passes through the plate as if it were not there. Thus, when the magnet and plate are both stationary, no forces are exerted and nothing happens.

But suppose we move the magnet to the right at a constant speed v_s. The flux will cut across the copper plate, and a voltage will be induced, which, in turn, will produce a current in the plate. The current is in the path of the flux created by the magnet (Fig. 17.2), and so a force acts on the plate. This force drives the plate in the same direction as the moving magnet. The plate is therefore dragged along with the magnet, at a certain speed v.

▼ **Figure 17.1**

Stationary permanent magnet above a copper plate.

▼ **Figure 17.2**

Moving the magnet to the right induces currents in the plate. The resulting force causes the plate to follow the magnet.

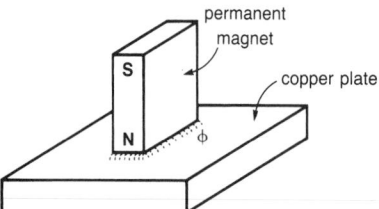

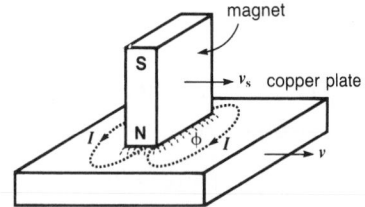

As the plate picks up speed, the flux lines cut across it less quickly, and so the induced voltage and the resulting induced current both begin to fall. The force dragging the plate along with the magnet therefore becomes smaller. If the plate moved at the same speed as the magnet, the flux lines would no longer cut across the plate. The induced current would become zero, and the force urging the plate to the right would disappear (Fig. 17.3). The magnitude of the induced current depends therefore upon the *relative* speed $(v_s - v)$ between the magnet and the plate. The greater the difference between v_s and v, the greater will be the current and the resulting force.

If we move the magnet to the left, the direction of current flow will reverse, and the plate will be dragged toward the left (Fig. 17.4).

▼ **Figure 17.3**

When the plate and magnet
move at the same speed, the
induced currents disappear and
the force on the plate is zero.

▼ **Figure 17.4**

When the magnet moves to
the left, it drags the plate
with it.

▼ **Figure 17.5**

A stationary magnet exerts a
braking force on the moving
copper plate.

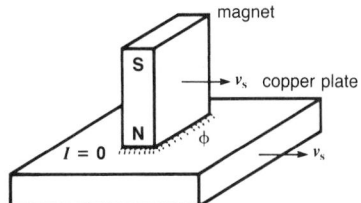

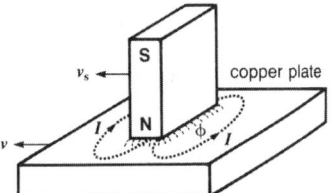

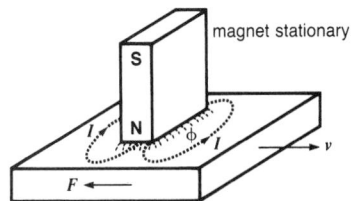

We conclude that the plate always tends to move in the same direction and at the same speed as the moving field.

Suppose now that the magnet is stationary and that the *plate* is moving toward the right at a speed *v*. The flux again cuts across the plate, and a current is again induced (Fig. 17.5). The resulting force on the plate acts against the direction of motion, and so a braking force *F* is exerted on the plate.

Thus, the magnet can cause the plate to move to the right or to the left, depending upon the direction of v_s. Furthermore, if the magnet is stationary, it will oppose the motion of the copper plate.

17.2 Torque Produced by a Rotating Magnetic Field

We can also produce rotary motion, based upon the principle of magnetic induction. Figure 17.6 shows a permanent magnet N-S that can be rotated manually by means of handle H. A rotor R, made of solid copper, is supported by bracket B, but is otherwise free to rotate. If we turn the handle clockwise at a speed n_s, the magnet will induce voltages and currents in the rotor. As in the case of the copper plate, the rotor will be dragged along by the revolving magnet. But as the rotor speed *n* increases, the induced voltage will become smaller, as will the induced current. Thus, the dragging force, or torque, will decrease as *n* approaches n_s. If *n* were to become equal to n_s, the induced voltage (and consequent current) would fall to zero, and the dragging force would disappear.

If we reverse the direction of rotation of the magnetic field, the rotor will turn in the opposite direction.

Finally, suppose that the magnetic field is stationary. If the rotor is turning, a braking force will act on it, which will quickly bring it to a halt.

The behaviour of a revolving rotor is therefore similar to that of a moving flat plate. This has given rise to two types of induction motors: standard (rotating) motors and linear motors.

Figure 17.6

A revolving permanent magnet
induces currents in the copper
rotor, causing the rotor to turn
in the same direction.

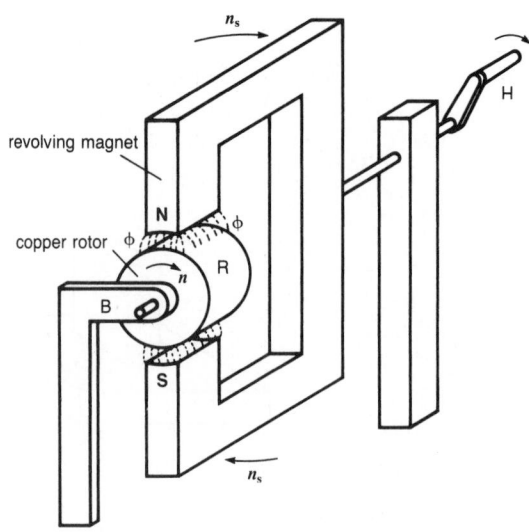

17.3 Number of Poles and Construction of the Rotor

The revolving magnetic field can have more than two poles. Figure 17.7 shows a field created by four poles that rotate as a group. Adjacent poles have opposite polarities N-S-N-S, as shown. The number of poles is always even because for every N pole there must be a corresponding S pole.

We mentioned that the rotor was made of solid copper. However, it could equally well be made of solid aluminum or solid steel. It will still be carried along by the magnetic field. However, to develop the largest possible torque, we must first ensure that a strong field is produced by the N and S poles. For this reason, the rotor should be made of iron, which has a high permeability. In addition, the air gap between the rotor and the magnetic poles should be as small as possible.

Figure 17.7

A revolving four-pole magnetic
field causes the rotor to turn.

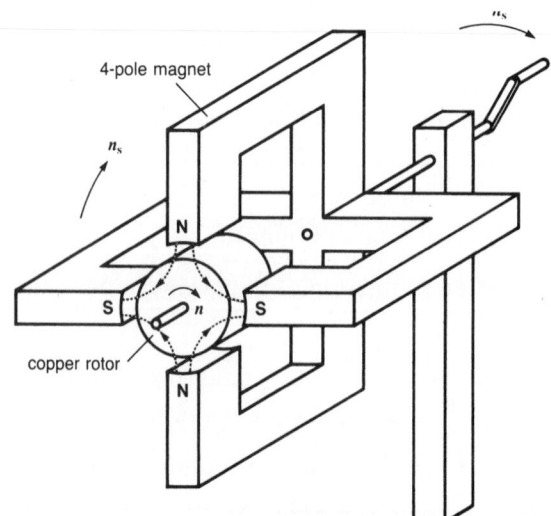

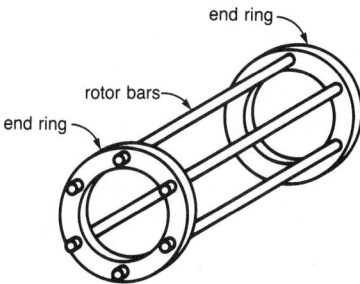

Figure 17.8

Elementary winding in a squirrel-cage rotor.

Second, to obtain a really strong torque, the rotor currents must be as large as possible. This means that the rotor should be made of a metal having a low resistivity. The best choice is copper or aluminum. Thus, to obtain the highest possible torque, we use a rotor made of iron in combination with a good conductor, such as copper and aluminum. In practice, we use a laminated iron rotor that has slots around the circumference. Aluminum or copper bars are inserted in the slots, and the ends are short-circuited by so-called end rings. The resulting winding looks like a squirrel cage (Fig. 17.8), and the rotor is often called a squirrel-cage rotor.

17.4 Slip and Synchronous Speed

Referring to Figs. 17.6 or 17.7, suppose the magnetic field is turning at a speed of n_s r/min, and the rotor is rotating in the same direction at a speed of n r/min. The relative speed is therefore $(n_s - n)$ r/min. The so-called **slip** of the rotor is given by the equation

SLIP

$$s = \frac{n_s - n}{n_s}$$

EQ. 17.1

The slip is zero when the rotor turns at the same speed and in the same direction as the magnetic field. On the other hand, the slip has a value of 1 when the rotor is stationary.

EXAMPLE 17.1

1. The field in Fig. 17.7 is turning cw at 1600 r/min, and the rotor is rotating cw at 1260 r/min. Calculate the slip.
2. Calculate the new value of slip if the rotor rotates cw at 1680 r/min while the field is still turning cw at 1600 r/min.

SOLUTION:

1. $s = (n_s - n)/n_s = (1600 - 1260)/1600 = 340/1600 = 0.21$ or 21%
2. $s = (n_s - n)/n_s = (1600 - 1680)/1600 = -80/1600 = -0.05$ or -5%

The slip is negative when the rotor turns faster than the field.

17.5 Producing a Revolving Field

So far we have used mechanical means to produce a rotating field. The question arises, how can we produce a field that turns without having to use a mechanical drive?

Consider the special electromagnet of Fig. 17.9, which is called a *stator*. It has six salient poles carrying six identical coils. The coils are arranged in pairs — a_1, a_2; b_1, b_2; and c_1, c_2 — spaced at 120° to each other. Coils that are diametrically opposite (such as a_1 and a_2) are connected in series in such a way as to create one N and one S pole. Three of the six coil ends are joined together to form a common neutral N, and the remaining coil ends A, B, and C are connected to a three-phase source. The coil arrangement is perfectly symmetrical, and so the three-phase currents I_a, I_b, and I_c are identical but are displaced in time by 120° (Fig. 17.10). This means that the currents reach their maximum positive values at different times. Thus, when I_a is maximum positive, flux ϕ_a acts in line with coils a_1–a_2, as shown in Fig. 17.11. Then, 120° later, when I_b reaches its maximum positive value, the flux ϕ_b acts in line with coils b_1–b_2 (Fig. 17.12). Another 120° later, current I_c reaches its maximum positive value, and flux ϕ_c is oriented in line with coils c_1 – c_2 (Fig. 17.13). After another 120° (Fig. 17.14), I_a is again maximum positive, and the flux takes up the same position it had in Fig. 17.11.

The flux in Figs. 7.11 to 17.14 is obviously moving clockwise inside the six-pole stator. The sequence ϕ_a – ϕ_b – ϕ_c – ϕ_a – ϕ_b repeats continually, and so the flux rotates continually. We can reverse the direction of rotation by interchanging any two stator leads. As we learned in Section 13.10, this reverses the phase sequence at the motor terminals.

In comparing Figs. 17.11 to 17.14, it is evident that the flux makes a complete turn in the time it takes I_a to go from one maximum positive value to the next. In other

Figure 17.9

Simplified stator winding of a three-phase motor. The three phases are connected in wye forming the common neutral N. When the switch is closed, the three-phase currents are equal in magnitude and displaced by 120° in time. The arrows show the direction of current when the respective currents are positive.

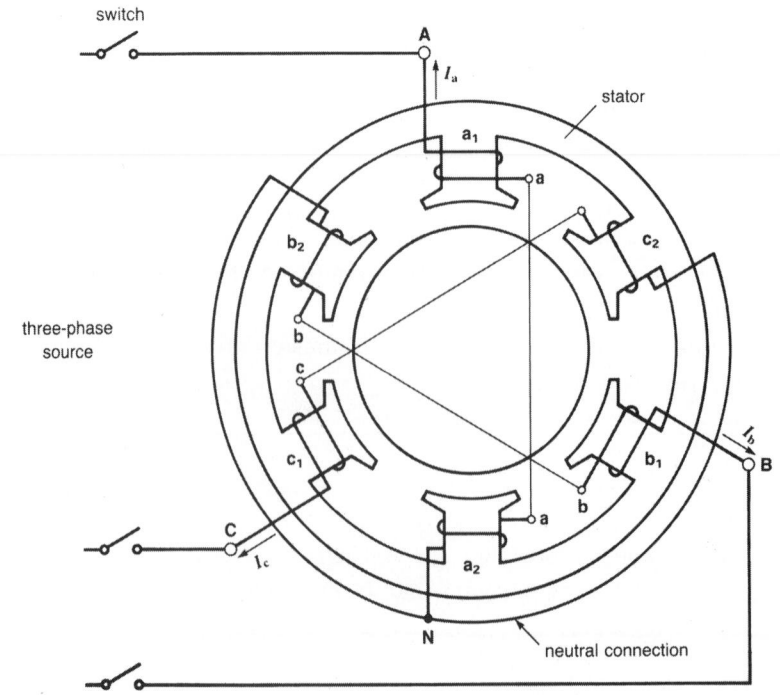

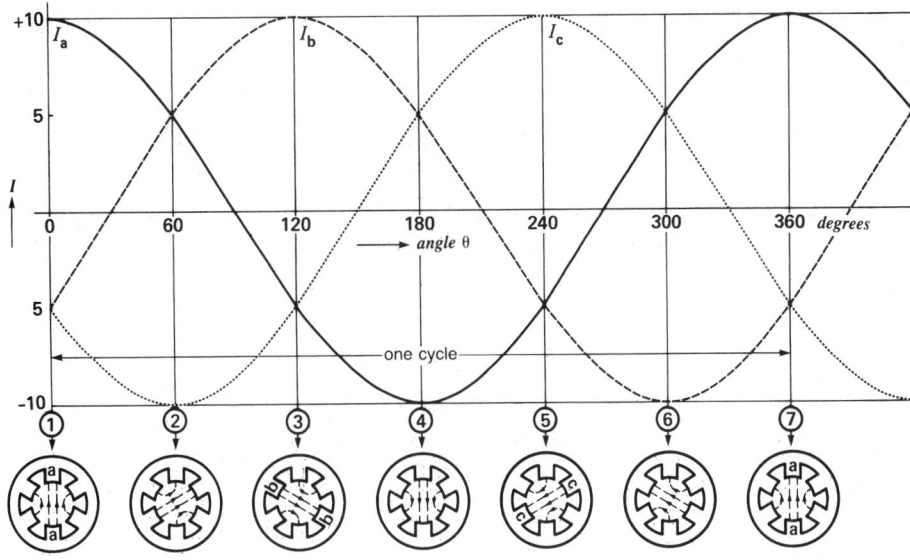

Figure 17.10

The currents in the windings vary sinusoidally. The resulting flux in the stator is shown at seven successive instants. The peak current is assumed to have a value of 10 A.

Figure 17.11

Flux produced by coils a_1–a_2 when I_a is +10 A

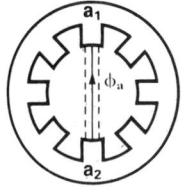

Figure 17.12

Flux produced by coils b_1–b_2 when I_b is +10 A

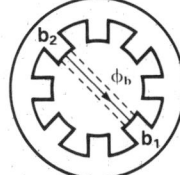

Figure 17.13

Flux produced by coils c_1–c_2 when I_c is +10 A

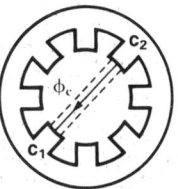

Figure 17.14

Flux produced by coils a_1–a_2 when I_a is again +10 A

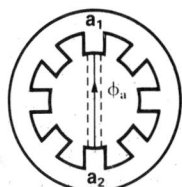

words, the flux makes a complete turn during each cycle. If the frequency of the source is 60 Hz, the flux makes one turn in 1/60 s. This corresponds to 60 revolutions per second, or 3600 r/min. The speed of rotation is therefore synchronized with the frequency of the source.

Although the stator has six poles, it only has two poles per phase. Thus, the three phases together produce a revolving magnetic field that has two poles. The shape of the field at successive intervals is also shown in Fig. 17.10.

17.6 Effect of the Number of Poles

We can increase the number of poles per phase from two to four to six (or to any higher even number) by changing the design of the stator. Increasing the number of poles reduces the speed of rotation of the magnetic field. For example, in Fig. 17.15, the four-pole stator (four poles per phase) produces a four-pole revolving field that turns at exactly half the speed of a two-pole stator. The four poles rotate together like the spokes of a wheel. Consequently, the rotating field is similar to that shown in Fig. 17.7.

Flux produced by the coils of phase A in a 4-pole stator when I_a is maximum positive. Note that the coil connections produce alternate N and S poles as we move around the stator. The coils of phases B and C are wound the same way but are shifted in space.

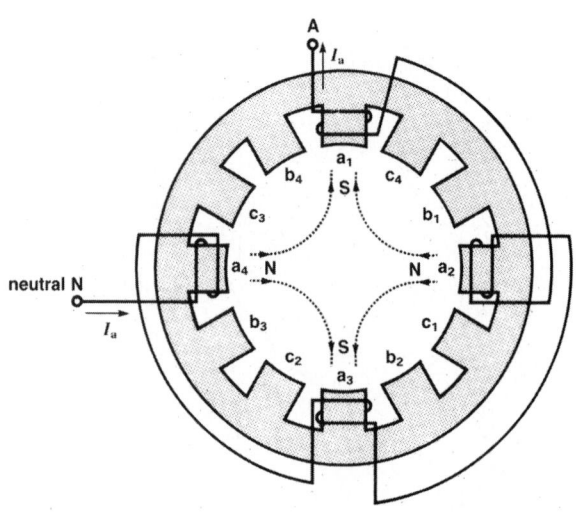

The speed of rotation of the magnetic field depends therefore upon the frequency of the source and the number of poles on the stator. Its value is given by the equation

EQ. 17.2

$$n_s = \frac{120\,f}{p}$$

where

n_s = synchronous speed, in revolutions per minute (r/min)

f = frequency of the source, in hertz (Hz)

p = number of poles per phase

SYNCHRONOUS SPEED

The speed of rotation is called **synchronous speed** because it is exactly in step with the frequency.

EXAMPLE 17.2

A three-phase induction motor has 16 poles on the stator. If it is connected to a special source that generates a frequency of 5 Hz, calculate the speed of rotation of the magnetic field.

SOLUTION:

EQ. 17.2 $n_s = 120\,f/p = (120 \times 5)/16 = 37.5$ r/min

The synchronous speed of the motor is therefore 37.5 r/min.

17.7 Construction of a Squirrel-Cage Induction Motor

Having covered the general principles, we will now examine the practical construction of an induction motor. A three-phase induction motor has two main parts: a stationary stator and a revolving rotor.

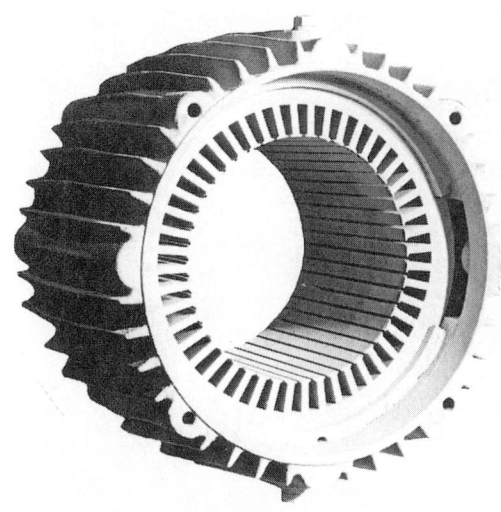

Figure 17.16

Stator core of a medium-power
(50 hp) three-phase motor.
The large number of slots
permits a distributed winding
that produces a better motor
performance than a salient-
pole winding does.

The stator produces the revolving field in a manner similar to the stator of Fig. 17.9
or Fig. 17.15. However, instead of having salient poles, it consists of a hollow cylindrical core made up of stacked laminations. A number of evenly spaced slots are
punched out of the internal circumference. The slots provide space for the stator
winding (Figs. 17.16, 17.17, and 17.18). The laminated core is supported inside a
steel frame that carries mounting feet and lifting lugs and also serves to accurate-
ly position the end-bells. End-bells are the two disk-shaped ends of the motor that
support the rotor shaft (Fig. 17.20).

Figure 17.17

Placing pre-formed coils into
the slots of a large-power
motor. Note the symmetrical
distribution of the winding.

(Courtesy General Electric)

The rotor is also made of punched laminations. The rotor slots are carefully lined up during the stacking process to provide space for the rotor winding. The winding is composed of copper bars that are inserted into the slots and then welded together at each end by means of two copper end rings. For motors below 100 hp, the rods and end rings are usually made of die-cast aluminum. In the manufacturing process, molten aluminum under high pressure is forced into a mould that surrounds the iron rotor. The squirrel-cage winding is thus formed in a fraction of a second. Figs. 17.19 to 17.21 show typical rotor construction and motor assembly.

The completed rotor is mounted on a steel shaft and then turned down in a lathe to create a small gap between the rotor and the stator. The length of the air gap depends upon the size of the motor, but it usually ranges from 0.4 mm to about 5 mm for very large machines. The air gap is made as small as mechanical tolerances will permit.

Figure 17.19

Squirrel-cage rotor of a large-power induction motor. The slots are just beneath the smooth outer surface and are therefore not visible. The thirteen radial ducts permit cooling along the length of the rotor. Additional cooling is provided by the two fans at each end. The very robust shaft is designed to resist mechanical shock and to prevent the rotor from coming in contact with the stator.

(Courtesy General Electric)

Figure 17.20

Exploded view of a squirrel-cage induction motor having copper rotor bars. The illustration shows the ball bearings mounted on each end of the shaft, the two end-bells next to the stator, the ventilating fan, and the protective shield on the extreme left. The windings are fed from the three terminals in the terminal box.

(Courtesy Brook Crompton Parkinson)

17.8 Locked-Rotor Conditions

At the instant a three-phase motor is connected to the line, the rotor is still at rest. However, the stator immediately creates a revolving field. This field cuts across the rotor bars, inducing a small voltage in them. However, large currents begin to flow in the rotor bars because they are short-circuited together. The bars are immersed

Figure 17.21

Cutaway view of a 5 hp
squirrel-cage induction motor
having a die-cast aluminum
rotor. This dual-voltage
230 V/460 V motor has nine
leads coming out of the
terminal box. Note that the
cooling fins are die-cast
integrally with the rotor bars
and end rings.

(Courtesy Siemens-Allis)

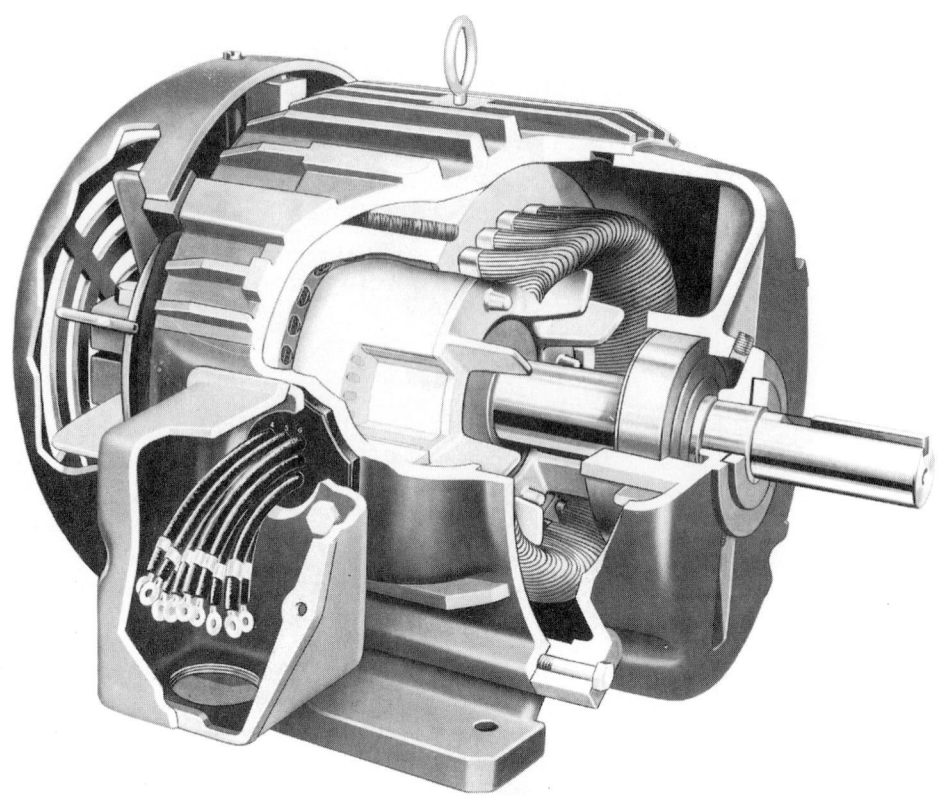

in the magnetic field created by the stator, and so a strong force ($F = BLI$) acts on each bar. The sum of the forces on all the bars produces a strong locked-rotor torque which acts in the same direction as the revolving field.

Under locked-rotor* conditions, the motor acts like a three-phase transformer whose secondary winding is short-circuited (remember that all the rotor bars are short-circuited together). Consequently, the rotor and stator windings begin to heat up very quickly because of the large I^2R losses. The current in the three lines of the stator is between 5 and 6.5 times the rated full-load current. Consequently, the I^2R losses are between 25 and 42 times their normal value. Furthermore. the power factor is usually below 40 percent.

Because of the large power that is drawn from the source and because of the high heating rate, we must never leave a motor in the locked-rotor condition for more than a few seconds.

17.9 Acceleration of a Squirrel-Cage Motor

If the rotor is free to turn, the locked-rotor torque will accelerate the rotor in the same direction as the rotating field. But as the motor picks up speed, the rotating field cuts across the rotor bars at a lower speed, and so the induced voltage begins to fall. This, in turn, causes the rotor current to decrease. Although the rotor torque may decrease, it continues to accelerate the rotor.

* The term locked-rotor is sometimes abbreviated LR.

How fast will the motor turn? The rotor can never reach synchronous speed because if it did, it would be moving at the same speed as the revolving field. The induced voltage would then be zero, the currents in the rotor bars would disappear, and the torque would become zero. Therefore, a three-phase induction motor always runs at slightly less than synchronous speed. That is why it is sometimes called an **asynchronous motor**. The difference between the rotor speed and synchronous speed amounts to a slip of less than one percent.

ASYNCHRONOUS
MOTOR

While the rotor is accelerating, a frequency effect also takes place. Where the rotor is locked, the frequency of the voltage and current in the rotor bars is the same as the line frequency. But as the rotor picks up speed, the frequency decreases progressively. For example, when the rotor is turning at one-half synchronous speed. the stator flux cuts across the rotor bars at half the speed it did when the rotor was locked. As a result, the frequency of the voltage and current in the rotor bars falls to one-half the line frequency.

By the same reasoning, if the rotor turns at 90 percent of synchronous speed (slip = 10 percent), the frequency of the voltage and current in the rotor bars will be only 10 percent of line frequency. The rotor frequency is therefore related to the slip by the equation:

$$f_r = sf$$

EQ. 17.3

where

f_r = rotor frequency, in hertz (Hz)
s = slip
f = frequency of the source, in hertz (Hz)

The progressive drop in rotor frequency causes the inductive reactance of the rotor to decrease with increasing speed. This tends to increase the torque during the acceleration period. On the other hand, the decrease in rotor current with increasing speed tends to decrease the torque. These two opposing effects produce the typical torque-speed curves shown in Fig. 17.22.

17.10 Squirrel-Cage Motor at No-Load

When a squirrel-cage motor is operating at no-load, it runs very close to synchronous speed. For example, a 100 hp motor having a synchronous speed of 1800 r/min has a typical no-load speed of 1799 r/min. This represents a slip of (1800 – 1799)/1800 = 0.00055, or about 0.05 percent. Under these conditions, the current in the rotor bars is very small. Thus, as far as the stator is concerned, it is as if the rotor bars were open-circuited. Consequently, the no-load current drawn by the stator is mainly that needed to produce the revolving magnetic field. Thus, at no-load the motor draws mainly reactive power from the line, and so the power factor is low. The no-load current is typically 30 percent to 50 percent of the full-load current, and the power factor is about 20 percent.

▼ Figure 17.22a

Typical torque-speed characteristic of a
2 hp, 3-phase squirrel-cage induction
motor. The curve illustrates the interpretation of locked-rotor, pull-up, breakdown and full-load torques.

▼ Figure 17.22b

Typical torque-speed characteristic of a
2000 hp, 3-phase squirrel-cage induction
motor. Note the low starting torque and
almost constant speed before the breakdown torque is reached.

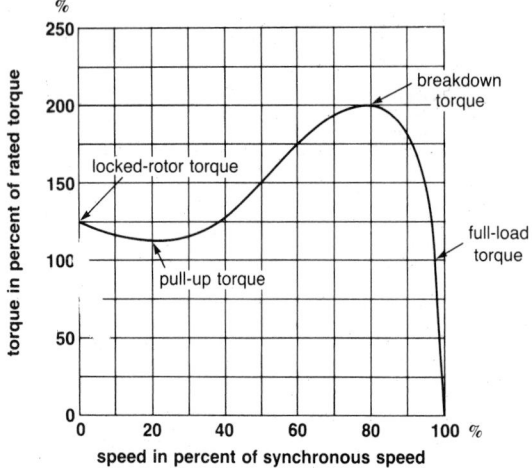

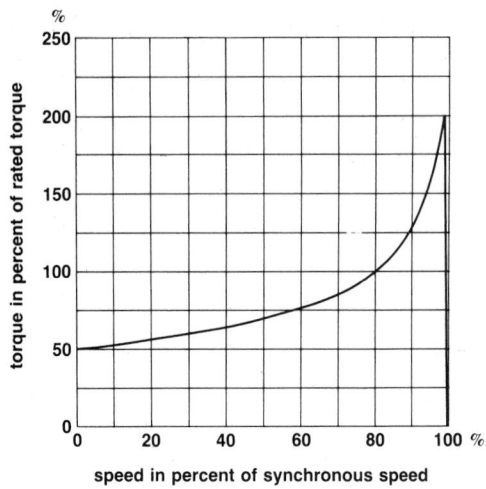

17.11 Squirrel-Cage Motor Under Load

Suppose an induction motor is initially running at no-load. If we suddenly apply a
mechanical load, the motor will begin to slow down. This causes the magnetic flux
to cut across the rotor bars more quickly. The voltage induced in the rotor bars
increases progressively, as does the rotor current. As a result, the motor develops
more and more torque. Eventually, when the motor has slowed down enough, the
torque it develops becomes equal to the load torque. The speed then remains stable (see Section 1.16).

The full-load speed is only slightly less than synchronous speed. Thus, a 1/4 hp
motor having a synchronous speed of 1800 r/min has a typical full-load speed of
1725 r/min. Similarly, a 5000 hp motor has a typical full-load speed of 1780 r/min.
Thus, induction motors are often called **constant-speed machines** because the
change in speed from no-load to full-load is very small.

**CONSTANT-SPEED
MACHINES**

Between no-load and full-load, the magnetic field in the motor is practically constant,
and so the reactive power (kvar) needed to produce it is practically constant.
However, the active power (kW) absorbed by the motor increases in almost direct
proportion to the mechanical load. Consequently, the power factor of an induction
motor improves as the load increases. Figure 17.23 shows the typical power factor
and efficiency curve of a 2 hp motor as the load increases from zero to rated output.

This curve shows that we should never select a 100 hp motor to do a 20 hp job.
The reason is that when a motor operates below its rated output, the power factor
and efficiency are always below their best values.

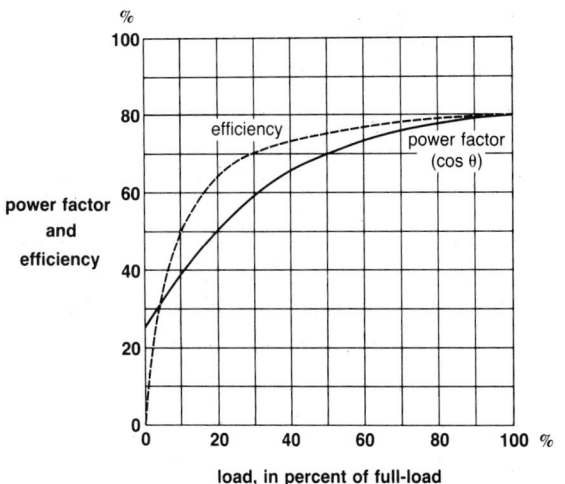

Figure 17.23

Typical efficiency and power factor of a 2 hp, 3-phase induction motor.

17.12 Squirrel-Cage Motor Under Overload

If we increase the mechanical load beyond the rated capacity of the motor, both the rotor and stator begin to overheat, which can reduce the useful life of the motor. However, as long as the excessive temperature does not last too long, no harm is done.

There is a limit, however, to the overload we can apply. If the load torque exceeds the so-called **breakdown torque** of the motor, the machine will stop and the circuit breakers will trip because of the resulting high current. The breakdown torque (Fig. 17.22) ranges between 1.5 and 2.5 times rated torque, depending upon the design of the motor.

BREAKDOWN TORQUE

17.13 Effect of Rotor Resistance

The resistance of the rotor has an important effect on the torque-speed characteristic of a three-phase induction motor. Fig. 17.24 shows the torque-speed curve of a standard 5 hp, 1760 r/min, 208 V motor having copper conductors in the rotor. If brass is used instead of copper, the torque-speed curve changes considerably, as shown. The locked-rotor torque increases from 30 N.m to 60 N.m and at the same time, the locked-rotor current *decreases* from 90 A to 75 A. This is a big advantage because we get more torque while drawing less current. Unfortunately, at rated torque, the speed falls from 1760 r/min to 1600 r/min when brass is used. In most cases, this decrease in speed is a disadvantage. Furthermore, the efficiency drops from 85 percent to 80 percent.

Thus, it would be desirable to have a motor whose rotor resistance is high under locked-rotor conditions and low when the motor runs at rated speed. This objective can be met by using a wound-rotor induction motor.

Figure 17.24

Effect on the torque-speed
characteristic when brass
instead of copper is used in
the rotor winding.

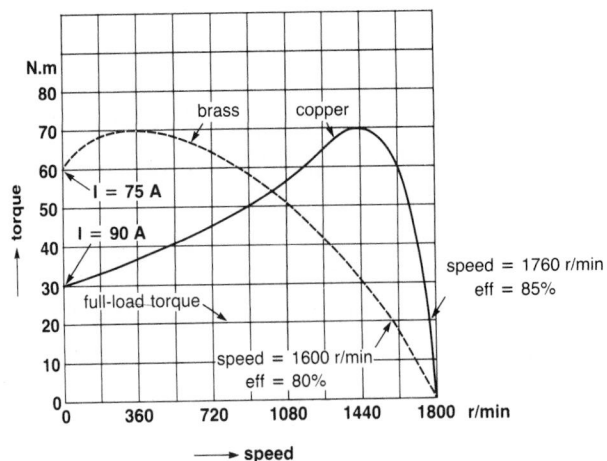

17.14 Sector Motor

Consider a standard 3-phase, 4-pole induction motor having a synchronous speed
of 1800 r/min. Let us cut the stator in half so that half the stator winding is
removed and only two complete poles (per phase) are left. Let us connect the three
phases in wye without making any other change to the existing coil connections.
This will give us a so-called **sector stator**, shown in Fig. 17.25. Let us mount the
original rotor above this sector stator, leaving a small air gap.

SECTOR STATOR

If we connect the stator terminals to a 3-phase, 60 Hz source, the rotor will again
turn at slightly below 1800 r/min. The reason is that the sector motor produces a
"revolving" flux that moves at the same linear speed as the ac in the original three-
phase motor. However, instead of making a complete turn, the field simply travels
continuously from one end of the stator to the other.

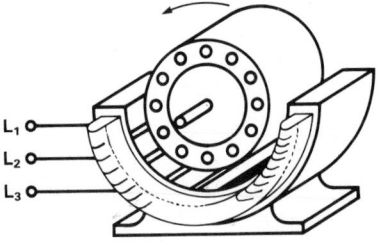

Figure 17.25

The sector stator causes
the squirrel-cage rotor to
rotate.

17.15 Linear Induction Motor

The sector stator could be laid out flat without affecting the linear speed of the
magnetic field. Such a flat stator produces a field that moves at constant speed in
a straight line.

If a flat plate is brought near the flat stator, the travelling field drags the plate along
with it, as was explained in Section. 17.1. In practice, we generally use a simple aluminum or copper plate as a "rotor" (Fig. 17.26). The combination of flat stator and
flat rotor is called a **linear induction motor**. The direction of the motor can be
reversed by interchanging any two stator leads.

LINEAR INDUCTION
MOTOR

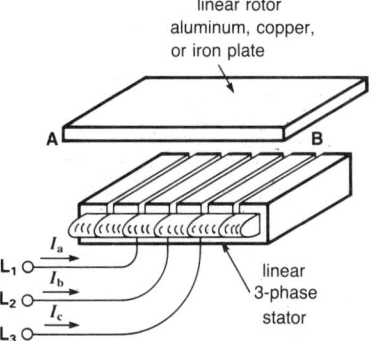

linear rotor
aluminum, copper,
or iron plate

A   B

L₁ ○ I_a
L₂ ○ I_b
L₃ ○ I_c

linear
3-phase
stator

Figure 17.26

Linear induction motor
produces a moving field
that drives the motor in a
straight line

EXAMPLE 17.3

The stator of a 600 hp, 3-phase, 60 Hz induction motor has six poles per phase and
an internal diameter of 460 mm. Calculate the speed at which the flux travels along
the internal surface of the stator.

SOLUTION:

a. The synchronous speed of the flux is:
    $n_s = 120 \, f/p = (120 \times 60)/6 = 1200$ r/min

    EQ. 17.2

b. The length L of the internal circumference is:
    $L = \pi d$
       $= 3.1416 \times 460 = 1445$ mm $= 1.445$ m

c. The flux makes 1200 turns per minute, and so it covers a distance of: $1200 \times$
    $1.445 = 1734$ metres per minute, or $(1734 \times 60) = 104\,040$ m/h

d. Knowing that 1609 m = 1 mile, the linear speed v_s is:
    $v_s = 104\,040 \, / \, 1609 = 64.7$ miles per hour

This means that if this particular stator were laid out flat, it would become a linear
motor having a synchronous speed of 64.7 miles per hour. By changing the design
of the windings, it is possible to obtain linear synchronous speeds of several hundred miles per hour.

17.16 Summary

Upon completion of this chapter you should have learned that:

• The three-phase rotating magnetic field (Figs. 17.11 through 17.14) causes a current to flow in the rotor by induction. The induced rotor current creates a magnetic field opposite to that of the stator field. The attraction between the rotor
   and the rotating magnetic field results in motion.

• A major advantage of the three-phase squirrel-cage induction motor is its simple
   construction (Fig. 17.20). Because it is an induction motor, there is no need for
   brushes and associated mechanical supports.

- The efficiency and power factor of a three-phase squirrel-cage induction increase as the motor load increases from no-load to full-load (Fig. 17.23).

- As the number of poles in a three-phase induction motor increases, the synchronous speed of the motor decreases. This relationship is shown in Equation 17.2.

- Changing the rotor resistance changes the torque-speed relationship of an induction motor. An example of changing rotor resistance is shown in Fig. 17.24.

- The three-phase sector motor (Section 17.14) and the linear induction motor (Section 17.15) are induction motors designed for special applications.

Key Terms

ASYNCHRONOUS MOTOR: Any motor in which the rotor turns at less than the synchronous speed.

BREAKDOWN TORQUE: The maximum torque that a motor is able to produce. If the motor attempts to produce torque higher than the breakdown torque, the rotor will stall.

CONSTANT-SPEED MACHINES: Any motor in which the speed change between no-load and full-load is minimal.

LINEAR INDUCTION MOTOR: A three-phase induction motor in which the stator is flat.

A copper or aluminum "rotor" moves in a straight line (linear) along the flattened stator.

SECTOR STATOR: A three-phase multipole induction motor in which the stator has only a single pole for each of the three phases.

SLIP: The difference in speed between the rotor and synchronous speed of the stator. Slip is usually expressed as a percentage of the synchronous speed.

SYNCHRONOUS SPEED: The speed, in rpm, at which the magnetic field rotates.

Test Your Knowledge

17.1   If a magnet moves swiftly across a sheet of non-magnetic material, it will drag the sheet along with it.

true _____   false _____

17.2   The field in a motor rotates at 3600 r/min, and the rotor turns in the same direction at 2700 r/min. The slip is
a. 0.33
b. 0.25
c. 2.5%

17.3   The field in a motor rotates at 3600 r/min, and the rotor turns in

the *opposite* direction at 2700 r/min. The slip is
a. −1.75
b. −0.25
c. 1.75

17.4   In Fig. 17.9, if the frequency of the source is 120 Hz, the speed of the rotating field is
a. 1800 r/min
b. 7200 r/min
c. 2400 r/min

17.5   A three-phase motor having eight poles per phase is connected to a

source whose frequency is 50 Hz.
The revolving field turns at
a. 250 r/min
b. 750 r/min
c. 750 r/s

17.6 The locked-rotor current relates to
the condition in which the rotor is
not turning.

true_____   false_____

17.7 A squirrel-cage motor rated at 440 V,
3-phase, 60 Hz runs at a no-load
speed of 1798 r/min. If the applied
voltage is reduced to 220 V, the new
speed will
a. drop to about 900 r/min

b. decrease only slightly
c. not change at all

17.8 A 3-phase, 60 Hz induction motor has
a full-load speed of 252 r/min. The
number of poles per phase is
a. 28
b. 29
c. 30

17.9 The copper bars of a squirrel-cage
rotor are replaced by aluminum. The
locked-rotor torque will
a. decrease
b. increase
c. remain the same

Questions and Problems

17.10 Name the principal components of an
induction motor.

17.11 Explain how a revolving field is
set up in a three-phase induction
motor.

17.12 Why does the rotor of an induction
motor turn slower than the revolving
field?

17.13 Describe the principle of operation of
a linear induction motor.

17.14 How can we change the direction of a
three-phase motor?

17.15 One of the bars in a squirrel-cage
rotor carries a current of 600 A. The
bar is 23 cm long, and it is momentarily in a field whose flux density is
0.5 T. Calculate the force on the bar,
in newtons and in pounds force.

17.16 a. Calculate the synchronous speed
of a 3-phase, 14-pole induction
motor excited by a 60 Hz source.
b. What is the full-load speed if the
slip is 6 percent?
c. What is the frequency of the current in the rotor bars at full-load?

18

Selection and Application of Three-Phase Induction Motors

LEARNING OBJECTIVES

Upon completion of this chapter you will be able to:

- Explain the difference between the various enclosure types
- Explain the difference between the various NEMA class induction motors
- Describe how plugging and dc injection can be used to stop an induction motor
- Describe the effect of several abnormal operating conditions on induction motors
- List several applications for three-phase induction motors

18.1 Standardization and Classification of Induction Motors

Industrial motors under 500 hp all have standardized dimensions. Thus a 60 hp, 1725 r/min, 60 Hz motor of one manufacturer can be replaced by that of any other manufacturer without having to change the mounting holes, shaft height, or type of coupling. The standardization covers not only frame sizes, but also establishes minimum requirements on starting torque, locked-rotor current, overload capacity, and temperature rise. These standards are set by organizations such as ANSI (American National Standards Institute), IEEE (Institute of Electrical and Electronics Engineers), and NEMA (National Electrical Manufacturers Association). In Canada, the CSA (Canadian Standards Association) is largely responsible for setting standards.

18.2 Classification According to Enclosure Type

Motors are grouped into several distinct categories, depending upon the environment in which they have to operate. Environmental conditions determine how well the motor must be sealed and cooled. We limit our discussion to five important **enclosure types**.

ENCLOSURE TYPE

1. *Drip-proof motors.* The frame protects the windings against liquid drops and solid particles that fall at any angle from 0 to 15 degrees from the vertical. The motor is cooled by a fan directly coupled to the rotor. Cool air is drawn into the motor through vents in the frame, blown over the windings, and then expelled. Drip-proof motors can be used in most locations (Figs. 18.1 and 18.2).

▼ **Figure 18.1**

Drip-proof induction motor rated 450 hp, 1770 r/min, 3-phase, 60 Hz.

(Courtesy Gould)

▼ **Figure 18.2**

Drip-proof induction motor in a particularly clean industrial environment.

(Courtesy General Electric)

2. *Splash-proof motors.* The frame protects the windings against liquid drops and solid particles that fall at any angle from 0 to 100 degrees from the vertical. Cooling is similar to that in drip-proof motors. These motors are mainly used in wet locations.

3. *Totally enclosed, non-ventilated motors.* These machines have closed frames which prevent the free exchange of air between the windings and the outside atmosphere. They are designed for very wet or dusty locations. Such motors are usually rated below 10 hp because it is difficult to get rid of the heat. The motor losses are dissipated by natural convection and radiation from the frame.

4. *Totally enclosed, fan-cooled motors.* Medium- and high-power motors that are totally enclosed are usually cooled by an external blast of air. An external fan, directly coupled to the shaft, blows air over the ribbed motor frame. A concentric outer shield prevents physical contact with the fan and serves to channel the air stream over the frame (Figs. 18.3 and 18.4).

5. *Explosion-proof motors.* These motors are used in highly inflammable or explosive surroundings such as in coal mines, oil refineries, and grain elevators. The motors are totally enclosed (but not airtight) and the frames are designed to withstand the enormous pressure that may build up inside the motor if an internal short-circuit should occur, and to prevent the arc from igniting the surrounding atmosphere (Figs. 18.5 and 18.6).

▼ **Figure 18.3**

Totally enclosed fan-cooled induction motor rated 350 hp, 1765 r/min, 60 Hz. Air blows over the ribbed frame from the rear to the shaft end of the motor. The ribs improve the heat transfer from the frame.

(Courtesy Gould)

▼ **Figure 18.4**

Totally enclosed fan-cooled induction motor rated 25 hp, 3515 r/min, 230 V/460 V, 3-phase, 60 Hz for a vertical pump.

(Courtesy General Electric)

▼ **Figure 18.5**

Explosion-proof induction motor, totally enclosed, fan-cooled.

(Courtesy Siemens-Allis)

▼ **Figure 18.6**

This 50 hp totally enclosed, fan-cooled, explosion-proof motor has given decades of service in a dusty and hazardous environment.

(Courtesy Canadian General Electric)

18.3 Classification According to Electrical and Mechanical Properties

In addition to special enclosures, three-phase squirrel-cage motors can be designed to produce various electrical and mechanical characteristics, as listed below.

1. *Motors with standard locked-rotor torque* (**NEMA Design B**). Most induction motors belong to this group. The locked-rotor torque depends upon the size of the motor and ranges from 130 to 70 percent of full-load torque as the power increases from 20 hp to 200 hp (15 kW to 150 kW). The corresponding locked-rotor current should not exceed 6.4 times the rated full-load current. These general-purpose motors are used to drive fans, centrifugal pumps, machine-tools, and so forth.

> **NEMA DESIGN CLASS**

EXAMPLE 18.1

A 75 hp, 460 V, 3-phase, 60 Hz, 880 r/min squirrel-cage induction motor has a NEMA Design B rating. The full-load efficiency is 92% and power factor is 81.5%. Calculate:

1. the slip at full-load.
2. the full-load torque, in ft.lbf.
3. the active power consumed by the motor.
4. the apparent power absorbed by the motor.
5. the full-load current.
6. the reactive power absorbed by the motor.

continued

SOLUTION:

1. a) The synchronous speed of the motor must be close to its rated speed of 880 r/min

    b) The nearest synchronous speed corresponds to that of an 8-pole motor:

    EQ. 17.2
    $$n_s = 120 \, f/p = 120 \times 60/8 = 900 \text{ r/min}$$

    c) The full-load slip is

    EQ. 17.1
    $$s = (n_s - n)/n_s$$
    $$= (900 - 880)/900 = 0.0222, \text{ or } 2.22 \text{ percent}$$

2. The full-load torque is:

    EQ. 1.10
    $$T = 5252 \, P/n = (5252 \times 75)/880 = 447.6 \text{ ft.lbf}$$

3. The active power P_i consumed by the motor is

    EQ. 1.11
    $$P = 100 \, P_o/eff = (100 \times 75 \times 746)/92 = 60\,815 \text{ W} = 60.8 \text{ kW}$$

4. The apparent power S absorbed by the motor is

    EQ. 13.2
    $$S = P_i/\cos \theta = 60.8/0.815 = 74.6 \text{ kVA}$$

5. The full-load current drawn by the motor is

    EQ. 13.3
    $$I = S/(1.732 \, V) = 74\,600/(1.732 \times 460) = 93.6 \text{ A}$$

6. The reactive power Q absorbed by the motor is

    EQ. 12.20
    $$Q = \sqrt{S^2 - P_i^2} = \sqrt{74.6^2 - 60.8^2} = 43.2 \text{ kvar}$$

This reactive power creates the magnetic field in the motor.

2. *High starting-torque motors (NEMA Design C).* These motors are used when starting conditions are difficult. Pumps and piston-type compressors that have to start under load are two typical applications. In general, these motors have a special double-cage rotor. In the range from 20 hp to 200 hp, the locked-rotor current should not exceed 6.4 times the rated full-load current.

    The excellent torque-speed characteristic of a double-cage rotor (Fig. 18.7) is based upon these facts:

    a) The frequency of the rotor current diminishes as the motor speeds up.

    b) A conductor that lies close to the rotor surface (cage 1) has a lower inductive reactance than one buried deep inside the iron core (cage 2).

    When the motor is starting up, most of the rotor current flows in cage 1 because of its relatively low reactance. Thus, cage 2 is effectively out of service during this period, and because the small rotor bars of cage 1 produce a relatively high rotor resistance, the starting torque is high. But as the motor approaches synchronous speed, the frequency of the current in the rotor falls. As a result, the reactance becomes negligible, and current begins to flow in cage 2, which has a much lower resistance than cage 1. Thus, the effective rotor resistance at rated speed is much lower than at standstill. For this reason, the double-cage rotor develops both a high starting torque, and a low slip at full-load (see Section 17.13).

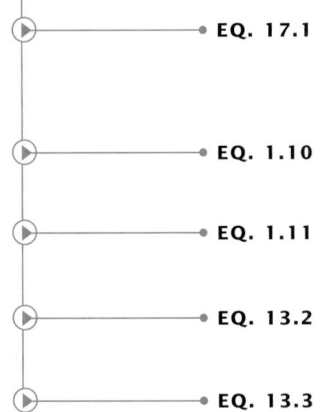

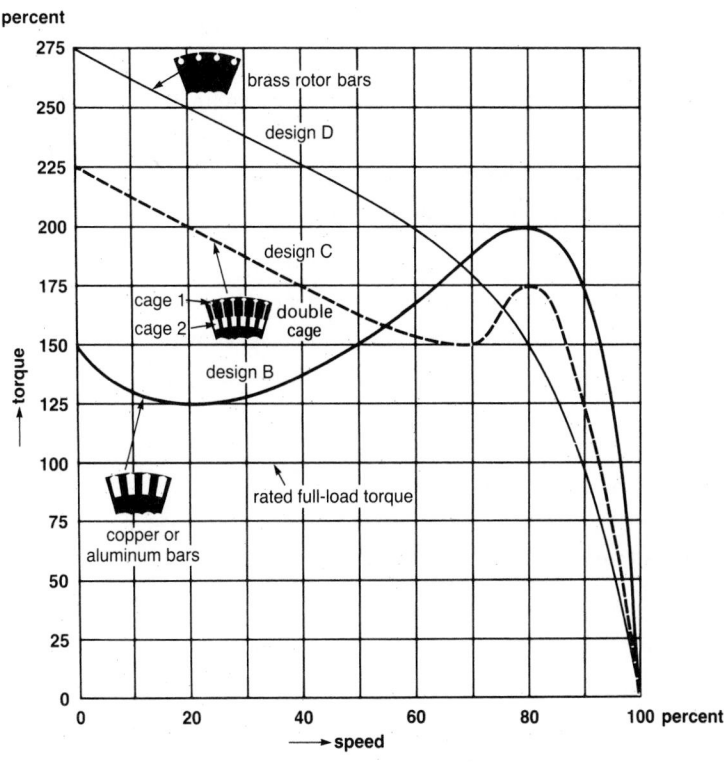

Figure 18.7

Torque-speed curves of three types of squirrel-cage induction motors.

EXAMPLE 18.2

A 3 hp, 575 V, 3-phase, 60 Hz, 1080 r/min induction motor has the NEMA Design C torque-speed characteristic shown in Fig. 18.7. Calculate the actual torque (in N.m) and speed at the 40 percent speed point.

SOLUTION:

a) The synchronous speed that is closest to 1080 r/min at 60 Hz corresponds to a 6-pole motor, for which n_s = 1200 r/min

b) The 40 percent speed corresponds to (40/100) × 1200 = 480 r/min

c) The full-load torque is given by Equation 1.9:
    $T = 9.55\ P/n = (9.55 \times 3 \times 746)/1080 = 19.8$ N.m

d) From the curve, the torque is 175 percent at 40 percent speed; the torque at 480 r/min is therefore
    $T = (175/100) \times 19.8 = 34.6$ N.m

3. *High-slip motors (NEMA Design D).* The rated speed of high-slip motors lies between 85% and 95% of synchronous speed. These motors develop high starting torques and can be used to drive high-inertia loads (such as centrifugal dryers) which take a relatively long time to reach full speed. The high-resistance squirrel cage is made of brass, and the motors are usually designed

for intermittent operation to prevent overheating. The large drop in speed with increasing load is also ideal to drive impact machine tools, such as shears and punch presses equipped with a flywheel. The flywheel gradually stores up mechanical energy during the idling period and releases it in a surge of power when the machine tool impacts. The power delivered by the flywheel during the short impact period is usually many times the nameplate horsepower rating of the motor.

The graphs of Fig. 18.7 enable us to compare the torque-speed characteristics of these motors. The rotor construction is also shown, and it can be seen that the distinguishing properties are obtained by changing the rotor design.

EXAMPLE 18.3

A 1.5 hp, 200 V, 3-phase, 60 Hz, 1620 r/min high-slip motor has the following characteristics:

full-load current = 5.1 A

locked-rotor current = 46 A

locked-rotor torque = 250 percent

We want to rewind this motor so that it can function on a 460 V, 3-phase, 60 Hz line. Calculate:

1. how the properties of the rewound motor compare with the original machine.
2. the winding changes that must be made.

SOLUTION:

1. a) The horsepower rating, the efficiency, power factor, and torque-speed characteristic are not affected when a motor is rewound for a different voltage.
   b) It follows that the apparent power at full-load is constant. Thus, when the voltage rating increases, the motor current must decrease in direct proportion. The full-load current at 460 V is
   $I_{FL} = 5.1 \times (200/460) = 2.22$ A
   c) The new locked-rotor current is
   $I_{LR} = 4 \times (200/460) = 1.74$ A

2. a) The full-load current is only 2.22 A, compared with the original value of 5.1 A. Consequently, the conductor size of the motor windings can be reduced by a factor of 5.1/2.22 = 2.3. For example, if the original motor was wound with No. 17 1/2 wire (0.924 mm²), the new winding would be made with No. 21 wire (0.402 mm²).
   b) The second important change is to increase the number of turns per coil in the ratio of the voltages—that is, 460/200 = 2.3. Thus, if the coils in the original motor were made of 13 turns of No. 17 1/2 wire, the new coils would have (13 × 2.3) = 30 turns of No. 21 wire. In effect, the volts per turn in the rewound motor must be the same as before.

18.4 Choice of Motor Speed

The synchronous speed of induction motors changes by jumps, depending upon the frequency and number of poles. Consequently, the choice of motor speed is rather limited. For example, it is impossible to build an efficient 2400 r/min, 60 Hz induction motor. For good efficiency, the motor must run close to synchronous speed; thus, at either 1800 or 3600 r/min.

The speed of a motor is obviously determined by the required speed of the load. At low speeds, it is often preferable to use a high-speed motor and a gear box instead of directly coupling a low-speed motor to the load. There are several advantages to the gear-box approach:

1. For a given power output, a high-speed motor is smaller and costs less than a low-speed motor. Furthermore, its efficiency and power factor are higher.

2. High-speed motors always have a greater locked-rotor torque (as a percentage of full-load torque) than that of low-speed motors of similar type and power.

When equipment has to operate at very low speeds (100 r/min or less), a gear box is unavoidable. The gears are often an integral part of the motor, making for a very compact unit (Fig. 18.8).

On a 60 Hz system, a gear box is also required when equipment has to run above 3600 r/min. For example, in one industrial application, a large gear unit is used to couple a 5000 r/min centrifugal compressor to a 3000 hp, 3560 r/min induction motor.

Figure 18.8

Three-phase gear motor rated 3 hp, 125 r/min, 460 V, 3-phase, 60 Hz. The motor speed is 1750 r/min.

(Courtesy Reliance)

EXAMPLE 18.4

A 1 hp, 1740 r/min induction motor is coupled to a gear box having a gear ratio of 200. Calculate the full-load output torque and speed.

continued

SOLUTION:

a) The shaft output speed is 1740/200 = 8.7 r/min
b) The output power is slightly less than 1 hp because of the losses in the gear box. If we assume a loss of 10 percent, the output power at the low-speed shaft is 0.9 hp.
c) The output torque is
   $T = 5252\, P/n = (5252 \times 0.9)/8.7 = 543$ ft.lbf

EQ. 1.10

Note that this torque exceeds the torque developed by the 75 hp motor in Example 18.1.

In some applications (Fig. 18.9), it is convenient to use a motor that can operate at two speeds. One obvious way to accomplish this result is to place two separate three-phase windings in the stator. For example, if a 60 Hz motor has a 2-pole and a 6-pole winding, it can operate at either 3600 or 1200 r/min. It is clear that for a given horsepower rating, such a two-winding motor will be bigger than a conventional single-speed motor.

However, when the speed ratio is 2:1, it is possible to use a single winding, and to obtain the required pole change by simply reconnecting a few external leads. Because there is never an idle winding, such two-speed machines are smaller and therefore cheaper. The single winding is sometimes called a Dahlander winding.

In two-speed blower applications, a speed ratio of 2:1 is too large a spread. In such cases, a so-called *pole-amplitude modulated* (PAM) winding can be reconnected to produce either 8 or 10 poles. Such PAM motors are built in sizes up to several hundred horsepower.

18.5 Plugging an Induction Motor

If we want to bring an induction motor to a rapid stop, we can simply interchange two stator leads. This causes the revolving field to turn suddenly in the opposite

Figure 18.9

Multispeed induction motors are often used to drive hoists and cranes in port facilities, and on ships equipped with ac power.

(Courtesy Brown Boveri)

direction and therefore opposite to the rotation of the rotor (Fig. 18.10). During this so-called *plugging* period, the motor acts as a *brake*.

It absorbs kinetic energy from the still-revolving load, causing its speed to fall. The energy is entirely dissipated as heat in the rotor. Unfortunately, the rotor also continues to receive power from the stator, and this power is also dissipated as heat. Consequently, plugging produces very high I^2R losses in the rotor. They are even greater than the I^2R losses when the rotor is locked. Motors should not be plugged too frequently because high rotor temperatures may melt the rotor bars or overheat the stator winding.

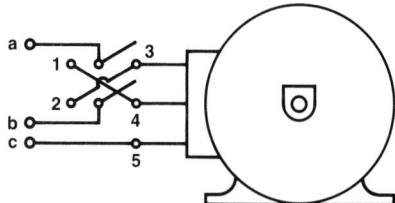

Figure 18.10

To plug a three-phase induction motor, a switch or contactor interchanges two leads.

EXAMPLE 18.5

A 50 hp, 575 V, 3-phase, 60 Hz, 1765 r/min motor is repeatedly plugged, as shown in Fig. 18.10. The motor is insulated with class B (120°C) insulation, for which the maximum permissible temperature rise (by resistance) is 80°C. The winding is made of copper.

To determine the temperature of the winding after 10 plugging cycles, the resistance of the winding was measured between terminals 4 and 5 immediately after the last reversal. The result gave 0.94 Ω, and the ambient temperature was 26°C.

The motor was then disconnected from the line and allowed to cool to room temperature during a 24-hour period. The resistance was again measured (0.62 Ω), as was the ambient temperature (t_c = 23°C). Calculate the temperature of the winding after the plugging period, and state whether the temperature rise is excessive.

SOLUTION:

a) The resistance of the copper winding at 0°C would be:
    $R_o = R_t/(1 + \alpha t_c)$
    $\qquad = 0.62/(1 + 0.004\ 27 \times 23) = 0.565\ \Omega$ **EQ. 3.3**

b) The temperature t_H of the winding after the plugging test is given by:
    $R_t = R_o(1 + \alpha t_H)$
    $0.94 = 0.565\ (1 + 0.004\ 27\ t_H)$
    $t_H = 155°C$

c) The ambient temperature at the time of the plugging test was 26°C. Thus, the temperature *rise* is (155 − 26) = 129°C. This temperature rise far exceeds the 80°C limit for Class B insulation. The motor is definitely running too hot.

18.6 Effects of Inertia

High-inertia loads put a heavy strain on induction motors because they prolong the starting period. The starting current in both the stator and rotor is high during this interval, and so overheating is a major problem. To limit the temperature rise, induction motors are often started on reduced voltage. This reduces the power and current which the motor draws from the line. Unfortunately, it also increases the time it takes to bring the load up to speed, but this is usually not too important.

When very high inertia loads have to be accelerated (or brought to a rapid stop), wound-rotor motors are recommended. The reason is that most of the heat produced in the rotor circuit is dissipated by the external resistors. Furthermore, we can maintain a consistently high torque by gradually varying the external rotor resistance during the acceleration or deceleration periods.

18.7 Braking with Direct Current

An induction motor and its high-inertia load can also be brought to a quick stop by disconnecting the three-phase line and circulating dc current in the stator winding (Fig. 18.11). This is known as **DC injection**. Any two stator terminals can be connected to the dc source.

| DC INJECTION |

The direct current produces stationary N and S poles in the stator. The number of poles created is equal to the number of poles the motor develops normally. Thus, a 3-phase, 4-pole induction motor produces four dc poles no matter how the motor terminals are connected to the dc source.

As the rotor sweeps past the stationary field, a voltage is induced in the rotor bars. The voltage produces a current, and the resulting rotor I^2R losses are dissipated at the expense of the kinetic energy stored in the revolving parts. The motor finally comes to rest when all the kinetic energy has been dissipated as heat in the rotor. (This is a practical application of the principle discussed in Section 17.1.)

The advantage of dc braking is that it produces far less heat than does plugging. In effect, the energy dissipated in the rotor is only equal to the original kinetic energy stored in the revolving masses. The energy dissipated in the rotor is independent of the magnitude of the dc current. However, a smaller dc current increases the braking time.

Figure 18.11

A three-phase induction motor can be braked by connecting the stator to a dc source.

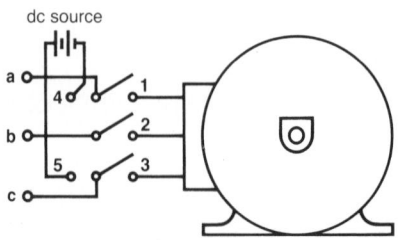

18.8 Abnormal Conditions

Abnormal motor operation may be due to internal causes (short-circuit in the stator, overheating of the bearings, etc.) or to external disturbances. External problems may be caused by:

1. mechanical overload.
2. line voltage changes.
3. single-phasing.
4. frequency variations.

We will now examine the effect of these external disturbances.

18.9 Mechanical Overload

Although standard induction motors can develop at least 1.5 times their rated power output for short periods, they should not be allowed to run continuously beyond their rated capacity. Overloads produce stator and rotor currents that are above the rated values. The consequent overheating deteriorates the insulation and reduces the useful life of the motor. In practice, the higher motor current causes thermal overload relays to trip, bringing the motor to a stop before its temperature rises too much.

Some drip-proof motors are designed to carry a continuous overload of 15 percent. This overload capacity is indicated on the nameplate by the so-called **service factor**.

SERVICE FACTOR

18.10 Line Voltage Changes

According to national standards, a motor shall operate successfully on any voltage within ±10% of the nominal voltage and for any frequency within ±5% of the nominal frequency.

A change in line voltage has an important effect on the torque-speed curve of the motor because the torque at any speed is proportional to the *square* of the applied voltage. Thus, if the line voltage drops 10%, the torque will fall 20%. Such voltage drops are often produced during start-up because of the large starting current.

On the other hand, if the line voltage is too high, the magnetic flux in the motor rises above its normal level. This increases both the iron losses and the magnetizing current, with the result that the temperature increases slightly, and the power factor is somewhat reduced.

Finally, a slight imbalance of the three-phase line voltage can produce a serious unbalance of the three line currents. This condition increases the stator and rotor losses, yielding a higher temperature. A voltage imbalance of as little as 3.5% can cause the temperature to increase by 15°C. The utility company should be notified whenever the phase-to-phase line voltages differ more than 1 percent.

18.11 Single-Phasing

SINGLE-PHASING

If one line of a three-phase line is accidentally opened, or if a fuse blows while the motor is running, the machine will continue to run as a single-phase motor. This condition is known as **single-phasing**. The current drawn from the remaining two lines will almost double, and the motor will begin to overheat. The thermal relays protecting the motor will eventually trip the circuit breaker, thereby disconnecting the motor from the line.

The torque-speed curve is seriously affected when a three-phase motor operates on single phase. The breakdown torque decreases to about 40% of its rated value, and the motor develops no starting torque at all. Consequently, a fully loaded three-phase motor may simply stop if one of its feeder lines is accidentally opened.

18.12 Frequency Variation

Important frequency changes never take place on a large electric utility system, except during a major disturbance. However, the frequency may vary significantly on isolated systems in which electrical energy is generated by diesel engines or gas turbines. The emergency supply in a hospital, the electrical system on a ship, and the generators in a lumber camp, are examples of this type of supply.

The most important consequence of a frequency change is the resulting change in speed: if the frequency drops 20%, the speed of the induction motor drops 20%.

Machine tools and other motor-driven devices imported from countries where the frequency is 50 Hz may cause problems when they are connected to a 60 Hz system. Everything runs 20% faster than normal, and this may not be acceptable in some applications. In such cases, we have to gear down the motor speed or supply an expensive auxiliary 50 Hz source.

A 50 Hz motor operates well on a 60 Hz line, but its terminal voltage should be raised to 60/50 (or 120%) of the nameplate rating. The new breakdown torque is then equal to the original breakdown torque, and the starting torque is only slightly reduced. Power factor, efficiency, and temperature rise remain satisfactory.

A 60 Hz motor can also operate on a 50 Hz line, but its terminal voltage should be reduced to 50/60 (or 83%) of its nameplate rating. The breakdown torque and starting torque are then about the same as before, and the power factor, efficiency, and temperature rise remain satisfactory.

18.13 Typical Applications of Induction Motors

The following list of typical applications show how induction motors are used in industry:

1. In Montana, a 900 hp, 2300 V, 3-phase, 60 Hz, 3600 r/min squirrel cage induction motor is used to drive a pipeline pump. The motor is weather-protected and is designed to operate in a 40°C ambient with a maximum temperature rise of 80°C by resistance.

2. In Sydney, Australia, a 12 000 hp, 11 kV, 3-phase, 50 Hz, 1490 r/min wound-rotor induction motor drives the feedwater pump in a thermal generating station. The motor is totally enclosed, and the closed-circuit cooling air gives up its heat to an air/water heat exchanger.

3. In Stuttgart, Germany, a 3300 kW, 5000 V, 3-phase, 425 to 595 r/min wound-rotor induction motor pumps water from Lake Constance to meet the needs of the city. The motor is totally enclosed, and a closed-circuit air/water heat exchanger ensures adequate cooling.

4. In Cleveland, Ohio, an overhead crane in a plant is propelled along its supporting I-beams by two linear three-phase motors. The stators are mounted on the crane a few millimetres away from the flat I-beam, which acts as the stationary rotor. The motors develop a thrust of 300 lbf.

5. The crane on a ship is driven by a 3-speed pole-changing induction motor rated at 19/7/3.3 hp, with synchronous speeds of 1800/900/450 r/min. A single winding is used for the 1800/900 r/min speeds and a second winding for the 450 r/min. The motor is totally enclosed, non-ventilated, and integrated with a gear box.

6. In Ontario, twelve 1500 hp, 3600 r/min squirrel-cage induction motors drive the heat transport pumps of the Pickering nuclear generating station. The 4.16 kV, 3-phase, 60 Hz motors are totally enclosed with an air/water heat exchanger. The motors are equipped with a heavy flywheel to ensure a brief period of continued operation in the event of a momentary power failure.

18.14 Summary

Upon completion of this chapter you should have learned that:

• Different types of NEMA enclosure have different mechanical sealing and cooling requirements. The operating environment determines the type of enclosure used.

• Different NEMA class induction motors have different starting characteristics. The NEMA class B induction motor is the most widely used induction motor.

• Plugging and dc injection are techniques used when it is necessary to stop a motor rapidly.

- Several abnormal operating conditions, including mechanical overload, line voltage changes, frequency variation and single-phasing, can result in overheating due to a motor's inability to produce the required torque.

- When a three-phase induction motor is selected, its operating characteristics must be matched to the torque requirements of the load.

Key Terms

DC INJECTION: The application of dc, usually to one phase of a three-phase induction motor stator winding after the ac has been disconnected. The stationary field created by the dc induces an opposite magnetic field on the rotor. The attraction between the stationary stator field and the rotor field slows the motor.

ENCLOSURE TYPE: A standardized classification system used to match the mechanical enclosure of a motor to the operating environment.

NEMA DESIGN CLASS: A classification system used to standardize the starting characteristics of a three-phase induction motor.

SERVICE FACTOR: A measure of the continuous overload capacity of a motor. A service factor of 1.15 means that a motor is able to draw 115 percent of its rated current on a continuing basis without overheating.

SINGLE-PHASING: The operation of a three-phase induction motor when one of the three lines supplying the motor opens circuits. Under these conditions, the motor will continue to operate until a change in motor torque is required.

Test Your Knowledge

18.1   An explosion-proof motor is designed to withstand *external* explosions.

true _____   false _____

18.2   A 500 hp, 3-phase, 2.4 kV squirrel-cage motor has a rated current of 125 A. The locked-rotor current is probably between
a.   700 A and 900 A
b.   600 A and 800 A
c.   40 A and 70 A

18.3   When a flywheel is part of a punch press, the driving motor must have:
a.   a high locked-rotor torque
b.   a high power factor
c.   a high slip at full-load

18.4   Two drip-proof NEMA Design B, three-phase induction motors have the following ratings: motor X—200 hp,

1760 r/min, 2.4 kV; motor Y—60 hp, 450 r/min, 460 V. Motor X is bigger than motor Y.

true _____   false _____

18.5   If a three-phase induction motor has to be plugged frequently, it is best to use
a.   a NEMA Design D motor
b.   a wound-rotor induction motor
c.   a wound-rotor induction motor with external resistors

18.6   A 40 hp, 460 V, 3-phase, 60 Hz induction motor has a full-load rated current of 45 A. The rated full-load current of an identical motor, but rated at 575 V, is:
a.   56.25 A
b.   36 A
c.   28.8 A

18.7 A 40 hp, 460 V, 3-phase, 60 Hz induction motor develops a locked-rotor torque of 74 ft.lbf. The torque expressed in newton metres is
a. 100.3 N.m
b. 54.57 N.m
c. 16.64 N.m

18.8 A 5 hp, 460 V, 3-phase, 60 Hz induction motor has a rated speed of 837 r/min and a locked-rotor torque of 114 N.m. When the motor is connected across the line, the terminal voltage falls to 410 V. The locked-rotor torque under these conditions is:
a. 101.6 N.m

b. unchanged
c. 90.56 N.m

18.9 A 50 Hz squirrel-cage induction motor has a rated speed of 419 r/min. It has
a. 16 poles
b. 14 poles
c. 15 poles

18.10 A 200 hp, 460 V, 3-phase, 60 Hz induction motor has to be installed on a 50 Hz system. The recommended 50 Hz voltage is
a. 383 V
b. 552 V
c. 460 V

Questions and Problems

18.11 Explain why a NEMA Design B motor is not the best choice to drive a pump.

18.12 Is it possible for a three-phase motor to run on a single-phase line?

18.13 What type of ac induction motor should you recommend for a variable-speed pump?

18.14 A three-phase induction motor can be brought to a quick stop by plugging it. Why *must* the line be disconnected when the motor has come to a halt?

18.15 If a dc current flows in the winding of a three-phase stator, the rotor is very hard to turn. Why?

18.16 Referring to Fig. 18.7, a 60 hp, NEMA Design B motor has a rated speed of 1152 r/min. Calculate:
a. the rated full-load torque, in N.m
b. the locked-rotor torque
c. the breakdown torque and corresponding breakdown speed
d. the pull-up torque and corresponding speed
e. the mechanical power developed when the motor is running at 600 r/min

18.17 Draw the typical torque-speed curve of a NEMA Design C motor rated at 25 hp, 60 Hz, 1750 r/min. Show the torque in newton metres versus the speed in revolutions per minute.

18.18 The resistance between two terminals of a stator is 3 Ω when the winding temperature is 22°C. Knowing that the winding is made of copper, calculate the resistance for a winding temperature of 95°C.

18.19 A 1.5 hp, 460 V, 3-phase, 60 Hz, 870 r/min induction motor has a full-load efficiency of 77%, and a power factor of 62%. Calculate:
a. the active power drawn by the motor
b. the reactive power absorbed by the motor
c. the rated line current

18.20 In Problem 18.19, calculate the impedance per phase at full-load, knowing that the stator is connected in wye.

19

Synchronous Motors

LEARNING OBJECTIVES

Upon completion of this chapter you will be able to:

- Describe the construction of synchronous motors
- Explain how a synchronous motor accelerates
- Describe the operation of a synchronous motor under load
- Explain the effect of torque angle on motor torque
- Explain how the rotor of a synchronous motor is excited

19.1 Construction of a Synchronous Motor

A synchronous motor is composed of a rotor and a stator. The stator is identical to that of a three-phase induction motor. Consequently, it is wound to produce 2, 4, 6 or more poles and may be connected in either delta or wye. When the stator is connected to a three-phase source, a revolving field is set up, as in the case of an induction motor.

The speed of the revolving field is again given by the equation

$$n_s = \frac{120\,f}{p}$$

EQ. 17.2

where

n_s = synchronous speed, in revolutions per minute (r/min)

f = frequency, in hertz (Hz)

p = number of poles, per phase

Figure 19.1 shows the typical construction of the stator of a synchronous motor. The rotor is composed of a set of salient poles that carry identical coils connected in series (Fig. 19.2). A dc current I_x flows through the coils, and the connections are made so that adjacent poles have opposite magnetic polarities. The rotor behaves, therefore, like a revolving dc field. The exciting current I_x is fed into the rotor by means of a set of brushes and two slip rings.

Figure 19.1

Stator of synchronous motor rated 600 hp, 1200 r/min, 2300 V, 3-phase, 60 Hz.

(Courtesy H. Roberge)

Figure 19.2

Figure 19.2

Schematic diagram of the rotor of
a four-pole synchronous motor.
The four coils are connected in
series to two slip rings.

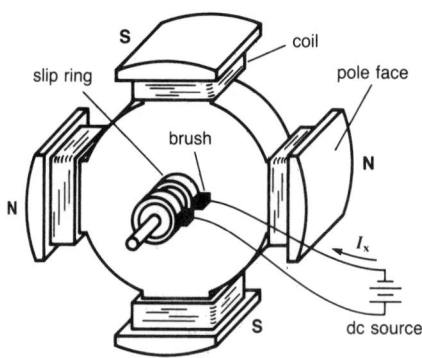

Figure 19.3 shows the construction of a 6-pole rotor. The number of poles on the
rotor is equal to the number of poles per phase on the stator. Thus, a 6-pole rotor
is always associated with a 6-pole stator.

The rotor also carries a squirrel-cage winding, similar to that in an induction motor.
This winding is composed of rotor bars that pass through slots in the pole faces. The
bars are short-circuited together by means of end rings (Fig. 19.4). In some motors,
the squirrel-cage winding does not form a continuous circle around the rotor. The
rotor bars are still short-circuited together, but only pole by pole (Fig. 19.6).

Figure 19.3

Partially assembled rotor of a
synchronous motor rated 600 hp,
1200 r/min, 2300 V, 3-phase,
60 Hz. The six salient poles are
dovetailed into the central core
so as to resist the centrifugal
forces.

(Courtesy H. Roberge)

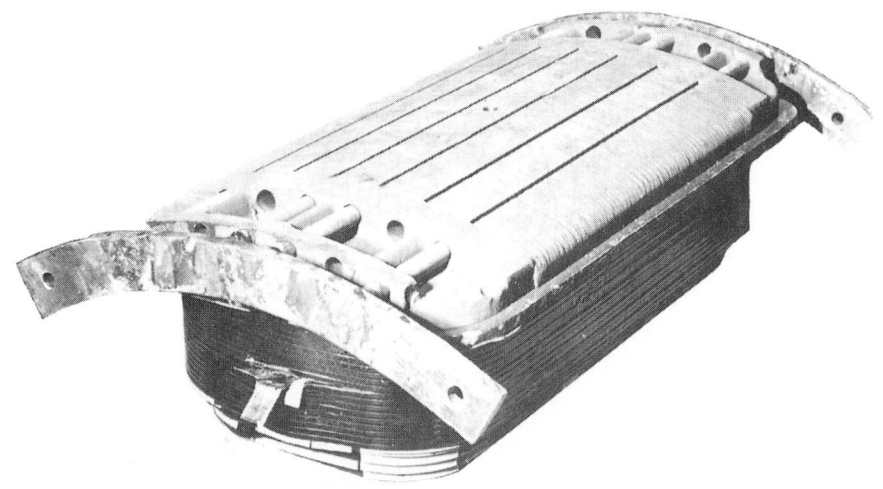

Figure 19.4

Closeup of the salient pole in Fig. 19.3, showing the rotor bars and end rings. The end rings of adjacent poles are later bolted together to form a closed circle.

(Courtesy H. Roberge)

Figure 19.5

Relative position of the rotor and stator laminations of a large synchronous motor. The air gap in the centre of the pole is smaller than near the pole tips. The deep stator slots carry pre-formed armature coils.

When the rotor is mounted inside the stator, a small air gap separates the two. The pole face on the rotor is shaped so that the length of the air gap increases gradually as we move away from the centre (Fig. 19.5). The variable length ensures that the ac voltages and currents in the stator remain as sinusoidal as possible.

19.2 Acceleration of a Synchronous Motor

We will first consider what happens when a 4-pole synchronous motor is connected, at standstill, to a 3-phase, 60 Hz source. The dc winding is not excited, but is connected to a low external resistance R (Fig. 19.6). The stator has four poles per phase, and so a 4-pole revolving field will be created that turns at 1800 r/min. Let us assume it turns clockwise.

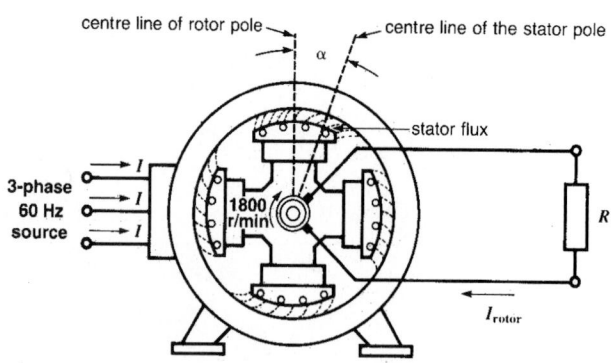

As the field cuts across the squirrel-cage rotor bars, the resulting induced current will produce a torque, and the rotor will quickly accelerate to a speed close to 1800 r/min. A current is also induced in the dc winding, and so it contributes to some of the accelerating torque. During this starting period, the machine behaves like an ordinary three-phase induction motor.

When the rotor reaches a speed of, say, 1795 r/min, the stator field is moving across the rotor poles at a relative speed of only $(1800 - 1795) = 5$ r/min. At this low speed, the currents induced in the rotor bars and the dc winding are small, and so the squirrel-cage torque is much weaker than before.

However, as the stator flux slowly moves across the iron pole face, it develops a strong force of magnetic attraction. The magnetic force produces a reluctance torque that pulls the rotor into synchronism with the field.* Once pull-in is achieved, the rotor runs at the same speed as the rotating field, namely at 1800 r/min. Thus, the induction motor has become a synchronous motor.

Once the motor attains synchronous speed, the stator flux no longer cuts across the squirrel-cage winding or the dc winding. As a result, the induced voltage (and current) in both windings is zero. However, the rotor poles are carried along by the field because of the reluctance torque. The lines of force are slanted at an angle, as shown in Fig. 19.6, because the windage and friction losses impose a drag on the rotor. This causes the centre line of the rotor poles to lag slightly behind the centre line of the stator poles. The mechanical angle α between the two centre lines increases with increasing mechanical load. However, at no-load, α is only a few degrees.

19.3 Effect of Dc Excitation

When the motor runs at no-load with no dc excitation, the ac current I drawn from the three-phase line is large, and lags almost $90°$ behind the voltage. The reason is that a lot of reactive power is needed to create the magnetic field. Consequently, the no-load current I in Fig. 19.6 may be greater than the rated full-load current of the machine.

If we circulate a dc current in the rotor winding in such a way as to create a flux in the same direction as the stator flux, a remarkable thing begins to happen. The stator

* The reluctance torque is produced in exactly the same way as was discussed in Section 5.19.

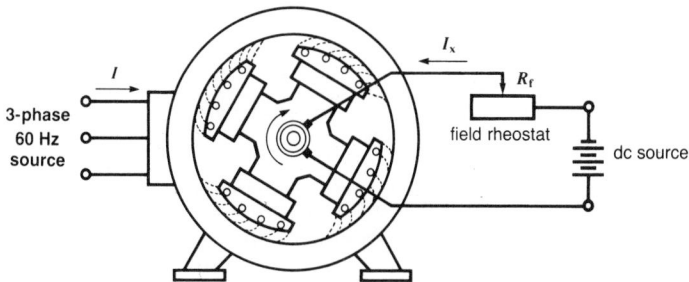

Figure 19.7

The stator current first decreases and drops to a minimum as the dc exciting current is increased. The current then increases again as I_x is further increased. The field rheostat permits control of I_x. Note that the centre line of the rotor poles always lags slightly behind the centre line of the stator poles.

current I begins to fall. In effect, the mmf created by the rotor reduces the mmf the stator has to develop, in order to produce the required magnetic field. Thus, the more we increase the mmf of the rotor, the less the stator mmf has to be.

Consequently, the stator current I decreases as the dc exciting current I_x is raised (Fig. 19.7).

As we continue to raise I_x, less and less reactive power has to be supplied by the stator to produce the required flux. Finally, when I_x is high enough, the stator needs to produce no reactive power at all. Under these conditions, the stator current I is in phase with the stator voltage because only active power is being supplied. The active power keeps the motor running and also supplies its iron and copper losses.

What happens if we continue to raise the dc excitation? The magnetic field tends to become greater than it should be and, to keep it at its original value, the stator mmf must now *oppose* the excess mmf created by the dc field. As a result, as I_x increases, current I again begins to increase. However, I acts in the direction opposite to what it did before, when I_x was small. Consequently, the reactive power becomes *negative.* This means that the synchronous motor is actually feeding reactive power back into the line! Consequently, the motor is now acting like a capacitor as far as the three-phase line is concerned.

Figure 19.8 shows the change in stator current I as the dc exciting current I_x is varied. When $I_x = 0$, $I = 100$ A, and the current lags almost $90°$ behind the voltage. But as we raise I_x, the stator current begins to fall and eventually reaches a minimum of 2 A when I_x is 5 A. The power factor of the motor is then 100 percent. As we continue to raise I_x, the stator current begins to increase, eventually reaching a value of 50 A when $I_x = 10$ A. The current now leads the voltage by almost $90°$.

When the dc current is less than 5 A, the motor draws reactive power from the line. The synchronous machine is said to be *under-excited,* and it behaves like a three-phase inductor. Conversely, when the dc current is greater than 5 A, the synchronous machine feeds reactive power into the line. The machine is said to be *over-excited,* and it behaves like a capacitor.

A synchronous motor that runs at no-load on a three-phase line can therefore act as a continuously variable three-phase inductor or capacitor. The amount of reactive power absorbed (or delivered) by the machine depends upon the level of dc excitation. When the excitation is "normal" (5 A in Fig. 19.8), the machine neither delivers nor absorbs reactive power.

Figure 19.8

V-curve showing the variation of stator current with
the dc exciting current.

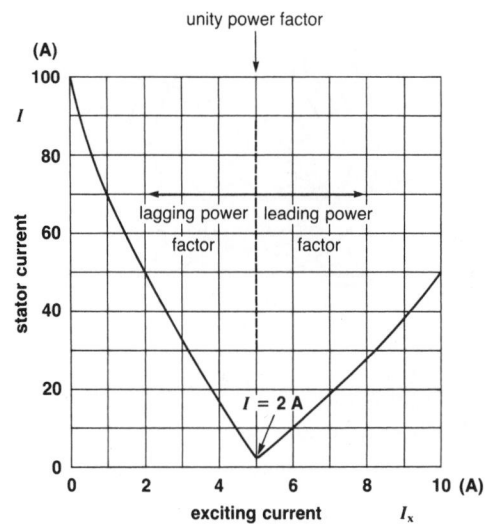

EXAMPLE 19.1

A synchronous motor operating on a 3-phase, 4 kV line has the V curve characteristic shown in Fig. 19.8. Calculate:

1. the magnitude of the reactive power for dc excitation currents of 1 A, 5 A, and
    10 A.
2. the equivalent capacitance of the motor when $I_x = 10$ A.

SOLUTION:

1. a) Referring to Figs. 19.7 and 19.8, for $I_x = 1$ A, $I = 70$A

    and from

    EQ. 13.3

    $S = 1.732\ VI$

    we have

    $S = 1.732 \times 4000 \times 70 = 485$ kVA

    At this level of excitation, the machine is under-excited, and so it draws
    nearly 485 kvar of reactive power from the line. (The motor is operating at
    no-load; therefore, the active power is negligible compared with the appar-
    ent power S of 485 kVA. Thus, the reactive power is nearly equal to the
    apparent power S.)

    b) For $I_x = 5$A, we find $I = 2$A, and so

    $S = 1.732\ VI = 1.732 \times 4000 \times 2 = 13.86$ kVA

    Because I is at its minimum value, the machine absorbs only active power
    from the line. This power (13.86 kW) is mainly used to overcome the fric-
    tion, windage, and iron losses. (The apparent power S is numerically equal
    to the active power at unity power factor.)

continued

c) When $I_x = 10A$, we find $T = 50$ A; therefore
$S = 1.732\ VI = 1.732 \times 4000 \times 50 = 346$ kVA

The machine is over-excited, and so it delivers nearly 346 kvar to the three-phase line. (The reactive power is again nearly equal to S because the motor absorbs very little active power.)

2. We can calculate the equivalent capacitance of the motor as follows (Fig. 19.9):
    a) Current in each "capacitor" = 50 A
    b) Voltage across each "capacitor" = 4000/1.732 = 2309 V
    c) Capacitive reactance per phase is
    $X_c = V/I = 2309/50 = 46.18\ \Omega$
    d) From $X_c = \dfrac{1}{2\pi fC}$

EQ. 13.2

$$C = \frac{1}{2\pi fX_c} = \frac{1}{2\pi \times 60 \times 46.18} = 57.4 \times 10^{-6} = 57.4\ \mu F$$

Thus, as far as the three-phase line is concerned, the synchronous motor has exactly the same effect as a three-phase, wye-connected capacitor bank composed of three 57.4 μF capacitors. That is why such a machine is sometimes called a synchronous capacitor (Fig. 19.10a and b).

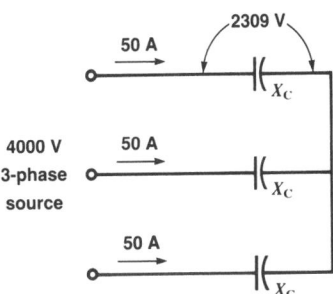

Figure 19.9

See Example 19.1

Figure 19.10a

Synchronous capacitor whose reactive power can be varied from −200 Mvar (supplying reactive power) to + 300 Mvar (absorbing reactive power). The 8-pole machine operates at no-load on a 16 kV, 3-phase, 60 Hz line.

(Courtesy Hydro-Québec)

Figure 19.10b

The synchronous capacitor is used to regulate the voltage of a 735 kV transmission line. It is enclosed in a steel shell that contains hydrogen to provide an efficient cooling system.

(Courtesy Hydro-Québec)

19.4 Synchronous Motor Under Load

Consider the synchronous motor of Fig. 19.11 running at no-load on a three-phase line. The rotor current is adjusted so that the ac line currents are minimum. This means that the machine is drawing only active power from the line, just enough to keep the machine running. We assume that the field created by the stator is turning clockwise.

The poles of the rotor are slightly behind the poles of the stator, and the angular displacement between them is α degrees. The displacement at no-load amounts to only a fraction of a degree. Thus, we can assume that the centre lines of the rotor poles and stator poles are lined up.

What happens when a mechanical load is suddenly applied to the rotor? The motor begins to slow down, causing the rotor poles to fall further behind the stator poles. Angle α increases, causing the flux lines between the rotor and stator poles to become more "stretched", and this produces a larger torque. When the torque developed by the motor is equal to the load torque, the so-called **torque angle** α

TORQUE ANGLE α

Figure 19.11

Synchronous motor operating at no-load and turning clockwise. The torque angle and stator current are small.

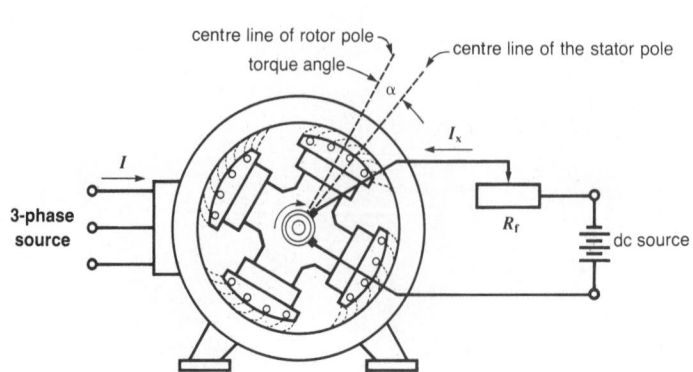

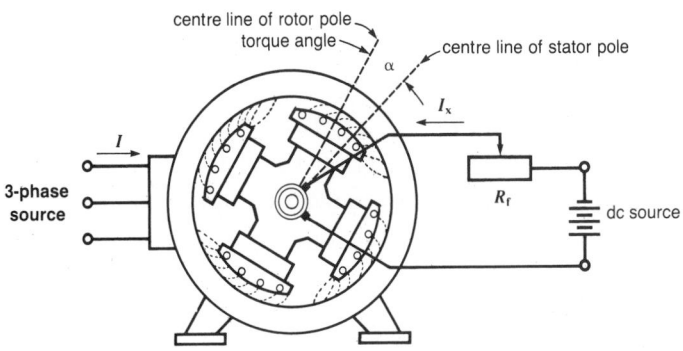

Figure 19.12

Synchronous motor operating under load causes the torque angle to increase.

again remains constant. However, its value (Fig. 19.12) is now greater than at no-load. In this new condition, current *I* drawn by the stator is also greater than before. However, the machine continues to run at synchronous speed because the rotor and stator poles remain locked together. Consequently, the machine still operates as a synchronous motor.

However, there is a limit to the mechanical load that can be applied. As we increase the load torque, the rotor poles lag farther and farther behind the stator poles, and current *I* becomes greater and greater. However, at a certain critical torque, called **pull-out torque**, the rotor poles break away from the stator poles and the motor starts running below synchronous speed. The motor is said to have "lost synchronism." When this happens, the average torque developed by the motor is only that due to the squirrel-cage winding. In effect, when the motor runs below synchronous speed, it behaves like an induction motor. The stator current increases greatly, and the circuit breakers protecting the machine will immediately trip.

PULL-OUT TORQUE

In a 4-pole machine, the pull-out torque occurs at an angle α of about 40°. This condition is shown in Fig. 19.13. Note how the flux lines between the rotor and stator poles are "stretched." They behave like rubber bands between the N and S pole faces (rotor and stator), tending to keep the poles together. However, in the critical position of Fig. 19.13, the "rubber bands" are about to snap.

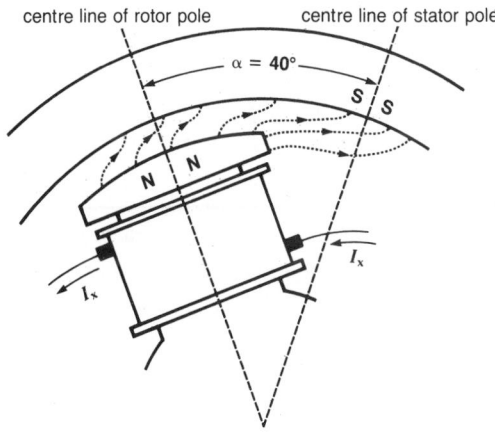

Figure 19.13

Position of rotor poles when a 4-pole synchronous motor has reached its pull-out torque.

19.5 Relationship between Torque and Torque Angle

We have seen that the torque developed by the synchronous motor depends upon the torque angle α. The relationship between the two is given by the graph of Fig. 19.14. Curve 1 applies for a level of dc excitation that produces unity power factor at rated load. In the case of our 4-pole motor, the pull-out torque T_m is 1.6 times the rated torque, and it occurs at an angle of about 40°. The motor continues to develop a positive torque when α exceeds 40°. However, the torque is smaller than T_m, and it falls to zero when $\alpha = 90°$.

The mechanical angle α_m at which pull-out occurs depends upon the number of poles on the synchronous machine. Thus, in a 2-pole machine α_m is about 90°, while in a 20-pole α_m machine it is about 9°.

Curve 2 shows the torque developed in the 4-pole motor when there is no dc excitation. This reluctance torque reaches a maximum of 20 percent of rated torque, and it occurs at an angle of 22.5°.

Figure 19.14

Typical torque versus torque angle curves for a 4-pole synchronous motor. Curve 2 is the reluctance torque developed by the motor when the poles are not excited.

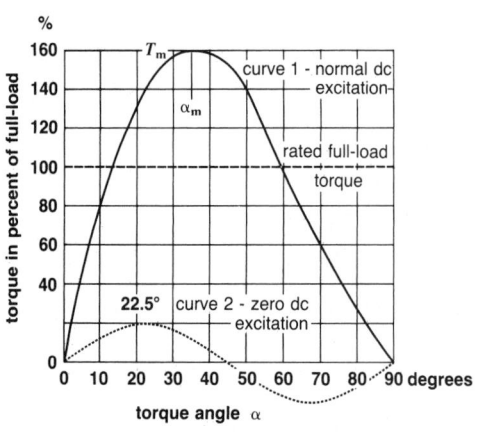

19.6 Excitation of Synchronous Machines

There are several ways to provide the dc excitation for a synchronous machine. One of the simplest is to use a dc generator G called an **exciter** (Fig. 19.15). The exciter output current I_x is varied by changing the exciter field excitation I_o, using a field rheostat R. The main exciting current I_x flows through a set of brushes and slip rings that are mounted on the rotor of the synchronous machine.

Another means of excitation is to use two dc generators, G_1 and G_2 (Fig. 19.16). Generator G_1 is called the **pilot exciter** because it provides the field excitation for the main exciter. Such excitation systems are used when generator G_2 has a rating of several hundred kilowatts. By using a pilot exciter, the small control power V_oI_o associated with I_o can be used to control the much larger power V_xI_x associated with I_x.

A third method of excitation is to use a three-phase generator (also called an exciter), and rectify its ac output (Fig. 19.17). The magnitude of I_x can be controlled

EXCITER

PILOT EXCITER

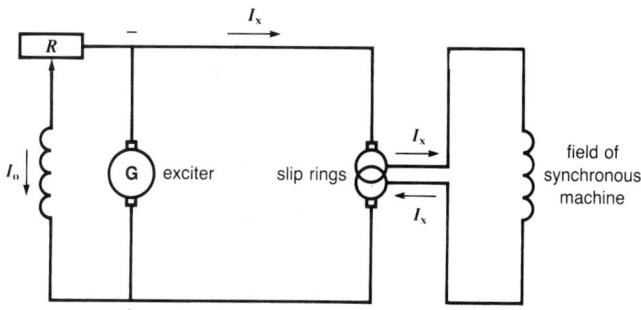

Figure 19.15

The dc excitation is provided by an exciter.

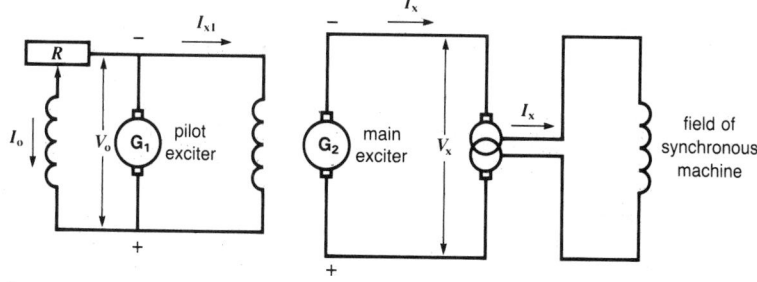

Figure 19.16

Large synchronous machines are sometimes excited by two exciters. The small pilot exciter requires little control power.

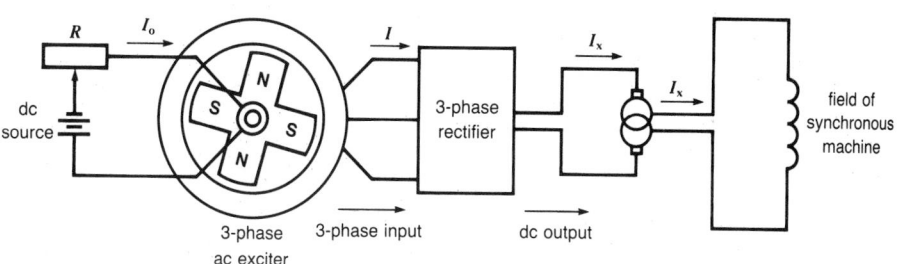

Figure 19.17

Exciting a synchronous machine with an ac exciter and rectifier.

by varying the dc excitation I_o of the exciter. The advantage of this system is that the brushes formerly associated with the dc generator are eliminated. But we still have the brushes riding on the slip rings of the synchronous machine.

Brushes are a source of trouble because they have to be replaced. Furthermore, in large machines, the wear of dozens of brushes causes carbon dust to be deposited at various places. Such conducting dust creates a serious hazard because it may cause flashovers and short-circuits. As a result, many synchronous machines today are equipped with so-called **brushless excitation** systems.

BRUSHLESS EXCITATION

Figure 19.18 illustrates the basic components of such a system. A three-phase exciter is mounted on the shaft of the synchronous machine, along with a three-phase **rectifier**. A dc control source (1) provides the dc excitation current I_{x1} for the exciter. The poles (2) of the exciter are stationary, and the armature (3) rotates. The three-phase output of the exciter is delivered by cable (4) to the rectifier (5). The dc output I_x of the rectifier is fed directly into the rotor of the synchronous machine without having to flow through brushes and slip rings.

RECTIFIER

Figure 19.18

Schematic diagram of a brushless excitation system for a synchronous motor or generator.

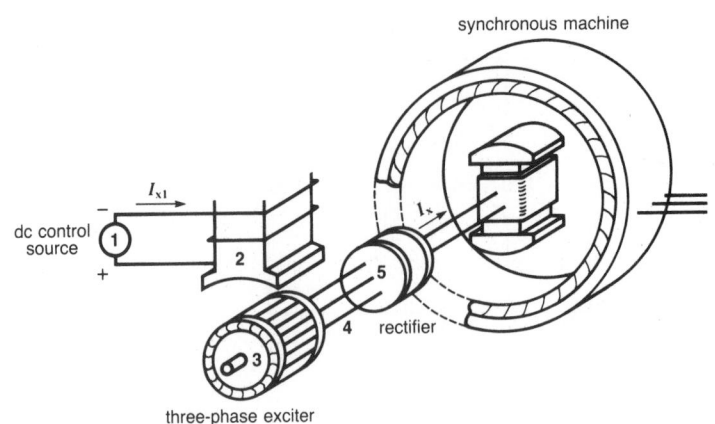

Table 19A **EXCITATION REQUIREMENTS OF SYNCHRONOUS MACHINES**

FUNCTION OF THE SYNCHRONOUS MACHINE	POWER RATING	DC EXCITATION (RATED VALUES)		
		Power	**Voltage**	**I_x**
motor	2 hp	120 W	120 V	1 A
motor	4000 hp	50 kW	250 V	200 A
generator	500 MVA	2400 kW	400 V	6000 A
generator	1500 MVA	6720 kW	600 V	11 000 A

Because of the high reliability of modern rectifiers, most synchronous motors and virtually all synchronous generators are now equipped with brushless excitation systems (Fig. 19.19). To appreciate the excitation requirements of synchronous machines, it is useful to refer to Table 19A.

19.7 Hunting of Synchronous Machines

Synchronous motors tend to oscillate for several seconds whenever they are subjected to sudden load changes. The reason is that the rotor and stator poles are held together by the "elastic" magnetic field. Thus, when a sudden load is applied to a synchronous motor, the rotor poles start moving toward a new position. However, in doing so, they briefly overshoot the mark and therefore the rotor oscillates around the new position until it finally comes to "rest." This temporary action of hide and seek is called **hunting**. The frequency of the oscillations is typically one or two per second. The frequency depends upon the mechanical inertia of the revolving parts and the electrical properties of the synchronous machine.

HUNTING

Hunting is particularly important in synchronous motors that drive pulsating loads, such as reciprocating compressors. If the load pulsates at close to the natural hunting frequency of the synchronous machine, the oscillations may build up, causing the machine to eventually lose synchronism. The oscillations also may be transmitted to the floor and through the building, causing damage to foundations and structures. However, such problems are usually foreseen (and corrected) in the design stage.

19.8 Rating of Synchronous Motors

Synchronous motors are rated according to horsepower, speed, line voltage, and power factor. The power factor rating is necessary because synchronous motors are often designed to operate at leading power factor. When they do, they deliver reactive power to the factory in which they are installed. The amount of reactive power is controlled by varying the dc excitation. The reactive power is absorbed by induction motors in the factory, and so the power factor of the entire plant can be maintained at the desired level.

Synchronous motors may be designed to operate at a leading power factor of as much as 80% (Fig. 19.19a and b). However, if there is no need for reactive power, a unity power factor motor can do the job just as well. It is slightly smaller and cheaper than the 0.8 power factor motor because less exciting current is needed. Consequently, the field windings are smaller. Furthermore, the rated stator current is smaller, which reduces the size of the stator windings.

Figure 19.19a

Synchronous motor rated 4000 hp, 200 r/min, 3-phase, 6.9 kV, 60 Hz, 80% power factor designed to drive an ore crusher. The brushless exciter is mounted on the overhung shaft and is rated 50 kW, 250 V.

(Courtesy General Electric)

Figure 19.19b

Closeup of the 50 kW
exciter showing the arma-
ture winding and five of the
six diodes used to rectify
the ac current.

EXAMPLE 19.2

A 3000 r/min, 400 V, 60 Hz, 3-phase synchronous motor has an efficiency of 96%
and a power factor rating of 0.9. Calculate the maximum reactive power it can deliver to the electrical system.

SOLUTION:

a) Power output of the motor is

$P_o = 3000 \times 746 = 2\ 238\ 000$ W $= 2238$ kW

b) Active power absorbed by the motor is

EQ. 1.11

$$P_i = \frac{100\ P_o}{eff} = \frac{100 \times 2238}{96} = 2331 \text{ kW}$$

c) Rated apparent power of the motor is

$S = P$ / power factor $= 2331 / 0.9 = 2590$ kVA

d) Reactive power the motor can deliver is

EQ. 12.20

$Q = \sqrt{S^2 - P^2}$

$= \sqrt{2590^2 - 2331^2} = 1129$ kvar

19.9 Starting Synchronous Motors

Special starters are used for synchronous motors. Many are designed for across-
the-line starting, but large motors may require reduced-voltage starting. These
starters are considered in Chapter 22, so for now we will discuss only the general
principles of starting synchronous motors.

During the acceleration phase, the dc field winding is connected to an external "discharge" resistor (Fig. 19.6). The presence of the discharge resistor improves the starting torque of the motor. It also limits the high voltage that would otherwise appear
across the field terminals while the motor speed is low. When the motor is running

at close to synchronous speed, the dc excitation is suddenly applied. The timing is done automatically, so as to develop the highest possible pull-in torque. We recall that the field produced by the stator sweeps slowly past the salient poles when the rotor is running at close to synchronous speed. Consequently, when dc excitation is applied, we must be sure that the resulting N and S poles on the rotor are facing the opposite S and N poles on the stator, so as to maximize the force of attraction.

If the load has high inertia, the pull-in torque may not be big enough to pull the machine into synchronism. In such cases, the synchronous motor must be synchronized alone and the load gradually brought up to speed by a using a magnetic clutch.

19.10 Application of Synchronous Motors

Synchronous motors are used to drive pumps, compressors, fans, pulp grinders, and other heavy industrial equipment. They are preferred to induction motors whenever the speed of rotation is low. At low speeds, induction motors tend to have a low power factor, whereas synchronous motors can operate at unity power factor.

At the opposite end of the power spectrum, we find tiny synchronous motors that are used in electric clocks and timing devices. They are single-phase devices having typical outputs of 0.75 W (1/1000 hp) at efficiencies of 15 percent. Motors that are geared down to 1 r/min have typical efficiencies of 1 percent.

19.11 Summary

Upon completion of this chapter you should learned that:

- A synchronous motor consists of a three-phase stator that is similar in construction to the stator of a three-phase squirrel cage motor. The rotor in a synchronous motor is composed of wound magnetic poles connected to a dc source.

- A synchronous motor accelerates in a manner similar to that of an induction motor. As rotor speed approaches synchronous speed, the induced rotor current decreases. At this time, the magnetic fields created by the dc windings of the rotor cause the rotor speed to be "pulled" up to the stator speed.

- When a load is applied to a synchronous motor, the rotor poles lag behind the stator poles by an angle called the torque angle. The increased torque angle causes the motor torque to increase and the rotor maintains synchronous speed. If the load exceeds the rated motor torque, the rotor poles will lag further and further behind the stator poles and the motor may drop out of synchronous operation.

- As the torque angle of a synchronous motor increases, the torque increases. The torque angle at which pull-out torque occurs is related to the number of poles in the machine. A typical graph of torque versus torque angle is given in Fig. 19.14.

- A synchronous motor requires dc excitation for the rotor windings in order to produce magnetic fields' synchronous speed. The dc source, called the exciter, may be supplied from an external dc source or from a generator attached to the rotor shaft of the synchronous motor.

Key Terms

BRUSHLESS EXCITATION: A system that uses a three-phase alternator and rectifier to supply excitation current. The rectifier is attached to the rotor of the synchronous motor, eliminating the need for brushes.

EXCITER: The dc source used to supply the rotor fields of a synchronous motor. The exciter may be supplied from a generator attached to the rotor shaft, or it may be supplied from a separate dc rectifier.

HUNTING: The oscillation of a machine's speed when the load is suddenly changed. The motor will usually stabilize its speed after a short period.

PILOT EXCITER: A small permanent magnet generator used to supply field current to the main exciter of a synchronous motor.

PULL-OUT TORQUE: The motor torque at which a synchronous motor will drop out of synchronous operation.

RECTIFIER: An electronic circuit that converts ac to dc.

TORQUE ANGLE α: The angle between the pole faces of the stator and rotor of a synchronous motor. The maximum torque angle is a function of the number of poles in the machine.

Test Your Knowledge

19.1   A synchronous motor can pull into step even in the absence of dc excitation.

      true _____   false _____

19.2   The dc excitation of a synchronous motor must not be applied until the motor is running at close to synchronous speed.

      true _____   false _____

19.3   A 500 hp, 2200 V, 3-phase, 60 Hz, 30-pole synchronous motor is connected to a line whose frequency is 60.3 Hz. Its speed is
     a.   240 r/min
     b.   720 r/min
     c.   241.2 r/min

19.4   A 28-pole synchronous motor draws an exciting current of 80 A from a 125 V dc source. The resistance of a rotor field coil is
     a.   43.75 Ω
     b.   55.8 mΩ
     c.   1.56 Ω

19.5   When a synchronous motor is under-excited,
     a.   its field coils overheat
     b.   its speed drops slightly
     c.   it absorbs reactive power from the ac line

19.6   In Fig. 19.8, the field current needed to obtain a leading power factor and a stator current of 40 A is
     a.   2.5 A
     b.   9A
     c.   5.196 A

19.7   A 4500 hp, 6900 V, 3-phase, 60 Hz, 1200 r/min, 0.8 power factor synchronous motor drives a centrifugal compressor in a coal mine. If it has an efficiency of 97.0%, calculate the ac line current when the motor operates at its rated output.
     a.   362 A
     b.   627 A
     c.   209 A

Questions and Problems

19.8 Why does the speed of a synchronous motor remain constant even under variable load?

19.9 What is meant by a synchronous capacitor?

19.10 Explain what causes a synchronous motor to hunt.

19.11 If we over-excite a synchronous motor, will it deliver more power to the load?

19.12 A synchronous motor driving a pump operates at unity power factor. If the dc excitation is increased, what happens to (a) the stator current and (b) the temperature of the motor?

19.13 A 10 000 hp, 6.6 kV, 3-phase, 60 Hz, 327 r/min, 0.9 power factor synchronous motor drives a pulpwood grinder in a paper mill. If it has a full-load efficiency of 97.8%, calculate the losses in the machine.

19.14 In Table 19A, calculate the ratio of excitation power to the power rating of (a) the 2 hp motor, (b) the 4000 hp motor, and (c) the 1500 MVA generator.

20

Synchronous Generators

LEARNING OBJECTIVES

Upon completion of this chapter you will be able to:

- Describe the construction of synchronous generators

- Describe the operation of a synchronous generator on an infinite bus

- Explain the operation of an asynchronous machine as a generator

- Explain how active and reactive power flow is controlled

- List the conditions that must be met in order to synchronize generators

- Construct phasor diagrams to illustrate the operation of a synchronous generator connected to an infinite bus

- Describe the operation of a generator supplying an isolated load

20.1 Stationary-Field Ac Generator

Commercial ac generators are built with either a stationary or a rotating dc field. A stationary-field ac generator (Fig. 20.1) has the same outward appearance as a dc generator. The salient poles create

▼ Figure 20.1

Three-phase stationary-field ac generator.

▼ Figure 20.2

Rotor of a stationary-field ac generator rated 20 kVA, 3600 r/min, 115/230 V, single-phase, 60 Hz unity power factor. The armature is 200 mm long and has a diameter of 143 mm. The two single-phase windings are brought out to four slip rings.

(Courtesy Electro-Mecanik)

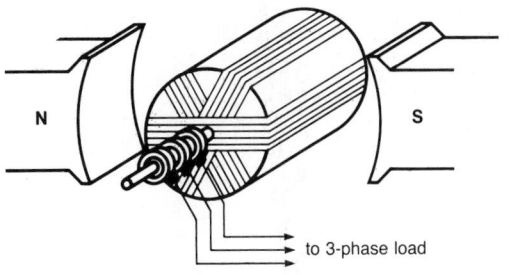

▼ Figure 20.1

Three-phase stationary-field ac generator.

to 3-phase load

the dc field, which is cut by a revolving armature. However, the armature has a three-phase winding whose terminals are connected to three slip rings mounted on the shaft. A set of brushes riding on the slip rings permits the armature to be connected to an external three-phase load. The armature is driven by a gasoline engine, water turbine, or some other source of motive power. As we learned in Section 13.2, a three-phase voltage is induced whose value depends upon the speed of rotation and the magnitude of the dc exciting current in the stationary poles.

Stationary-field generators are satisfactory when the output power is less than 50 kVA (Fig. 20.2). However, for greater outputs, it is cheaper, safer, and more practical to employ a stationary armature and a revolving dc field.

20.2 Revolving-Field Ac Generator

From an electrical standpoint, the stator of a revolving-field ac generator is identical to that of a three-phase synchronous motor. However, the windings are always connected in wye and the neutral is grounded. We prefer a wye connection to a delta connection because the voltage per phase is only 1/1.732 or 58 percent of the voltage between the lines. This means that the highest voltage between a stator conductor and the grounded stator core is only 58 percent of the line voltage. Thus, by using a wye connection, we can reduce the amount of insulation in the slots. Figures 20.3 and 20.4 show the typical construction of large ac generators.

The rated voltage of a synchronous generator depends upon its power rating. In general, the greater the power, the higher the voltage. However, the rated voltage seldom exceeds 25 kV.

Figure 20.3

Stator of a steam turbine
generator rated 722 MVA,
3600 r/min, 19 kV, 60 Hz,
3-phase. The windings are
water-cooled and the entire
stator will later be enclosed
in a metal housing (see
background). The housing
contains hydrogen under
pressure to further improve
the cooling.

(Courtesy Brown Boveri)

Revolving-field generators are built with two types of rotors: *salient-pole* rotors and smooth, *cylindrical* rotors. Salient-pole rotors are used in low-speed generators, such as those driven by hydraulic turbines. Cylindrical rotors are used in high-speed generators driven by steam turbines. The turbines or driving engines are

PRIME MOVER

called **prime movers**.

Figure 20.4a

The stator of a large, slow-speed synchronous genera-tor is composed of steel laminations that are stacked at the generator site. This picture shows the stator of a 500 MVA, 200 r/min, 15 kV, 60 Hz, 3-phase generator designed to operate at a lagging power factor of 95%. The internal diameter is 9250 mm and the axial length is 2500 mm.

(Courtesy Marine Industrie)

Figure 20.4b

The 376 pre-formed coils are placed in the 376 slots and interconnected to produce a 3-phase wye-connected winding. The current per phase is 19 250 A.

(Courtesy Marine Industrie)

20.3 Number of Poles

The number of poles on a synchronous generator depends upon the speed of rotation and the frequency we wish to produce. The frequency is given by the basic equation

$$f = \frac{pn_s}{120}$$

EQ. 17.2

where

f = frequency of the induced voltage (Hz)

p = number of poles on the rotor

n_s = speed of the rotor (r/min)

EXAMPLE 20.1

A hydraulic turbine turning at 150 r/min drives a synchronous generator rated at 400 MVA, 14 kV, 3-phase, 60 Hz.

1. How many poles does the rotor have?
2. What is the armature current per phase?

SOLUTION:

1. $p = 120f/n_s = 120 \times 60/150 = 48$ poles

    EQ. 17.2

2. From Equation 13.3 we have $S = 1.732\ VI$

    therefore $I = \dfrac{S}{1.732\ V} = \dfrac{400 \times 10^6}{1.732 \times 14\ 000} = 16\ 500$ A

20.4 Salient-Pole Rotors

Most hydraulic turbines must turn at low speeds (between 50 and 300 r/min) in order to extract the maximum power from a waterfall. Because the rotor is directly coupled to the waterwheel and because a frequency of 60 Hz is required, a large number of poles must be placed on the rotor. The salient poles are mounted on a circular steel frame that is fixed to a revolving vertical shaft (Fig. 20.5).

In addition to the dc winding, we often add a squirrel-cage winding embedded in the pole faces (Fig. 20.6). Under normal conditions, this winding does not carry any current because the rotor turns at synchronous speed. However, when the load on the generator changes suddenly, the rotor begins to hunt, producing momentary speed variations above and below synchronous speed. This induces a voltage in the squirrel-cage winding, causing a large current to flow. The current reacts with the magnetic field of the stator, producing forces that dampen the oscillation of the rotor. For this reason, the squirrel-cage winding is sometimes called a **damper winding**.

> **DAMPER WINDING**

20.5 Cylindrical Rotors

Steam turbines are smaller and more efficient when they run at high speed. The same is true of synchronous generators. Thus, there is an economic advantage

▼ **Figure 20.5**

Salient-pole rotor of a 500 MVA, 200 r/min synchronous generator being lowered inside its stator. The diameter is 9.1 m (30 feet).

(Courtesy Marine Industrie)

▼ **Figure 20.6**

Salient-pole of a low-speed, 250 MVA synchronous generator showing the twelve slots that will carry the squirrel-cage damper winding.

Figure 20.7a

Cylindrical rotor of a steam-turbine generator showing the slots being milled out along its length. They will carry the dc winding. The generator is rated 1530 MVA, 1500 r/min, 27 kV, 50 Hz. It has an effective pole length of 7490 mm and a diameter of 1800 mm.

(Courtesy Allis-Chalmers Power Systems Inc., West Allis, Wisconsin)

Figure 20.7b

Cylindrical rotor with its 4-pole dc winding. The total mass is 225 tons and the exciting current of 11 200 A is supplied by a 600 V dc brushless exciter. The air gap between the revolving rotor and stationary stator is 120 mm.

to using high-speed equipment. However, to produce the desired frequency, we cannot use fewer than two poles, and this fixes the highest possible speed. On a 60 Hz system, it is 3600 r/min. The next lower speed is 1800 r/min, corresponding to a 4-pole machine. Consequently, these so-called *steam-turbine generators* have either two or four poles. The rotor is a long solid-iron cylinder which has slots milled lengthwise out of the cylindrical mass (Fig. 20.7a). Concentric field coils, firmly wedged into the slots, serve to create the dc poles (Figs. 20.7b and 20.8).

The high speed of rotation produces strong centrifugal forces which impose an upper limit on the diameter of the rotor. For this reason, cylindrical rotors have to be very long when the power output of the generator is in the 1000 MW range.

Figure 20.8

End view of a two-pole cylindrical rotor. Each pole is composed of eight concentric coils that carry the dc current. Flat, bare conductors are placed at the top of each slot and extend outwards in artistic display. They will be flattened down over the dc winding and short-circuited to create the damper winding.

(Courtesy Brown Boveri)

20.6 Ac Generator Under Load

The performance of an ac generator depends upon the type of load it has to supply. Although there are many types of loads, they can all be grouped into two basic categories:

1.   Isolated loads, powered by a single generator.

2.   A fixed-voltage, fixed-frequency infinite bus.

From the standpoint of power generation, the second category is by far the most important, so we will discuss it first.

20.7 Ac Generator on an Infinite Bus

A large electric utility system, fed by dozens of big generators, is so powerful that the frequency and line voltage are, to all practical purposes, fixed. Thus, when a single generator is added to or disconnected from the system, it cannot affect either the voltage or the frequency of the system. Such a system is called an **infinite bus**.

INFINITE BUS

Once connected to an infinite bus, an ac generator becomes part of a network comprising dozens (sometimes hundreds) of other generators that deliver power to millions of loads. It is impossible, therefore, to specify the nature of the load (large or small; resistive, inductive, or capacitive) connected to the terminals of this particular generator. What, then, determines the power the machine delivers?

Part of the answer lies in what we learned in Chapter 19 on synchronous motors. We recall that a synchronous motor is effectively connected to an infinite bus because the voltage and frequency of the line are constant. When a load torque is applied to the motor, it *absorbs* active power from the line. Similarly, if a prime mover exerts a *driving* torque on a generator, it will *deliver* active power to the line.

In effect, whenever a generator is connected to an infinite bus, we can raise the active power (kilowatts) it delivers to the system by increasing the torque of the turbine. On the other hand, if we want to vary the amount of reactive power (kilowatts), we sim-

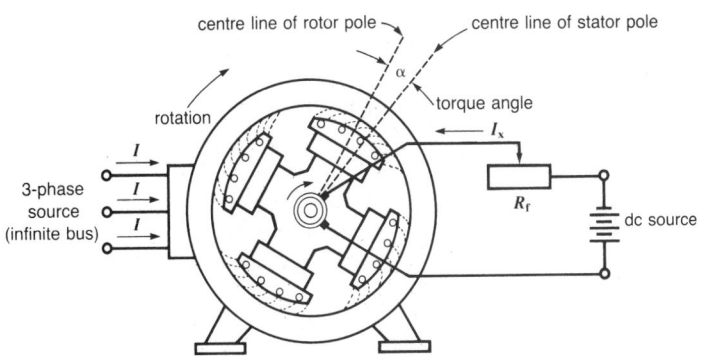

Figure 20.9

Synchronous motor connected to an infinite bus and running at no-load. The arrows show the positive direction of the current in each phase. The dc current is adjusted so that the motor operates at unity power factor.

ply vary the dc excitation. These two basic methods — torque control and excitation control — are the way in which the generator output is adjusted. Because the kW and kvar output can be varied independently, the power factor and the magnitude of the generator load are actually determined by the generator and its prime mover.

We will now examine in more detail what actually happens when an ac generator is connected to an infinite bus. Such an ac generator is often called a *synchronous generator* because its average speed has to be directly proportional to the frequency of the system to which it is connected.

20.8 Synchronous Machine Operating as a Generator

In order to observe the smooth transition from motor action to generator action, let us begin our study with a synchronous motor operating at no-load (Fig. 20.9). Because the voltage and frequency of the ac source are fixed, the motor is actually connected to an infinite bus. The rotor is turning clockwise, and it lags behind the stator poles by a small angle α. The excitation is adjusted so that the motor operates at unity power factor; the line current I is therefore small.

Instead of applying a mechanical load to the shaft (thus tending to slow the machine down), let us apply a driving torque, tending to speed it up. This can be done by connecting a gasoline engine or other prime mover to the motor shaft (Fig. 20.10). As the driving torque is increased, angle α will gradually decrease and eventually become zero

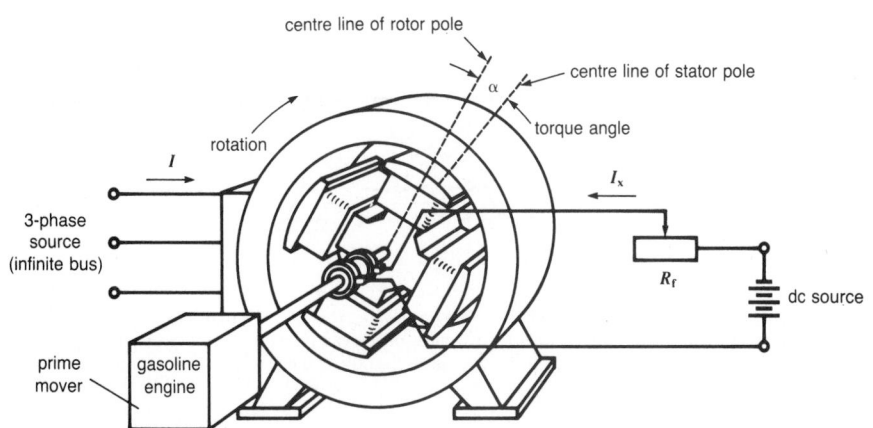

Figure 20.10

When a prime mover, such as a gasoline engine, is coupled to the shaft, the torque angle can gradually be reduced to zero.

when the rotor and stator poles are perfectly lined up. When this happens, the windage and friction losses are entirely supplied by the driving engine, and no more power is drawn from the three-phase line. Consequently, line current *I* becomes zero (Fig. 20.11).

Let us continue to increase the driving torque by opening the throttle of the engine. The rotor poles will pull ahead of the stator poles, and so the flux between them will have the shape shown in Fig. 20.12. The magnetic "rubber bands" exert a pull on the rotor that acts *against* the direction of rotation. Consequently, the engine has to exert a torque to maintain this position of the poles. The engine is therefore delivering mechanical power to the synchronous machine. What happens to this power?

It is entirely converted into electric power, which is returned to the three-phase line. As a result, the synchronous machine now operates as a generator. It is called a synchronous generator because its frequency is determined by the three-phase line to which the generator is connected.

As we continue to increase the driving torque of the engine, angle α increases, as does the power delivered to the three-phase system. The stator current *I* also increases. However, there is a limit to the driving torque that can be applied to the rotor. If we exceed the **pull-out torque** of the generator, the rotor poles will suddenly break away from the stator poles, and the generator is said to lose synchronism. When this happens, the net power delivered to the three-phase line falls abruptly to zero. The line current *I* increases dramatically, and the circuit breakers protecting the machine will trip.*

PULL-OUT TORQUE

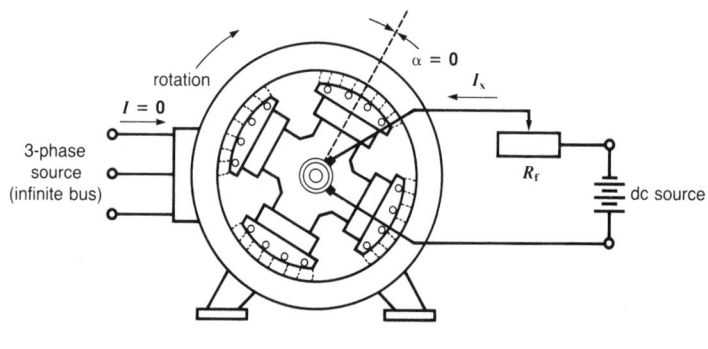

Figure 20.11

When the torque angle is zero, the prime mover supplies all the power needed to drive the rotor. The ac line current becomes zero. Note that the flux is now symmetrically distributed over the pole face.

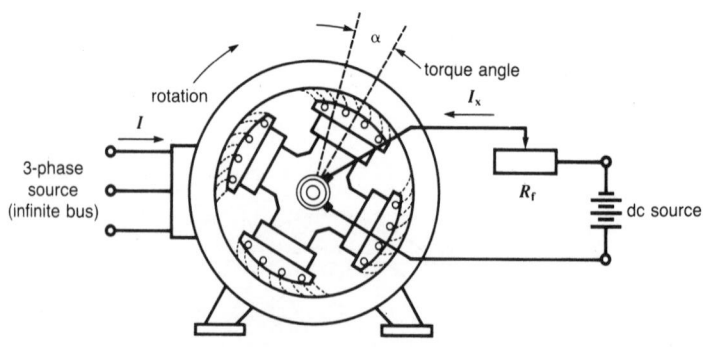

Figure 20.12

When the torque of the prime mover is increased, the rotor poles pull ahead of the stator poles. The poles continue to attract each other; therefore, a continuous braking torque is exerted on the rotor as it rotates.

* The sudden disappearance of any opposing torque causes the driving engine to start racing unless automatic means are used to limit its speed. Such overspeeds can be dangerous because the centrifugal forces acting on the poles may tear the rotor apart, literally causing a mechanical explosion inside the machine.

The pull-out torque T_m of the synchronous generator has the same magnitude as when the machine was operating as a synchronous motor (see Fig. 19.14). Furthermore, the critical angle α_m where pull-out occurs is also the same. The only difference is that the torque acts in the opposite direction and α_m is positive instead of negative.

In summary, we can increase the active power (kilowatts) delivered to an infinite bus by increasing the mechanical power input to the synchronous generator. The increased mechanical power is obtained by raising the torque of the turbine or driving engine.

As a final point of comparison, Fig. 20.13 shows the flux pattern between the rotor poles and stator poles when the machine is acting as a motor ($\alpha = -30°$), and as a generator ($\alpha = +30°$). Note that the rotor poles are always ahead of the stator poles when the machine runs as a generator.

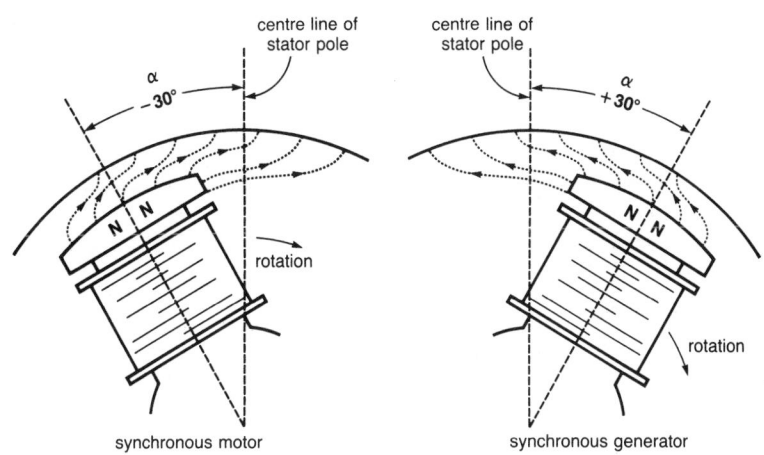

Figure 20.13

Comparison of the rotor position and flux pattern when a synchronous machine is connected to an infinite bus and running as a motor or a generator.

20.9 Active and Reactive Power Flow

We have seen that when a synchronous machine is connected to a three-phase line, it can operate as either a motor or a generator, depending upon the torque that is exerted on the shaft. When the machine operates as a motor, it *draws* active power P from the line. When it operates as a generator, it *delivers* active power to the line. Thus, if a 3-phase wattmeter is connected between the synchronous machine and the line, it will give a positive reading when power flows into the machine (Fig. 20.14). Conversely, it will give a negative reading when power flows out of the machine, in which case it is acting as a synchronous generator (Fig. 20.15). Note that the dc exciting current I_x is the same in both cases. We conclude that the magnitude of the active power received or delivered by the synchronous machine depends only upon the magnitude of the torque exerted on the shaft.

What happens if we vary the dc excitation? This will vary the amount of reactive power that flows into (or out of) the machine.

Figure 20.14

Wattmeter reading and active power flow when the synchronous machine is operating as a motor. The torque exerted on the shaft is opposite to the rotation.

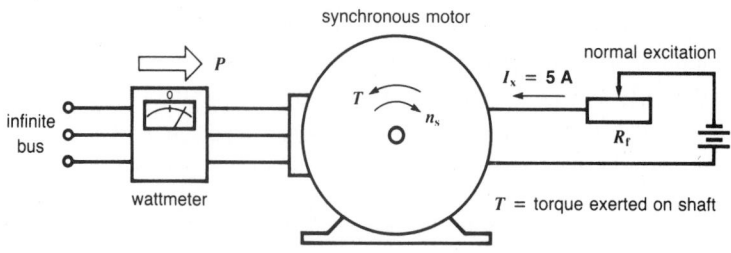

Figure 20.15

Wattmeter reading and active power flow when the synchronous machine is operating as a generator. The torque exerted on the shaft is in the direction of rotation.

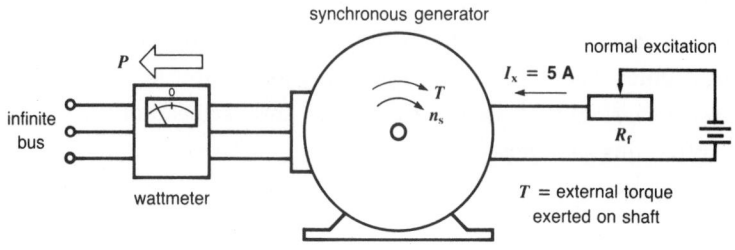

Figure 20.16

Varmeter reading and reactive power flow when a synchronous motor (or generator) is under-excited.

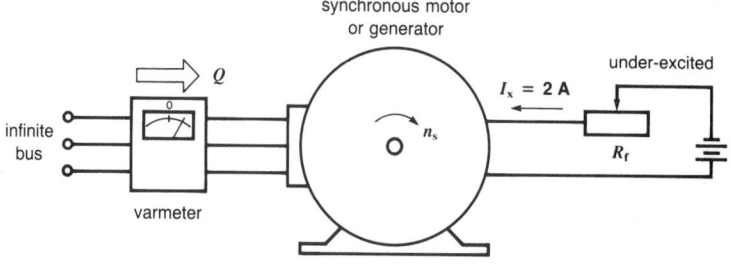

Figure 20.17

Varmeter reading and reactive power flow when a synchronous motor (or generator) is over-excited.

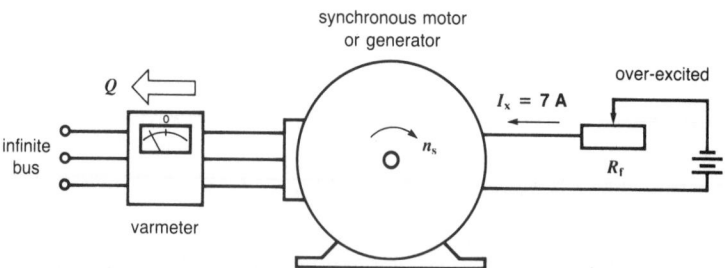

If we decrease the excitation below its "normal" value, the synchronous machine will absorb reactive power from the line. This is true whether the machine operates as a motor or as a generator. If a three-phase varmeter is connected into the line, it will give a positive reading (Fig. 20.16).

Conversely, if we raise the excitation above its normal value, the machine will deliver reactive power to the line, whether it is acting as a motor or as a generator. The varmeter will give a negative reading (Fig. 20.17).

20.10 Synchronization of an Ac Generator

On a large electric utility system, dozens of synchronous generators are effectively connected in parallel to supply the enormous power requirements of a geographical region. As the demand builds up during the day, generators are successively added to the system to provide the extra power. Later, as the power demand falls, selected machines are successively disconnected from the system until the utility load again builds up the following day. Synchronous generators are therefore continually being connected and disconnected from a power grid in response to consumer demand. However, before a generator is connected to a system, it must first be *synchronized*. We cannot just throw it on the line by closing a switch. A generator is said to be synchronized when it meets the following conditions:

1. the generator frequency is equal to the system frequency,

2. the generator voltage is equal to the system voltage,

3. the generator voltage is in phase with the system voltage, and

4. the generator phase sequence is the same as the system phase sequence.

To synchronize a generator, we proceed as follows:

1. Adjust the speed of the turbine (or other prime mover) so that the generator frequency is very close to the system frequency.

2. Adjust the dc excitation so that the generator terminal voltage V_o is equal to the system voltage V (Fig. 20.18).

3. Observe the phase angle between V_o and V by means of a **synchroscope**. This instrument has a pointer that indicates the phase angle between the two volt-

SYNCHROSCOPE

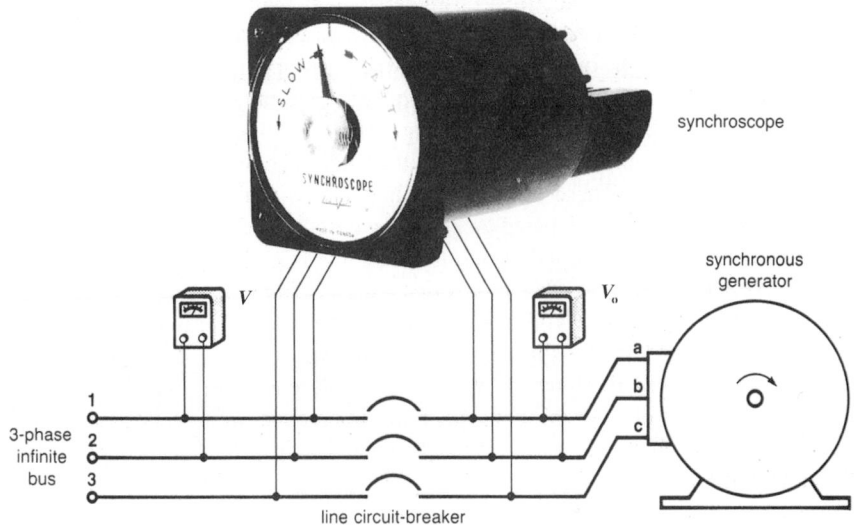

synchroscope

synchronous generator

3-phase infinite bus

line circuit-breaker

Figure 20.18

Method of synchronizing a generator.

(Courtesy Lab-Volt)

ages, covering the entire range from zero to 360°. Although the degrees are not shown, the dial has a zero marker to indicate when the voltages are in phase. In practice, when the frequency of the generator is close to system frequency, the pointer rotates slowly as it tracks the changing phase angle between the generator and system voltages. If the generator frequency is higher than the system frequency, the pointer rotates clockwise. Otherwise, it rotates counterclockwise.

4. Carefully adjust the speed regulator of the turbine so that the pointer of the synchroscope just barely creeps across the dial.

5. Make a final check to see that the generator voltage is equal to the system voltage.

6. Then, the moment the pointer crosses zero, close the line circuit breaker, thus connecting the generator to the system.*

The same synchronizing procedure is followed in isolated systems when a generator has to be connected in parallel with another generator. In modern generating stations, synchronization is done automatically.

20.11   Equivalent Circuit of an Ac Generator

In the study of dc machines, we found it useful to employ an equivalent circuit showing the essential components of the armature and field. It enabled us to predict the voltages and currents when the machine was under load. In the same way, it is useful to have an equivalent circuit of a synchronous machine. It should represent, as simply as possible, the electrical characteristics of the armature and field.

The three armature (stator) windings of a synchronous machine have identical electrical properties. The only difference among them is that the voltages and currents are displaced (in time) by 120°. Consequently, we can use one winding on the stator to represent all three. Referring to Fig. 20.19, a voltage V_o is induced in this winding by the revolving flux ϕ created by the rotor. The winding has a resistance R_s and a reactance X_s. These elements are in series with the induced voltage V_o. The external terminals are labelled A and N, where N is the neutral of the three-phase machine. The corresponding terminal voltage is V.

The revolving field is connected in series with a field rheostat R_s to a dc source V_x. The resulting current I_x produces the flux ϕ. The external terminals of the field are marked 1 and 2, but the slip rings are not shown.

The equivalent circuit shown in Fig. 20.19 represents with good accuracy the electrical properties of a synchronous machine. In practice, R_s is much smaller than X_s, and so we usually neglect it. The reactance X_s is called the *synchronous reactance* of the machine.

---

* If the phase sequence 1-2-3 of the infinite bus is not the same as the phase sequence a-b-c of the "incoming" generator, it will be impossible to observe the slow rotation of the synchroscope pointer. If the circuit breaker is closed, a short-circuit will result.

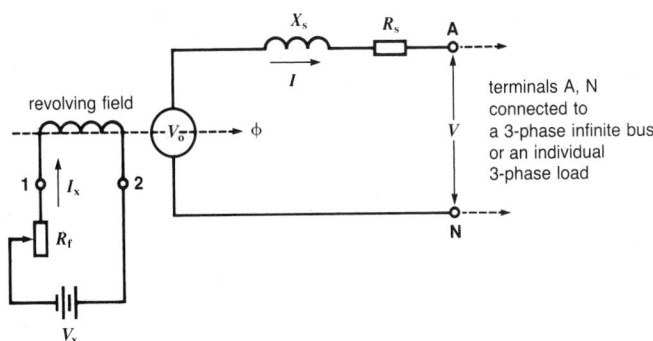

Figure 20.19

Equivalent circuit of a three-phase generator, showing only phase A and the dc exciting circuit.

20.12 Phasor Diagram of a Synchronous Generator

To illustrate the use of the equivalent circuit, let us draw the phasor diagram when the synchronous machine operates as a generator on a three-phase line (infinite bus). We assume that I_x is adjusted so that the generator operates at unity power factor. This means that I is in phase with the terminal voltage V (Fig. 20.20).

Next, because the machine is operating as a synchronous generator, we know that the rotor poles *lead* the stator poles by a certain mechanical angle α (see Fig. 20.13). As a result, voltage V_o that is induced in the stator by the rotor must *lead* V by a corresponding *electrical* angle δ. Finally, the IX_s drop must be at 90° to I, because of the inductive nature of X_s. The complete phasor diagram for the synchronous generator is shown in Fig. 20.20.

It can be proved that the electrical torque-angle δ is related to the mechanical torque-angle α by the equation

$$\delta = \alpha p/2$$

EQ. 20.1

where p is the number of poles on the synchronous machine.

Suppose we raise I_x so that the generator is over-excited. How will this affect the phasor diagram, knowing that the mechanical power remains the same? The theory tells us that over-excitation causes the generator to deliver reactive power to the line. Thus, as far as the generator is concerned, the load across its terminals is inductive. This means that I lags behind the terminal voltage V. However, the component I_p that

▼ **Figure 20.20**

Circuit and phasor diagram when a 3-phase generator is connected to an infinite bus and operating at unity power factor.

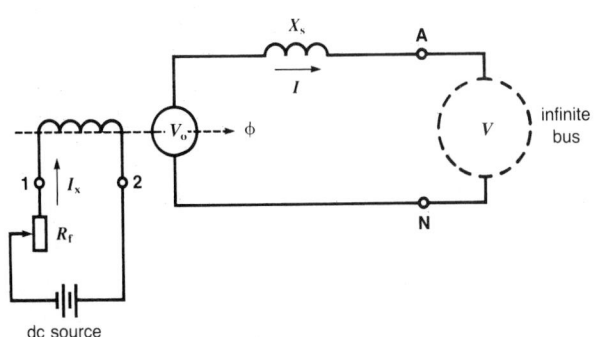

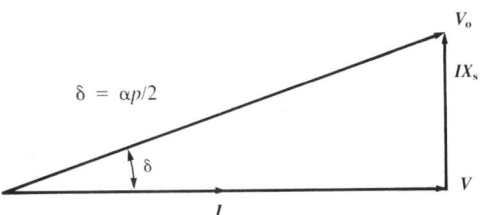

Figure 20.21

Phasor diagram when the
generator excitation in
Fig. 20.20 is increased
without changing the
power input of the prime
mover.

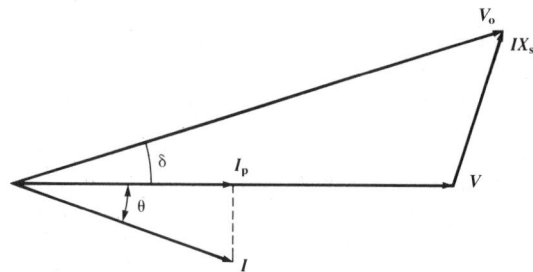

is in phase with V must be the same as before. The reason is that the active power
delivered by the generator is unchanged because the mechanical power input is the
same. The resulting phasor diagram is shown in Fig. 20.21. Note that IX_s is again 90°
ahead of I. The power factor of the synchronous generator is equal to cos θ, and the
torque angle δ is slightly smaller than in Fig. 20.20.

EXAMPLE 20.2

A 150 MVA, 15 kV, 3-phase, 200 r/min, wye-connected synchronous generator has
a synchronous reactance of 1.4 Ω per phase. We want it to deliver 120 MW of active
power and 60 Mvar of reactive power to the 15 kV infinite bus to which the generator is connected. Calculate:

1. the current per phase and the line-to-neutral voltage.
2. the phase angle between the line current and line-to-neutral voltage.
3. the internal voltage drop due to the synchronous reactance.
4. the excitation voltage V_o that is required.
5. the electrical torque angle α.
6. the mechanical torque angle δ.
7. the mechanical torque exerted by the prime mover.

SOLUTION:

This may appear to be a complicated problem, but if we attack it step by step, it is
fairly easy to solve.

1. a) The apparent power delivered by the generator is

$$S = \sqrt{P^2 + Q^2} = \sqrt{120^2 + 60^2} = 134 \text{ MVA}$$

    b) The current per phase is

$$I = S/1.732V = 134 \times 10^6/(1.732 \times 15\ 000) = 5158 \text{ A}$$

    c) The line-to-neutral voltage is

$$V/1.732 = 15\ 000/1.732 = 8660 \text{ V}$$

continued

2. a) The power factor of the generator is

    $\cos \theta = P/S = 120/134 = 0.895$

    b) The phase angle between I and the line-to-neutral voltage is

    $\theta = \arccos 0.895 = 26.4°$

3. The internal IX_s drop is $IX_s = 5158 \times 1.4 = 7221$ V

    Note that the internal voltage drop is almost as great as the terminal voltage of the generator: this is quite common in synchronous machines. However, unlike in a dc generator, this voltage drop produces no heat because it is associated with a reactance.

4. a) To determine the excitation voltage V_o, we draw a phasor diagram of the values we have calculated so far (see Fig. 20.22). The IX_s drop is at 90° to current 1, and so the phase angle between 7221 V and 8660 V is (90 + 26.4) = 116.4°.

    b) The magnitude of V_o can be found using the cosine law. Thus

    $$V_o^2 = 8660^2 + 7221^2 - 2 \times 8600 \times 7221 \cos 116.4 \qquad \text{EQ. 1.15}$$

    from which the required excitation voltage is found to be $V_o = 13\ 518$ V

5. The electrical torque angle δ can also be found using the cosine law. Thus

    $7221^2 = 13\ 518^2 + 8660^2 - 2 \times 13\ 518 \times 8660 \cos \delta$

    from which $\cos \delta = 0.878$, and so $\delta = \arccos 0.878 = 28.6°$

6. a) The number of poles on the generator is

    $$p = 120\ f/n_s = 120 \times 60/200 = 36 \qquad \text{EQ. 17.2}$$

    b) The mechanical torque angle is

    $$\alpha = 2\ \delta/p = 2 \times 28.6/36 = 1.59 \qquad \text{EQ. 20.1}$$

    The centre line of the rotor poles is therefore only 1.59° ahead of the stator poles. Thus, it takes a very small mechanical displacement to produce the 120 MW output.

7. The torque of the prime mover is:

    $$T = 9.55P/n = 9.55 \times 120 \times 10^6/200 = 5.73 \text{ MN.m} \qquad \text{EQ. 1.9}$$

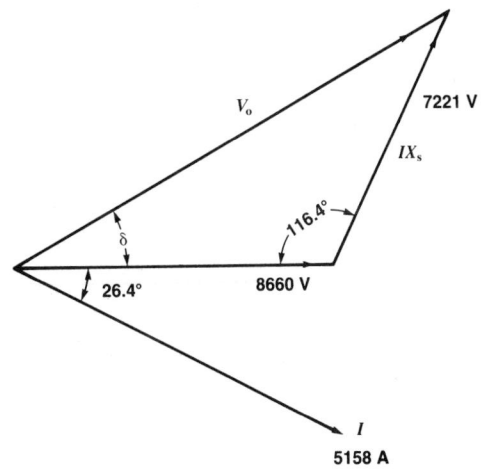

Figure 20.22

See Example 20.2.

20.13 Ac Generator Feeding an Isolated Load

When an ac generator feeds an isolated load, the terminal voltage does not remain constant, as in the case of an infinite bus. The voltage regulation from no-load to full-load can be quite large, depending upon the power factor of the load. In order to maintain a constant line voltage, the dc excitation has to be varied whenever the load varies. Furthermore, the speed of the prime mover also has to be regulated to maintain a constant frequency,

Figure 20.23 shows a generator feeding an isolated load Z. The generator is operating at full-load, delivering rated current I_N at rated voltage V_N. We wish to determine the magnitude of the excitation voltage V_o for various load power factors with the generator delivering its rated output.

For a unity power factor load, we obtain the phasor diagram of Fig. 20.24.

For a lagging power factor load, current I_N lags the terminal voltage V_N. The resulting phasor diagram is shown in Fig. 20.25. Note that V_o is now greater than in Fig. 20.24. This means that the dc exciting current I_x has to be raised at lagging power factors in order to obtain the same terminal voltage.

For a leading power factor, current I_N leads V_N. The resulting phasor diagram is shown in Fig. 20.26. The induced voltage V_o is now *less* than the terminal voltage V_N. This surprising result is due to the partial resonance effect between the capacitance of the load and the synchronous reactance X_s.

Figure 20.23

Equivalent circuit of a three-phase generator feeding an isolated load. Only phase A is shown, and the dc exciting circuit.

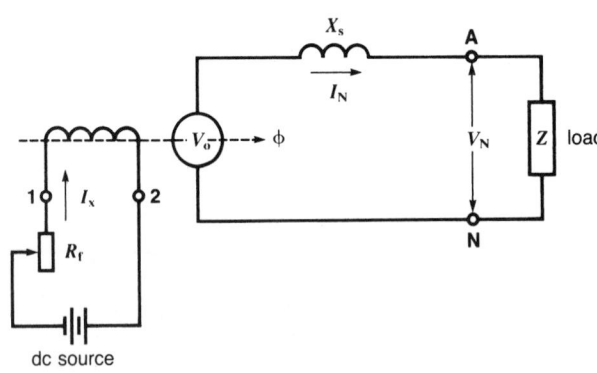

Figure 20.24

Phasor diagram and magnitude of V_o when a generator operates at full-load and unity power factor.

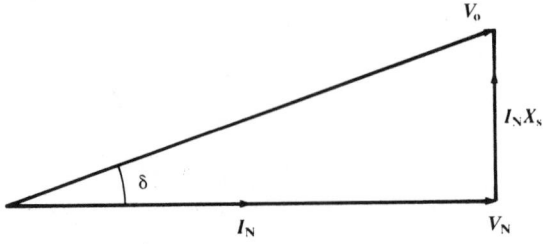

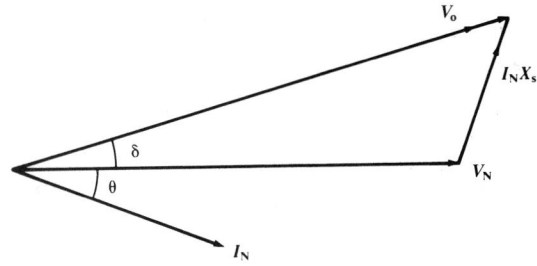

Figure 20.25

Phasor diagram and magnitude of V_o when a generator operates at full-load and lagging power factor.

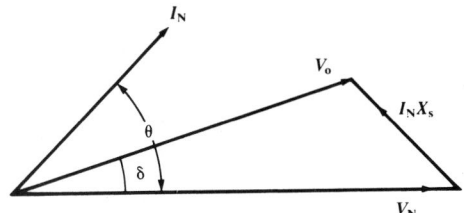

Figure 20.26

Phasor diagram and magnitude of V_o when a generator operates at full-load and leading power factor.

20.14 Voltage Regulation of an Isolated Generator

The previous phasor diagrams enable us to predict the full-load to no-load voltage regulation of an ac generator when it supplies an isolated load. However, the power factor of the load must be specified.

The voltage regulation in percent can be calculated from the equation

$$\text{percent regulation} = \frac{V_o - V_N}{V_N} \times 100 \qquad \textbf{EQ. 20.2}$$

where

V_N = rated voltage of the alternator
V_o = open-circuit voltage (at the same speed and excitation level)

EXAMPLE 20.3

A 3-phase generator having a rating of 72 MVA, 21 kV has a synchronous reactance of 5 Ω per phase. Calculate:
1. the rated current I_N of the generator.
2. the induced voltage V_o that is required at rated load, 80 percent power factor lagging.
3. the no-load to full-load voltage regulation, in percent, at this load.

SOLUTION:

1. $I_N = \dfrac{S}{1.732V} = \dfrac{72 \times 10^6}{1.732 \times 21\ 000} = 1980\ \text{A}$ **EQ. 13.3**

continued

Figure 20.27

See Example 20.3.

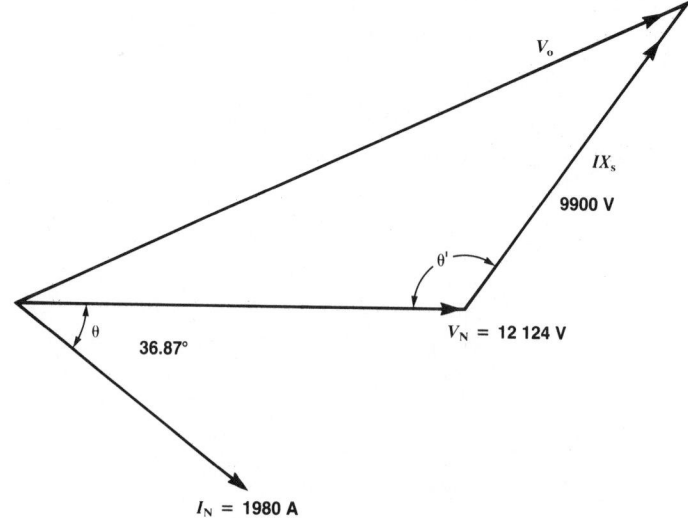

V_o

IX_s

9900 V

θ'

V_N = 12 124 V

θ

36.87°

I_N = 1980 A

2. a) Referring to Fig. 20.27, the line-to-neutral voltage is

$$V_N = \frac{21\ 000}{1.732} = 12\ 124\ \text{V}$$

b) The current lags behind V_N by an angle arcos 0.8 = 36.9°

c) The internal voltage drop due to the synchronous reactance of the machine is

$$IX_s = 1980 \times 5 = 9900\ \text{V}$$

This voltage drop is at 90° to phasor I_N, as shown. Consequently, angle

$$\theta' = 90 + \theta = 90 + 36.87 = 126.9°$$

d) From the cosine law we have

EQ. 1.15

$$V_o^2 = 9900^2 + 12\ 124^2 - 9900 \times 12\ 124\ \cos 126.87$$
$$= 98.01 \times 10^6 + 147 \times 10^6 + 72 \times 10^6 = 317 \times 10^6$$

hence $V_o = \sqrt{317\ 000\ 000} = 17\ 804$ V

3. If the load is disconnected, the induced voltage V_o will appear across the generator terminals. The voltage regulation is

EQ. 20.2

$$\text{percent regulation} = \frac{V_o - V_N}{V_N} \times 100$$

$$= \frac{17\ 804 - 12\ 124}{12\ 124} \times 100 = 46.85\%$$

Figure 20.28 shows the typical voltage regulation curves for a generator having a rated voltage of 1500 V and a rated current of 100 A. The curves show how the terminal voltage varies with the load current at unity power factor, at 80 percent power factor lagging, and at 80 percent power factor leading. In each case, the dc excitation current was adjusted to give rated voltage V_N at the rated current I_N of the machine. Once adjusted, the current was then kept fixed.

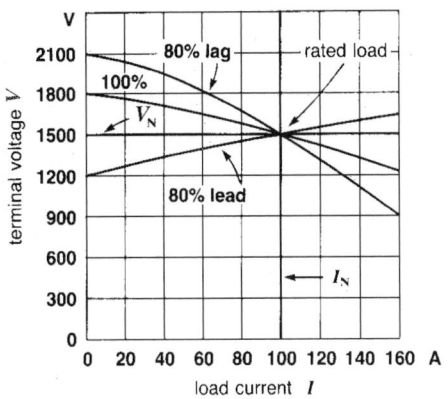

Figure 20.28

Typical voltage regulation curves of a 260 kVA, 1500 V, 3-phase, 60 Hz ac generator.

20.15 Summary

Upon completion of this chapter you should have learned:

- The construction and application of salient and cylindrical rotors. Salient pole rotors are used in low speed applications such as waterfalls. Cylindrical pole rotors are used in high-speed applications, such as steam turbine installations.

- One synchronous generator operating on a network is unable to alter the system voltage or frequency. By varying the prime mover torque or the excitation level of the machine, the active and reactive power levels supplied to the infinite bus may altered.

- A synchronous machine can operate as either a motor or a generator. When the torque supplied from the prime mover exceeds the torque produced by a synchronous motor, the machine generates power.

- Active power is controlled by varying the torque supplied by the prime mover, while the reactive power flow is controlled by varying the dc excitation.

- When two generators are to be synchronized, the following conditions must be met:

   i) The frequencies must be the same.

   ii) The voltages must be equal.

   iii) The voltages must be in-phase.

   iv) The phase sequence must be the same.

- Phasor diagrams can be used to illustrate the operation of a synchronous generator connected to an infinite bus. The equivalent circuit for a synchronous generator can be used to construct a phasor diagram that will show the effect of excitation and load.

- When supplying an isolated load, a generator's speed of rotation must be kept constant in order to maintain frequency. The level of excitation must be varied whenever the load changes.

Key Terms

DAMPER WINDING: A squirrel cage winding embedded in the rotor of a generator. When the generator load changes quickly, the magnetic fields resulting from the induced rotor current dampen the oscillations due to hunting.

INFINITE BUS: A large system, typically a power distribution grid, in which a single generator is unable to affect the system voltage and frequency.

PRIME MOVER: The mechanical force used to turn a generator is the prime mover. Prime movers commonly include steam turbines, water wheels, and diesel engines.

PULL-OUT TORQUE: In a generator, the pull-out torque represents the maximum torque that the prime mover can supply without causing the generator to lose synchronization.

SYNCHROSCOPE: A meter that shows the phase angle between two voltages. If the generator frequency is higher than the system frequency, the needle rotates clockwise; otherwise, the needle rotates counterclockwise.

Test Your Knowledge

20.1   A wye-connected synchronous generator has a rated line voltage of 19 kV. The *peak* voltage between a conductor in a slot and the stator core is
a. 15.5 kV
b. 10.97 kV
c. 19 kV

20.2   A 400 Hz aircraft generator is driven at 12 000 r/min. The number of poles is
a. 30
b. 4
c. 2

20.3   A steam-turbine generator is rated at 722 MVA, 19 kV, 3-phase, 60 Hz. The rated current per phase is
a. 38 A
b. 38 kA
c. 21 940 A

20.4   Figure 20.13 represents the mechanical angle of a 4-pole synchronous machine. The corresponding electrical angle delta is
a. 60°
b. 15°
c. 30°

20.5   When a synchronous generator is under load, the rotor poles are always ahead of the centre-line of the stator poles.

    true_____   false_____

20.6   If a synchronous generator is connected to an infinite bus, it will absorb reactive power if it is over-excited.

    true_____   false_____

20.7   If a synchronous motor is connected to an infinite bus, it will absorb reactive power if it is over-excited.

    true_____   false_____

20.8   A synchronous machine neither delivers nor receives active power when the centre lines of the rotor and stator poles are lined up.

    true_____   false_____

20.9   A synchronous generator can deliver active power at the same time that it *absorbs* reactive power.

    true_____   false_____

20.10 When a synchronous generator delivers only reactive power to an infinite bus, it has the same effect on the bus as a capacitor.

true_____   false _____

20.11 When a synchronous generator delivers only reactive power to a load, the prime mover must exert a large torque.

true_____   false _____

20.12 In Fig. 20.28, the voltage regulation for an 80 percent power factor lagging load is
a. 23.09%
b. 40%
c. 28.6%

20.13 In Fig. 20.28, the dc exciting current is greatest when the load has a leading power factor.

true_____   false _____

20.14 In a revolving-field ac generator, the armature is the stator.

true_____   false _____

Questions and Problems

20.15 What are the advantages of using a stationary armature in large synchronous generators?

20.16 State the main differences in construction between salient-pole and steam-turbine generators. For a given power output, which of these machines requires the bigger torque? Which machine is larger?

20.17 In analyzing a hydropower site, it is found that the turbines should turn at close to 350 r/min in order to develop the maximum mechanical power. If a directly coupled generator must produce a frequency of 60 Hz, calculate (a) the number of poles on the rotor and (b) the exact turbine speed.

20.18 An ac generator delivers power to an isolated load having a lagging power factor. If the no-load line voltage is 600 V, must the excitation be increased or decreased to maintain the same voltage under load? Draw a phasor diagram to explain your answer.

20.19 State the procedure to synchronize a generator with an infinite bus.

20.20 An ac generator turning at 1200 r/min generates a no-load line voltage of 6.9 kV, 60 Hz. How will the terminal voltage be affected if the following loads are connected to its terminals?
a. resistive load
b. inductive load
c. capacitive load

20.21 In Problem 20.20, calculate the no-load voltage and frequency if the speed is (a) 100 r/min and (b) 5 r/min. The dc exciting current is held constant.

21

Single-Phase Motors

LEARNING OBJECTIVES

Upon completion of this chapter you will be able to:

- Explain the operation of split-phase induction motors
- Explain the operating characteristics of the resistance start, capacitor start, and capacitor-run split-phase induction motors
- Explain the operation of small synchronous motors
- Explain the operation of the stepper motor
- Explain the operating principle of the watthourmeter
- Select a single-phase motor based upon the requirements of the load

21.1 Single-Phase Induction Motors

If one of the three lines feeding a three-phase induction motor is disconnected, the motor will continue to rotate and will develop a substantial mechanical torque. This is proof that an induction motor can run on single-phase power. However, if the motor is initially at rest, it will not start when single-phase power is applied. Thus, a single-phase induction motor is not self-starting.

But if we spin the shaft in one direction or the other, the motor will immediately pick up speed until it runs at close to synchronous speed. The synchronous speed is given by the same equation as that for three-phase motors, namely

n_s = 120 f/p

EQ. 21.1

where

n_s = synchronous speed, in revolutions per minute (r/min)

f = frequency of the single-phase source, in hertz (Hz)

p = number of poles on the stator

Figure 21.1 is the schematic diagram of a 2-pole, single-phase induction motor. It is composed of a stator and a squirrel-cage rotor. When an ac voltage is applied to the stator winding, the resulting current I_m produces a flux ϕ_m. This is an ac flux which increases, decreases, and reverses periodically, in step with the line frequency. However, it is not a rotating flux, and so the rotor does not turn. The ac flux induces large ac currents I_{r1} in the rotor bars of the stationary rotor. Consequently, the rotor bars are subjected to a force F because the currents are immersed in the flux ϕ_m. Unfortunately, the sum of these forces is zero because some of them tend to make the rotor turn cw, while others tend to make it turn ccw (Fig. 21.1). For this reason, the motor cannot start by itself.

21.2 Theory of the Revolving Field

If the motor is started, it unexpectedly develops a torque in the same direction of rotation, and it rapidly picks up speed. What produces this driving torque when the motor starts turning?

One of the theories explaining the torque of a single-phase motor may be stated as follows. As soon as the motor begins to rotate, a weak revolving field is set up in the machine. This field is caused by the combined action of the mmf of the stator and the mmf produced by the currents in the rotor. As the motor picks up speed, the rotating field becomes stronger and stronger. It reaches its maximum strength when the rotor runs at synchronous speed. The rotating field is then similar to that produced by a three-phase motor. Indeed, if we placed a conventional three-phase winding on the stator (in addition to the single-phase winding), we would discover that the voltages induced in the three windings are displaced at 120° to each other. This is perhaps the best proof that a revolving field is produced in a single-phase motor when it runs at close to synchronous speed. But how is this field produced?

Referring to Fig. 21.2, when the motor is turning, a voltage is induced in every conductor in sections ϕ_m and ϕ_a of the rotor because these conductors are cutting across the flux lines ϕ_m. The induced voltages produce rotor currents I_{r2}, which together develop an mmf that produces a flux ϕ_R. This flux did not exist when the rotor was stationary. It so happens that ϕ_R reaches its maximum value 90° after ϕ_m is maximum. The combined action of this 90° time delay and the 90° mechanical displacement between ϕ_m and ϕ_R produces the revolving field.

▼ **Figure 21.1**

The forces in the rotor of a stationary single-phase motor cancel each other and so the starting torque is zero.

▼ **Figure 21.2**

When the rotor turns, the induced currents I_{r2} produce a rotor flux ϕ_R that is at right angles to the stator flux ϕ_m. The two fluxes together produce a revolving field.

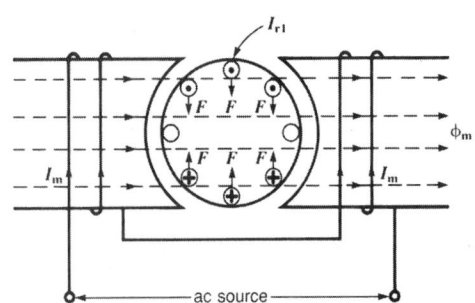

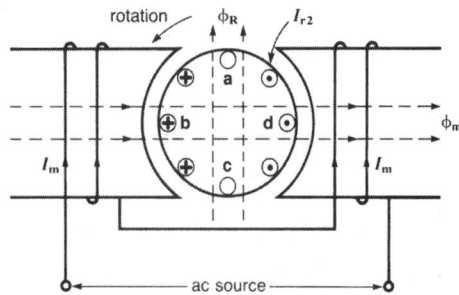

21.3 Means of Starting Single-Phase Motors

STARTING WINDINGS

To make a single-phase motor self-starting, we add an extra winding to the stator. This *auxiliary* winding, or **starting winding**, has the same number of poles as the main winding. However, the poles are shifted in space from those of the main winding. In most cases, they are placed exactly midway between the poles of the main winding (Fig. 21.3).

When the main and auxiliary windings are connected to a single-phase source, the main winding produces a flux ϕ_m and the auxiliary winding a flux ϕ_a. If the two fields are out of phase, a revolving field is produced. It rotates at a fixed, synchronous speed given by Equation 21.1. We obtain a perfect rotating field when ϕ_m and ϕ_a are equal in magnitude and out of phase by 90°. However, a strong rotating field and good starting torque can still be produced for phase shifts as small as 20° between ϕ_m and ϕ_a.

SPLIT-PHASE

In order for ϕ_m and ϕ_a to be out of phase, currents I_m and I_a in the main and auxiliary windings must be out of phase. The desired phase shift can be obtained by using different R/X ratios for the two windings, where R and X are the resistance and reactance of the windings. In some cases, we connect a capacitor in series with the auxiliary winding so that I_m leads I_a. These phase-shift methods go under the general term **split-phase.**

▶ **Figure 21.3**

To make a single-phase motor self-starting, a starting winding is added.

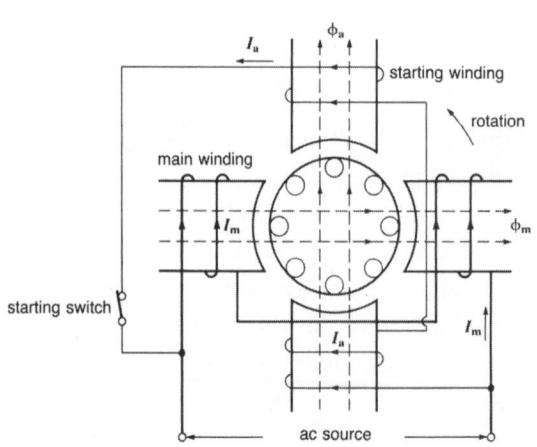

Once the motor has reached about 80 percent of synchronous speed, the auxiliary winding is disconnected from the source by an automatic switch. The motor then continues to run as a true single-phase machine, with only the main winding in service.

The automatic switch is usually actuated by the centrifugal force that acts on spring-loaded weights mounted on the rotor shaft. When the motor approaches its rated speed, the centrifugal force causes the weights to suddenly fly out, which opens the circuit of the auxiliary winding. In some motors, the automatic switch consists of a current-sensitive relay.

Figures 21.4 to 21.10 illustrate the components and construction of a single-phase motor.

Figure 21.4

The construction of a single-phase motor is very similar to that of a three-phase motor. The laminated stator on the left has treated-paper slot liners to insulate the windings from the core. The squirrel-cage rotor on the right is identical to that of a three-phase induction motor. The rotor bars end rings and fan blades are made of die-cast aluminum.

(Courtesy Lab-Volt)

▼ **Figure 21.5**

The main coils of this four-pole motor each consist of four concentric coils connected in series. The connections are made so that adjacent poles have opposite magnetic polarities. The two wires are the terminals of the main winding. Note that the laminated core is supported by a rolled iron frame that will also support the end bells.

(Courtesy Lab-Volt)

▼ **Figure 21.6**

The next step consists of threading the auxiliary winding into the slots. The four poles of the auxiliary winding are arranged to straddle the poles of the main winding. The adjacent poles of the auxiliary winding are connected in series and produce alternate N and S poles.

(Courtesy Lab-Volt)

▼ **Figure 21.7**

Schematic diagram showing how (a) the main and (b) the auxiliary winding are
connected in a 4-pole motor. The turns per coil and wire size are typical for a
1/4 hp, 120 V, 60 Hz motor.

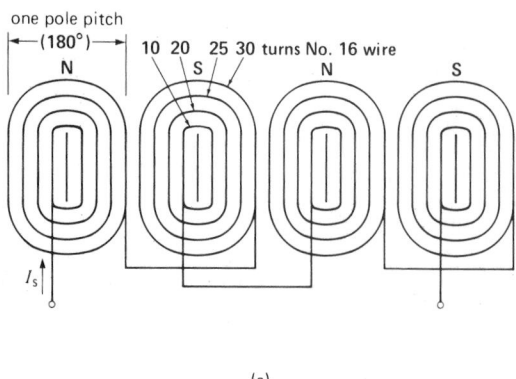

(a)

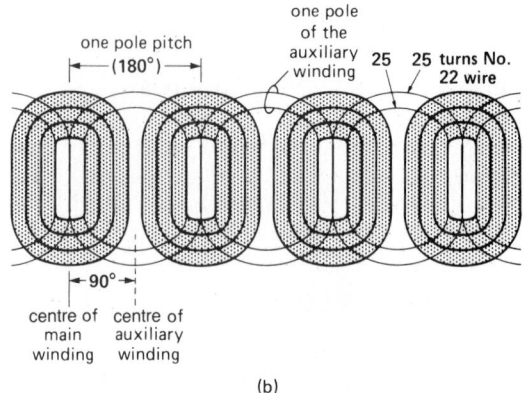

(b)

▼ **Figure 21.8**

After assembly, the centrifugal switch is
mounted on the end bell and the spring-
loaded weights are mounted on the shaft.
When the motor is at rest, the spring pushes
a plastic collar against the switch, thus closing the circuit of the starting windings.

▼ **Figure 21.9**

When the motor approaches synchronous
speed, the weights suddenly fly outward,
as shown above. The plastic collar moves
to the left, opening the starting circuit. In
most commercial motors, the action of
the centrifugal switch cannot be observed
because it is mounted inside the frame.

(Courtesy Lab-Volt)

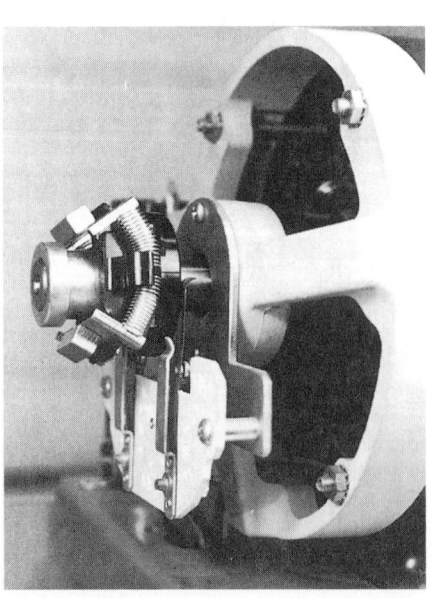

Figure 21.10

Cutaway view of a 5 hp, 1725 r/min, 230 V, 60 Hz single-phase motor. The centrifugal switch mechanism can be seen between the fan and the die-cast end ring.

(Courtesy Gould)

21.4 Resistance Split-Phase Motors

In a *resistance split-phase* motor (Fig. 21.11), the main winding has many turns of relatively large wire. Its inductive reactance is therefore large and the resistance is low. As a result, current I_m lags considerably behind the applied voltage V.

On the other hand, the starting winding has relatively few turns of small wire. Consequently, it has a high resistance compared with its inductive reactance. The current I_a in the staring winding lags therefore only slightly behind voltage V.

Figure 21.12 shows the resulting phase angle β between I_m and I_a. This angle is obviously the same as that between ϕ_m and ϕ_a. The two fluxes produce the rotating field that starts the motor. The locked-rotor current I_T is the phasor sum of I_m and I_a. It is usually 6 to 7 times the rated full-load current of the motor.

▼ **Figure 21.11**

Schematic diagram of a resistance split-phase motor.

▼ **Figure 21.12**

Phasor diagram of a resistance split-phase motor under locked-rotor conditions.

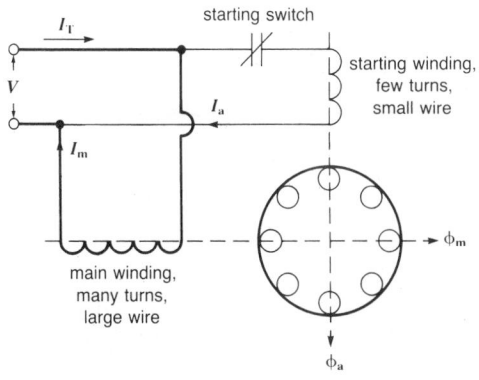

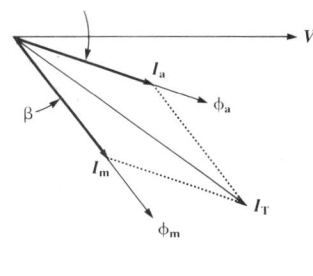

Because the wire used in the starting winding is small, it heats up very quickly. To prevent excessive temperatures, the motor should reach its running speed in 2 to 3 seconds. If the starting period exceeds 5 seconds, the auxiliary winding will start to smoke, and unless the protective devices trip, the winding will burn out.

A resistance split-phase motor is therefore not adapted to frequent starts and stops. Furthermore, it cannot be used to bring high-inertia loads up to speed. When heavy-duty starting conditions are encountered, it is preferable to use a capacitor-start motor.

21.5 Capacitor-Start Motors

The *capacitor-start* motor (Fig. 21.13) is identical to the resistance split-phase motor except that the auxiliary winding has about the same number of turns as the main winding. A capacitor is connected in series with the auxiliary winding and a starting switch again disconnects it when the speed reaches about 80 percent of synchronous speed.

The capacitive reactance of the capacitor is high enough so that current I_a in the auxiliary winding is *ahead* of the applied voltage V (Fig. 21.14). However, current I_m in the main winding lags behind the voltage by the same angle as before. It follows that the phase angle between currents I_m and I_a (and between fluxes ϕ_m and ϕ_a) is greater than the angle in the resistance split-phase motor. Consequently, the locked-rotor torque is greater. Furthermore, if currents I_m and I_a have the same magnitude as those of the resistance split-phase motor, the total current I_T drawn from the line will be smaller.

Thus, a capacitor-start motor has the double advantage of producing a larger locked-rotor torque with a smaller locked-rotor current. The current is only 4 to 5 times the nominal full-load current. This means that the starting time can be longer than in the case of a resistance split-phase motor without causing the auxiliary

▼ **Figure 21.13**

Schematic diagram of capacitor-start motor.

▼ **Figure 21.14**

Phasor diagram of a capacitor-start motor under locked-rotor conditions.

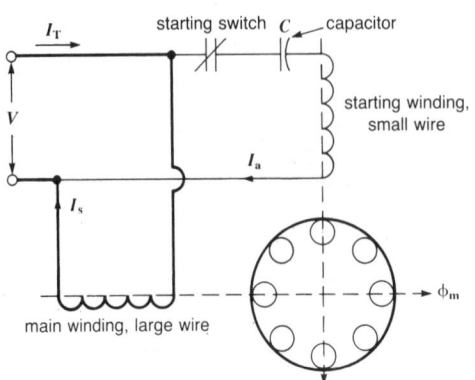

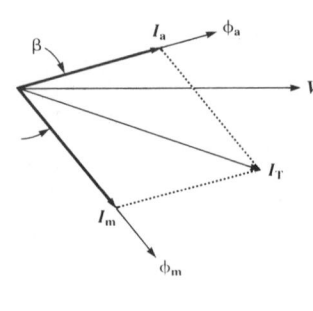

winding to overheat. However, it is only the starting characteristics that are better; under normal running conditions, capacitor-start and resistance split-phase motors have exactly the same properties. The reason is that only the main windings are then in service, and they are the same in both machines.

The increasing use of capacitor-start motors is due to the excellent characteristics and low cost of modem **electrolytic capacitors**. These capacitors have relatively large microfarad ratings compared to their size. Although they cannot remain in continuous service, they are well adapted for intermittent use. Before the development of these capacitors, repulsion-induction motors were used when starting conditions were severe. Repulsion-induction motors with their commutators and brush gear are still in use, but they are becoming obsolete.

```
ELECTROLYTIC
 CAPACITOR
```

21.6 Properties of Split-Phase Induction Motors

The efficiency and power factor of split-phase motors are usually low. Thus, at full load, a 1/4 hp motor has a power factor and efficiency of about 60%, compared with values of 70% for three-phase motors of equal power.

Considerable reactive power is needed to create the magnetic field. As a result, the no-load current may be as high as 80 percent of full-load current. Thus, even at no-load these motors have a temperature rise approaching its full-load value.

Another disadvantage of single-phase motors is the mechanical vibration they produce. The mechanical frequency is exactly twice the electrical frequency. For example, any single-phase motor that operates on a 60 Hz source will vibrate at a mechanical frequency of $2 \times 60 = 120$ Hz. If the motor is mounted on a rigid base, the vibration may be amplified, producing a loud noise. To eliminate the noise, we can mount the motor on a special cradle support. The end bells are supported on rubber rings that dampen the 120 Hz vibrations so they are not transmitted to the base (Fig. 21.15). Three-phase motors do not produce this vibration and so they are quieter.

Figure 21.15

Capacitor-run motor supported in a resilient mount to prevent the vibrations from being transmitted to the base.

(Courtesy Brook Crompton Parkinson)

The speed of split-phase motors is essentially constant. Thus, a 1/4 hp motor having a synchronous speed of 1800 r/min will have a full-load speed of about 1730 r/min. The direction can be reversed by interchanging the terminals of either the main winding or the auxiliary winding. However, the direction cannot be reversed while the motor is running. Unlike a three-phase motor, a conventional single-phase motor cannot be plugged.

As in the case of three-phase motors, the torque of a single-phase motor varies as the square of the voltage across its terminals. Thus, at a given speed, if the line voltage is 10 percent below the rated voltage of the motor, the corresponding torque will be 20 percent lower. This rule also applies when the motor is starting up with both windings in service.

EXAMPLE 21.1

A 1/4 hp, 120 V, 60 Hz, 1725 r/min resistance split-phase motor develops a locked-rotor torque of 1.5 N.m.

1. What is the magnitude of the rated locked-rotor torque, in percent?
2. If the line voltage drops to 112 V, what is the value of the locked-rotor torque?

SOLUTION:

1. a) The rated torque of the motor is

   EQ. 1.9
   $$T = 9.55 \ P/n$$
   $$= 9.55 \times 0.25 \times 746/1725 = 1.032 \text{ N.m}$$

   b) The LR torque in percent $= \dfrac{\text{locked-rotor torque}}{\text{rated torque}} \times 10\phi$

   $$= \frac{1.5}{1.032} \times 100$$

   $$= 145\%$$

2. When the line voltage falls from 120 V to 112 V, the locked-rotor torque drops from 1.5 N.m to
   $$T = 1.5 \times (112/120)^2 = 1.31 \text{ N.m}$$

EXAMPLE 21.2

The motor in Example 21.1 has a full-load efficiency of 61% and a power factor of 58%. Calculate:

1. the rated full-load current.
2. the reactive power absorbed by the motor.
3. the slip.

continued

SOLUTION:

1. a) The active power input to the motor is:

$$P_I = 100\ P_o/eff$$
EQ. 1.11

$$P_i = 100 \times (0.25 \times 746)/61 = 305.7\ \text{W}$$

   b) The apparent power of the motor is:

$$S = P/\text{power factor} = 305.7/0.58 = 527\ \text{VA}$$
EQ. 12.22

   c) The full-load current is $I = S/V = 527/120 = 4.39\ \text{A}$

2. The reactive power absorbed by the motor is:

$$Q = \sqrt{S^2 - P^2} = \sqrt{527^2 - 305.7^2} = 429.3\ \text{var}$$
EQ. 12.20

3. The slip is found the same way as for a 3-phase motor:

$$s = (n_s - n)/n_s$$
EQ. 17.1

$$s = (1800 - 1725)/1800 = 0.0417,\ \text{or}\ 4.17\%.$$

21.7 Capacitor-Run Motors

The capacitor-run motor is basically a two-phase motor. It is composed of a main winding and an auxiliary winding that is *permanently* connected to the line in series with a capacitor. These motors are used in hospitals and studios because they are particularly quiet. Their mechanical construction is simpler than that of split-phase motors because they do not contain a starting switch. The starting torque is inherently low, but because the motors are often used to drive fixed, low starting-torque loads such as fans and pumps, this presents no problem. The power factor at full-load is about 90 percent because the capacitor is always in service.

21.8 Shaded-Pole Motors

Shaded-pole induction motors are often used when the power output is less than 1/20 hp. These small squirrel-cage motors have salient poles on the stator and the main winding is a simple coil. The auxiliary winding is composed of a single turn of heavy copper that is short-circuited on itself. The turn, or ring, is wrapped around the "shaded" portion of each salient pole, as shown in Fig. 21.16.

Part of the flux ϕ_m created by the coil links with the ring, inducing a large current I_a. This current produces a flux ϕ_a. Because of the inductance of the ring, I_a, and therefore ϕ_a, lag behind ϕ_m. At the pole face, the mechanical displacement between ϕ_m and ϕ_a, together with the phase lag between them, causes a revolving field to be produced. This weak revolving field produces a weak torque that starts the motor going.

Although the starting torque, efficiency, and power factor are very low, the simplicity of the windings and the absence of a starting switch give this motor a distinct advantage. The direction of rotation cannot be changed; it is fixed by the location of the short-circuiting rings. In effect, the time lag between ϕ_m and ϕ_a causes the flux to continually shift from the unshaded toward the shaded portion of the pole face. This continual shift determines the direction of rotation of the motor. For example, the direction of rotation of the motor in Fig. 21.16 is clockwise.

▼ **Figure 21.16**

Shaded-pole motor and the fluxes and currents it produces.

▼ **Figure 21.17**

Shaded-pole motor rated 5 millihorse-power, 2900 r/min, 115 V, 60 Hz.

(Courtesy Gould)

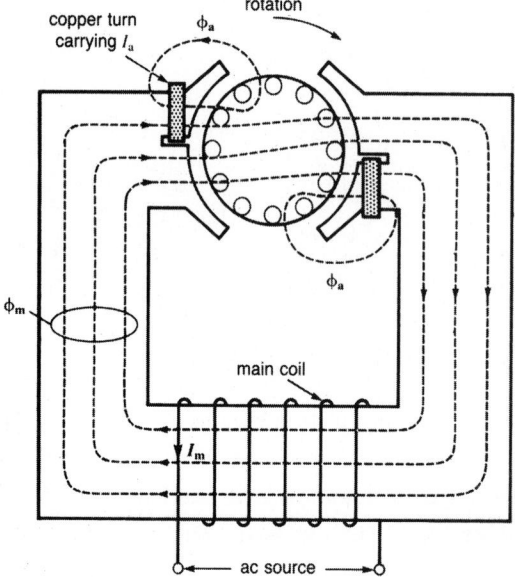

Figure 21.18 shows a slow-speed shaded-pole motor in which the rotor is a simple aluminum disc. The phase shift between ϕ_m and ϕ_a produces a revolving field that drives the disc in the direction shown. Figure 21.19 shows such a single-coil shaded-pole motor driving a set of contacts that open and close in sequence to create an incandescent-lamp display.

▼ **Figure 21.18**

Shaded-pole motor in which the phase shift between ϕ_m and ϕ_a causes an aluminum disc to turn.

▼ **Figure 21.19**

Small shaded-pole motor using a single coil to drive a copper disc to open and close a set of four contacts.

(Photo Denys Pelletier)

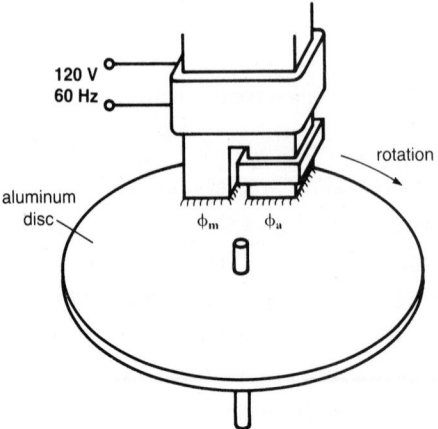

21.9 Series Motors

The single-phase series motor (Fig. 21.20) is similar to a dc series motor, and so it is equipped with a commutator. However, both the field and armature are laminated because they carry an ac flux. An ac series motor can therefore operate on both dc and ac. That is why it is often called a **universal motor**.

UNIVERSAL MOTOR

The main advantage of fractional-horsepower series motors is their high speed, which may range from 5000 to 25 000 r/min. Unlike induction motors, their speed does not depend upon the frequency or the number of poles. They are used to drive vacuum cleaners and small, powerful hand tools, such as hand drills and circular saws.

When an ac voltage is applied to the terminals of a series motor, both the armature current and the flux produced by the poles change direction simultaneously. As a result, the torque developed by the rotor always acts in the same direction. There is no revolving field in such a motor; the operating principle is the same as that of a dc series motor.

The starting torque of a series motor is high, and its speed decreases rapidly from no-load to full-load. This is an advantage in such tools as circular saws and electric drills for which we want the speed to drop significantly as the torque increases.

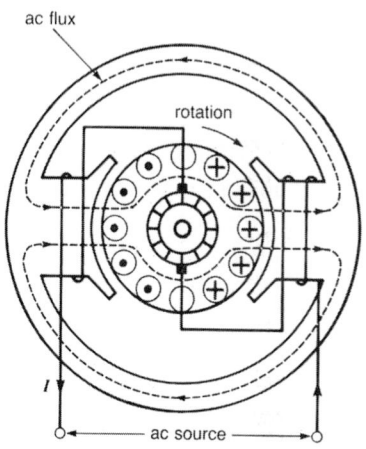

Figure 21.20

Series single-phase motors can run at very high speeds and will operate on both dc and ac power. The photograph shows a 1/3 hp, 120 V, 10 000 r/min series motor used in a domestic vacuum cleaner.

21.10 Choice of Single-Phase Motors

Because of its relatively low cost, the split-phase resistance motor is the one most commonly used. However, it is applied to drives in which the starting periods are infrequent. It is mainly built in ratings between 1/20 hp and 1/4 hp. Motors of this type are used to drive fans, centrifugal pumps, washing machines, oil burners, and small machine tools, such as lathes, drill presses, and grinding wheels.

The capacitor-start motor is used for applications that require a high or prolonged starting torque. It has built-in ratings between 1/8 hp and 10 hp. Such motors are used on compressors, large fans, and centrifugal pumps.

Single-phase series motors are manufactured in many types and sizes, ranging from small toy motors to large traction motors of several hundred horsepower. They operate on frequencies that range from 60 hertz to 16 2/3 hertz.

Finally, there is a great variety of tiny synchronous motors, rated below 1/50 hp. They drive electric clocks and timing devices, and will be covered next.

21.11 Hysteresis Motors

The operation of a hysteresis motor is based upon a revolving field and the permanent magnetism in a rotor. The revolving field is created by a single-phase stator in one of the various split-phase methods we have just learned. The rotor is composed of a permanent-magnet (PM) material. In order to eliminate eddy-current effects, suppose the rotor is made of a ceramic PM material having very high resistivity (Section 5.6). The revolving field created by the stator can be represented by two magnets N, S that rotate around the PM rotor (Fig. 21.21). As previously explained in Sections 5.21 and 5.22, poles of opposite polarity are continually being induced in the rotor under the N and S poles of the stator. A torque is therefore produced which drags the rotor along with the field. Thus, a hysteresis motor produces its torque in a way fundamentally different from that in an induction motor.

Because the torque is due to the magnetic attraction between the rotor and stator poles, it does not depend upon the relative speed of the rotor with respect to the stator. In other words, the torque is the same whether the N, S poles barely creep around the rotor or whether they move quickly.

Thus, the main advantage of a hysteresis motor is that it produces a *constant* torque up to, and including, synchronous speed. This means that a hysteresis

▼ Figure 21.21

The revolving field produced by a stator creates poles of opposite polarity in the permanent magnet rotor. As a result, the rotor is subjected to a driving torque even when it runs at the same speed as the revolving field.

▼ Figure 21.22

Rotor and stator of a 32-pole, 115 V, 60 Hz single-phase hysteresis motor. The rim of the rotor is made of a ferrite ceramic material.

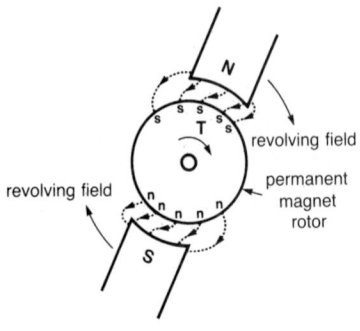

motor can bring high-inertia loads, such as tape decks and heavy turntables, up to synchronous speed. Then, because the frequency of the electric utility system is constant, the speed remains fixed like a clock.

Hysteresis motors are synchronous motors, and they are used in millions of electric clocks and timing devices. On large electric utility systems, the frequency is kept very constant, although not with quartz-watch precision. However, the frequency is monitored and adjusted so that during a 24-hour day on a 60 Hz system, the number of cycles generated is *exactly* $24 \times 3600 \times 60 = 5\ 184\ 000$. Thus, although electric clocks may run slow or fast during certain times of the day, they are absolutely precise over any 24-hour period. (This of course is true only if the system has not suffered an outage).

Figure 21.22 shows a 32-pole, shaded-pole hysteresis motor used to drive a kitchen clock.

21.12 Stepper Motors

Stepper motors have salient poles on both the rotor and stator. The stator poles carry windings that are excited in sequence, either slowly or in rapid succession. The reluctance torque causes the rotor to advance in response to these excitation pulses. Stepper motors are not really single-phase motors because they are often powered by a dc source. The source is connected in sequence to individual windings that are equally spaced around the stator. This causes the rotor to advance in steps.

Stepper motors are made for digital-control systems. They enable an object to be positioned with high precision. The object (tracing pen, drill, or punch) is coupled to the motor by gears, and so each step of the motor corresponds to a precisely known distance, or angular movement.

One of the simplest stepper motors consists of a 3-pole stator and 2-pole iron rotor (Fig. 21.23). The rotor is shown at rest in the vertical position. Current I_1 flows so

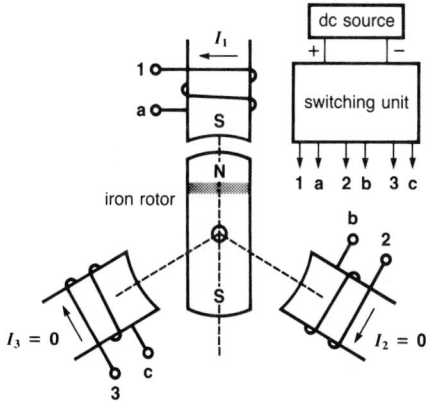

Figure 21.23

Stepper motor with rotor in the vertical position because of the flux produced by I_1. The band across the rotor is merely to identify the pole.

▼ **Figure 21.24**

The rotor turns cw through 60° when I_1
is switched off and I_3 is switched on.

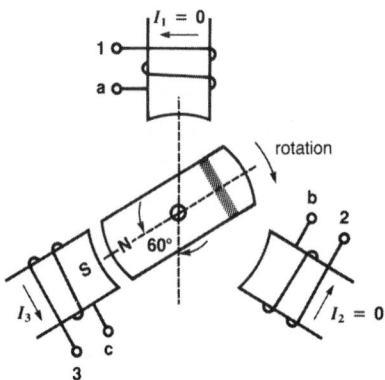

▼ **Figure 21.25**

The direction of rotation can be reversed
by turning off I_1 and turning on I_2.

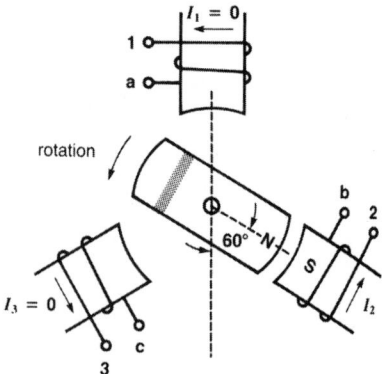

as to keep the rotor locked in this position. To make the rotor turn cw, we interrupt I_1 and cause I_3 to flow by means of the switching unit. This will cause the rotor to step cw by an angle of precisely 60°. Current I_3 is then maintained for as long as we want the rotor to stay in this new position (Fig. 21.24).

If we want the rotor to turn ccw, we energize winding 2 instead of winding 3, and the rotor again moves through an angle of 60° (Fig. 21.25).

It is clear that we can cause the rotor to move cw or ccw in 60° steps. Thus, a pulse rate of one per second will produce a speed of 10 r/min. The number of successive exciting pulses are stored electronically to keep accurate track of what is going on. Knowing which coils were excited in the past, the system "knows" precisely where the rotor is at any instant. However, because we must be sure that each pulse does in fact correspond to a 60° step, we must adjust the stepping rate so that the rotor has time to respond.

For example, if we apply stepping pulses at the rate of 200 per second when the rotor is at standstill, it will only vibrate in place. The rotor cannot follow these rapid signals because of its inertia and the inertia of the load. However, if the motor is already running at 1900 r/min (corresponding to a pulse rate of 190/s), an increase in the pulse rate to 200 per second presents no problem. The rate at which the pulses may be generated depends therefore upon the speed at which the stepper motor is turning. This is true whether the motor is accelerating or decelerating. Fast response pulsing must therefore be computer-controlled to reduce the risk of missing a step.

We can diminish the angular motion per step by increasing the number of poles. For example, Fig. 21.26 shows a stepper motor that advances 30° per pulse. There are many types of stepper motors, but the basic principle remains the same: to control the position of an object by digital means.

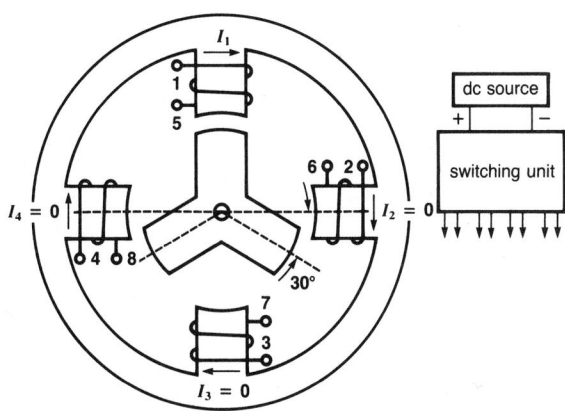

Figure 21.26

Stepper motor that advances 30° per pulse.

21.13 Precision Motors in a Watthourmeter

Watthourmeters that measure the energy consumed in domestic homes and industry contain extremely accurate single-phase motors. They rotate at a speed that is directly proportional to the active power (kilowatts) used by the consumer. Thus, it is possible to measure the energy consumed during a given period of time by recording the number of turns on a register.

The motor is similar to the shaded-pole disc motor illustrated in Fig. 21.18, except that ϕ_m is created by the line voltage and ϕ_a by the line current at the consumer's service entrance. Figure 21.27 shows schematically how the voltage and current coils are placed above the disc and how they are connected to the consumer's line. The voltage coil is highly inductive, and so current I_v (and the corresponding flux) lags almost 90° behind the line voltage V. A small short-circuiting ring around the core adjusts the phase so that the net flux ϕ_m crossing the disc is exactly 90° behind V. The flux ϕ_a created by the current coil is in phase with the line current I.

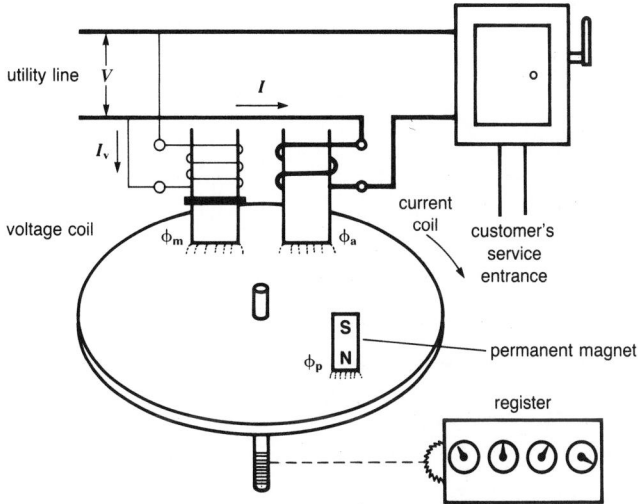

Figure 21.27

Principle of the watthourmeter.

When the line current is in phase with the line voltage, ϕ_m and ϕ_a are 90° out of phase, and so a torque is exerted on the disc. However, if the current lags 90° behind the voltage, ϕ_m and ϕ_a are in phase and no revolving field is produced. Consequently, the torque is zero. In general, the torque exerted on the disc is given by the expression $T = k_1\phi_m\phi_a\cos\theta$, which can be reduced to the form

EQ. 21.2 $T = kVI\cos\theta$

where

T = torque, in newton metres (N.m)

V = line voltage, in volts (V)

I = line current, in amperes (A)

θ = phase angle between V and I, in degrees (°)

k = constant that depends upon the design of the instrument motor

Thus, the torque is proportional to the active power $VI\cos\theta$ consumed. However, if the motor is free to rotate, it will turn at a speed that is limited only by electrical losses and mechanical friction. As a result, the speed will not be linearly related to the torque. To obtain a linear relationship (speed proportional to torque) a permanent magnet is introduced so that the disc sweeps across its flux ϕ_p.

The resulting braking torque T_b is directly proportional to the speed. Thus, $T_b = k_2 n$. But we recall from Section 1.15 that the speed of a motor is stable when the driving torque is equal to the load torque. Consequently, because $T = T_b$, the speed of rotation n is directly proportional to the active power.

These highly precise motors are calibrated so that each revolution corresponds to a definite amount of electrical energy, expressed in *watthours*. This energy is indicated by the constant K_h inscribed on the nameplate.

Figure 21.28

Single-phase watthourmeter for a 120/240 V, 60 Hz service entrance. The rotating aluminum disc can be observed through the narrow slot immediately below the label "kilowatthours."

(Courtesy General Electric)

EXAMPLE 21.3

The disc of a watthourmeter makes 5 complete turns in 78 s. If the nameplate shows $K_h = 7.2$, calculate the active power consumed.

SOLUTION:

a) The energy consumed during the interval is
    W = 5 turns × 7.2 W.h/turn = 36 W.h
b) The duration of the interval is 78 s = 78/3600 h = 0.0217 h
c) The power is $P = W/t$ = 36 W.h/0.0217 h = 1659 W

21.14 Summary

Upon completion of this chapter you should have learned that:

- Split-phase induction motors contain a start winding and a run winding. A built-in centrifugal switch controls the operation of the start windings used to develop starting torque.

- Resistance start, capacitor start, and capacitor run split-phase induction motors have different starting and running characteristics that need to be matched to the load requirements.

- Shaded-pole motors are synchronous motors used in applications requiring less than 1/20 hp. Shaded-pole motors are used in low torque applications such as clocks and timers.

- Single-phase series motors (universal motors) develop high starting torque and operate at speeds of 5000 to 25 000 . These motors are commonly found in applications for power tools such as drills and power saws.

- Stepper motors are precision-control motors used in digital electronic systems. The stepper motors are rated in degrees of rotation per step.

- The motors used in watthourmeters are similar to shaded-pole motors, except that the speed of rotation is proportional to the available active power.

- The selection of a single-phase motor should be based upon the requirements of the load.

Key Terms

ELECTROLYTIC CAPACITOR: A type of capacitor that is polarity sensitive. An ac electrolytic capacitor contains two series-connected capacitors with opposite polarities. This allows the capacitor to operate on ac.

SPLIT-PHASE: By controlling the ratio of R and X in the start and run windings of a single-phase motor, the phase shift between the supply voltage and the current through the two motor windings is controlled. This phase shift is known as a split-phase.

STARTING WINDINGS: A secondary set of windings located midway between the main windings. The starting windings allow split-phase motors to develop sufficient torque to begin rotating under load.

UNIVERSAL MOTOR: Another name for the series motor (Section 21.9). The universal motor is used in applications requiring high speed and high starting torque. This motor can operate on both ac and dc. It is commonly used in power tools.

Test Your Knowledge

21.1 If the main winding and auxiliary winding of a single-phase motor are connected in series, it is impossible to obtain a starting torque.

true _____   false _____

21.2 The auxiliary winding of a split-phase motor must be disconnected quickly to
a. prevent overheating
b. produce a good starting torque
c. reduce the power drawn from the line

21.3 The rated full-load speed of a 50 Hz single-phase motor is 2850 r/min. If the motor is connected to a 60 Hz source, the speed
a. will be close to 2375 r/min
b. will be close to 3420 r/min
c. will not run on a 60 Hz line

21.4 At no-load, the line current of a single-phase motor lags 72° behind the line voltage. The no-load power factor is
a. zero
b. 30.9%
c. 95.1%

21.5 A capacitor-start motor develops a high torque because
a. it increases the auxiliary flux ϕ_a
b. it increases the phase angle between ϕ_a and ϕ_m

c. it absorbs less reactive power from the line

21.6 A single-phase motor is connected to a 400 Hz source. It will vibrate at a frequency of
a. 400 Hz
b. 200 Hz
c. 800 Hz

21.7 The direction of rotation of a shaded-pole motor can be reversed by interchanging the leads of the ac source.

true _____   false _____

21.8 The direction of rotation of an ac series motor can be reversed by interchanging the armature leads.

true _____   false _____

21.9 A hysteresis clock motor incorporated with a gear box has a no-load speed of 1.00 r/min when connected to a 120 V, 60 Hz source. If the voltage increases to 120 V, the speed will be
a. 1.05 r/min
b. 0.952 r/min
c. 1.00 r/min

21.10 In stepper motors, the number of poles on the rotor and stator is usually different.

true _____   false _____

Questions and Problems

21.11 A 10-pole split-phase motor is connected to a 60 Hz source. What is its synchronous speed?

21.12 What is the purpose of the auxiliary winding in a single-phase induction motor? How can we change the rotation of such a motor?

21.13 State the main differences between a capacitor-start motor and a resistance split-phase motor. What are their relative advantages?

21.14 Explain the operation of a shaded-pole motor.

21.15 Why are some single-phase motors equipped with a resilient mounting? Is such a mounting necessary on three-phase motors?

21.16 What is the main advantage of a capacitor-run motor?

21.17 Which of the motors discussed in this chapter is best suited to drive the following loads:
   a. small portable drill
   b. 3/4 hp air compressor
   c. vacuum cleaner
   d. 1/100 hp blower
   e. 1/3 hp centrifugal pump
   f. 1/4 hp fan for use in a hospital ward
   g. electric timer
   h. stereo turntable

21.18 The palm of the human hand can just barely tolerate a temperature of 130°F. If the no-load temperature of the frame of a 1/4 hp motor is 64°C in an ambient temperature of 76°F
   a. can a person keep his hand on the frame?
   b. is the motor running too hot?

21.19 A 115 V, 60 Hz shaded-pole motor develops a rated mechanical output of 6 W at 2990 r/min. The corresponding input power is 21 W, and the line current is 0.33 A. Calculate the
   a. efficiency of the motor
   b. power factor of the motor
   c. torque developed by the motor, in millinewton metres (mN.m)
   d. slip
   e. phase angle between the line voltage and line current
   f. losses in the motor

21.20 The motor in Problem 21.19 has a locked-rotor current of 0.35 A and a locked-rotor torque of 10 mN.m. The power input is 24 W. Compare the locked-rotor losses with the full-load losses.

21.21 If the rotor of the stepper motor in Fig. 21.26 had four poles instead of three, it would be impossible to make it rotate. Explain.

21.22 If the 3-pole rotor of the stepper motor in Fig. 21.26 is replaced by a 5-pole rotor, calculate the smallest angular motion per pulse when the coils are excited in sequence. *Hint*: Draw a diagram of the rotor and stator.

21.23 A 4-pole, 60 Hz single-phase motor is equipped with a centrifugal switch taken from a 2-pole, 60 Hz motor. Explain why the auxiliary winding may burn out and why the motor can never operate properly.

22

Industrial Motor Control

LEARNING OBJECTIVES

Upon completion of this chapter you will be able to:

- List the components used in a control system and recognize their symbols

- List the four types of control diagrams and explain where each is used

- Describe the operation of an automatic dc motor starter

- Describe the operation of three-phase manual and automatic motor starters

- Explain the operation of reduced voltage motor starters

- Describe the operation of cam switches

- Explain the operation of a three-phase synchronous motor starter

22.1   Typical Control Devices

Every control circuit is composed of a number of basic components connected together to achieve the desired performance. The size of the components varies with the power they handle, but the principle of operation remains the same. Using only a few basic components, we can design control systems that are very complex.

The basic components are:

1. Disconnecting switches
2. Manual circuit breakers
3. Cam switches
4. Pushbuttons
5. Relays
6. Magnetic contactors
7. Thermal relays and fuses
8. Pilot lights
9. Limit switches and other special switches
10. Resistors, reactors, transformers, capacitors

Table 22A illustrates these devices and states their main purpose and application. The symbols for these and other devices are given in Table 22B.

Table 22A   BASIC COMPONENTS FOR CONTROL CIRCUITS

DISCONNECTING SWITCH (FIG. 22.1)

A fused disconnecting switch isolates the motor from the power source. It consists of three knife-switches and three line fuses enclosed in a metal box. An external handle opens and closes the knife-switches simultaneously. An interlocking mechanism prevents persons from opening the hinged cover when the switch is closed. Disconnecting switches are designed to carry the rated full-load current indefinitely and to withstand short-circuit currents for brief intervals. Some disconnecting switches have no fuses: they serve only to isolate a circuit, not to protect it.

Figure 22.1

Fused disconnecting switch, rated 600 V, 30 A, 3-phase.

(Courtesy Square D)

MANUAL CIRCUIT BREAKER (FIG. 22.2)

A manual circuit breaker opens and closes a circuit, like a toggle switch. It trips (opens) automatically when the current exceeds a predetermined limit. After tripping, it can be reset manually. Circuit breakers are often used instead of fused disconnecting switches because no fuses have to be replaced.

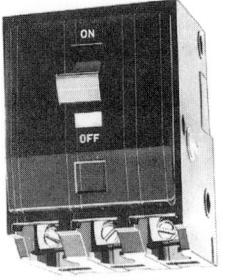

Figure 22.2

Manual circuit breaker rated 600 V, 100 A, 3-phase.

(Courtesy Square D)

CAM SWITCH (FIG. 22.3)

A cam switch has a group of fixed contacts and an equal number of movable contacts. The contacts can be made to open and close in a preset sequence by rotating a handle or knob. Cam switches are used to control the motion and position of hoists, cranes, and machine tools.

Figure 22.3

Three-position cam switch rated 250 V, 10 A.

(Courtesy Siemens)

continued

Figure 22.4

Pushbutton with NO and NC contacts rated to interrupt an ac current of 6 A one million times.

(Courtesy Siemens)

PUSHBUTTON (FIG. 22.4)

A pushbutton is a switch that is actuated by finger pressure. Two or more contacts open or close when the button is depressed. Pushbuttons are usually spring-loaded, so they will return to the normal position when pressure is removed.

Figure 22.5

Single-phase control relay rated 25 A, 115/230 V, 60 Hz.

(Courtesy Potter and Brumfield)

CONTROL RELAY (FIGS. 22.5 AND 22.6)

A control relay is an electromagnetic switch that opens and closes a set of contacts when the relay coil is energized. The coil produces a strong magnetic field that attracts a movable armature bearing the contacts. Control relays are mainly used in low-power circuits. They include time-delay relays whose contacts open or close after a definite time interval.

Figure 22.6

Time-delay relay continuously variable from 5 s to 1.5 min.

(Courtesy Siemens)

THERMAL RELAY (FIG. 22.7)

A thermal relay (or overload relay) is a small protective device whose *contacts* open when the line current exceeds a preset limit. The current flows through a calibrated heating element which raises its temperature. When the temperature exceeds a certain limit, the relay trips and its control contacts open. Thermal relays are inherent time-delay devices because the temperature cannot follow the instantaneous changes in current.

Figure 22.7

Thermal overload relay rated 400 A.

(Courtesy Siemens)

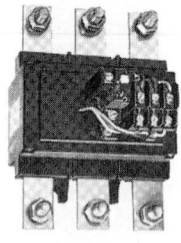

MAGNETIC CONTACTOR (FIGS. 22.8 to 22.10)

A magnetic contactor is basically a large control relay designed to open and close a power circuit. It has a relay coil that actuates a set of contacts. Magnetic contactors are used to control motors ranging from 0.5 hp to several hundred horsepower. The size, dimensions, and performance of contactors are standardized.

Figure 22.8

Magnetic contactor sizes are standardized according to NEMA specifications. This picture shows the range.

(Courtesy Ward Leonard Electric)

continued

▼ **Figure 22.9**

Magnetic contactor with the arc
shield removed, exposing the
three-phase contacts.

(Courtesy Siemens)

▼ **Figure 22.10**

Direct current contactor rated 65 A, 600 V,
showing the holding coil on the right and
two arc shields on the left. Arc suppres-
sion is more difficult in dc contactors.

(Courtesy Siemens)

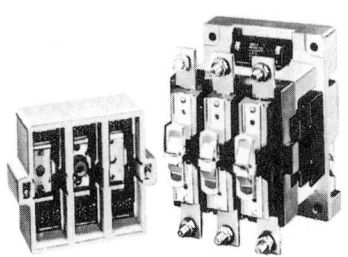

PILOT LIGHT (FIG. 22.11)

A pilot light indicates the on/off state of a remote
component in a control system.

LIMIT SWITCH AND SPECIAL SWITCHES (FIGS. 22.12 AND 22.13)

A limit switch is a low-power snap-action device that
opens or closes a control contact, depending upon
the position of a mechanical part. Other limit switches are sensitive to pressure, temperature, liquid
level, direction of rotation, and so forth.

Figure 22.11

Start-stop pushbutton
station with pilot light.

(Courtesy Siemens)

▼ **Figure 22.12**

Limit switch with one NC contact
rated for ten million operations;
position accuracy is 0.5 mm.

(Courtesy Square D)

▼ **Figure 22.13**

Liquid level switch.

(Courtesy Square D)

22.2 Normally Open and Normally Closed Contacts; Graphic Symbols

NORMALLY OPEN CONTACTS

NORMALLY CLOSED CONTACTS

Control circuit diagrams always show components in a state of rest—that is—when they are not energized (electrically) or actuated (mechanically). In this state, some electrical contacts are open while others are closed. They are respectively called **normally open contacts** (NO) and **normally closed contacts** (NC). They are designated by the symbols given in Table 22B.

Table 22B   GRAPHIC SYMBOLS FOR ELECTRICAL DIAGRAMS

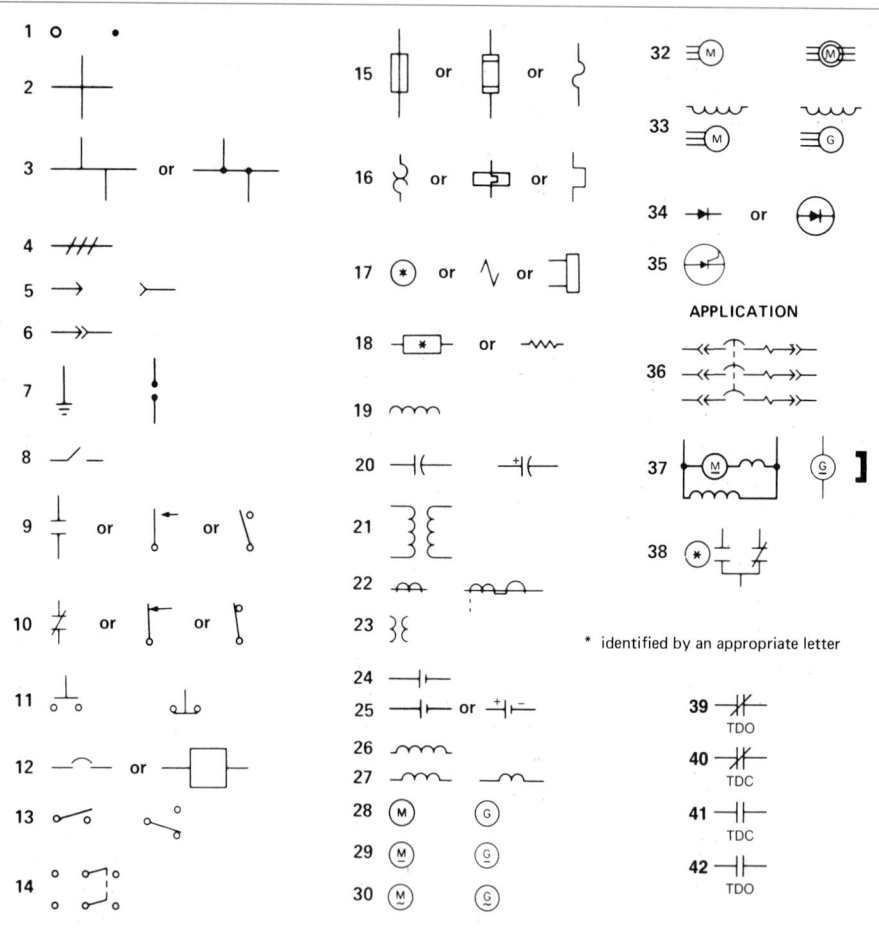

* identified by an appropriate letter

1. terminal; connection   2. conductors crossing   3. conductors connected   4. three conductors   5. plug; receptacle
6. separable connector   7. ground connection; arrester   8. disconnecting switch   9. normally open contact (NO)
10. normally closed contact (NC)   11. pushbutton NO; NC   12. circuit-breaker   13. single pole switch; three-way switch
14. double pole double throw switch   15. fuse   16. thermal overload element   17. relay coil   18. resistor
19. winding, inductor or reactor   20. capacitor; electrolytic capacitor   21. transformer   22. current transformer; bushing type
23. potential transformer   24. dc source (general)   25. cell   26. shunt winding   27. series winding; commutating pole or compensating winding
28. motor; generator (general symbols)   29. dc motor; dc generator (general symbols)   30. ac motor; ac generator (general symbols)
32. 3-phase squirrel-cage induction motor; 3-phase wound-rotor motor   33. synchronous motor; 3-phase alternator   34. diode
35. thyristor or SCR   36. 3-pole circuit breaker with magnetic overload device, drawout type
37. dc shunt motor with commutating winding; permanent magnet dc generator   38. magnetic relay with one NO and one NC contact.
39. NC contact with time delay opening   40. NC contact with time delay closing   41. NO contact with time delay closing
42. NO contact with time delay opening

For a complete list of graphic symbols and references see *IEEE Standard and American National Standard Graphic Symbols for Electrical and Electronics Diagrams* (ANSI Y32.2/IEEE No. 315) published by the Institute of Electrical and Electronic Engineers, Inc., New York, N.Y. 10017. Essentially the same symbols are used in Canada and several other countries.

The coil of a control relay or contactor is usually represented by a small circle. The circle bears a letter, such as A, M, F, or a combination of letters and numbers, such as IA, 2A, 1M, 2M, CR and CX, in order to identify the relay or contactor. The contacts that are associated with a given relay bear the same letter or letter-number as the relay coil. This is important because the contacts of a given relay can appear in quite different places in a schematic diagram.

Most contactors are equipped with one or more **auxiliary contacts** in addition to the main power contacts. The auxiliary contacts are small control contacts that form part of the low-power control circuit. The auxiliary contacts are sometimes identified by the letter-number of the coil and a subscript, such as A_x or $1A_a$. The subscripts simplify the description of the control circuit.

AUXILIARY CONTACTS

22.3 Control Diagrams

Depending upon the amount of information that is required, a control system can be represented by four types of circuit diagrams. They are listed here in order of increasing detail and completeness:

1. block diagram
2. one-line diagram*
3. wiring diagram
4. schematic diagram

A *block diagram* (Fig. 22.14) is composed of a set of rectangles, each representing a control device, together with a brief description of its function. The rectangles are connected by arrows which indicate the direction of power flow.

A *one-line diagram* (Fig. 22.15) is similar to a block diagram except that the components are shown by their symbols rather than by rectangles. The symbols give an idea of the nature of the components; consequently, one-line diagrams contain more information. The single lines connecting the various components represent one, two, or more wires.

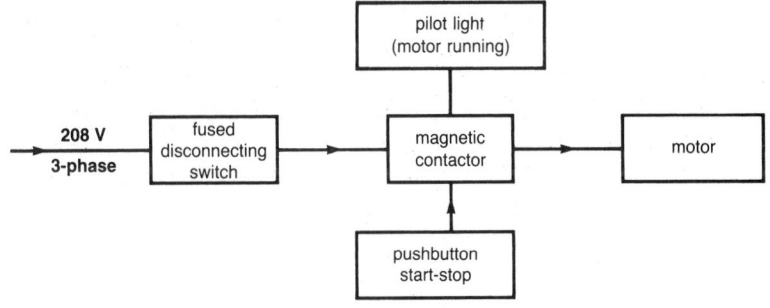

Figure 22.14

Block diagram of a combination starter.

---

* Also called single-line diagrams.

Figure 22.15

One-line diagram of a
combination starter.

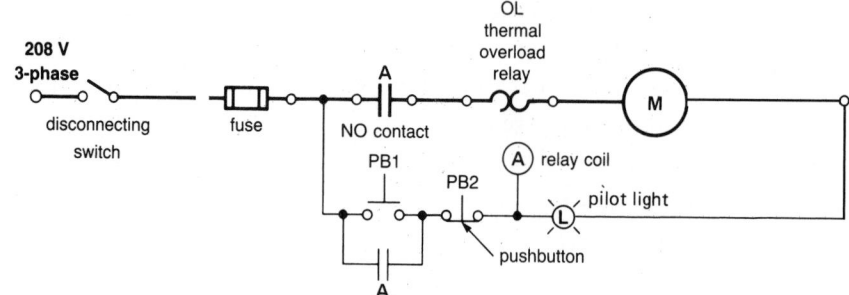

Figure 22.15

One-line diagram of a
combination starter.

A *wiring diagram* (Fig. 22.16) shows the connections between the components, taking into account the location of the terminals and even the colour coding of the
wires. These diagrams are employed when installing equipment or troubleshooting
a circuit.

A *schematic diagram* (Fig. 22.17) shows all the electrical connections between components but without regard to their location or terminal arrangement. This type of
diagram is indispensable when troubleshooting a circuit or analyzing its mode of
operation.

Note that the four diagrams in Figs. 22.14 to 22.17 describe the same control circuit. The symbols used to designate the various components are given in Table 22B.

Figure 22.16

Wiring diagram of a
combination starter.

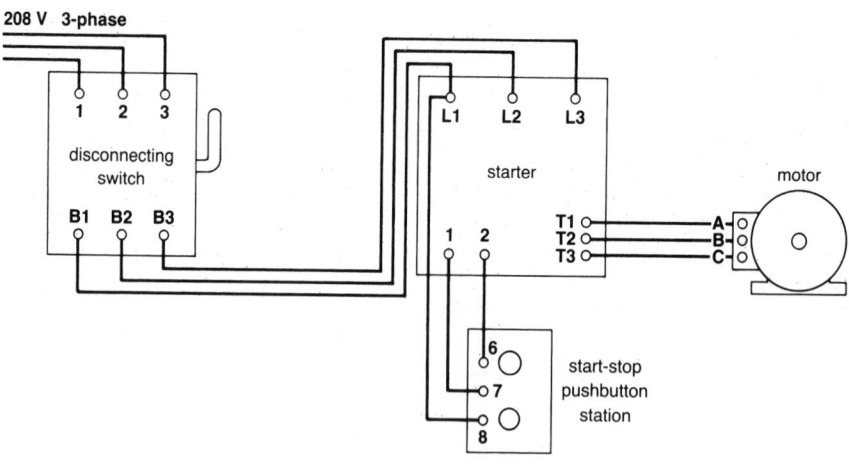

Figure 22.17

Schematic diagram of a
combination starter.

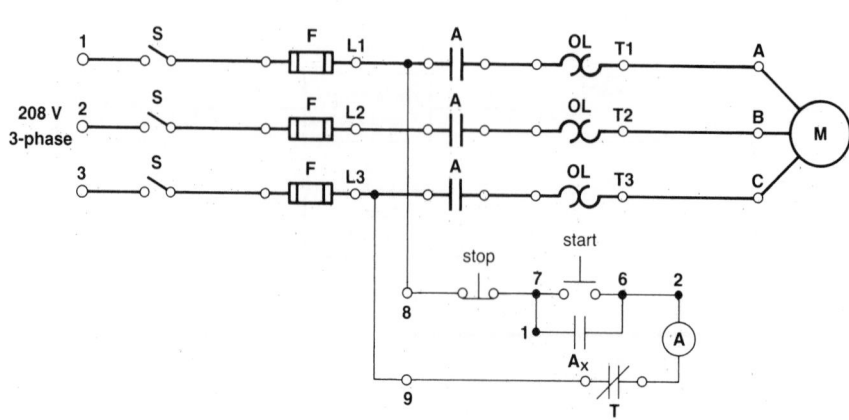

22.4 Automatic Dc Starters

In Chapter 16 on dc motors, we learned that a resistor must be placed in series with the armature during the starting period. This can be done manually by using a face-plate starter, but in modern equipment an automatic starter is preferred. We will describe a very simple dc starter in order to explain the basic principles that are common to all dc starters. We shall proceed in two steps. The first step will show the basic circuit that will bring the motor up to speed; the second step introduces the additional components needed to adequately protect the motor and electrical system.

Figure 22.18 is the schematic diagram of a dc starter for a shunt-wound motor. The armature terminals are labelled Al and A2, and the field terminals FI and F2. In addition to the start-stop pushbuttons, the circuit contains a main contactor M and a starting contactor A. The associated main contacts M and A are designed to carry the rated armature current. The auxiliary contacts M_{1x}, M_{2x}, and A_{1x} carry control currents, and so they are much smaller than the main contacts.

Contactor A is designed so that its contacts operate as soon as voltage is applied to relay coil A. However, when the coil is de-energized, it takes several seconds for the NC contact A to return to its normal closed position. This property is designated by the letters TDC (time delay closing). Similarly, it takes several seconds for the NO contact A_{1x} to return to its normal open position. This property is designated by the letters TDO (time delay opening).

The motor is brought up to speed in two steps because the starter has only one series resistor R. In larger motors, at least two resistors would be used to obtain a more gradual acceleration.

Figure 22.18

Basic control circuit of a dc starter for a shunt motor. The relay coils and contacts on the right show even more clearly how they are associated and how they relate to the control diagram.

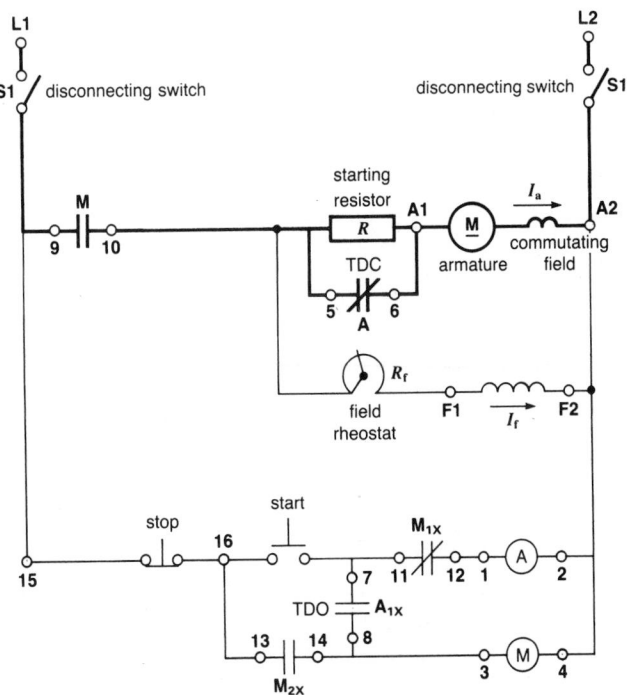

The circuit operates as follows. When the disconnecting switch is closed, the dc line voltage between L1 and L2 becomes available to drive the motor. When the start pushbutton is pressed, relay coil A becomes energized, causing contact A to open and A_{1x} to close. This removes the short-circuit across R, just a fraction of a second before A_{1x} closes. The closing of A_{1x} energizes relay coil M, and main contact M closes. This applies full voltage across the field circuit, as well as the armature circuit. The armature current I_a is established at once, but the field current I_f takes time to build up because of the high inductance of the shunt field.

When M is energized, contact M_{1x} opens, which removes the excitation of coil A. However, because of the TDC, TDO time-delay feature mentioned above, contact A remains open and contact A_{1x} remains closed for several more seconds.

Contact M_{2x} closes at the same time as main contact M. It plays an important role. In effect, it provides a current path to energize relay coil M, even when the start push-button returns to its normal position. As a result, to start the motor we have to depress the start pushbutton only momentarily. Auxiliary contact M_{2x} is sometimes called a **self-sealing contact** because it "seals" the current path of its own relay coil.

As soon as contact A closes, full voltage appears across the armature and the motor runs normally. To stop it, we momentarily depress the stop pushbutton, which de-energizes coil M, causing main contact M and self-sealing contact M_{2x} to open. The motor will coast to a stop. During this interval it acts as a self-excited shunt generator.

The simple circuit of Fig. 22.18 has some serious drawbacks because it provides no protection against overloads, short-circuits, or overspeeding of the motor. This deficiency is overcome in Fig. 22.19. It requires the addition of fuses, a thermal overload relay OL, a field-loss relay FL, and an extra contact A_{2x} on contactor A.

SELF-SEALING CONTACTS	

Figure 22.19

Basic control circuit of the dc starter, including circuit-protective devices.

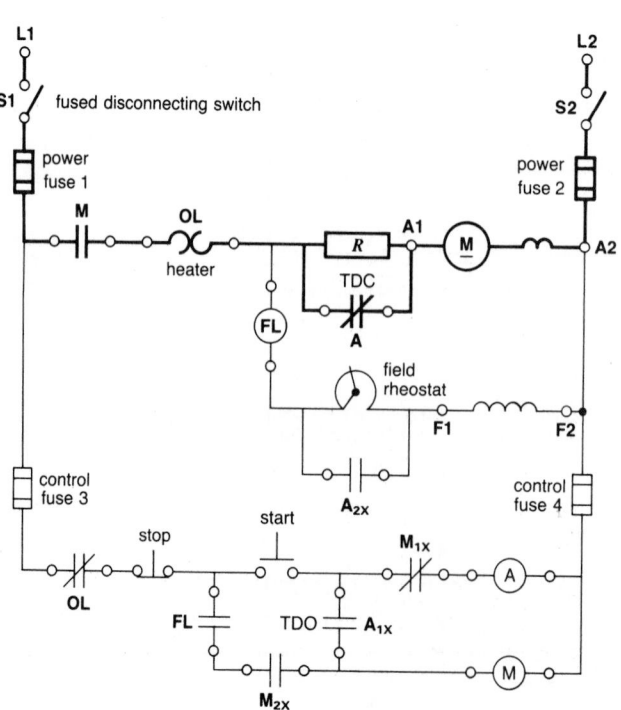

The *power* fuses will blow if a short-circuit occurs in the starter box or in the armature circuit. The *control* fuses have a much smaller current rating because they protect the smaller components and smaller wiring of the control circuit. The heater of the overload relay carries the full motor current. If a sustained overload occurs, the heat given off by the heater will cause the normally closed OL contact to open, which in turn opens the circuit of relay coil M, causing contactor M to drop out.

The extra contact A_{2x} is closed whenever contact A is open. This means that the field rheostat is shorted-circuited during the acceleration period when resistor R is in service. As a result, the field strength is maximum, which ensures the highest possible starting torque.

The field-failure relay coil FL is energized as long as the shunt field current is above a predetermined minimum. If, for any reason, the shunt field becomes too weak, the FL contact will open, causing main contactor M to drop out. Thus, the FL relay protects the motor from overspeeding.

22.5 Starting Methods for Three-Phase Induction Motors

Three-phase squirrel-cage motors are started either by connecting them directly across the line or by applying reduced voltage to the stator. The starting method (and type of starter) depends upon the power capacity of the supply line and the type of load.

Across-the-line starting is simple and inexpensive. The main disadvantage is the high starting current. It can produce a significant voltage drop, which may affect other customers connected to the line. Voltage-sensitive devices such as incandescent lamps, computer monitors, and high-precision machine tools respond poorly to such voltage dips. The voltage drop can also seriously reduce the torque of the motor while it is starting up.

Mechanical shock is another problem that should not be overlooked. Equipment can be damaged if full-voltage starting produces a hammer-blow impulse. Thus, printing presses, paper mills, electric trains, and elevators are always started on reduced voltage. Conveyor belts are another example for which sudden starting may not be acceptable.

In large industrial installations, we can sometimes install across-the-line starters for motors rated up to as much as 10 000 hp. The fuses and contactors must be chosen to carry the starting current during the acceleration period.

A disconnecting switch or manual circuit-breaker is always placed between the supply line and the starter. The switch and starter are sometimes mounted in the same enclosure to make what is called a **combination starter**. The line fuses (when used) are rated at about 3.5 times full-load current; consequently, they do not protect the motor against continuous overloads. Their primary function is to protect the motor and supply line against catastrophic currents resulting from a short-circuit in the motor or starter, or a failure to start up. The fuse rating, in amperes, must comply with the requirements of the Canadian Electrical Code.

COMBINATION STARTER

22.6 Manual Across-the-Line Starters

Manual three-phase starters (Figs. 22.20 and 22.21) are composed of a circuit breaker and either two or three thermal relays, all mounted in an enclosure. They are used for small motors (usually 10 hp or less) at voltages ranging from 115 V to 575 V. The thermal relays trip the circuit breaker whenever the current in one of the phases exceeds the rated value.

▼ **Figure 22.20**

Manual starters for single-phase motors rated at 1 hp: left—surface mounted; centre—flush mounted; right—waterproof enclosure.

(Courtesy Siemens)

▼ **Figure 22.21**

Manual three-phase starters rated between 1/4 hp and 40 hp and for voltages between 200 V and 575 V. Photograph shows starters for surface, flush, and special mounting.

(Courtesy Klockner-Moeller)

22.7 Magnetic Across-the-Line Starters

Magnetic across-the-line starters are used whenever we have to control a motor from a remote location. Figures 22.22 and 22.23 show a typical combination magnetic starter and its schematic diagram.

▶ **Figure 22.22**

Combination across-the-line starter rated 100 hp, 575 V, 3-phase, 60 Hz. The disconnecting switch is controlled by an external handle. The three fuse supports are immediately below the switch and the magnetic contactor is mounted in the lower left-hand corner. The small 575/115 V transformer in the lower right-hand corner supplies low-voltage power for the control circuit.

(Courtesy Square D)

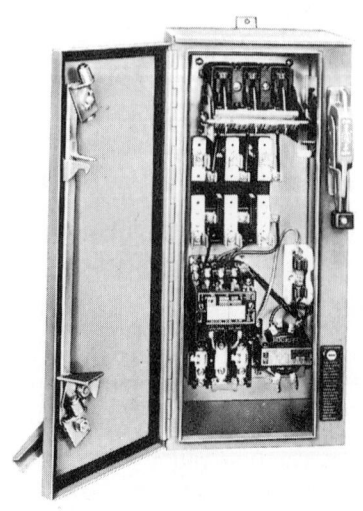

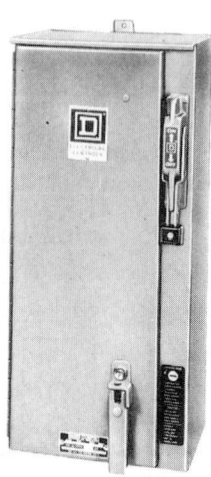

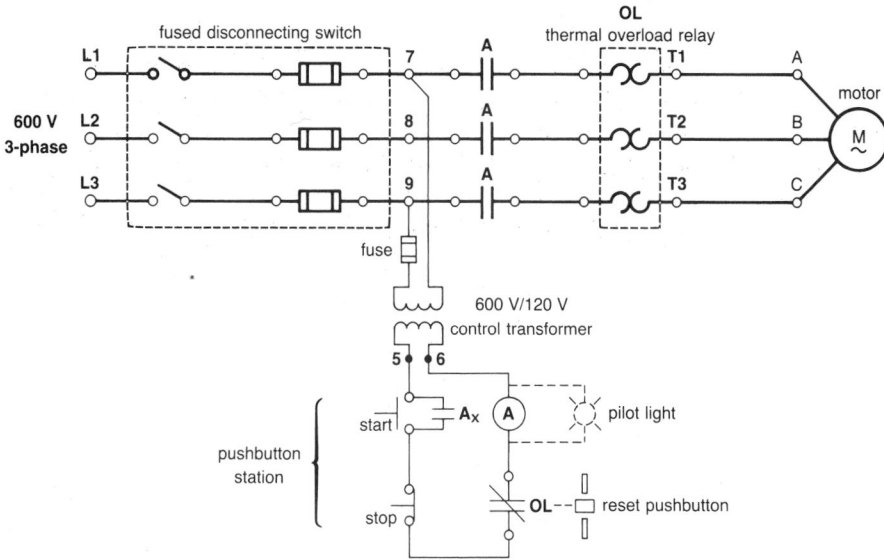

Figure 22.23

Schematic diagram of a three-phase combination starter using a low-voltage control circuit.

The starter has five main components: a magnetic contactor, a thermal relay, a control transformer, a disconnecting switch and a fuse block, and an external control station that permits the motor to be started and stopped.

1. The *magnetic contactor* A has three main contacts, A, and one small auxiliary contact, A_x. Contacts A must be big enough to carry the starting current and the rated full-load current without overheating. Contacts A and A_x remain closed as long as the relay coil A is energized.

2. The *thermal relay* OL protects the motor against sustained overloads. The relay is composed of three individual heater elements connected in series with the three phases. A small, normally closed contact OL forms part of the relay assembly. It opens when the relay gets too hot and stays open until the relay is manually reset.

   The current rating of the thermal relay is chosen to protect the motor against sustained overloads. Contact OL opens after a period of time that depends upon the magnitude of the overload current.

3. The 600 V/120 V *control transformer* steps down the line voltage to a standard 120 V control voltage. The control circuit is protected by a low-calibre fuse.

4. The fused *disconnecting switch* serves to isolate the motor and starter during routine inspection or repairs. The *fuses* protect the motor and starter components against catastrophic failure. To start the motor, we first close the disconnecting switch and then depress the start pushbutton momentarily. Relay coil A is immediately energized, contacts A and A_x close, and full voltage appears across the motor. When the pushbutton is released, it returns to its normal position, but relay coil A remains excited because auxiliary contact A_x is now closed. Contact A_x is a self-sealing contact.

5. The *control station,* composed of start-stop pushbuttons, may be located either close to, or far away from, the starter. The pilot light is optional.

   To stop the motor, we push the stop button, which opens the circuit to the relay coil. In case of an overload, the opening of contact OL produces the same effect.

Figure 22.24

Control circuit and pushbutton station for start-stop-jog operation. Terminals 5 and 6 are connected to the secondary of the control transformer.

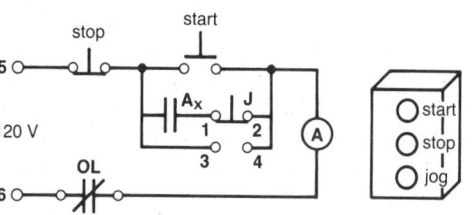

22.8 Inching and Jogging

In some mechanical systems, we have to adjust the position of a motorized part very precisely. To accomplish this, we energize the motor in short pulses so that it barely starts before it again comes to a halt. A double-contact pushbutton J is added to the usual start-stop circuit, as shown in Fig. 22.24. This arrangement permits conventional start-stop control as well as so-called *jogging,* or *inching.*

Jogging imposes severe duty on the power contacts because they continually make and break currents that are six times greater than normal. When jogging is required, the contactor is usually selected to be one NEMA size bigger than normal duty.

22.9 Reduced-Voltage Starting

As mentioned previously, some industrial loads have to be started very gradually. Examples are coil winders, printing presses, and other machines that process fragile products. In other industrial applications, we cannot connect a motor directly to the line because the starting current may be too high.

REDUCED-VOLTAGE STARTING

In such cases, we have to reduce the voltage applied to the motor, either by connecting resistors (or reactors) in series with the line or by employing an autotransformer. In **reducing-voltage starting**, we should remember that:

1. The locked-rotor stator current is proportional to the stator voltage: reducing the voltage by half reduces the current by half.

2. The locked-rotor torque is proportional to the square of the voltage: reducing the stator voltage by half reduces the torque by a factor of four.

22.10 Primary Resistance Starting

Primary resistance starting consists of placing three resistors in series with the stator during the start-up period (Fig. 22.25).* After a time sufficiently long so the motor is running close to rated speed, a second magnetic contactor B short-circuits the resistors. This method gives a very smooth start with negligible mechanical shock. The resistors are short-circuited after a delay that depends upon the setting of time-delay relay 1A. Note that contact 1A bears the letters TDC for time delay closing.

Figure 22.26 shows a typical primary resistance starter.

---

* Secondary resistance starting consists of placing three resistors in the rotor circuit of a wound-rotor induction motor.

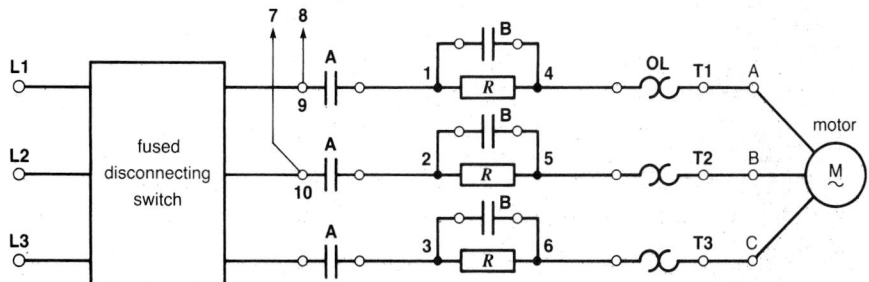

Figure 22.25

Schematic diagram of a reduced-voltage primary resistance starter.

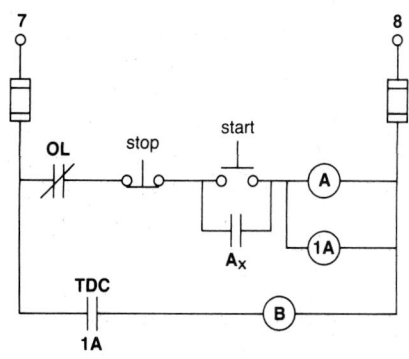

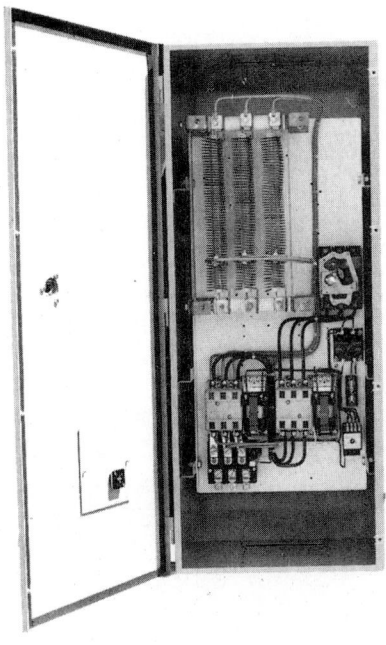

Figure 22.26

Primary resistance starter for a 50 hp, 575 V, 3-phase, 60 Hz motor. The three resistors are in the upper left-hand corner and the two magnetic contactors are mounted side by side below.

(Courtesy Siemens)

22.11 Autotransformer Starting

For a given locked-rotor torque, autotransformer starters draw a lower line current than do resistance starters. The disadvantages are that autotransformers cost more and the transition from reduced voltage to full voltage is not quite as smooth.

The autotransformer is equipped with taps that may be selected to give output voltages equal to 80%, 65%, or 50% of the rated motor voltage. The corresponding starting torques are 0.64, 0.42, or 0.25 of the full-voltage starting torque; further-more, the starting currents on the line side are reduced to 0.64, 0.42, or 0.25 of the full voltage locked-rotor current.

Figure 22.27 shows a starter using two autotransformers connected in open delta. Its schematic diagram is shown in Fig. 22.28, making use of the 65% tap. The time-delay relay CR has three contacts, CR_1, CR_2 and CR_3. Contact CR_1, in parallel with the start pushbutton, closes as soon as relay coil CR is energized. The two other contacts operate after an interval that depends upon the time-delay setting. Contactors A and B are mechanically interlocked to prevent them from closing simultaneously.

Contactor A closes as soon as the start pushbutton is depressed because contact CR_2 is closed. This excites the autotransformer, and reduced voltage (65 percent of full-line voltage) appears across the motor terminals. A few seconds later, the two CR contacts in series with coils A and B respectively open and close. Contactor A drops out, followed almost immediately by the closing of contactor B. This action applies full voltage to the motor and simultaneously disconnects the auto-transformer from the line. Note that relay coil B cannot become excited before contact A_x closes. Consequently, contactor B cannot come into service before contac-tor A has dropped out.

In transferring from contactor A to contactor B, the motor is momentarily discon-nected from the line. This creates a problem because when contactor B closes, a large transient current is drawn from the line. This transient surge is hard on the contacts and also produces a mechanical shock. For this reason, we sometimes employ more elaborate circuits in which the motor is never completely disconnected from the line.

Because the autotransformers are in service for only a short time (usually less than 10 s), they can be wound with much smaller conductors than continuously rated transformers. This enables manufacturers to reduce the size, weight, and cost of these starters.

Figure 22.27

Autotransformer reduced voltage starter rated 100 hp, 575 V, 3-phase, 60 Hz.

(Courtesy Square D)

EXAMPLE 22.1

A 200 hp, 460 V, three-phase, 60 Hz, 1785 r/min induction motor has a locked-rotor torque of 600 ft.lbf and a locked-rotor current of 1350 A. The motor is connected to an autotransformer starter, as shown in Fig. 22.28. Calculate:

1. the locked-rotor stator current.
2. the locked-rotor torque.
3. the current flowing in the 460 V supply lines L1, L2, and L3.

SOLUTION:

1. a) The locked-rotor stator current is proportional to the stator voltage
    b) The stator voltage is 65% × 460 V = 299 V
    c) The stator current is $I_{\text{locked-rotor}}$ = 1350 × (299/460) = 877.5 A

2. a) The locked-rotor torque is proportional to the square of the voltage, across the stator. Thus, the locked-rotor torque is
        $T = 600 \times (299/460)^2 = 254$ ft.lbf

3. a) The apparent power delivered to the motor is
        $S = 1.732 \, VI = 1.732 \times 299 \times 877.5 = 454\,429$ VA = 454 kVA
    b) The autotransformer consumes a negligible amount of apparent power. Consequently, the apparent power furnished by the 460 V lines is nearly 454 kVA
    c) The line current in phases L1, L2, and L3 is therefore
        $I = S/(1.732 \, V) = 454\,000/(1.732 \times 460) = 569$ A

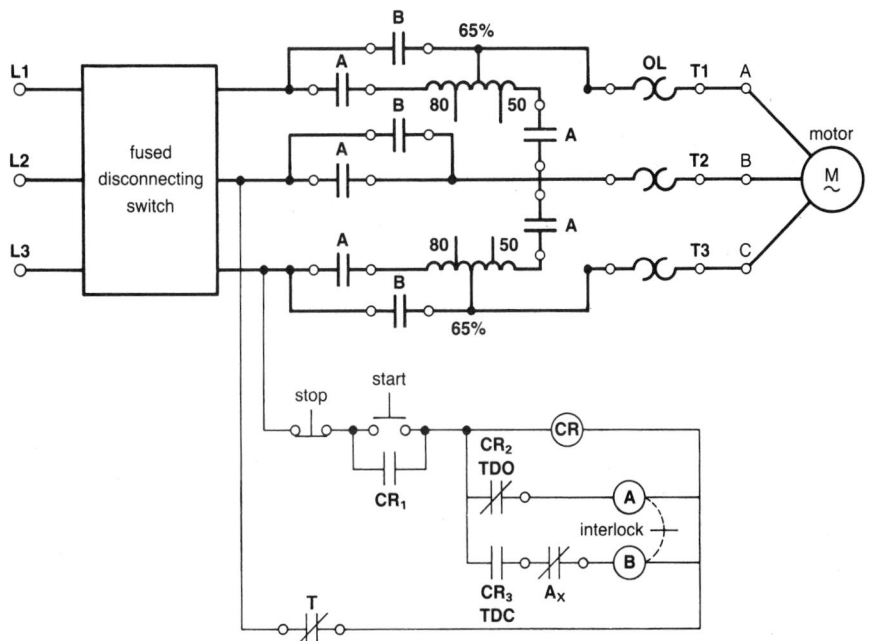

Figure 22.28

Simplified schematic diagram of an autotransformer starter.

22.12 Other Starting Methods

Several other methods are used to limit the current and torque when starting induction motors. Some require only a change in the stator winding connections. Thus, with **part-winding starting**, the motors have two identical sets of wye-connected windings, only one of which is energized during the starting period. When the motor approaches its rated speed, the second set is connected to the line. Thus, under running conditions, the two sets of windings operate in parallel. When one set of windings is energized, the locked-rotor torque is about 50 percent of what it would be if both sets were connected across the line. Furthermore, the locked-rotor current is about 65% of its "full-winding" value.

PART-WINDING STARTING

In **wye-delta starting**, all six stator leads are brought out to the terminal box. The windings are connected in wye during start-up and in delta during normal running conditions. This starting method produces the same results as an autotransformer starter having a 58 percent tap. The reason is that during start-up, the voltage across each wye-connected winding is only 1/1.732 (=0.58) of its rated value.

WYE-DELTA STARTING

EXAMPLE 22.2

A 40 hp, 575 V, three-phase, 60 Hz, 875 r/min induction motor is equipped with a delta-connected winding, and all six leads are brought out to the terminal box. The locked-rotor current is 232 A and the locked-rotor torque is 300 ft.lbf. The motor is installed in a small plant where across-the-line starting is not feasible. If wye-delta starting is used, calculate:

1. the locked-rotor current drawn from the line.
2. the locked-rotor torque.

SOLUTION:

1. a) The rated voltage per phase is 460 V
   b) The rated locked-rotor current in each winding when the motor is connected in delta is
      $I = 232/1.732 = 134$ A (Fig. 22.29)
   c) The voltage per phase when the motor is connected in wye is
      $V = 460/1.732 = 265.6$ V
   d) The current per phase is proportional to the voltage per phase. The current in each winding is therefore
      $I = 134 \times (265.6/460) = 77.4$ A
   e) The locked-rotor line current is therefore 77.4 A, which is only one-third of 232 A (Fig. 22.30).

2. The locked-rotor torque is proportional to the square of the voltage per winding. The locked-rotor torque with the windings connected in wye is
   $T = 300 \times (265.6/460)^2 = 100$ ft.lbf

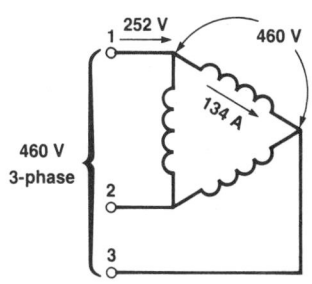

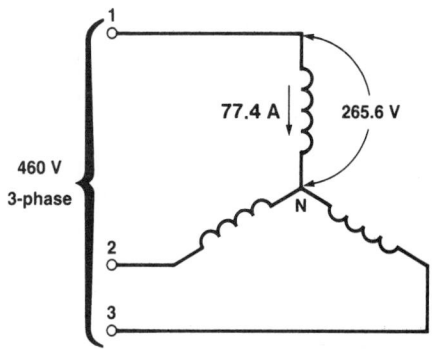

22.13 Cam Switches

Some industrial operations must remain under the continuous control of an operator. In hoists, for example, an operator has to vary the lifting and lowering rate, and the load has to be carefully set down at the proper place. Such a control sequence can be accomplished with manually operated cam switches.

Figure 22.31 shows a 3-position cam switch designed for the forward, reverse, and stop operation of a three-phase induction motor. For each position of the knob, some contacts are closed while others are open. This information is given in a table (Fig. 22.31b), usually attached to the side of the switch. An × designates a closed contact, while a blank space is an open contact. In the forward position, for example, contacts 2, 4, and 5 are closed, and contacts 1 and 3 are open. When the knob is turned to the stop position, all contacts are open. Figure 22.31c shows the shape of the cam that controls the opening and closing of contact 1.

The schematic diagram (Fig. 22.32) shows how to connect the cam switch to a three-phase motor. The state of the contacts (open or closed) is shown on the diagram for each position of the knob. For example, in the reverse position, contacts 1, 3, 5 are closed (see crosses) and contacts 2, 4 are open. The three-phase line and the motor are connected to the appropriate cam-switch terminals. Note that four jumpers J are required to complete the connections.

▼ **Figure 22.31**

Cam switch: (a) external appearance; (b) table listing the on-off state of the five contacts; (c) detail of the cam that controls contact 1, in the "off" position.

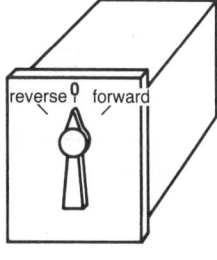

contact	forward	stop	reverse
1			X
2	X		
3			X
4	X		
5	X		X

contact 1

reverse   forward

cam shown in off position

(a)   (b)   (c)

Figure 22.32

Schematic diagram of a cam switch permitting forward and reverse operation of a 3-phase motor.

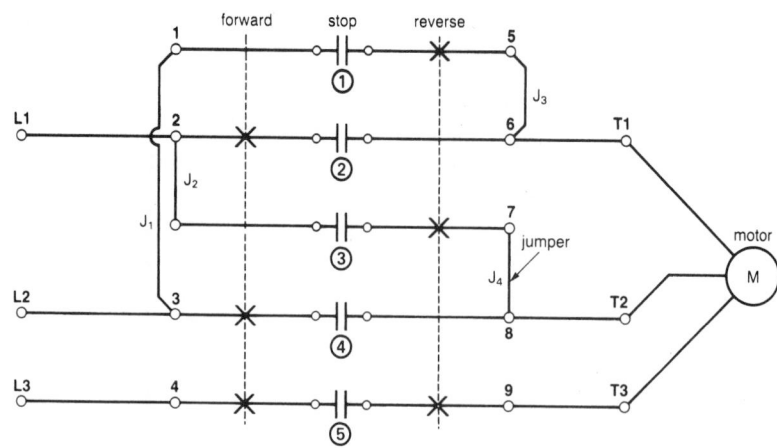

Some cam switches are designed to carry several hundred amperes, but magnetic contactors are often preferred to handle large currents. In such cases, a small cam switch is used to control the coils of the contactors. Very elaborate control schemes can be designed with multicontact cam switches.

22.14 Starting Three-Phase Synchronous Motors

In Section 19.9, we learned that synchronous motors are started as induction motors. Consequently, the same across-the-line and reduced voltage starting methods can be applied to synchronous motors as are used for induction motors. However, a special method is needed to control the dc field so that the synchronous motor will develop (1) a satisfactory locked-rotor torque and (2) maximum pull-in torque.

The first objective is met by connecting the field across an external "discharge" resistor, with the dc source disconnected. The second objective is met by connecting the field to the dc source only when the motor is running close to synchronous speed *and* when the N and S rotor poles are in the correct position with respect to the N and S stator poles. How can we meet this objective?

It so happens that the ac voltage V_f, induced in the field winding during start-up, enables us to determine both the speed of the rotor and the position of the poles. The speed is directly related to the induced frequency, and the position of the poles is related to the polarity and slope of the induced voltage. Figure 22.33 shows the voltage V_f induced in the field of a synchronous motor when it is running below synchronous speed. It is the voltage that would appear across the field terminals on open circuit. Whenever V_f is maximum, the rotor poles are midway between the stator poles. On the other hand, when V_f is zero, the rotor poles are directly facing the stator poles. Furthermore, if care is taken to properly identify the field terminals, the following relationships are true:

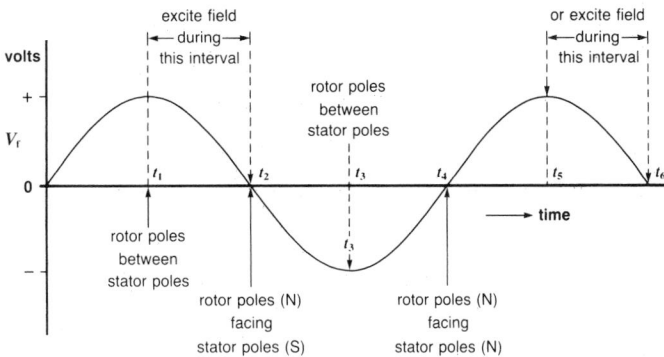

Figure 22.33

Voltage induced in the field winding and critical intervals during which field excitation may be applied.

1. When V_f is maximum positive (instant t_1), the N pole of the rotor is approaching the S pole of the stator.

2. When V_f is zero and the rate of change is negative (instant t_2), the N pole of the rotor is facing the S pole of the stator.

3. When V_f is maximum negative (instant t_3), the N pole of the rotor is approaching the N pole of the stator.

4. When V_f is zero and the rate of change is positive (instant t_4), the N pole of the rotor is facing the N pole of the stator.

Knowing that instants t_1, t_2, and t_3 are related to the position of the poles, it is possible to apply field excitation at the best moment. If possible, the field strength should be maximum when the N and S poles are facing each other (instant t_2). Consequently, field excitation should be applied slightly *before* instant t_2 so that the field current has had time to build up. However, excitation must not be applied before instant t_1. Referring to Fig. 22.33, field excitation should be applied between instants t_1 and t_2. It should be noted, however, that small, lightly loaded synchronous motors will pull into synchronism no matter when the excitation is applied.

As the motor picks up speed, the frequency and magnitude of V_f decreases progressively, just as in the rotor bars of a squirrel-cage motor. This means that the frequency of V_f can be used as an indicator of the rotor speed. If the slip is s and the stator line frequency is f, the frequency of V_f is given by Equation 17.3:

$$f_r = sf$$

EQ. 17.3

One method of detecting the speed and position of the rotor poles is shown in Fig. 22.34. The field terminals are connected to a discharge resistor R_d in series with a reactor X_m. The instantaneous magnitude of the voltage v across X_m is related to the instantaneous value of V_f. As a result, v can be used as a measure of V_f. Voltage v is detected by an electrical or electronic device D. The output of the device actuates a relay coil P at that moment when the rotor speed and position are such as to produce the highest pull-in torque. When P operates, the discharge resistor is automatically disconnected from the circuit, and the dc source is simultaneously connected to F1 and F2.

Figure 22.34

Method of detecting the
position and speed of the
rotor poles.

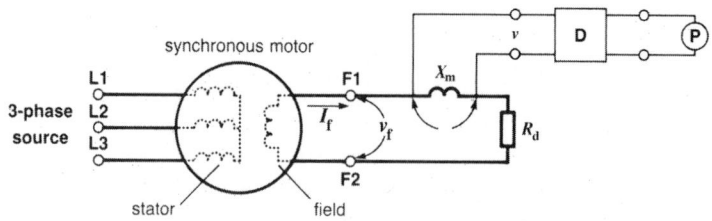

EXAMPLE 22.3

Figure 22.35 shows schematically the rotor and stator poles of a multipolar synchronous motor that has not yet come up to speed. The stator poles are moving at
synchronous speed to the left. The rotor poles are also moving to the left, but at a
lower speed. Although they are not yet excited, the rotor poles *will* have the polarities shown when they are connected to the dc source. What is the polarity of V_{ab}
across the winding of the (future) N pole at this moment?

SOLUTION:

From the viewpoint of the rotor, the stator flux is moving slowly toward the left.
Consequently, the flux ϕ linking coil a-b is increasing. By applying Lenz's law
(Section 7.5), we find that V_{ab} is positive. Thus, when the (future) N pole of the rotor
is approaching the S pole of the stator, V_{ab} is positive. Note that the field coils a-b,
c-d, etc., are connected in series and so the induced voltage V_f is the sum of the
voltages induced in each coil.

EXAMPLE 22.4

The field of a 500 hp, 2300 V, three-phase, 60 Hz, 300 r/min synchronous motor has
a resistance R_f of 1.5 Ω and an inductance L_f of 240 mH. At standstill, the ac voltage
V_f induced in the field is 5200 V. The field is connected to X_m and R_d as shown in
Figs. 22.34 and 22.36. If X_m has an inductance L_m of 5 mH and R_d = 5 Ω, calculate:

1.   the voltage across F_1 and F_2 if R_d is disconnected.
2.   the value of I_f at standstill.
3.   the voltage across X_m at standstill.

SOLUTION:

1.   With the field circuit open, the full value of V_f = 5200 V appears across the
     terminals F_1F_2

2.   a)   To determine the value of I_f we must first calculate the impedance of the
          field circuit (Fig. 22.36)
     b)   The total inductance of the circuit is
          $$L = L_f + L_m = 240 + 5 = 245 \text{ mH}$$

continued

c) The total reactance of the circuit is
$$X_L = 2\pi fL$$
$$X_L = 2 \times 3.1416 \times 60 \times 0.245 = 92.4 \ \Omega$$
EQ. 11.1

d) The total resistance of the circuit is
$$R = R_d + R_f = 5 + 1.5 = 6.5 \ \Omega$$

e) The impedance of the circuit is
$$Z = \sqrt{R^2 + X_L^2}$$
$$Z = \sqrt{6.5^2 + 92.4^2} = 92.6 \ \Omega$$
EQ. 12.11

f) The current I_f is $I_f = V_f/Z = 5200/92.6 = 56$ A

3. a) The value of X_m is
$$X_m = 2\pi fL_m = 2 \times 3.1416 \times 0.005 = 1.88 \ \Omega$$

b) The voltage across X_m at standstill is
$$v = I_f X_m = 56 \times 1.88 = 105.3 \text{ V}$$

▼ **Figure 22.35**

See Example 22.4.

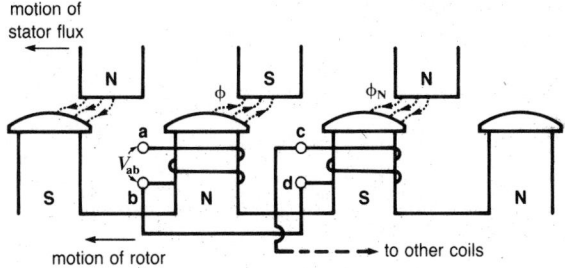

▼ **Figure 22.36**

See Example 22.5.

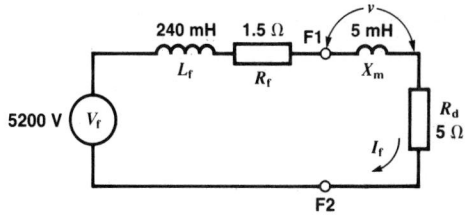

22.15 Automatic Starter for a Synchronous Motor

Figure 22.37 shows the schematic diagram of an automatic across-the-line starter for a 500 hp, 2300 V, three-phase, 60 Hz, 300 r/min synchronous motor. The motor has a rated full-load current of 104 A and a locked-rotor current of 411 A, and the rated field current is 80 A at 125 V dc. The starter has the following notable features:

1. The fused disconnecting switch has its blades connected to ground when it is in the open position. This is a safety feature to ensure zero voltage during maintenance and repair.

2. A 2400 V/120 V control transformer T_1 isolates the control circuit from the high-voltage line.

3. The main contactor relay coil M is fed by a rectifier D1 that converts the ac current into dc. The main advantage is to eliminate contactor vibration and noise.

4. Relay A is small compared with contactor M, and so the pushbutton stations can be of conventional size.

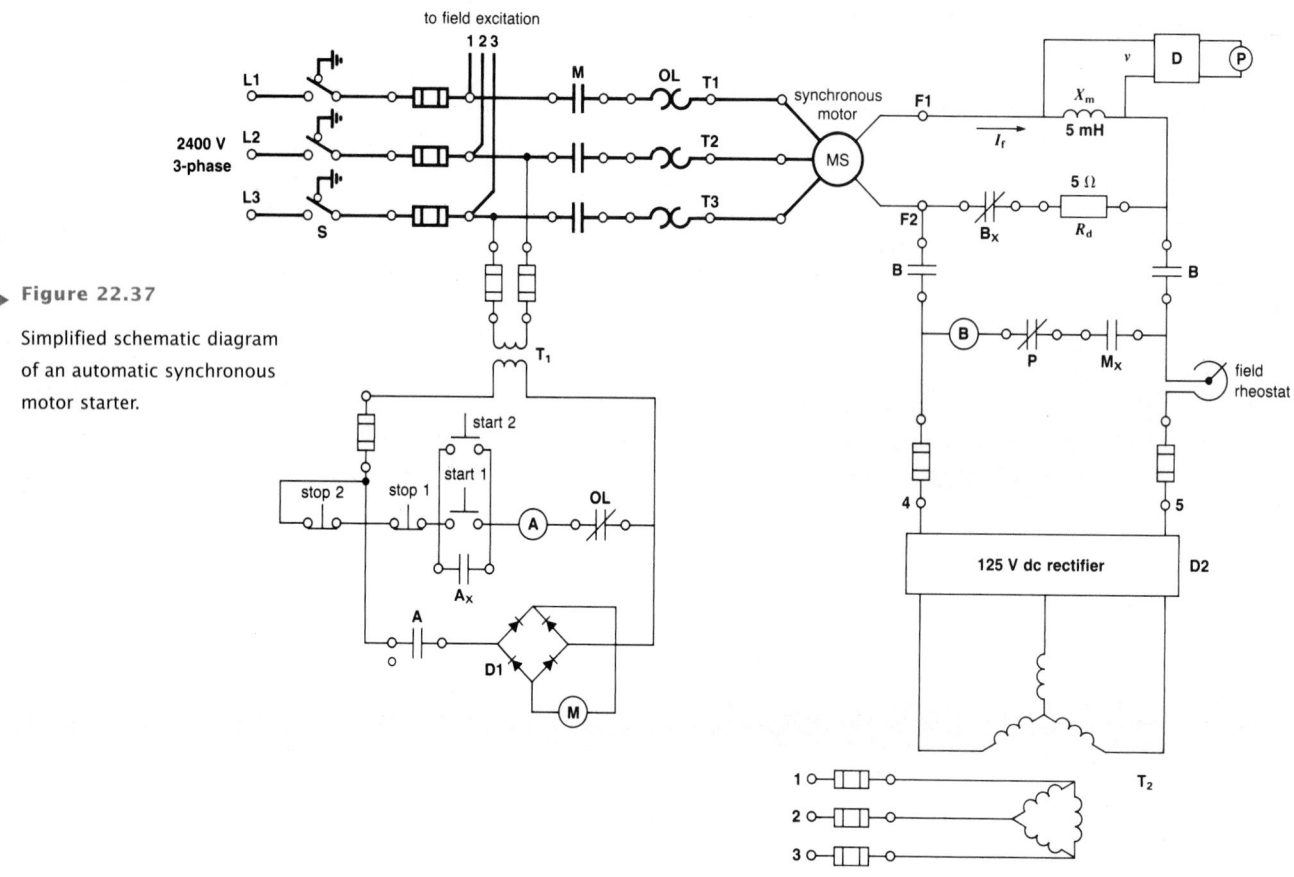

Figure 22.37

Simplified schematic diagram
of an automatic synchronous
motor starter.

5.   The 125 V dc source for the field is provided by a three-phase rectifier D2 that
     is powered by a delta-wye step-down transformer T2.

6.   Note that all circuits are protected by fuses to limit the damage if an acciden-
     tal short-circuit should occur.

7.   The field discharge resistor has a value of 5 Ω, and the inductance of X_m is 5 mH.

8.   The motor can be started from two locations and can also be stopped at two
     locations. Note that the start pushbuttons are in parallel, while the stop push-
     buttons are in series.

The circuit operates as follows. When the main disconnecting switch S is closed. the
control transformer T_1 is energized, as well as the field excitation transformer T_2.
A dc voltage appears across terminals 4 and 5 but does not reach the field because
contacts B are open. When one of the start pushbuttons is depressed, the following
sequence takes place.

1.   Relay A is excited, which causes relay coil M to close main contacts M, thus
     applying full voltage to the stator.

2.   An ac voltage is induced in the field, causing ac current I_f to flow in reactor X_m
     and field discharge resistor R_d. The locked-rotor value of I_f is 56 A and the fre-
     quency is 60 Hz. The voltage across R_d is $V_R = I_f R = 56 \times 5 = 280$ V.

The voltage across X_m is $v = I_f X_m = 56 \times 1.88 = 105.3$ V. This high input voltage V to detector D immediately actuates relay P, which keeps the circuit of relay coil B open, despite the fact that auxiliary contact M_X is now closed. With relay B out of service, the field circuit remains in the state shown in Fig. 22.37.

3. As the motor picks up speed, the induced field voltage begins to fall, which reduces the magnitude of I_f. Furthermore, the frequency of I_f decreases rapidly with increasing speed. Consequently, the voltage V across X_m falls very quickly. Its value is about 4 V when the motor turns at 285 r/min. The corresponding slip is 5 percent and the frequency is 3 Hz.

4. When the slip is below 5 percent (speed greater than 285 r/min), v is so small that detector D is about ready to allow relay P to drop out. As already mentioned, the drop-out will occur at the precise moment that will ensure the maximum pull-in torque.

5. As soon as P is de-energized, relay coil B becomes excited because contact M_X is still closed. As a result, contact B_X opens and resistor R_d is removed from the circuit. At the same time, contacts B close and dc excitation is applied to the field. Current I_f is now a dc current, and so the voltage v across X_m falls to zero, which ensures that relay P will remain de-energized.

A complete circuit diagram would show many more details, most of which relate to safety features and overload protection of the squirrel-cage and stator windings.

22.16 Summary

Upon completion of this chapter you should have learned that:

• A control system has a number of components and their symbols as shown in Table 22B. These symbols are used to simplify control diagrams.

• There are four types of control diagrams, each with a common use:

  i) Block diagrams are used to illustrate the function of various sections of a control diagram.

  ii) One-line diagrams are used to shown the operation of a control system.

  iii) Wiring diagrams show the relationship between components of the control system and the interconnecting wiring.

  iv) Schematic diagrams show the sequence of operation without regard to physical location. Schematics are useful for troubleshooting.

• An automatic dc motor starter inserts a resistance in series with the motor armature. After a preset period of time, the resistor is short-circuited by a set of timing contacts and the armature current increases to its rated value.

• Three-phase manual starters include a disconnect switch and a set of thermal overloads. The motor is started by closing the disconnect. Automatic motor starters have five components: magnetic starter, thermal overloads, control transformer, disconnecting switch and fuse block, and control station. The use of control devices allows the motor to be started or stopped from one or more remote locations.

- Reduced voltage starters limit the starting current of a motor by lowering the terminal voltage of the motor. Reducing the starting voltage also reduces the motor torque. The torque developed by a motor is proportional to the square of the voltage: 80% of the rated voltage results in 64% of rated torque.

- Cam switches are used in situations where continuous operator control is required, such as in cranes and hoists. Cam switches control multiple sets of contacts, as shown in Figure 22.32.

- Three-phase synchronous motors can be started in the same way as induction motors. However, a means of controlling the dc field must be included in order to achieve rated synchronous torque and maximum pull-in torque. The control system also connects a discharge resistor across the field windings as the motor accelerates and connects the dc source to field windings as the motor approaches synchronous speed.

Key Terms

AUXILIARY CONTACTS: Low current contacts operated by the coil of a motor starter. These contacts may be NO or NC as required, and operate at the same time as the main contacts.

COMBINATION STARTER: When a motor starter and its disconnect switch are mounted in the same enclosure, it is referred to as a combination starter.

Normally closed contacts: A set of contacts that are closed (not conducting current) when no electrical or mechanical force is applied.

NORMALLY OPEN CONTACTS: A set of contacts that are open (conducting current) when no electrical or mechanical force is applied.

PART-WINDING STARTING: A three-phase motor with two sets of wye-connected windings. During start, only a single set of the windings is connected to the source. After the motor accelerates to a pre-determined speed, the second set of wye-connected windings are connected to the source.

REDUCED VOLTAGE STARTING: A means of starting a three-phase motor that provides a motor with a lower than terminal voltage during start. Reducing the starting voltage reduces the starting torque of the motor (torque is proportional to the square of the voltage). Primary resistance and autotransformer starters are examples of reduced voltage starting techniques.

SELF-SEALING CONTACTS: A set of NO contacts in parallel with the start button in a starter's control circuit. These contacts are used to supply current to the starter after the start button is released. Self-sealing contacts are also known as holding contacts, seal-in contacts or maintaining contacts.

WYE-DELTA STARTING: A reduced voltage starting method requiring a six-lead motor. During start, the motor is connected in wye and during run the motor is connected in delta.

Test Your Knowledge

22.1   A thermal relay can be used for short-circuit protection.

       true _____   false _____

22.2   A fused disconnecting switch can often be used instead of a circuit breaker.

       true _____   false _____

22.3   A normally closed contact of a relay is a contact that is closed when the relay coil is in operation.

       true _____   false _____

22.4   In a large three-phase starter, three fuses are sufficient to adequately protect against short-circuits.

       true _____   false _____

22.5   A stop pushbutton always has at least one normally closed contact

       true _____   false _____

22.6   A field-failure relay in a dc starter prevents the motor from overspeeding when the series field circuit is interrupted.

       true _____   false _____

22.7   The rated locked-rotor current of a 460 V, 3-phase squirrel-cage motor is 250 A. If the starting voltage across the motor is reduced to 230 V, the new locked-rotor stator current will be

    a.   125 A

    b.   250 A

    c.   62.5 A

22.8   If one of the line fuses is removed in Fig. 22.23, the motor will not start.

       true _____   false _____

22.9   A 28-pole, 3-phase, 60 Hz synchronous motor pulls in at 247 r/min. The frequency in the field circuit at that moment is

    a.   3.94%

    b.   2.37 Hz

    c.   2.4638 Hz

22.10   In Fig. 22.33, if V_f has a frequency of 2 Hz, the time interval during which the field excitation can be applied is

    a.   0.5 s

    b.   8 s

    c.   0.125 s

Questions and Problems

22.11   Name four types of circuit diagrams, and describe the purpose of each.

22.12   Without referring to the text, describe the operation of the starter shown in Fig. 22.17, and state the use of each component.

22.13   Draw the symbols for an NO contact, an NC contact, and a thermal relay.

22.14   If the start and stop pushbuttons of a starter are pushed simultaneously, what will happen?

22.15   In Fig. 22.17, if the A_x contact were removed, what effect would it have on the operation of the starter?

22.16   In Fig. 22.19, if a short-circuit occurs across the armature while the motor is running, which of the following devices will interrupt the circuit: power fuses, control fuses, or OL?

22.17   In Fig. 22.19, if the motor is overloaded by 30 percent, which device will protect the motor? Describe how this protection works.

22.18   A partial short-circuit between the turns of the stator in Fig. 22.37 causes the currents in lines L1 and L2 to be above normal. Which device will trip the motor? Describe how the protection operates.

22.19   An ac magnetic contactor can make 3 million "normal" circuit interruptions before its contacts have to be replaced. If a motor is started and stopped 15 times per day, 7 days a week, after how many years will the contacts have to be replaced?

22.20   Without referring to the text, describe the sequence of operations that occurs when the start pushbutton in Fig. 22.19 is momentarily depressed. (The disconnecting switch is closed.)

22.21   The motor in Fig. 22.28 is on the 65% tap, and draws a stator current of 800 A when the speed is 710 r/min. Calculate the current in the three phases of lines L1, L2, and L3.

22.22   How many three-phase ac contactors are needed to start a motor using the part-winding method?

22.23   A delta-connected induction motor has a rated locked-rotor current of 360 A. Calculate the locked-rotor current if the motor is started with the windings connected in wye.

22.24   A delta-connected induction motor has a rated locked-rotor torque of 60 N.m. Calculate the locked-rotor torque if the motor is started with the windings connected in wye.

22.25   Without referring to the text, describe the sequence of operations that takes place when the start pushbutton is momentarily depressed in the starter of Fig. 22.28.

22.26   In Fig. 22.35, the field of the stator rotates to the left at 1800 r/min and the rotor rotates to the left at 1720 r/min. Using Lenz's law, determine the polarity of V_{cd} due to flux ϕ.

22.27   The field voltage induced across the open-circuit terminals of a 720 r/min, 60 Hz synchronous motor is 6000 V. What is the induced voltage per pole?

22.28   The synchronous motor starter in Fig. 22.37 works well with the connections as shown. What would happen if terminals 4 and 5 were reversed?

22.29   Without referring to the text, describe the sequence of events that takes place when the start pushbutton of Fig. 22.37 is depressed.

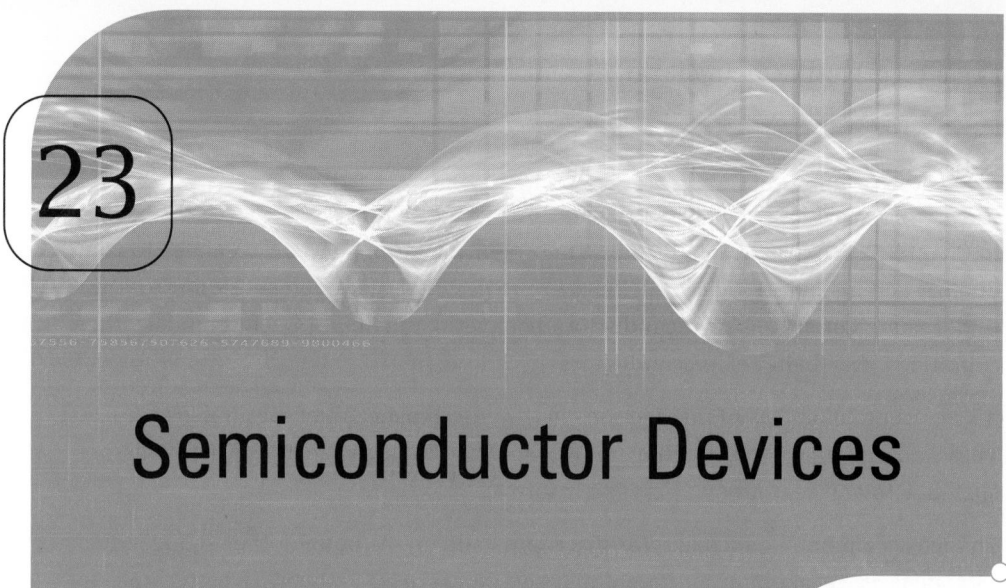

23

Semiconductor Devices

LEARNING OBJECTIVES

Upon completion of this chapter you will be able to:

- Describe the characteristics of p-type and n-type semi-conductor materials

- Explain forward and reverse biasing of the p-n junction

- Describe the characteristics of a junction diode

- Explain the operation of a half-wave and full-wave bridge rectifier

- Describe the construction and operation of a junction transistor

- Describe the characteristics of the junction transistor

- Explain the operation of a transistor switching circuit

- Describe the operation of the silicon controlled rectifier (SCR)

- Describe the characteristics of the SCR

- Explain the how an SCR can be controlled using static switching

- Explain how an SCR can be controlled using a gate pulse generating circuit

- Explain the operation of a snubber circuit

23.1 Semiconductor Materials

SEMICONDUCTOR

In Chapter 2 you learned about the structure of the atom and how it relates to conductors and insulators. There is a third group of materials called **semiconductors**. Under some conditions semiconductors behave like insulators, while under other conditions they behave like conductors.

All semiconductors have four electrons in the outermost orbit of the atom (Fig. 23.1). These atoms are called bonding or valence electrons. When these electrons are shared with adjacent atoms, a crystal is formed.

The most common semiconductor material is silicon. Although other semiconductors such as germanium and gallium-arsenide are used, silicon is better able to withstand heat.

Figure 23.1

A crystal is formed when a semiconductor atom shares its valence electrons with four other atoms.

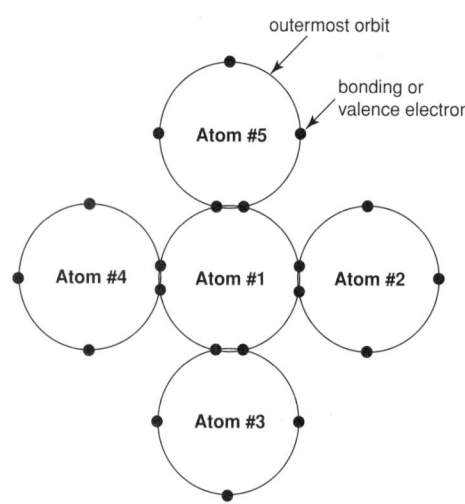

23.2 P-Type and N-Type Materials

If we add a very small amount of material that has five valence electrons to a silicon crystal, the fifth electron will not be able to bond with an adjacent silicon atom. The crystal formed in this process will have an excess number of electrons, resulting in an excess of negative charges. Such crystals are called **n-type materials** (Fig. 23.2).

N-TYPE MATERIAL

If we take the same silicon crystal and add a small amount of material with only three valence electrons, it will only be able to bond fully with three adjacent silicon atoms. Crystals formed in this way will have a number of unfilled bonding sites called **holes** (Fig. 23.3). The unfilled bonding sites will result in a positive charge and such material is called **p-type material.**

HOLES

P-TYPE MATERIAL

The excess electrons in n-type material and the holes in p-type material are charge carriers. In n-type material, the electrons are called majority carriers and holes are called minority carriers. In p-type material, the holes are the majority carriers and the electrons become the minority carriers.

▼ **Figure 23.2**

A crystal with an excess
number of valence electrons
is called n-type material.

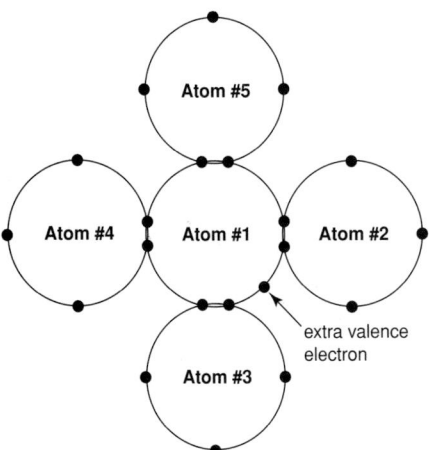

extra valence
electron

▼ **Figure 23.3**

A crystal with fewer valence
electrons is called p-type
material.

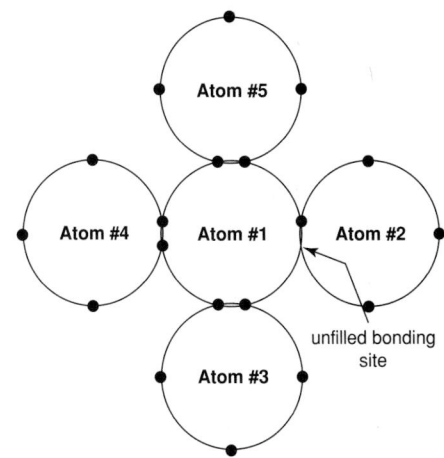

unfilled bonding
site

23.3 The P-N Junction

If a block of p-type material is brought into direct electrical contact with a block of
n-type material along a line called the **junction**, a migration of charge will occur.
The negative charges of the n-type material will migrate across the junction and
combine with the positive charges of the p-type material.

The recombination of the positive and negative charges will continue until the
force of attraction between them is too weak to cause the migration of the charges.
The attraction between the charges is limited by the square of the distance between
the charges; doubling the distance will result in one-quarter the attraction. This
process will result in a narrow band along the junction that has no electrical charge.
This band is called the **depletion zone** (Fig. 23.4).

JUNCTION

DEPLETION ZONE

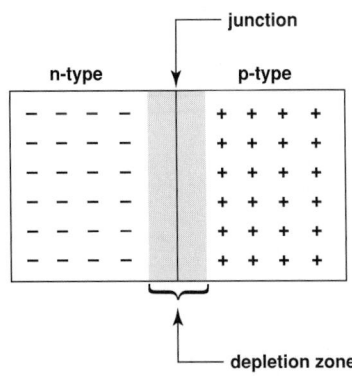

Figure 23.4

The migration across a p-n
junction results in an area
with no electrical charge
called the depletion zone.

23.4 Biasing the P-N Junction

When the p-n junction is connected to a voltage source, the p-n junction is said to be biased. A p-n junction can be reverse biased or forward biased.

If the negative terminal of the source is connected to the p-type material and the negative terminal to the n-type material, the junction is reverse biased. When this occurs, the negative charges in the n-type material will be attracted to the positive terminal of the source, and the positive charges in the p-type material are attracted to the negative terminal of the source. As a result, the depletion zone widens (Fig. 23.5) and no current flows in the circuit.

If the electrical connection to the junction is now reversed, the negative terminal of the source will be connected to the n-type material and the positive terminal to the p-type material, and the junction will be forward biased. Under these conditions, the negative charges in the n-type material will be repelled away from the negative terminal toward the junction. Likewise, the positive charges in the p-type material will be repelled from the positive terminal toward the junction. As a result, the depletion zone will be narrowed (Fig. 23.6).

As the depletion zone narrows, the distance between the positive and negative charges decreases. If enough voltage is applied across the terminals of the junction, electrons will cross through the depletion zone and recombine with the holes in the p-type material and current begins to flow. The voltage required to cause current flow is called the **breakover voltage (V_{bo})**. For silicon, V_{bo} is 0.7 V. If the voltage across the junction is less than this value, no current will flow.

BREAKOVER VOLTAGE (V_{bo})

23.5 The Junction Diode

The junction diode is simply a p-n junction manufactured to meet a predetermined set of operating conditions. Although a diode is designed to include a large number

▼ **Figure 23.5**

When a p-n junction is reverse biased, the depletion zone widens and no current flows

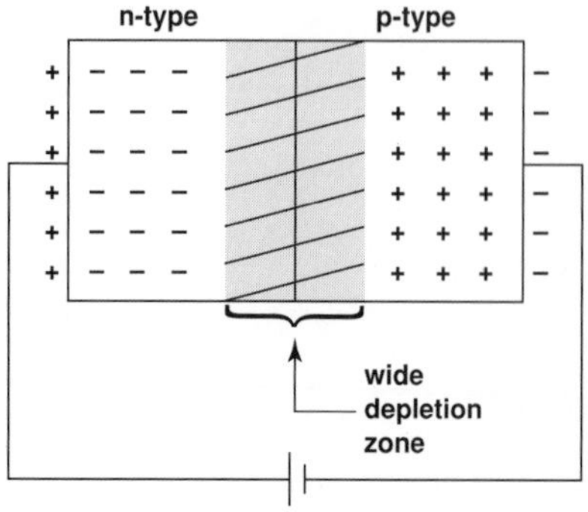

▼ **Figure 23.6**

When a p-n junction is forward biased, the depletion zone narrows and current flows.

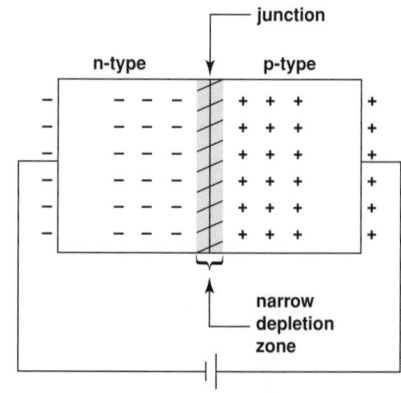

of characteristics, only a few of these need be considered in most applications. These include the forward current (I_F), surge current (I_s), and peak inverse voltage (*PIV*).

The forward current is the maximum current permitted to flow through the diode when it is forward biased. Exceeding this value will result in heat build-up within the p-n junction and may result in failure of the diode.

In some operating conditions, the diode may be subject to surges in load current. If the surge current is an occasional event lasting for a limited time, the heat build-up within the diode may be minimal and the diode will continue to operate normally. The magnitude of the surge current depends upon whether it is repetitive or non-repetitive in nature.

In Section 23.4 we saw that when a p-n junction was reverse biased, the depletion zone widened and no current flowed through the diode. If the reverse voltage is increased in value, the diode will eventually be forced into reverse current flow and the diode will probably fail. The voltage at which this occurs is called the reverse breakdown voltage (V_{rev}). The maximum reverse voltage a diode can withstand without breaking down is known as the **peak inverse voltage (*PIV*)**. The *PIV* rating of a diode is just as important as the forward current, since the diode must not only be able to conduct the load current when it is forward biased, it must be able to prevent current flow when the diode is reverse biased.

Fig. 23.7 shows the characteristic curve for a typical silicon junction diode.

PEAK INVERSE VOLTAGE (*PIV*)

23.6   The Half-Wave Rectifier

In Section 23.4 we forward biased a diode using a dc source and then reversed the connection in order to reverse bias the diode. If we replace the dc source with an ac source, the diode will be forward and reverse biased by the changing polarity of the source.

The circuit in Fig. 23.8 shows a diode (D_1) series with a load resistor (R_{Load}). The circuit is supplied from an ac voltage source. When the ac source is positive, the

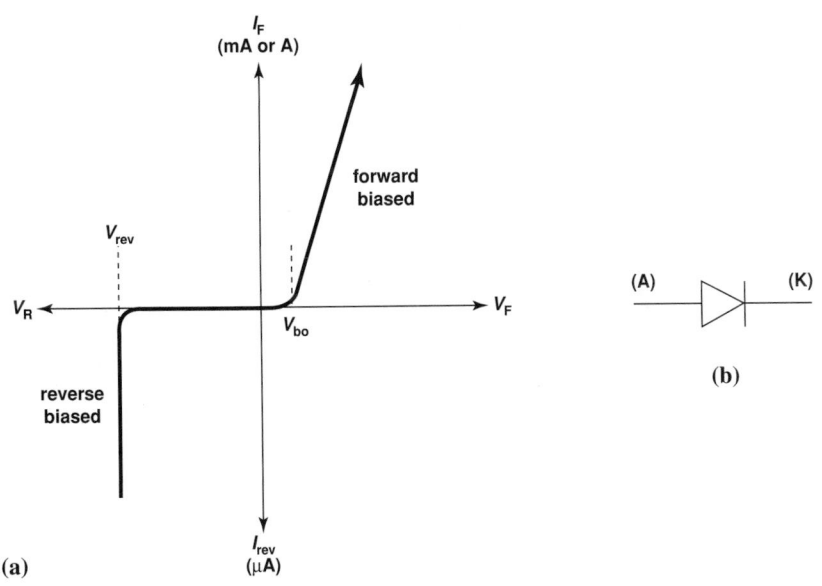

(a)

Figure 23.7

(a) The characteristic curve for a silicon p-n junction diode. Note the change in current units between the forward and reverse currents.
(b) The symbol for a junction diode. The positive terminal is called the anode (A) and the negative terminal is called the cathode (K).

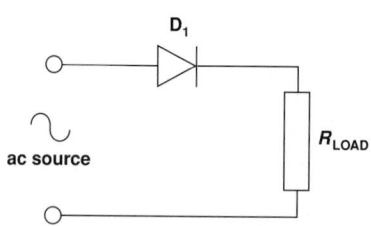

Figure 23.8

An ac series circuit including a diode and load resistor.

anode of the diode will be positive with respect to the cathode and the diode will be forward biased. When the supply voltage exceeds 0.7 V, current will flow through the series circuit formed by the diode and the load. When the supply voltage goes negative, the anode will be negative with respect to the cathode and no current will flow through the circuit.

The waveforms for this circuit are shown in Fig. 23.9. Note that when the diode is forward biased, the supply voltage (less the 0.7 V) appears across the resistor, and when the diode is reverse biased, the voltage appears across the diode. Since only

Figure 23.9

By averaging the voltage across the load resistor, it can be shown that the load voltage will be 0.318 V_{Supply}.

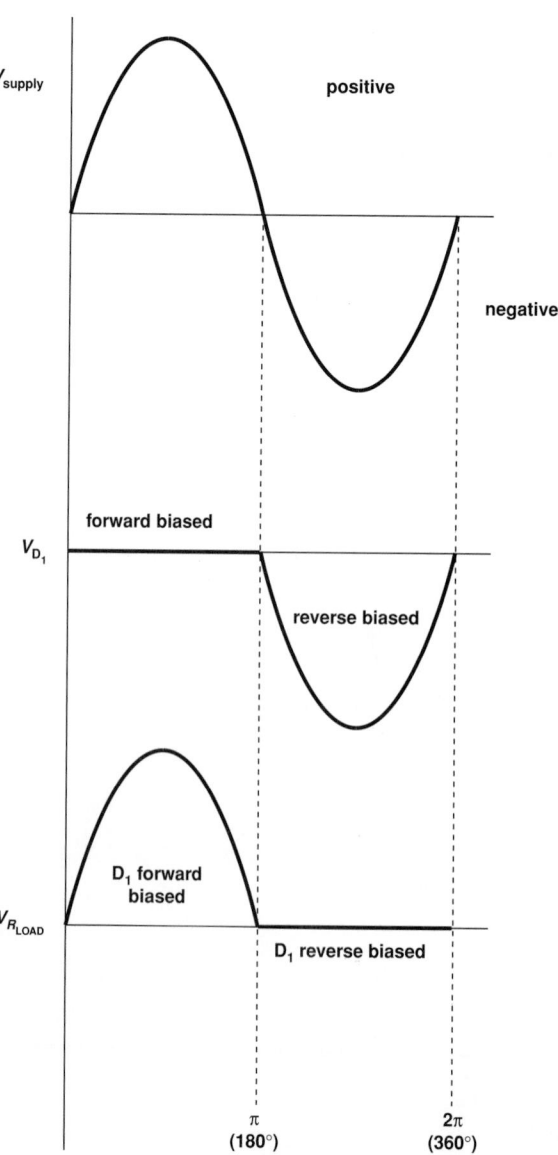

the positive portion of the supply voltage appears across the load resistor, the load voltage is dc. This circuit has converted the ac supply voltage to a dc load voltage. This process is called rectification and the circuit is called a **rectifier**.

RECTIFIER

EXAMPLE 23.1

A 100 Ω load resistor is connected in series with a junction diode and supplied from a 120 V ac source. Determine the load current.

SOLUTION:

a) $V_{\text{Max}} = V_{\text{Supply}} / 0.7071$

$\qquad = 120/0.7071$

$\qquad = 170 \text{ V}$

b) $V_{\text{DC}} = (V_{\text{Max}} - V_{\text{bo}}) \times 0.318$

$\qquad = (170 - 0.7) \times 0.318$

$\qquad = 53.8 \text{ V}$

c) $I_{\text{Load}} = V_{\text{DC}} / R_{\text{Load}}$

$\qquad = 53.8/100$

$\qquad = 0.538 \text{ A}$

23.7 The Bridge Rectifier

Because the dc output voltage of the half-wave rectifier is relatively low, it is has little practical application. The bridge rectifier, the most common of the full-wave rectifiers, produces a higher dc output voltage and is easily adaptable to many applications. For this reason, the bridge rectifier is the most widely used rectifier circuit.

When the ac supply shown in Fig. 23.10 is positive, point A will be positive with respect to point B. The cathode of diode D_1 will be negative with respect to the anode

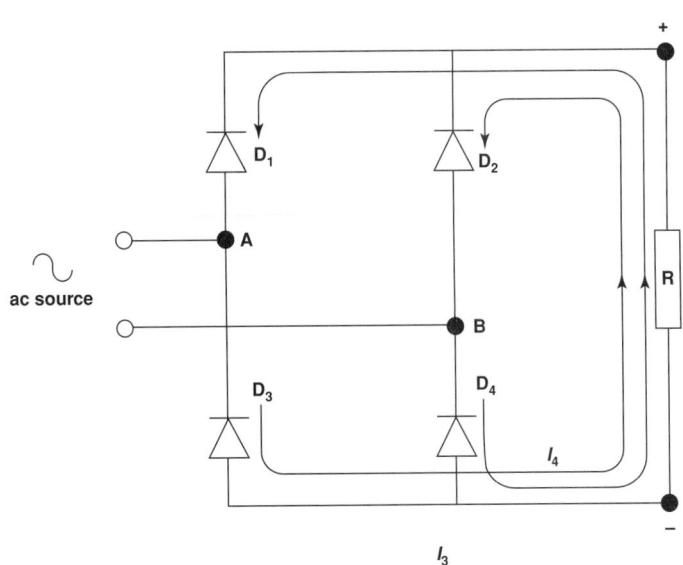

Figure 23.10

A load resistor connected to a bridge rectifier. The bridge rectifier is the most widely used rectifier circuit.

and the anode of diode D_4 will be positive with respect to the cathode. As a result, both diodes will be forward biased. Diodes D_2 and D_3 will be reverse biased. When the voltage exceeds the sum of the two breakover voltages (1.4 V), current (I_4) will flow from point B through diode D_4 to the load and return to the positive terminal of the supply through diode D_1 and point A. When the supply voltage swings negative, point B will be positive with respect to point A and diodes D_2 and D_3 will be forward biased. Diodes D_1 and D_4 will be reverse biased. Again, when the supply voltage exceeds 1.4 V, current (I_3) will flow from point A through diode D_3 to the load resistor and return to point B through diode D_2. In both cases, current flows from the negative terminal of the load resistor to the positive terminal.

The various waveforms for the bridge rectifier are shown in Fig. 23.11. Notice that each pair of diodes (D_1, D_4 and D_2, D_3) is forward biased half the time while the other pair is reverse biased. Because the currents are steered in this way that causes the current always to flow in the same direction through the load, the voltage across the load is always positive.

Figure 23.11

Comparing Fig. 23.11 with Fig. 23.9, it is apparent that the bridge rectifier output has twice the number of pulses of single-phase rectifier. It can be shown mathematically that the output voltage of the bridge rectifier will be double that of the single-phase rectifier. Thus, the output voltage for the bridge rectifier will be 0.637 V_{Max}.

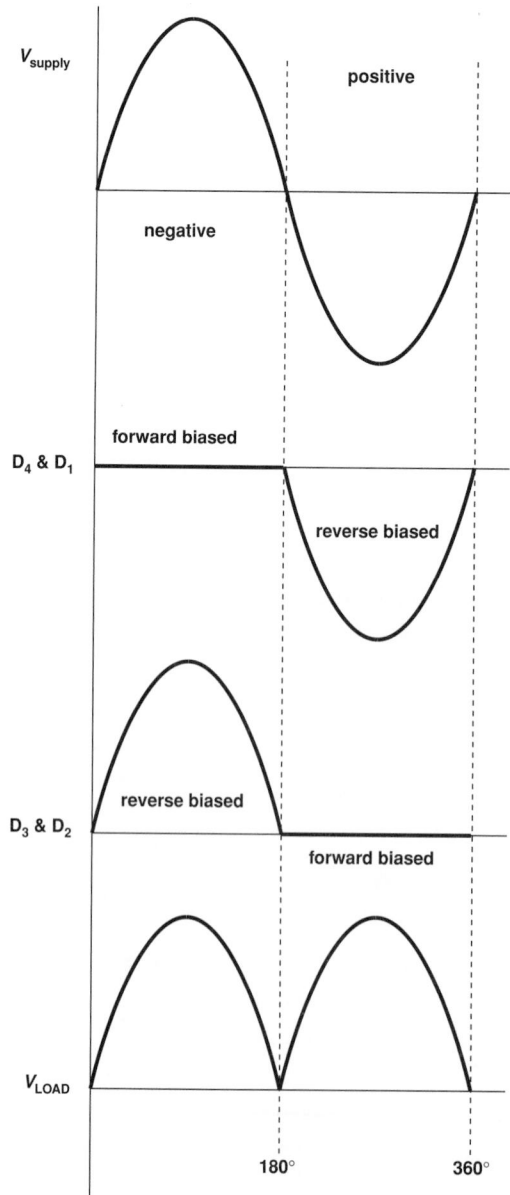

EXAMPLE 23.2

Repeat example 23.1, replacing the half-wave rectifier with a bridge rectifier.

SOLUTION:

a) $V_{max} = V_{supply} / 0.7071$
$$= 120/0.7071$$
$$= 170 \text{ V}$$

b) $V_{dc} = (V_{max} - 2V_{bo}) \times 0.637$
$$= (170 - 1.4) \times 0.637$$
$$= 107.4 \text{ V}$$

c) $I_{load} = V_{dc} / R_{load}$
$$= 107.4/100$$
$$= 1.074 \text{ A}$$

23.8 Construction of the Junction Transistor

Like the junction diode, the junction transistor is made from p-type and n-type semiconductor materials. Unlike the diode, however, the junction transistor is made from three blocks of semiconductor material. These blocks are layered in one of two ways: either as a piece of n-type material sandwiched between two pieces of p-type material (Fig. 23.12(a)) or as a piece of p-type material sandwiched between two pieces of n-type material (Fig. 23.12(b)). The first type is called a PNP transistor and the latter is called an NPN transistor.

Regardless of the type, the centre section of a transistor is called the base (b) and the other two sections are called the emitter (e) and the collector (c). The base region is typically very thin compared to the emitter and collector regions (about 1/150 the thickness). This means that the depletion zones at the base-emitter and base-collector junctions will almost extend across the base region.

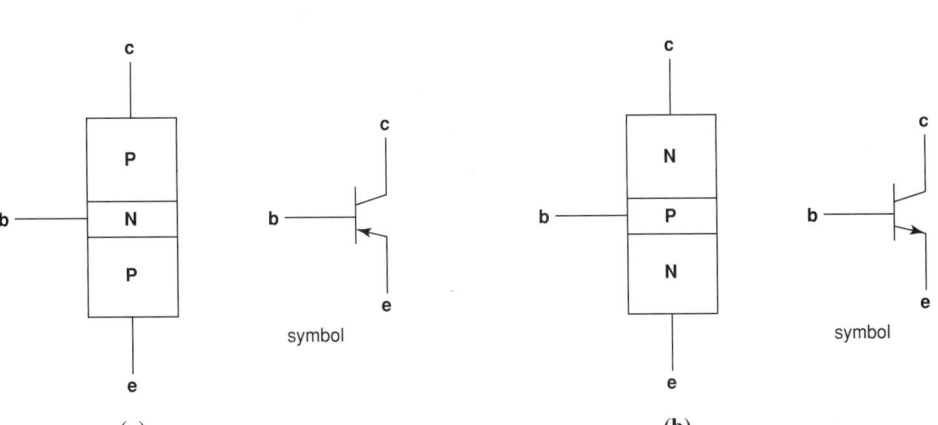

(a)   (b)

Figure 23.12

Transistors are three-layer devices available in two types: (a) the PNP transistor and (b) the NPN transistor. The schematic symbol for the two devices is also shown.

In industrial applications, the NPN transistor is more commonly used than the PNP. Therefore, we will restrict our discussion of transistors to the NPN type.

23.9 Operation of the NPN Transistor

Figure 23.13 shows a properly biased NPN transistor. The base-emitter junction is forward biased by the voltage source V_{bb} and the collector-emitter junction is reverse biased by the voltage source V_{cc}. Because the emitter forms part of the base circuit and part of the collector circuit, this configuration is known as a common emitter connection. The base-emitter circuit is the input and the emitter-collector circuit is the output.

If the switch S1 in Fig. 23.13 is open, the voltage across the base-emitter junction will be less than 0.7 V and no current will flow through the transistor. When switch S_1 is closed, the base-emitter will be forward biased and current will flow just as it

| MAJORITY CARRIERS |

| MINORITY CARRIERS |

would in a diode circuit. Large numbers of electrons, which are **majority carriers** in the emitter region, migrate across the base-emitter junction and become **minority carriers** in the base region. Because the base region is very thin, only a small number of electrons are able to flow out of the base connection to the positive terminal of the base-emitter voltage source. However, minority carriers are not affected by the depletion zone and as a result most of the base region minority carriers (electrons) migrate into the collector region (Fig. 23.14). This means that only a small current will flow in the base circuit and a larger current will flow in the collector circuit. Controlling the small base current allows us to control the much larger collector current.

A transistor is manufactured to carry a specified collector current (I_c) and specific base current (I_b). The emitter current (I_e) will be the sum of these two currents. Because the transistor may be operating at less than the rated current, the rated

Figure 23.13

Biasing for a common emitter circuit configuration using an NPN transistor. The base-emitter circuit is forward biased and the emitter-collector circuit is reverse biased.

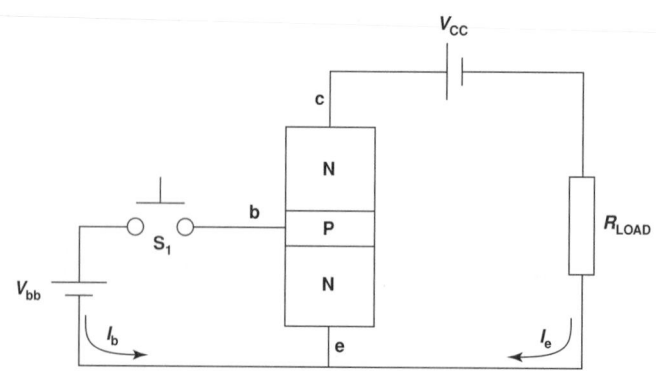

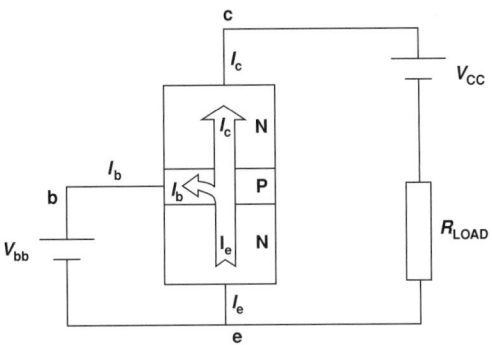

collector current and the ratio of the currents is used to describe the current characteristics of the transistor.

The two current ratios are called alpha (α) and beta (β). Alpha is the ratio of the emitter current to the collector current and is expressed as:

$$\alpha = I_c \, / \, I_e \qquad\qquad \textbf{EQ. 23.1}$$

Typically, α will be 0.98 or higher. As a result, α can usually be considered to be 1.0. This assumption has little effect on the theoretical circuit operation.

The second current ratio, β, is the more important of the two ratios. Beta is the ratio of the base current to the collector current and is expressed as:

$$\beta = I_c \, / \, I_b \qquad\qquad \textbf{EQ. 23.2}$$

Beta can have a wide range of values. Manufacturers' data sheets will show the maximum value of β for a particular transistor. In amplifying transistors, β may be as high as 500, while the same transistor will have a β of 30 for switching applications. For this reason, transistors designed as amplifiers make poor transistor switches and switching transistors make poor amplifiers.

EXAMPLE 23.3

A transistor has a beta of 25 and an alpha of 0.96. If the maximum collector current is 5.0 A, find (a) I_b and (b) I_e.

SOLUTION:

a) $I_b = I_c \, / \, \beta$
    $= 5.0 \text{ A}/25$
    $= 200 \text{ mA}$

b) $I_e = I_c \, / \, \alpha$
    $= 5.0 \, / \, 0.96$
    $= 5.2 \text{ A}$

23.10 The Transistor Characteristic Curve

The characteristic curve is a graphic means of depicting transistor behaviour at various operating base current levels. The transistor output characteristic curve for a common-emitter configuration as shown in Fig. 23.15 has three distinct regions: the **saturation region**, the active region, and the cut-off region.

SATURATION REGION

A typical characteristic curve has on the horizontal or x-axis the maximum collector-emitter voltage. For a given circuit, this value equals V_{cc}. The vertical or y-axis represents the collector current. A number of base currents are plotted against these two axes. The ratio between the base and collector currents represents β for the transistor. It is important to note that the collector current is controlled by the base current, not by the collector-emitter voltage.

CUT-OFF REGION

The **cut-off region**, below the $I_b = 0$ line, shows that the collector current is greater than 0. In fact, I_c would be in the microampere or nanoampere range. This current represents very small surface and leakage currents within the transistor. For all practical purposes the collector current would equal 0 A.

To the left of the base current curves is the saturation region. This region represents the area of maximum current flow with minimum V_{CE}.

The balance of the characteristic curve is called the active region. Transistor amplifiers operate in this region.

The operation of a specific transistor circuit can be shown on the characteristic curve by drawing a load line. The load line is constructed by first defining the end-points. On the x-axis, the end-point is defined as V_{cc} since this represents the maximum voltage that can occur between the collector and emitter of the transistor. The maximum current that can flow in the circuit can be found using Ohm's law:

$$I_{Max} = V_{cc} / R_{Load}$$

This value is plotted as the second end-point on the characteristic curve y-axis. Drawing a straight line between these two points defines the load line for the circuit. The operating point (Q point) for the circuit is represented by the point where I_C, V_{CE}, and I_B intersect. This operating point will move back and forth along the load line as the base current changes.

Figure 23.15

A typical output characteristic curve for an NPN transistor showing the saturation region, the active region, and the cut-off region.

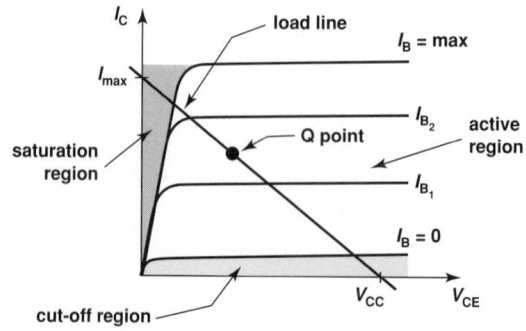

23.11 The Transistor as a Switch

Transistors are commonly used as switching devices in industrial applications. In order to accomplish this task, the transistor must be able to quickly move between the cut-off and saturation regions of the output characteristic curve.

In the cut-off region, the transistor behaves like an open switch. The collector-to-emitter voltage (V_{CE}) will equal the supply voltage (V_{CC}) and the collector current (I_C) will be 0 A. In the saturation region, the transistor behaves like a closed switch. V_{CE} will typically be less than 0.1 V and I_C will equal the load current. Ideally, the transistor will develop little heat in either cut-off or saturation since the product of I_C and V_{CE} will be close to zero.

As the transistor operating point shifts along the load line from cut-off to saturation or vice versa, it must pass through the active region. While in the active region, both V_{CE} and I_C will be greater than zero. Consequently, the power dissipated by the transistor will be highest when the transistor is passing through this region. The time required to move through the active region is the transistor's switching speed. Switching speed is a characteristic set during the manufacturing process. The shorter the switching time, the faster the transistor will be able to change from cut-off to saturation.

Figure 23.16 shows a transistor switching a resistive load. The transistor collector current must at least equal the load current and the base current must be sufficient to saturate the transistor. When the switch S_1 is open, the base current will be 0 A and the transistor will be cut off ($I_C = I_b \times \beta$). When switch S_1 is closed, a base current will flow. If the base current is sufficient, the transistor will saturate. The resistor, R_{base}, limits the base current. To find the value of R_{base}, we first find the base current:

$$I_b = I_C / \beta$$

Then we can find R_{base}:

$$R_{base} = (V_{cc} - V_{be}) / I_b$$
$$= (V_{cc} - 0.7 \text{ V}) / I_b$$

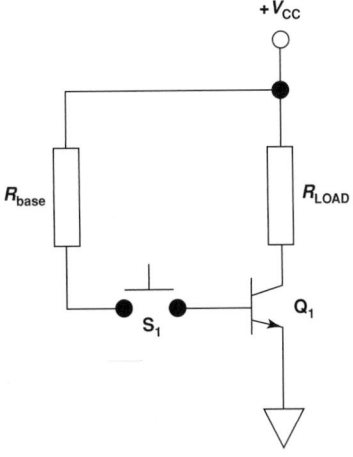

Figure 23.16

A transistor switching circuit supplied from a single voltage source. The switch S_1 controls the base current in this circuit.

EXAMPLE 23.4

A 5 A 12 V resistive load is to be controlled by a 7.5 A NPN transistor with a β of 25. Determine the value of R_{base}.

SOLUTION:

a) $I_b = I_C / \beta$

$= 5\ A / 25$

$= 0.2\ A$

b) $R_{base} = (V_{cc} - V_{be}) / I_b$

$= (12\ V - 0.7) / 0.2\ A$

$= 11.3\ V / 0.2\ A$

$= 56.5\ \Omega$

A voltage pulse from an external source can also supply the base current for a transistor switching circuit. The pulse could be supplied from a piece of field equipment or from another electronic circuit. Although the circuit will look a little different (Fig. 23.17), its operation will be the same as the circuit shown in Fig. 23.16.

So far we have examined switching circuits controlling resistive loads. Transistor switches can also be used to control inductive loads, such as relay coils and dc motors. Whenever inductive devices are turned off, the decaying magnetic fields will generate a voltage opposite in polarity to the source voltage, and it may be high enough in magnitude to destroy the controlling transistor. Connecting a diode across the inductive device, as shown in Fig. 23.18, can eliminate the problem. This diode is known as a freewheeling diode (FWD). Notice that the anode of the diode is connected to the positive terminal of the supply voltage. When the relay is energized, the diode will be reverse biased and therefore the current (I_F) will be 0 A. When the inductive device is turned off, the energy generated by the collapsing magnetic fields will be discharged through the FWD.

Although transistor switching circuits are widely used in industrial applications, they suffer from a number of limitations. Power transistors are limited to approximately 1200 A collector current. While this may sound like a very large current, other semiconductor devices are easily available with current ratings in excess of 3500 A.

Figure 23.17

A transistor switching circuit with the base current supplied from an external source.

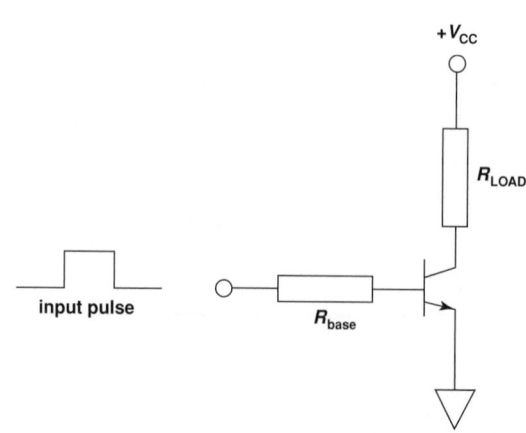

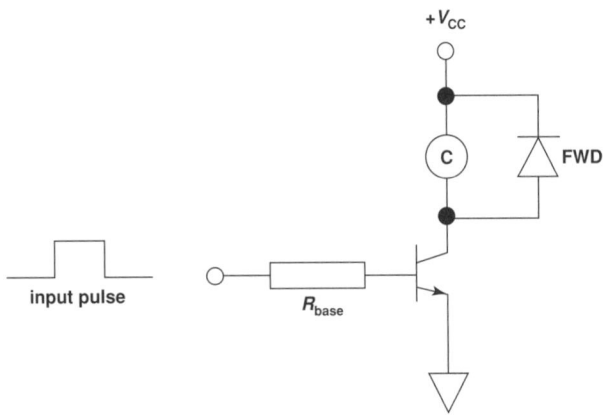

Figure 23.18

A transistor switching circuit controlling an inductive load. The freewheeling diode (FWD) discharges the inductive energy generated when the coil is turned off.

Because switching transistors have a relatively low β, they require a high base current in order to saturate the transistor and this base current must be maintained throughout the conduction period.

23.12 The Silicon Controlled Rectifier (SCR)

Silicon controlled rectifiers (SCRs) are four-layer P-N-P-N semiconductor devices (Fig. 23.19) belonging to a family of devices known as **thyristors**. SCRs have a number of advantages over switching transistors. They are available in larger current capacities than transistors and they can be turned on with a short duration control pulse. Their main disadvantage is that they must be forced to turn off in direct current applications.

THYRISTORS

The operation of the SCR is best shown using a two-transistor equivalent circuit. The four-layer device shown in Fig. 23.19 can be separated into two transistors as shown in Fig. 23.20(a). Re-drawing the transistors using standard symbols yields the circuit shown in Fig. 23.20(b). Note that the collector of each transistor is connected to the base of the other. The SCR gate is connected to the base of Q_1.

If a positive voltage is applied across the base-emitter junction of Q_1, the transistor will saturate and current will flow through the emitter-collector circuit to the base-emitter junction of Q_2. This causes Q_2 to saturate. The collector current of Q_2 in turn

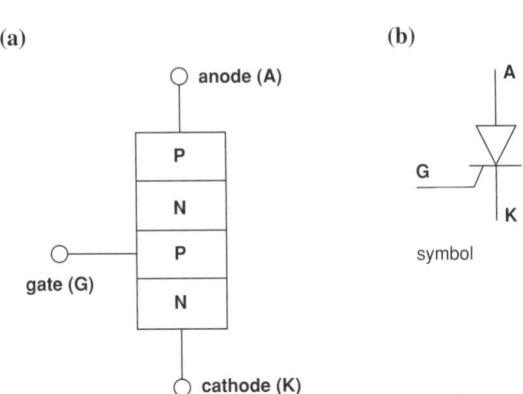

Figure 23.19

The SCR is a four-layer semiconductor device with three terminals: anode, cathode, and gate. The schematic symbol for the SCR is shown in (b).

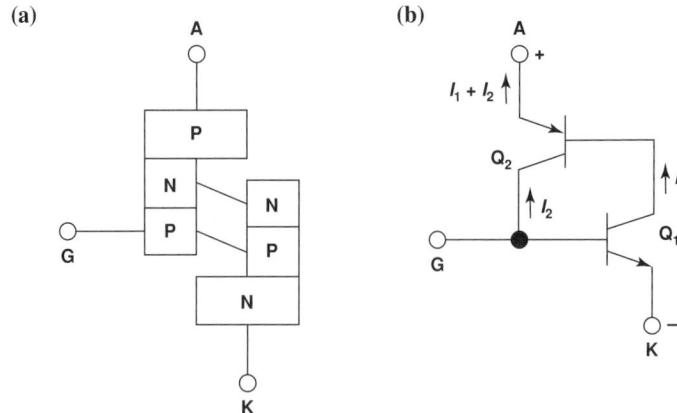

maintains the base-emitter current of Q_1, allowing the positive voltage to be removed
from the gate terminal of the circuit. Current flow from the cathode to anode of the
circuit is now maintained. It is important to note that removing the voltage source
from the gate connection will not cause Q_1 to turn off. The only way this circuit can
be turned off is to interrupt the collector current of one of the transistors.

23.13 The SCR Characteristic Curve

The operating characteristics of a typical SCR are shown in Fig. 23.21. The reverse
characteristics are similar to those of the junction diode (Fig. 23.7). If the breakdown voltage ($V_{breakdown}$) is exceeded, the SCR will likely fail due to excess heat
buildup resulting from high current. The forward characteristics, though similar to
a junction diode, show the conditions required to turn the device on.

If the anode to cathode voltage (V_{A-K}) is gradually increased, the SCR will turn on
when the breakover voltage (V_{bo}) is reached. A gate pulse is not required. Using a
gate pulse to turn on the device reduces V_{bo}, causing the SCR to turn on at a voltage lower than V_{A-K}. In Fig. 23.21, the lowest value of V_{A-K} is shown as the "ideal gate
pulse." Once the SCR turns on, it will remain in conduction so long as the forward
current (I_F) is greater than the holding current (I_H). The only way the SCR can be
turned off is to cause I_F to be less than I_H.

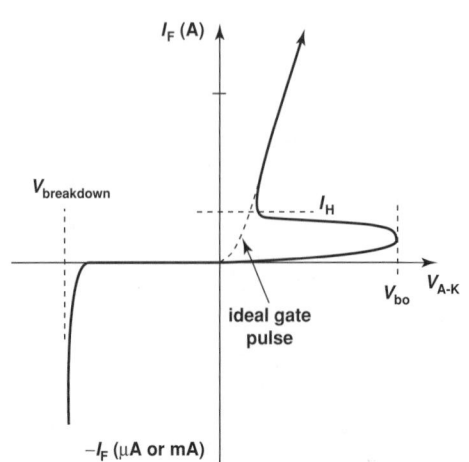

23.14 SCR Static Control

The process of controlling an SCR is known as commutation. An SCR must be commutated on and off.

An SCR can be turned on using either a gate pulse supplied from some form of pulse-generating circuit or by a static switching circuit using pushbuttons. In either case, the control circuit must be able to supply enough gate current to cause the SCR to conduct. A **static switching circuit** is shown in Fig. 23.22. Closing the pushbutton S_1 causes current to flow in the gate circuit, commutating the SCR on. The resistor (R_G) limits the gate current to the value specified by the manufacturer.

To turn off an SCR, the current flowing through the SCR must be less than the holding current. The circuit in Fig. 23.23 shows two pushbuttons (S_2 and S_3) in addition to the on pushbutton (S_1). Pressing pushbutton S_2 interrupts the circuit current, causing the forward current to drop to zero. Since 0 A will be less than the holding current, the SCR commutates off and remains off until the pushbutton S_1 is again pressed. Pressing pushbutton S_3 causes the load current to flow around the SCR. Again, this causes the forward current to drop below the holding current and the SCR to commutate off. As before, the SCR will remain in the off state until S_1 is pushed. Practically, static switching methods have limited application because the off pushbuttons (S_2 and S_3) must carry the full load current.

In addition to the static switching methods described, a variety of electronic control systems are possible. The electronic control systems cause a short duration

STATIC SWITCHING
CIRCUIT

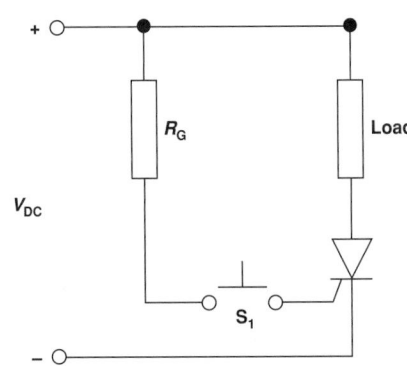

Figure 23.22

A static switching circuit can be used to turn an SCR on. Closing pushbutton S1 generates the gate pulse.

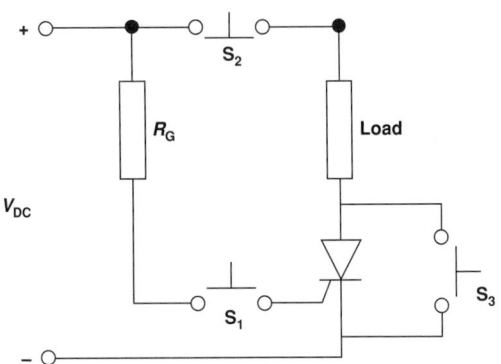

Figure 23.23

A complete static switching circuit showing an on switch (S_1) and two possible off buttons (S_2 and S_3).

current to flow opposite to SCR forward current. The vector sum of these two currents results in a current that is less than the holding current, allowing the SCR to commutate off.

23.15 Controlling SCRs with Pulse Generators

Although SCRs are unidirectional devices, like diodes and transistors, they can be — and are — widely used in many ac control applications.

In Chapter 8, we learned that an ac sinewave crosses the reference axis at 180° and 360°, and that one-half the waveform will be positive and the other will be negative. At each of the crossing points, a current waveform will have a value of zero amperes. In an SCR circuit, it is common to assume that the positive portion of the sinewave will cause the SCR anode to be positive and the cathode to be negative.

The circuit in Fig. 23.24(a) shows an SCR in series with a resistive load and supplied from an ac source. The gate current is supplied from the same source and it is limited by the resistor R_G. When the sinewave is positive, the anode of the SCR will be

Figure 23.24

(a) An SCR circuit with a continuous gate current and (b) the waveforms associated with the circuit. Compare these waveforms with those in Fig. 23.9.

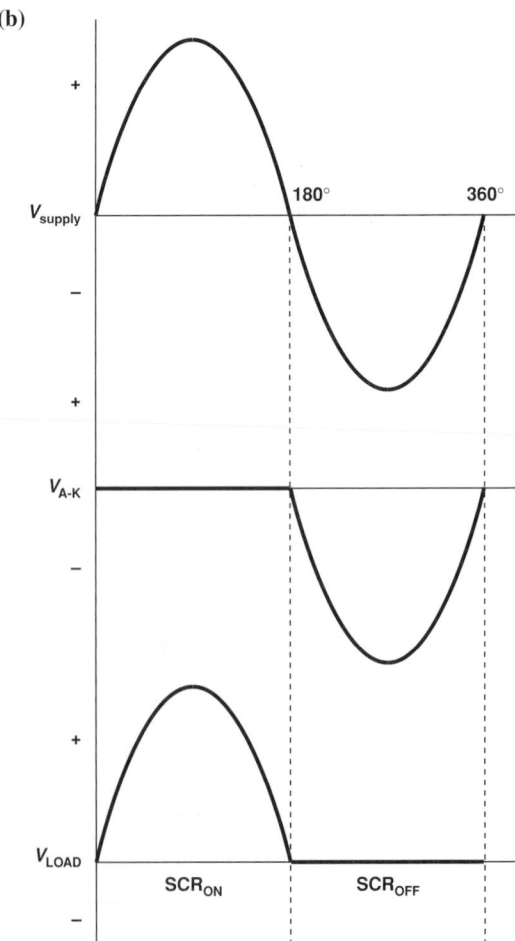

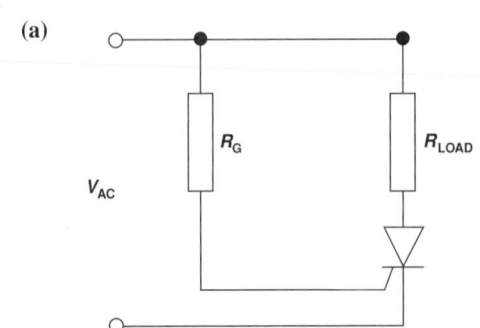

positive with respect to the anode and the positive gate current will cause the SCR to commutate on at a point very close to 0°. The SCR will continue to conduct until the load current drops below the holding current. This will occur very close to 180°. As the sinewave changes to the negative side of the reference axis, the SCR anode will be negative with respect to the cathode. The gate current will also be negative. As a result, the SCR will not turn on and no current flows in the circuit. The waveforms associated with this circuit are shown in Fig. 23.23(b). Comparing these waveforms with those for the half-wave rectifier waveforms in Fig. 23.9, we find they are virtually identical. There is little advantage in using an SCR as a simple rectifier. But by controlling the timing of the gate pulse, the voltage across the load can be varied — a clear advantage over the diode rectifier.

The key to controlling the operation of an SCR is controlling the gate current. Since at 60 Hz an ac waveform is only positive for 8 ms, practical control of the gate current is not possible using pushbuttons. A variety of electronic circuits can be used to generate gate pulses capable of commutating an SCR on during this relatively short time period. Since the operation of such circuits is beyond the scope of this text, Fig. 23.25 provides a summary showing the pulse-generating circuit as a block diagram with a number of inputs and outputs. The two connections to the ac source supply power to the block and the output is connected to the SCR gate terminal. A variable resistor connected to the block allows the operator to vary the time between gate pulses.

Because the pulse generator is supplied from the same ac source as the load, the voltage across the generator will be zero each time the ac sinewave crosses the reference axis. This means that the pulse generator will always begin a new timing cycle at 0°. When this condition is met, the circuit is said to be "line synchronized." As a result of **line synchronization**, the first voltage pulse will always occur at the same time with respect to 0° on the sinewave (Fig. 23.26).

LINE SYNCHRONIZATION

In Fig. 23.26 (a) ii and (b) ii show a stream of gate pulses separated by time (*t*). Only the position of the first pulse is significant, because the first pulse will commutate the SCR on. Since it is the first pulse that turns on the SCR, the remaining pulses have no effect. The SCR behaves like an open switch until the first gate pulse commutates it on; as a result, a portion of the positive source voltage appears across

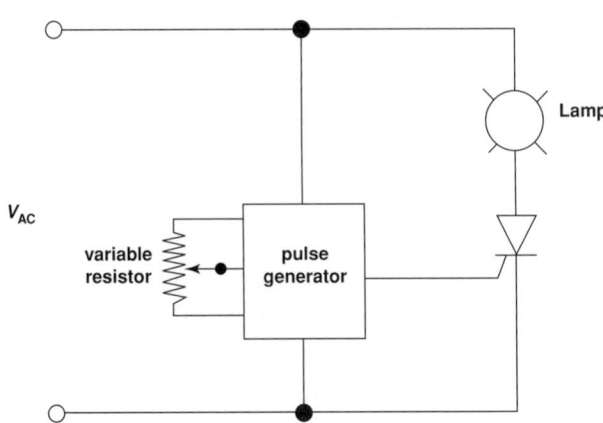

Figure 23.25

SCR control of a lamp using an electronic pulse generator to gate the SCR. Changing the variable resistor changes the time between the gate pulses. Waveforms for this circuit are shown in Fig. 23.26.

▼ **Figure 23.26**

Waveforms associated with a line synchronized circuit
shown in Fig. 23.25: (a) waveforms resulting from a short
timing period and (b) waveforms resulting from a longer
timing period.

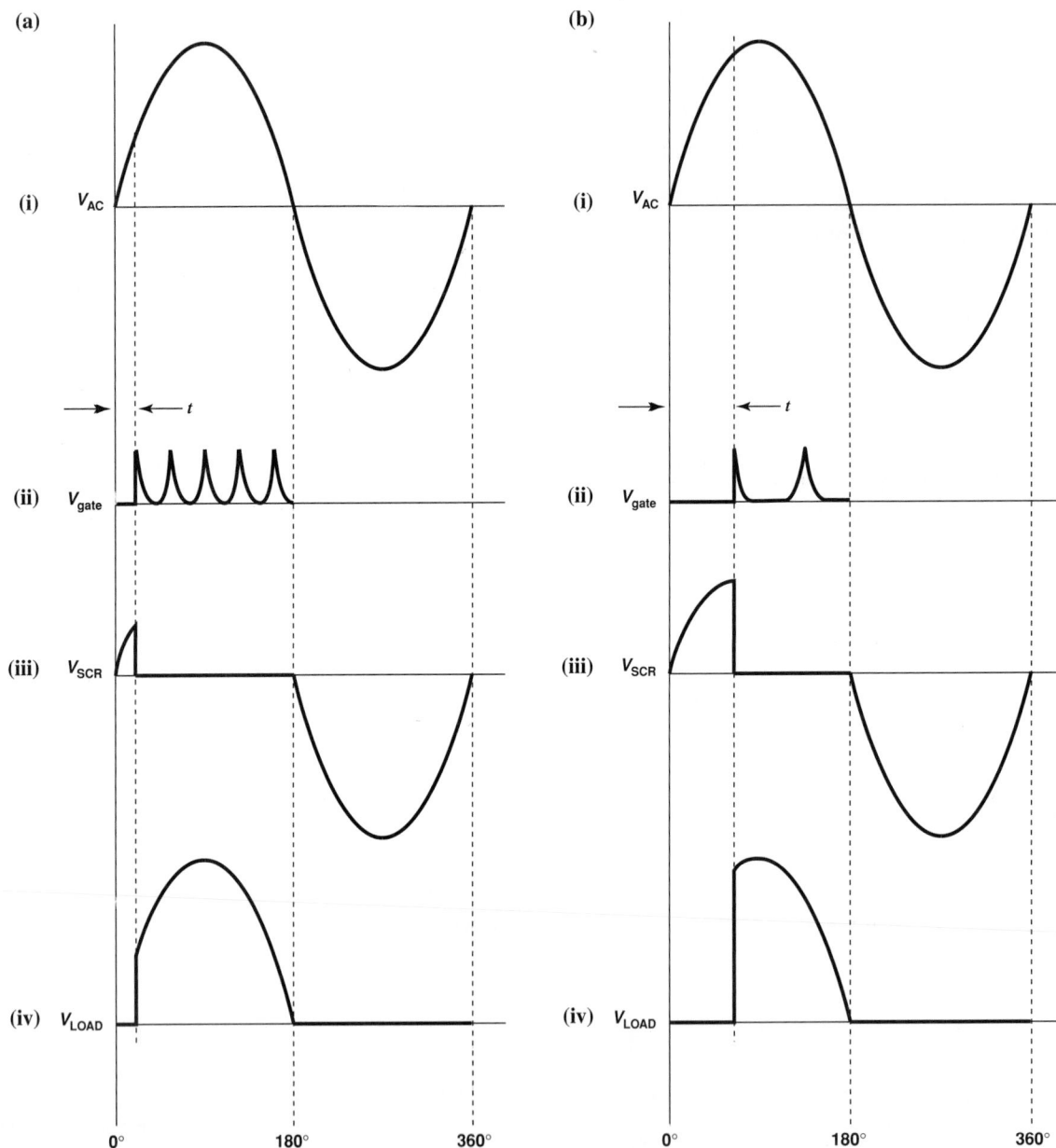

the SCR (Fig. 23.26 (a) iii and (b) iii). The voltage across the load will be zero whenever the SCR is off (Fig. 23.26 (a) iv and (b) iv). At the instant the SCR turns on, the
voltage across the SCR drops to zero and the voltage across the load rises to the
source value. By changing the setting of the variable resistor, the SCR can be turned
on at almost any point between 0° and 180°.

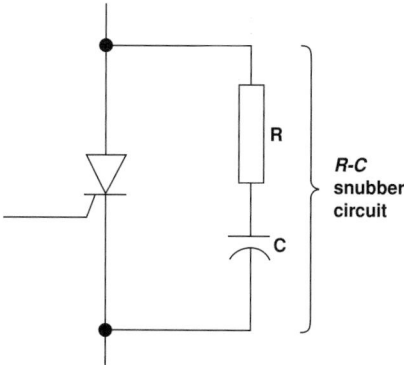

Figure 23.27

Accidental or nuisance turn-on
of an SCR can be minimized
by using a snubber circuit. A
snubber is an *R-C* circuit connected across the anode and
cathode of an SCR.

23.16 Snubber Circuits

Although SCRs are normally turned on using a gate pulse, they are sensitive to the
rate at which the anode-to-cathode voltage changes. This rate of voltage change is
known as dv/dt and this is one of the characteristics given by the device manufacturer. If the off-state dv/dt rating is exceeded, the SCR may turn on even though no
gate pulse is present. Should the SCR turn on under these conditions, it is unlikely
that the device will be damaged. It may simply be a nuisance or may result in the
faulty operation of equipment. The probability of nuisance turn on can be mini-
mized by using an SCR with a higher dv/dt rating or by using a **snubber circuit**. •———— | **SNUBBER CIRCUIT.** |

A snubber circuit (Fig. 23.27) is a series *R-C* circuit connected across the anode and
cathode of an SCR. The *R-C* circuit limits the rate at which the voltage across the SCR
is changing. Sizing of the components is often determined by experience and exper-
imentation, but many SCR manufacturers supply design techniques for snubbers.

23.17 Summary

Upon completion of this chapter you should have learned that:

- There are two types of semiconductor materials: n-type and p-type. N- type material has an excess of electrons and p-type material has an excess of positive
  charges called holes.

- When p-type and n-type material are joined, a narrow region depleted of electrical charge, the depletion zone, is formed.

- When a p-n junction is forward biased, a positive voltage is connected to the
  p-type material and the negative terminal is connected to the n-type material, the
  depletion zone narrows, and current is able to pass through the depletion zone.

- When a p-n junction is reverse biased, the negative terminal of the voltage source
  is connected to the p-type material and the positive terminal is connected to the
  n-type material, the depletion zone widens, and current cannot pass through the
  depletion zone.

- Junction diodes are p-n junctions designed with a specific set of characteristics.
  They are commonly used in rectifiers to convert ac to dc.

- A junction transistor is a three-layer device that can be either NPN or PNP. Transistors allow a small input current to control a larger output current.

- The silicon controlled rectifier (SCR) is a four-layer device that conducts current when a gate current is applied.

- The SCR can be controlled using either static switching circuits or gate pulse generating circuits.

Key Terms

BREAKOVER VOLTAGE (V_{bo}): The voltage level required to cause a forward biased p-n junction to conduct current. For silicon material, the breakover voltage is 0.7 V.

CUT-OFF REGION: On a transistor characteristic curve, the cut-off region is the area below the line where the base current is 0 A. A transistor does not conduct current in this region.

DEPLETION ZONE: An area depleted of electrical charge that forms about a p-n junction.

HOLES: A space that a bonding electron could occupy in the outermost orbit of a semiconductor material. Holes are considered positive charges.

JUNCTION: A semiconductor structure formed when a block of p-type material is brought into contact with a block of n-type material.

LINE SYNCHRONIZATION: A timing circuit that uses 0° of the supply voltage sinewave as a timing reference is line synchronized.

MAJORITY CARRIERS: In n-type material, electrons are majority carriers. In p-type material, majority carriers are the holes. In the p-n junction, the depletion zone limits the movement of majority carriers.

MINORITY CARRIERS: In n-type material, holes are minority carriers. In p-type material, electrons are minority carriers. Minority carriers are not affected by the depletion zone in a p-n junction.

N-TYPE MATERIAL: A semiconductor material with an excess of electrons.

PEAK INVERSE VOLTAGE (*PIV*): The maximum reverse voltage that a PN junction can withstand without damage.

P-TYPE MATERIAL: A semiconductor material with an excess of positive charges.

RECTIFIER: A circuit used to convert ac to dc.

SATURATION REGION: On a transistor output characteristic curve, the saturation regions to the left of the base current curve. In this region, the transistor is conducting maximum current.

SEMICONDUCTORS: Materials that under some conditions behave as insulators and under other conditions behave as conductors. Silicon is a commonly used example of a semiconductor.

SNUBBER CIRCUIT: A series R-C circuit used to limit dv/dt of an SCR circuit.

STATIC SWITCHING CIRCUIT: A type of control circuit using only switches and resistors. Static switching circuits are one means of commutating an SCR on and off.

THYRISTORS: A family of semiconductors made with four layers of P-N material. The SCR is a thyristor.

Test Your Knowledge

23.1   All semiconductor material is either p-type or n-type.

true _____   false _____

23.2   The barrier potential for a p-n junction depends on the current of the device.

true _____   false _____

23.3   In p-type material, holes are the majority carriers and electrons are the minority carriers.

true _____   false _____

23.4   A depletion zone forms anytime p-type and n-type materials are brought into direct electrical contact.

true _____   false _____

23.5   Rectifiers are electronic circuits used to increase the magnitude of a current.

true _____   false _____

23.6   When a transistor is in saturation, the current is minimal and the voltage across the emitter to collector is maximum.

true _____   false _____

23.7   Thyristors comprise a semiconductor family with four layers of PN material.

true _____   false _____

23.8   An SCR can be turned off by removing the gate potential.

true _____   false _____

23.9   Static switching of an SCR uses a static charge to gate the SCR on.

true _____   false _____

23.10   A snubber circuit is used to prevent an SCR turning on due to dv/dt.

true _____   false _____

Questions and Problems

23.11   A diode is connected in series with a resistive load. If the circuit is supplied by an ac sinewave, sketch the waveforms across each of the circuit components.

23.12   A bridge rectifier is supplied from a 208 V 60 Hz source. The load is a 25 Ω resistor. Calculate the load current.

23.13   A transistor has an emitter current of 0.5 A and a collector current of 0.48 A. Calculate α and β for the circuit.

23.14   A transistor used as a switch has a β of 25. If the collector current is 2.5 A, calculate the base current required to saturate the transistor.

23.15   Design a transistor switch to control a 12 V, 5 A resistive load. Beta for the transistor is 22; the base circuit is supplied from the dc source and is controlled by a pushbutton.

23.16   An SCR used to control a 10 Ω load is supplied from a 120 V, 60 Hz ac source. Sketch the waveforms for the circuit if the SCR turns on at 30°.

23.17   Repeat Problem 23.16 if the SCR turns on at 135°.

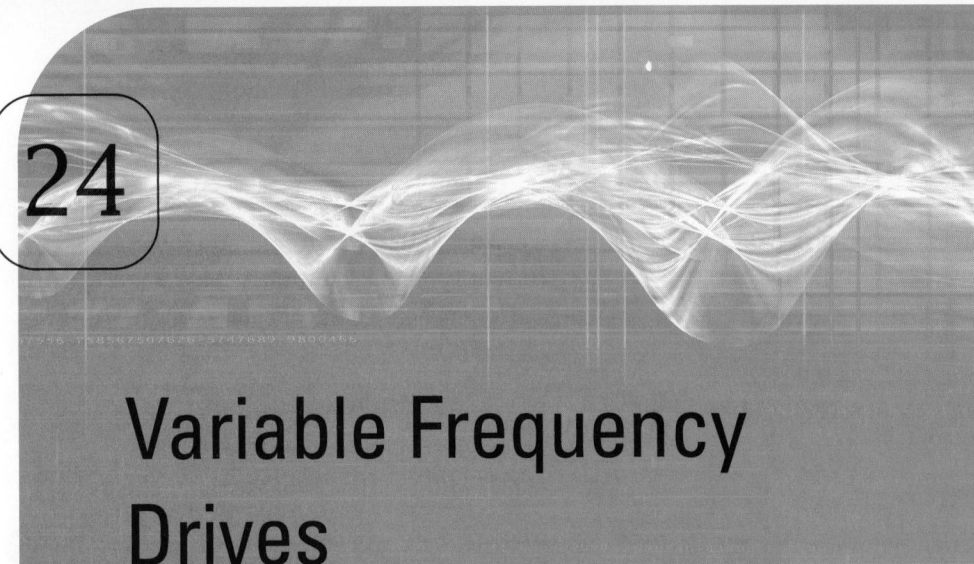

24 Variable Frequency Drives

LEARNING OBJECTIVES

Upon completion of this chapter you will be able to:

- Explain the operation of half-wave three-phase controlled and uncontrolled rectifiers

- Explain the operation of six-step and pulse width modulation type inverters

- Describe the operation of a variable voltage inverter (VVI) drive

- Describe the operation of a pulse width modulation (PWM) drive

- Describe the operation of a flux vector drive (FVD)

- Explain the difference between a current source inverter (CSI) and a voltage source inverter (VSI)

- Describe the effect of operating a standard three-phase squirrel cage induction motor on a non-sinusoidal source

24.1 Power Electronics

Power electronics is the branch of electronics that deals with the control of industrial loads. Single-phase systems used in light industrial and home electronics are usually

POWER ELECTRONICS

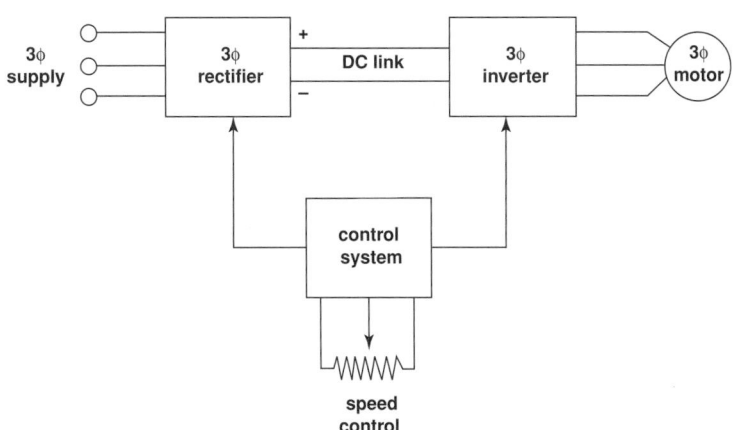

Figure 24.1

A block diagram of a typical
three-phase VFD showing
six components typical of a
VFD: (a) supply; (b) rectifier;
(c) dc link; (d) three-phase
inverter; (e) motor load.

limited to power ratings of less than 5000 watts. Power electronic systems are usually three-phase systems capable of controlling loads up to the megawatt range. Examples of power electronic systems include the control of electric motors up to 20 000 hp, standby power systems capable of supplying several hundred kilowatts of power, and the control and distribution of electric power in the megawatt range.

One of the most common applications for power electronics is the control of three-phase squirrel-cage induction motors. The most common electronic motor control method is the **variable frequency drive (VFD).** A typical VFD consists of six components (Fig. 24.1):

1. A single-phase or three-phase ac source.

2. A rectifier that converts the ac supply to a dc output.

3. A dc link that connects the rectifier output to the input of the **inverter.**

4. An inverter that converts the dc supplied by the rectifier to an ac supply at a new frequency.

5. A control system that generates the necessary pulses used to control the firing of the semiconductor control devices such as SCRs and power transistors.

6. A controlled three-phase ac load such as a motor.

| VARIABLE FREQUENCY DRIVE (VFD) |
| INVERTER |

24.2 Half-Wave Three-Phase Rectifier

The half-wave three-phase rectifier is the simplest and least used of the polyphase rectifiers. These systems require large transformers for a given load size and they have relatively high ripple voltages.

This system normally includes a three-phase delta-wye transformer with each secondary phase terminal connected to the anode of a diode. The cathode of each diode is connected to a common output bus. The load is connected between the common bus and the neutral point of the transformer secondary (Fig. 24.2).

Figure 24.2

A ha'f-wave 3∅ rectifier with
a resistive load.

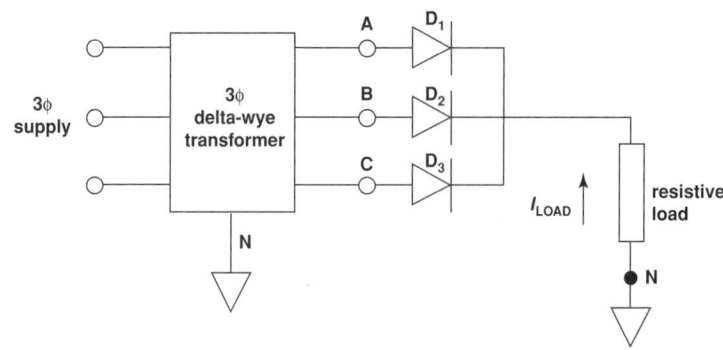

The diode connected to phase A will conduct whenever the anode is positive with respect to the cathode. This will occur when the phase A voltage is more positive than either of phases B or C. The same will happen to the diodes connected to phases B and C. The diode with the highest instantaneous anode-to-cathode voltage will supply current to the load. Since each phase has the highest instantaneous voltage for 120° or 1/3 of the total time, each of the rectifier diodes will supply 1/3 of the total load current. The voltage waveform for phase A will peak at 90° and the load voltage pulse will be symmetric about the peak. Therefore, the phase A load voltage will be highest at 90° ± 60°, which is 30° to 150°. This results in a load voltage characterized by three pulses (Fig. 24.3(b)). For this reason, such rectifiers are often referred to as three-pulse circuits.

The load voltage waveform shown in Fig. 24.3(b) contains a dc component and a ripple component. The ripple component is the sinusoidal portion of the input waveform between 30° and 150°. From these two components, two voltage values can be defined for any unfiltered rectifier: the dc voltage and RMS voltage, which includes the dc component plus the RMS of the ripple component. The dc output voltage will be 0.827 of the peak input voltage and the RMS voltage will be 0.84 of the peak input voltage. With a resistive load, these constants can be used to determine the dc and RMS currents using Ohm's law.

For the 120° during which a diode is conducting, $V_{A\text{-}K}$ will be 0 V (the voltage drop across the diode being negligible in circuits where the peak voltage is more than a few volts). Outside this period, $V_{A\text{-}K}$ will be the difference between the instantaneous voltage of phase A and the instantaneous voltage of the dc bus. For the period between 150° and 270°, the voltage across D_1 will be the line voltage A-B. Between 270° and 390°, the voltage across D_1 will be the voltage between phases A and C. The voltage across diode D_1 is shown in Fig. 24.3(c). Note in the figure that the negative peak of the reverse voltage is shifted 30° from the peak of the load voltage. This shift occurs because the load voltage is a phase voltage, but when the diode is reverse biased, $V_{A\text{-}K}$ is a line voltage. Each of the diodes in this rectifier circuit must be able to withstand this reverse voltage, which is the peak line-to-line voltage. Therefore the minimum *PIV* for the diodes will be:

EQ. 24.1 $PIV = \sqrt{3}\ V_{PK}$

(a)

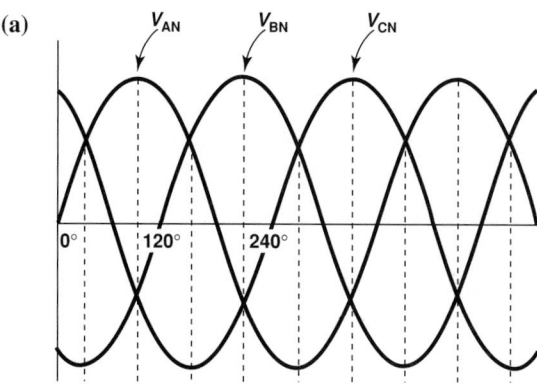

(b)

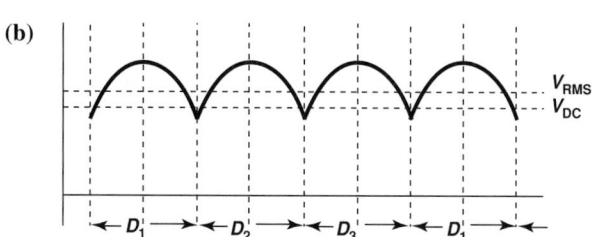

(c)

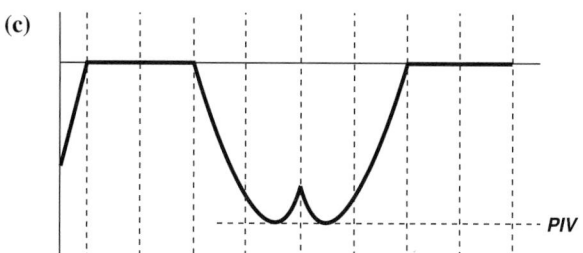

(d)

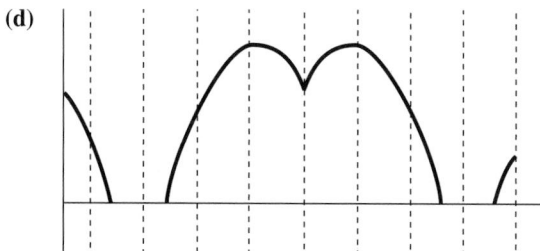

(e)

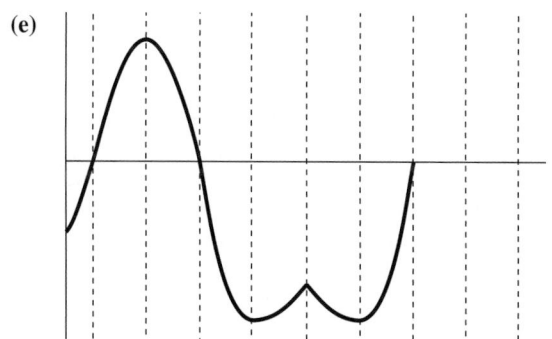

Figure 24.3

The voltage waveforms for the half-wave rectifier in Fig. 24.1: (a) V_{Supply}; (b) V_{Load}; (c) V_{Diode}; (d) V_{Load} with D_1 open-circuited; (e) V_{Diode} when D_1 is open-circuited.

EXAMPLE 24.1

A three-phase half-wave rectifier circuit is supplied from a 120/208 V 3-phase, 60 Hz source. If the load is a 24 Ω resistor, determine:

1   RMS current of the load.
2. RMS current through each of the diodes.
3. Dc power of the load.
4. Minimum *PIV* rating for the diode.

SOLUTION:

1. $I_{RMS} = \dfrac{V_{RMS}}{R}$

    $= \dfrac{\sqrt{2} \times 120 \times 0.84}{25} = \dfrac{\sqrt{2} \times 120 \times 0.84}{25}$

    $= \dfrac{142.6}{25}$

    $= 5.70 \text{ A}$

2. Each of the diodes must carry one current pulse or 1/3 the total current, therefore:

    $I_{Diode} = \dfrac{I_{RMS}}{3}$

    $= \dfrac{5.70}{3}$

    $= 1.9 \text{ A}$

3. $P_{LOAD} = \dfrac{V^2{}_{DC}}{R}$

    $= \dfrac{(\sqrt{2} \times 120 \times 0.827)^2}{25}$

    $= \dfrac{140.3^2}{25}$

    $= 787 \text{ W}$

4. $PIV = \sqrt{3} \; V_{PK}$

    $= 1.73 \times (120 \times 1.414)$

    $= 1.73 \times 170$

    $= 294 \text{ V}$

24.3 Full-Wave Three-Phase Rectifier

The three-phase full-wave bridge rectifier is the most commonly used of all the polyphase rectifiers. Typically, the supply transformer is a delta-wye configuration and does not have any special features. The rectifiers are connected in bridge fashion (Fig. 24.4), similar to the single-phase bridge. The cathodes of the upper diode bank are connected to the positive dc output bus, while the anodes of the lower bank are connected to the negative dc bus. The output terminals of the wye-

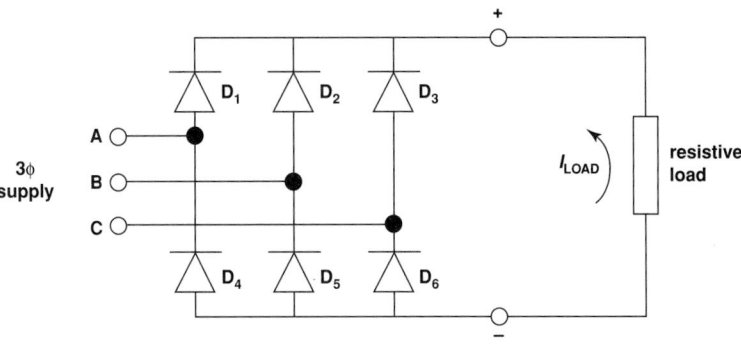

Figure 24.4

A full-wave 3∅ rectifier with a resistive load.

connected supply transformer are connected to the common anode/cathode junction joining the upper and lower diode banks. The load is connected across the negative and positive output buses.

Sixty degrees after phase A becomes positive, diode D_1 will be forward biased because the anode is positive with respect to the cathode. At this time current will flow through diode D_1, through the load, and return to the source that is most negative. This means that for the first 30° of the conduction period, current returns to phase B through diode D_5 (Fig. 24.5(a)). For the second 30° portion of the conduction period, current returns to phase C through diode D_6. A similar pattern of conduction will occur in phase B and phase C. As a result, each of the diodes within the bridge conducts two current pulses in every 360° period. Although each diode conducts two current pulses, each diode is only responsible for supplying 1/6 of the load current. Therefore, each load voltage pulse will have a duration of 60° (Fig. 24.5(b)). For phase A this pulse will be symmetrically distributed about the voltage peak, which means the pulse will have a duration of 90° ± 30°. In Fig. 24.5, note that there is a 30° phase shift between the source voltage and the load voltage. This phase shift occurs since the source is shown as a phase value, while the voltage across the load is a line-to-line value.

When diode D_1 conducts, $V_{A\text{-}K}$ is effectively 0 V for 120°. This may seem to contradict previous statements regarding the conduction period being 60°; however, it must be remembered that each of the rectifying diodes must provide a return path for a second current pulse, resulting in a conduction period of 120°. When diode D_1 is reverse biased, $V_{A\text{-}K}$ will be the voltage from the anode of D_1 to highest instantaneous voltage at the cathode (Fig. 24.5(c)). This waveform is the same as that for the half-wave rectifier because the voltage developed across the reverse-biased diode represents a line-to-line value. Thus, during the course of normal operation, the diodes must have a minimum *PIV* of $\sqrt{3} \times V_{\text{PHASE}}$.

As with all rectifier circuits, the voltage across the load will be composed of a dc component and a ripple component. Since the pulses are 60° in duration, the magnitude of the ripple is less than those in the three-phase half-wave rectifier circuit and therefore the dc and RMS values for the load will be higher. The dc component will be 0.9549 or 0.955 of the peak input voltage and the RMS component will be 0.955 or 0.96 of the peak input voltage. Note that as the magnitude of the ripple component decreases, the difference between the dc and RMS voltages becomes less.

Figure 24.5

The voltage waveforms for the full-wave rectifier in Fig. 24.4: (a) V_{Supply}; (b) V_{Load}; (c) V_{Diode}; (d) V_{Load} with D_1 open-circuited; (e) V_{Diode} when D_1 is open-circuited.

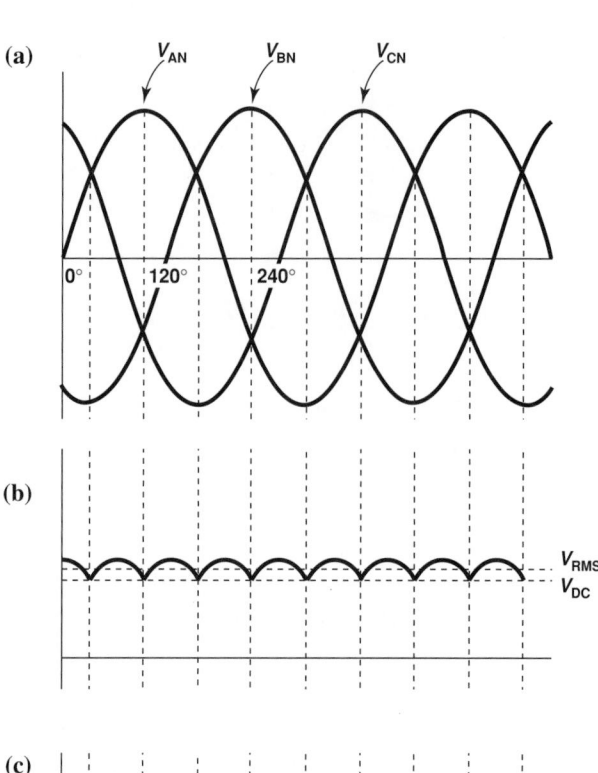

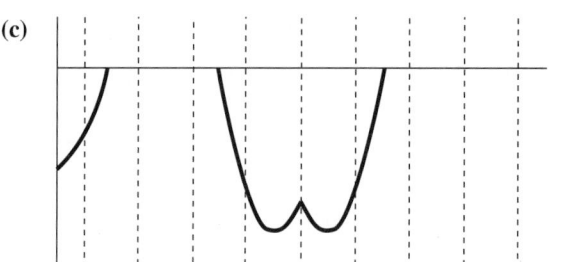

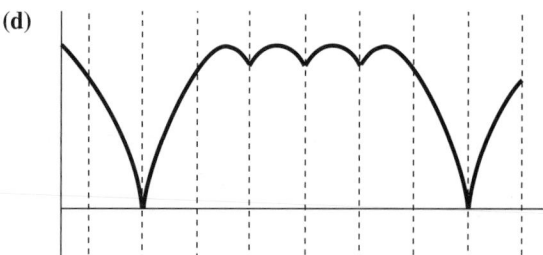

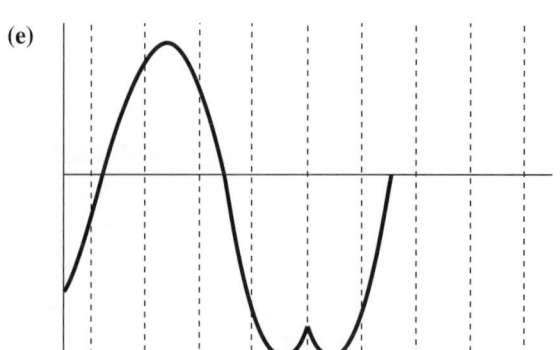

EXAMPLE 24.2

Repeat Example 24.1 for the three-phase full-wave rectifier.

SOLUTION:

1. There is no neutral connection in this system; therefore, the supply voltage is a line to line value:

$$I_{RMS} = \frac{V_{RMS}}{R}$$

$$= \frac{\sqrt{2} \times 208 \times 0.955}{25} = \frac{\sqrt{2} \times 208 \times 0.955}{25}$$

$$= \frac{280.9}{25}$$

$$= 11.24 \text{ A}$$

2. Each of the diodes conducts two current pulses; therefore:

$$I_{Diode} = \frac{I_{RMS}}{3}$$

$$= \frac{11.24}{3}$$

$$= 3.75 \text{ A}$$

3. $$P_{LOAD} = \frac{V^2_{DC}}{R}$$

$$= \frac{(\sqrt{2} \times 208 \times 0.954)^2}{25}$$

$$= 3150 \text{ W}$$

4. $$PIV = \sqrt{3} \ V_{PK}$$

$$= 1.73 \times (120 \times 1.414)$$

$$= 1.73 \times 170$$

$$= 294 \text{ V}$$

24.4 Controlled Half-Wave Three-Phase Rectifier

In this circuit, SCRs are substituted for the rectifying diodes used in the half-wave three-phase rectifier circuit (Fig. 24.6). If the SCRs were turned on at zero degrees of the phase voltage, the circuit would behave as a half-wave three-phase rectifier. By controlling the firing of the SCRs, the output voltage of the rectifier can be varied. In single-phase circuits, the firing and conduction angles are measured relative to zero degrees of the source voltage waveform; however, in three-phase systems, the firing and conduction angles are measured relative to the point at which a particular phase voltage has the highest instantaneous value (Fig. 24.7).

Figure 24.6

A controlled half-wave controlled rectifier with a resistive load.

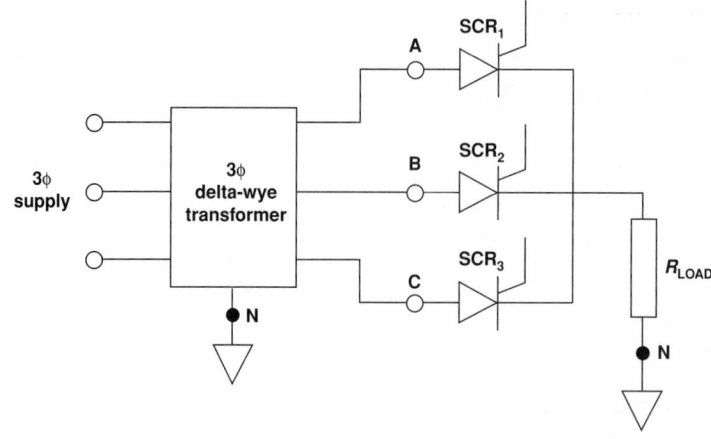

Figure 24.7

The voltage waveforms for the half-wave controlled rectifier in Fig. 24.6: (a) V_{Supply}; (b) V_{Load} when $\alpha = 30°$; (c) V_{T1} when $\alpha = 30°$; (d) V_{Load} when $\alpha = 60°$.

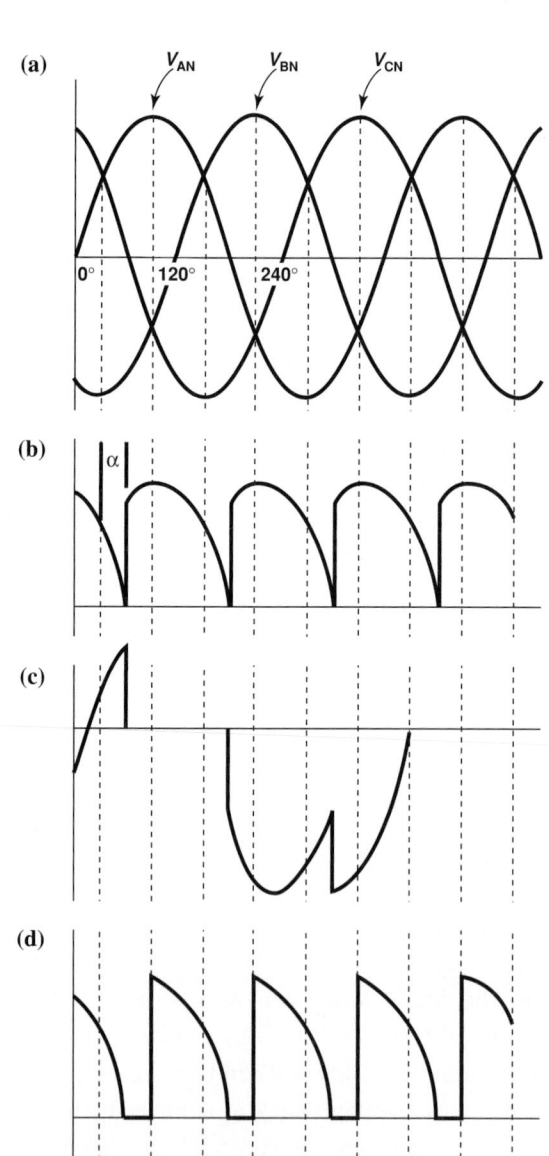

Changing the SCR firing angle alters the voltage waveform across the load. A delay in firing an SCR of 30° (for example, the SCR in phase A) will delay the dc load voltage pulse by the firing angle (α), resulting in a lower dc load voltage. The load voltage decreases because the portion of the supply voltage that occurs before 30° will be dropped across the SCR (Fig. 24.7(c)). Because the load voltage pulse is delayed by α, the preceding voltage pulse (generated by phase C) will be apparent across the load for a longer period that equals α (Fig. 24.7(b)). The input waveform will equal the sum of the voltage waveform across the SCR and the voltage across the load (Fig. 24.7(c) and 24.7(b)).

When the firing angle exceeds 30°, the point at which the SCR should turn off is beyond the 180° point of the supply phase voltage waveform. This supply voltage, which is now negative, would attempt to cause a reverse polarity current flow; however, this reverse current flow is not possible because the SCRs are unidirectional devices. As a result, the load voltage drops to zero and remains at zero until the SCR in the following phase conducts (Fig. 24.7(d)). It is possible to advance the firing angle of the SCR to a point at which the rectifier output voltage is zero, even though the rectifier is functioning properly.

24.5 Fully Controlled Full-Wave Rectifier

This rectifier retains the configuration of the full-wave uncontrolled rectifier, except the rectifying diodes have been replaced with SCRs (Fig. 24.8). Since there are six devices conducting for equal portions of time, there will be six voltage pulses across the load and each pulse will be 60° in duration (Fig. 24.9(b)). The rectifier network is connected line-to-line; consequently, two devices must conduct each for current pulse. Thus, each device will carry two current pulses over the period of one cycle. This means that although each SCR supplies current for 60°, each SCR will conduct for 120°.

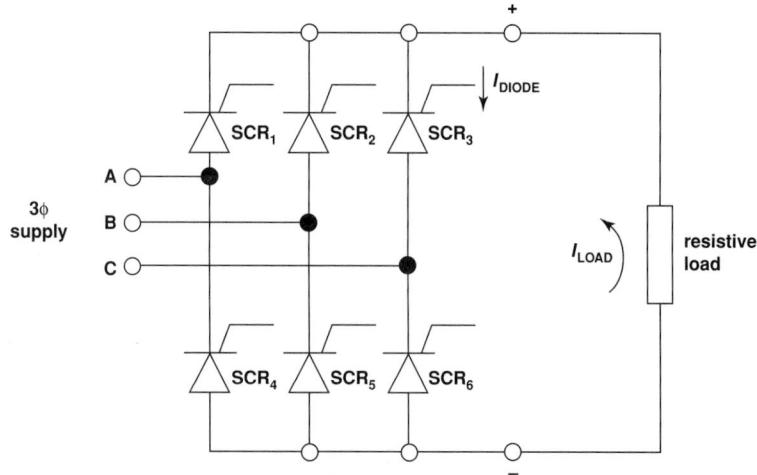

Figure 24.8

A fully controlled full-wave 3∅ rectifier with a resistive load.

Figure 24.9

The voltage waveforms for
the full wave fully controlled
rectifier in Fig. 24.8: (a) V_{Supply};
(b) V_{Load} when $\alpha = 30°$;
(c) V_{TI} when $\alpha = 30°$;
(d) V_{Load} when $\alpha = 45°$.

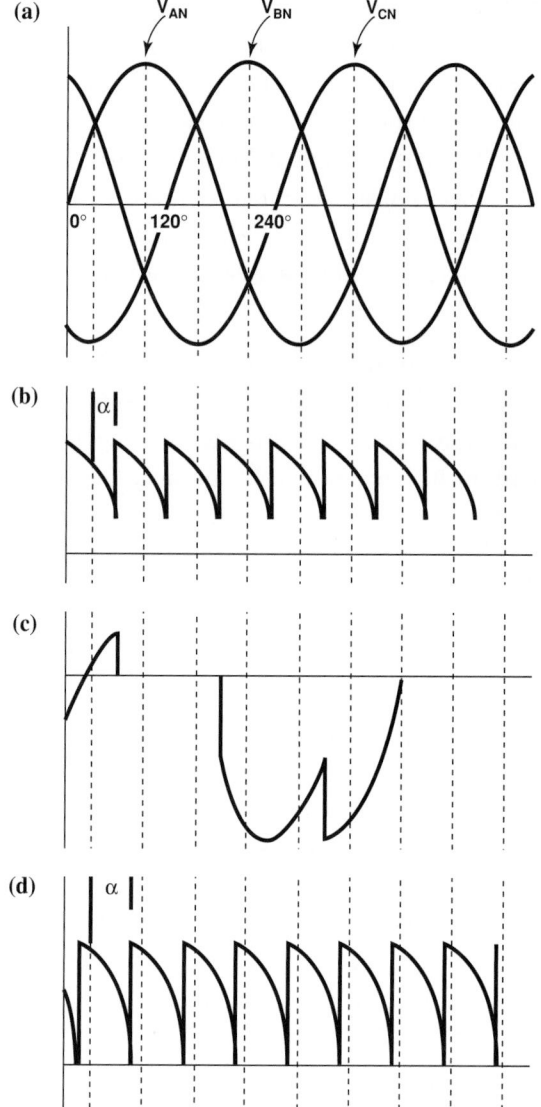

Unlike the half-controlled rectifier system, gate pulses must be supplied to two SCRs every 60° in order to provide a complete current path. In addition, when the system is first turned on, gate pulses must be supplied to two thyristors in order for load current to flow. This requires a significantly more complex triggering system than that required for the half-controlled full-wave rectifier. Description of such a triggering system is beyond the scope of this text; it is assumed that proper gate pulses are provided to each SCR at the appropriate time and in the proper sequence.

24.6 Six-Step Inverter

SIX-STEP INVERTER

The **six-step inverter** is similar to the full-wave three-phase rectifier (Fig. 24.4), but with the rectifying diodes replaced with power transistors (Fig. 24.10). The common connection point of each transistor pair is connected to one phase of the three-phase load. Since six voltage steps characterize the output, each of the steps in the output of this inverter will have a duration of 60° (360°/6).

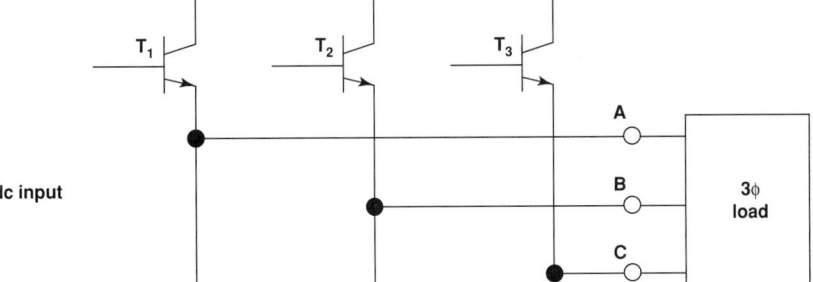

Figure 24.10

A 3Δ Inverter using transistors as the switching elements.

Fig. 24.11(a) shows a six-step inverter connected to a balanced three-phase wye-connected resistive load in which $R_a = R_b = R_c$. A series-parallel network is created when two of the resistors are paralleled and connected in series with the remaining resistor. In the series equivalent network, the parallel portion would have a resistance equal to one-third the total resistance. The remaining two-thirds of the total resistance is attributed to the single series connected resistor (Fig. 24.11(b)). When the network is connected to a source, we can use Ohm's and Kirchoff's laws to show that the voltage developed across each of the parallel-connected resistors will be one-third of the source voltage, and the remaining two-thirds of the source voltage will appear across the series-connected resistor. In the six-step inverter, causing various combinations of the six transistors to conduct creates the neces-

(a)

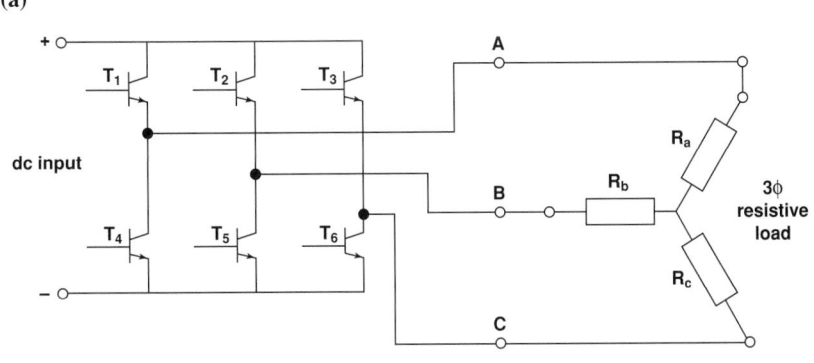

(b)

Figure 24.11

A six-step inverter connected to (a) three-phase resistive load; (b) series-parallel circuit created by the inverter.

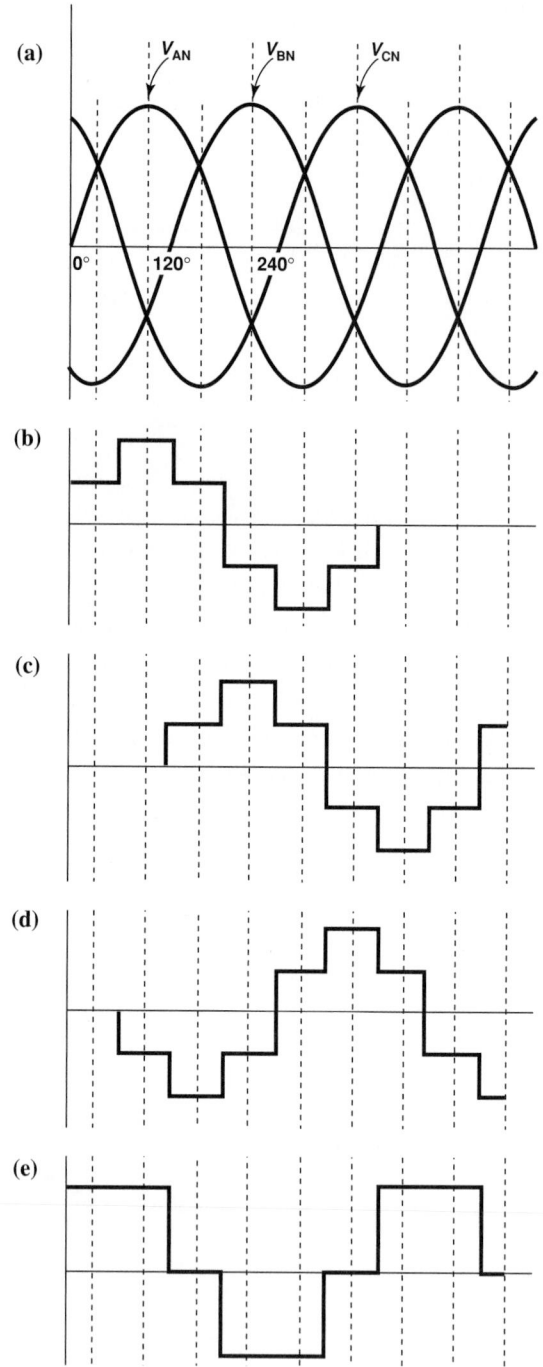

sary series-parallel networks required to produce the load voltage waveform shown
in Fig. 24.12(b). In order to create the various series-parallel load networks, three
transistors must be conducting at any time. The DC input rails supply the network
source voltage. Depending upon which transistors are conducting, the load voltage
may be either positive or negative.

To develop the three-phase voltages for the first 60° period of the load voltage,
Fig. 24.13(a) shows phases A and C to be positive while phase B will be negative. To

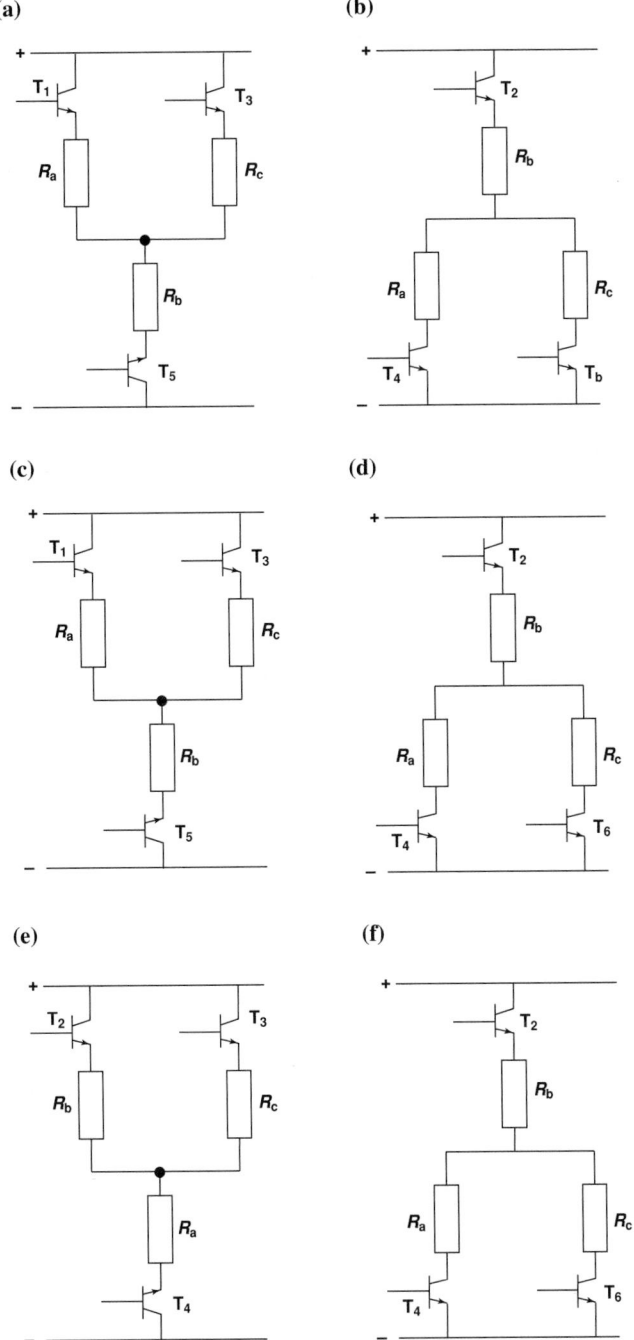

Figure 24.13

The load switching arrange-
ments required to produce
the six-step inverter output:
(a) 0-60°; (b) 60-120°;
(c) 120-180°; (d) 180-240°;
(e) 240-300°; (f) 300-360°.

accomplish this, phase A will be initially connected to the positive dc bus by transistor T_1, phase C will be connected to the positive dc bus by transistor T_3, and phase
B will be connected to the negative DC bus by transistor T_5 (Fig. 24.13(a)). In this configuration, R_a is paralleled with R_c, which in turn are connected in series with R_b. The
voltage across R_a and R_c, which are connected in parallel, will be one-third the dc rail
voltage and the voltage across R_b will be the remaining two-thirds of the dc rail voltage. With respect to the load neutral point, V_{an} and V_{cn} will be positive, while V_{bn} will
be negative. The resulting voltages are shown in Fig. 24.12(b).

In the second output voltage step, phases B and C will be negative, while phase A will be positive (Fig. 24.12(a)). Driving transistors T_1, T_5, and T_6 into saturation will connect R_a in series with R_b and R_c, which will be in parallel (Fig. 24.13(b)). The voltage across R_a will be positive: two-thirds the dc rail voltage, with the remaining one-third appearing across R_b and R_c. The voltage across R_b and R_c will be negative with respect to the load neutral point, while the voltage across R_a will be positive (Fig. 24.12(b)).

This process is repeated for the remaining four steps, using Fig. 24.12(a) to determine the polarity of the three phases for each 60° step. Based upon this pattern, Fig. 24.13 can be used to determine the conduction pattern for the six transistors needed to produce the six output voltage steps. The conduction pattern for the output sequence is summarized in Table 24.1.

So far, only the phase voltages have been considered, but any three-phase system also has three line voltages (V_{ab}, V_{bc}, and V_{ca}). Mathematically these are represented by:

$$V_{AB} = V_{An} - V_{Bn}$$

$$V_{BC} = V_{Bn} - V_{Cn}$$

$$V_{CA} = V_{Cn} - V_{An}$$

The magnitudes of both the phase and line voltages are summarized in Table 24.2 in terms of the DC rail voltage. Note that while the phase voltages are, at most, two-thirds of the rail voltage, the line voltages equal the rail voltage. It is also important to recognize that because the voltage waveforms are not sinusoidal, the usual $\sqrt{3}$ relationship between phase and line values is not valid.

In a six-step inverter, the output voltage is determined by the dc voltage supplied to the inverter input, while the frequency of the output voltage is determined by the speed at which the transistors are turned on and off. A high switching rate will result in a high frequency output and a lower switching rate will result in a lower output frequency.

Table 24.1   CONDUCTING TRANSISTORS FOR EACH 60 DEGREE PERIOD IN PHASE A OF THE SIX-STEP INVERTER SHOWN IN FIGURE 24.10

DEGREES	CONDUCTING TRANSISTORS
0–60	T1, T3, T5
60–120	T1, T4, T6
120–180	T1, T3, T5
180–240	T4, T6, T2
240–300	T2, T3, T4
300–360	T4, T6, T3

Table 24.2   THE OUTPUT VOLTAGE FOR A SIX-STEP INVERTER AS
A PROPORTION OF THE DC INPUT VOLTAGE.

	0–60	60–120	120–180	180–240	240–300	300–360
A	1/3	2/3	1/3	−1/3	−2/3	−1/3
B	−2/3	−1/3	1/3	2/3	1/3	−1/3
C	1/3	−1/3	−2/3	−1/3	1/3	2/3
A-B	1	1	0	−1	−1	0
B-C	−1	0	1	1	0	−1
C-A	0	−1	−1	0	1	1

24.7 Pulse Width Modulation (PWM) Inverter

Pulse width modulation (**PWM**) was a technique originally devised as a means of
representing analog telecommunications data in a digital (on/off) format. It has
since been adapted to power electronics as a triggering method for solid-state
devices. This process provides a means for generating sinusoidal currents at a
desired voltage and frequency.

PULSE WIDTH
MODULATION

The basic PWM principle can be illustrated using a simple operational amplifier and
two signal generators (Fig. 24.14). The **operational amplifier** is an integrated circuit amplifier with two inputs and a single output. One input (the inverting input)
produces an output that is 180° out-of-phase with the input. The second input,
called the non-inverting input, produces an output that is in-phase with the input.
The operational amplifier's output will be one of two voltage values, called the positive and negative saturation voltages ($\pm V_{\max}$). A sinusoidal reference waveform is
connected to the non-inverting input and a triangular waveform, called the carrier,
is connected to the amplifier's inverting input. Fig. 24.15(a) shows the relationship
between the two input waveforms when plotted on a common reference axis. When
the instantaneous voltage at the non-inverting input (the reference waveform) is
higher than instantaneous voltage at the inverting input (the carrier waveform), the
op-amp will be $+V_{\max}$. When the instantaneous voltage at the inverting input

OPERATIONAL
AMPLIFIER

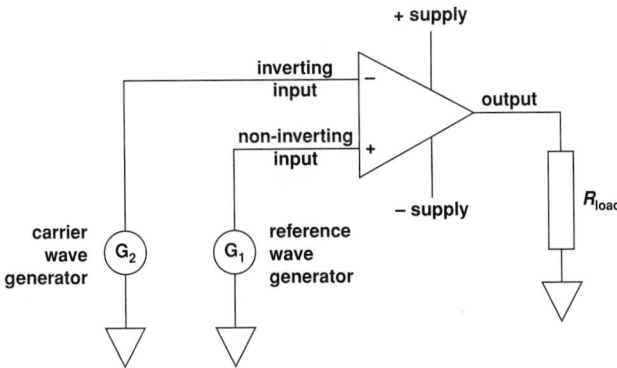

Figure 24.14

The basic principle of the
pulse width modulator
(PWM) using an operational
amplifier. The two input
voltages, the carrier and the
reference, are supplied by
signal generators.

Figure 24.15

The voltage waveforms
associated with the PWM
circuit illustrated in
Fig. 24.14: (a) the carrier
waveform superimposed
on the reference waveform;
(b) the output voltage
waveform.

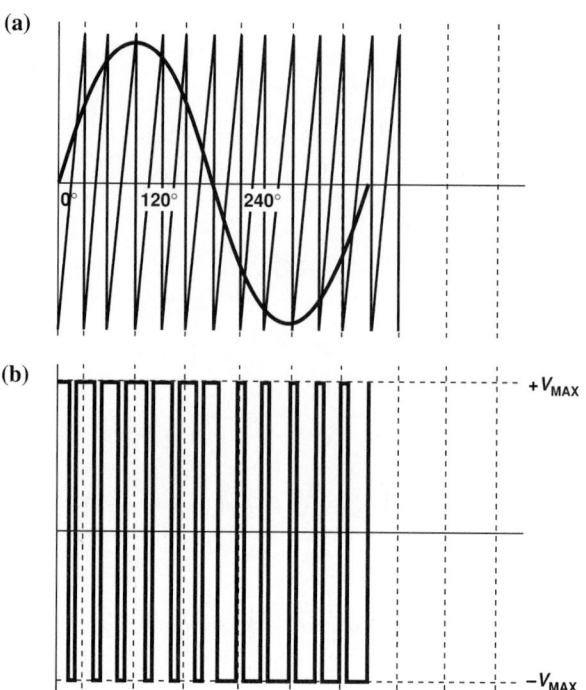

exceeds the instantaneous voltage at the non-inverting input, the amplifier output voltage will equal $-V_{max}$. Over time, the sinusoidal waveform will be represented by a series of constant height voltage pulses with a variable width and varying time between the individual pulses. The pulses will be narrowest near the beginning and end of each alternation, and they will be widest near the peak of each alternation (Fig. 24.15(b)). Negative-going alternations will be similarly represented, but with a pattern inverted with respect to the positive-going alternation.

A three-phase PWM inverter works in a similar if somewhat more complex fashion. Pulse width modulation represents a different means of transistor control, and it is important to note that the inverter circuitry is the same as that for the six-step inverter (Fig. 24.10); only the method of control is different. Since the output of a three-phase inverter produces a line-to-line voltage, the transistor biasing system must generate appropriate base pulses. Phase A, phase B, and a triangular carrier wave are shown plotted on a common reference in Fig. 24.16(a). The PWM equivalent for phase A and phase B voltages are shown in Fig. 24.16(b) and 24.16(c), respectively. These waveforms are generated in the same manner as the single-phase waveform in Fig. 24.15. The instantaneous difference between the phase voltages is the line-to-line voltage.

A high frequency carrier frequency results in an output waveform composed of a large number of voltage pulses. Practically, the carrier ratio is limited by the switching characteristics of the semiconductors used in the inverter system. Inverters using SCR technology are limited to switching speeds under 1 kHz, while systems using high-speed transistor technology are capable of switching at speeds in excess of 20 kHz. The higher switching speeds result in output voltage waveforms with a large number of individual voltage pulses. It is the large number of pulses that enable the PWM inverter to produce a load current waveform that closely approximates a sinusoidal waveform.

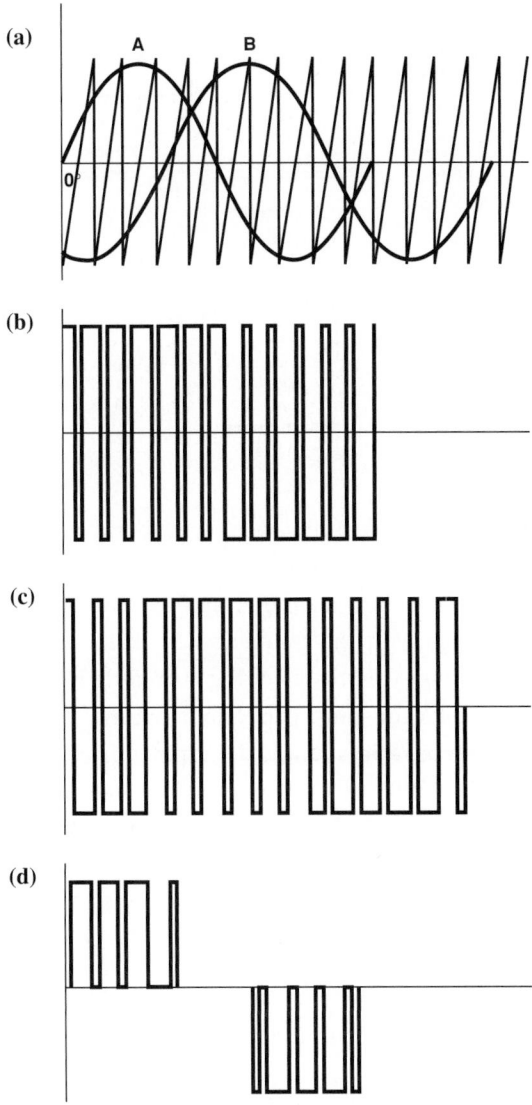

Figure 24.16

The voltage waveforms associated with the polyphase PWM: (a) the voltage waveforms for phases A and B, with the reference wave superimposed; (b) the output voltage for phase A; (c) the output voltage for phase B; (d) the line voltage V_{A-B}.

24.8 Variable Voltage Inverter (VVI) Drive

**VARIABLE VOLTAGE
INVERTER (VVI)**

The **variable voltage inverter (VVI)** is a technology introduced in the late 1970s and early 1980s. As the name implies, the VVI inverter controls the motor speed by varying both the load voltage and frequency. The VVI drive in its simplest form comprises a single-phase or three-phase controlled rectifier supplying the input of a six-step inverter (Fig. 24.17). The operator's speed potentiometer varies the input voltage to a control board, which is used to vary the firing of both the rectifier and inverter transistors. Varying the switching rate of a six-step inverter alters the drive output frequency, while altering the firing angle of the controlled rectifier alters the output voltage by varying the dc bus voltage. The capacitor connected across the dc bus is used to maintain a constant output voltage over one cycle. In practice there are a number of inherent drawbacks to such a simplistic system.

It is important in a variable frequency drive that motor loads produce constant torque at all speeds. In order to produce a constant torque, the magnetizing flux must remain constant over the motor's operating range. The magnetizing flux links the stator and rotor; this is also known as the air-gap flux. Since the

Figure 24.17

The basic components of a
variable frequency drive.
The rectifier may be sup-
plied from either a single or
polyphase power system.

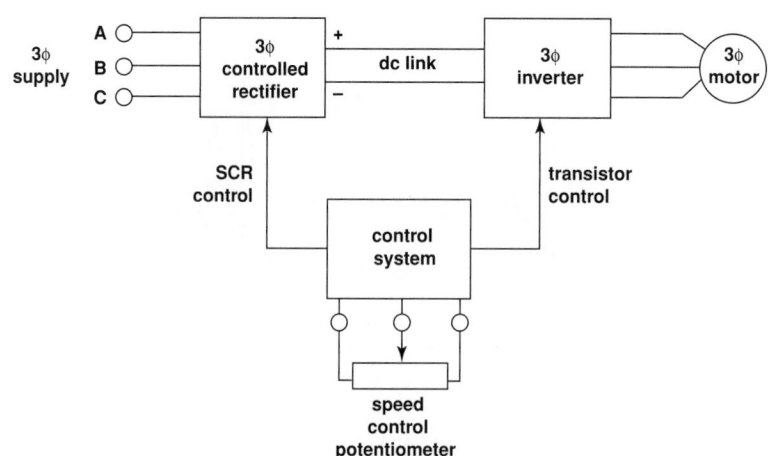

motor magnetizing reactance is a function of frequency, varying the frequency
results in variations in the magnetizing current and thus the motor's magnetizing
flux. In order to maintain a constant magnetizing flux, the voltage across the magnetizing circuit must change with the frequency. By maintaining a constant ratio
between frequency and voltage, the magnetizing current is held constant and thus
the motor torque also remains constant. The ratio between voltage and frequency is
known as the **volts per hertz ratio** and it is determined from the motor nameplate
data as:

**VOLTS PER
HERTZ RATIO**

EQ. 24.2

$$VHz^{-1} = \frac{V_{Nameplate}}{f_{Nameplate}}$$

where:

$V_{Nameplate}$ = the motor voltage obtained from the nameplate

$f_{Nameplate}$ = the nameplate frequency of the motor

Setting the VH^{-1} ratio too high will cause excessive magnetizing current, which may
saturate the motor core, resulting in reduced output torque. In addition, the higher current will result in additional heat build-up within the motor due to increased
I^2R losses in both the stator and the rotor. Excessive magnetizing current may also
result in distortion of the supply voltage and current. Should the VH^{-1} ratio be set
at too low a value, the motor will be unable to develop sufficient low-speed torque
due to insufficient magnetizing current.

Depending upon the architecture of the control system, the VH^{-1} ratio may be set
using a potentiometer or by the setting of switches. Once set, the VH^{-1} need not be
changed unless the attached motor is changed.

Any change in the bus voltage will affect the VH^{-1} setting and consequently the
motor torque. Therefore, it is important that the dc bus voltage remain constant. To
attain this, a feedback system between the bus and the control circuitry is required.
To achieve the necessary feedback, a sensing circuit is connected across the positive and negative lines of the dc bus. The sensing circuit in Fig. 24.18 consists of a
resistive voltage divider that is selected such that when the dc bus is at its maximum, a known voltage is applied to the controller. At less than the maximum bus

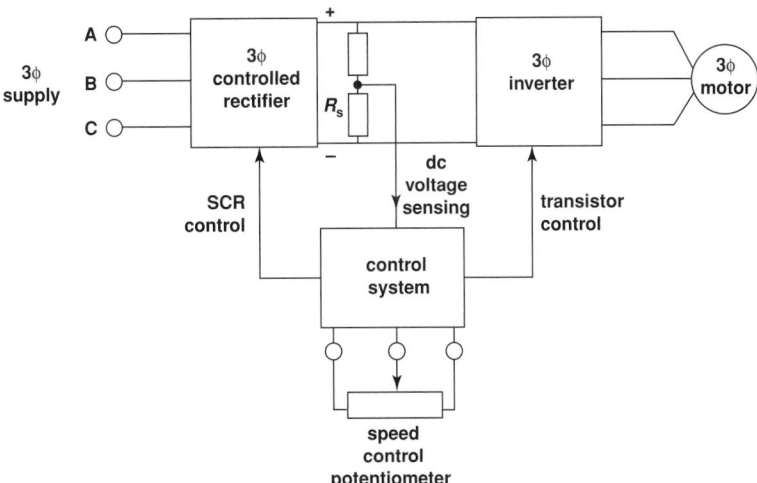

Figure 24.18

A functional block diagram
for a VVI drive system.

voltage, the voltage developed across the sensing resistor (R_S) will be proportional
to the bus voltage. Any fluctuation in the bus voltage will be reflected as change
in voltage across R_S. The output frequency of the inverter is sensed through a
frequency-to-voltage converter connected to the inverter output. Within the controller, the bus voltage and inverter frequency are compared to the set speed voltage. The firing angle of the thyristors in the rectifier is adjusted to maintain the
voltage, and the inverter frequency is adjusted to maintain the voltage/frequency
relationship. In situations where precise speed controls are not required, this type
of control system allows the controller to compensate for any variation in the dc
bus voltage due to changes in motor loading.

In order to produce the six-step inverter output, the inverter semiconductors need
only switch at a rate equal to six times the output frequency, which typically ranges
between 0 and 200 Hz. As a result, drives may be constructed using SCR technology
which have slower speed switching capabilities but higher current-carrying capacity
than the newer high-speed switching devices such as power transistors. For this reason, VVI drives are used in large load applications requiring currents up to 10 000 A.

At low speeds, 3∅ induction motors tend to produce a pulsating torque known as
"cogging." Cogging occurs because the high magnitude, low-order harmonics inherent in the six-step inverter produce positive and negative sequence torque, which
are apparent at low speeds because the rotor lacks significant momentum.

The input power factor to a VVI drive is directly related to rotor speed of motor
loads. Because of the VH^{-1} relationship, as the firing angle of the rectifier section
is advanced or retarded, the peak of the current waveform may be significantly
displaced from the peak of the input voltage. This displacement between the input
voltage and input current represents the drives' input power factor.

The torque produced by any 3∅ induction motor is proportional to the square of
the rotor voltage. When a VVI drive is operating at or near rated frequency, the voltage drop across the stator resistance and the leakage reactance are relatively small,
and as a result the magnetizing voltage and the motor terminal voltages are nearly equal. At lower operating frequencies the voltage drop across the stator imped-

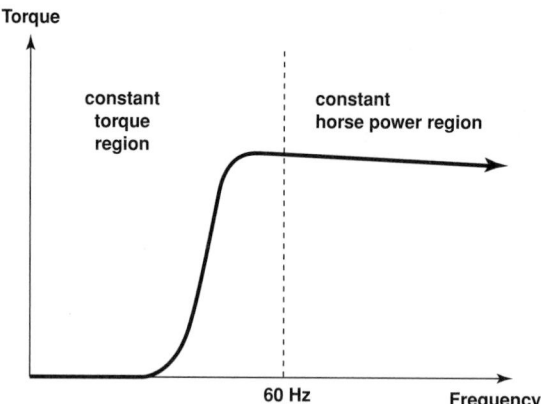

ance rises, causing a significant difference between the motor terminal voltage and the magnetizing voltage. As a result, the magnetizing current decreases and the motor is unable to maintain output torque. Since the output voltage of a VVI drive is directly proportional to the output frequency, VVI-controlled motors are only able to produce constant torque over a limited range of output frequencies (Fig. 24.19). To compensate for low motor torque at lower output frequencies, many VVI drives employ voltage boost. At lower operating frequencies the terminal voltage of the motor is increased in order to maintain a more constant magnetizing current. Voltage boost is a means of compensating for increased voltage drop across the motor impedance at lower operating speeds.

Below the motor nameplate frequency, the motor operates as a constant torque machine. It operates in this condition because as the motor frequency changes, the voltage is adjusted to maintain a constant magnetizing current. Applying a voltage greater than the motor nameplate value may damage the motor insulation; consequently, at frequencies above the motor nameplate frequency, the motor terminal voltage is held constant. As a result, above the rated frequency the motor operates as a constant horsepower motor.

24.9 Pulse Width Modulated Drives

A pulse width modulated (PWM) drive can be constructed by connecting an uncontrolled 3Ø full-wave rectifier to the input of a PWM inverter. Like the VVI drive, PWM drives are VH^{-1} drives and the ratio must be set based upon the nameplate data. In operation, the motor speed is set with a speed potentiometer (Fig. 24.20) that adjusts the inverter output frequency and voltage. A sensing resistor (R_S) transmits a signal to the control module that is proportional to the dc bus voltage. Should the bus voltage change the VH^{-1} rating of the inverter, output must remain constant. Thus either the inverter frequency of the PWM must be adjusted by varying the carrier frequency, or the inverter output voltage must be adjusted.

PWM drives have a number of advantages over VVI-type drives. The input power factor remains constant regardless of motor speed, since the line current supplying the

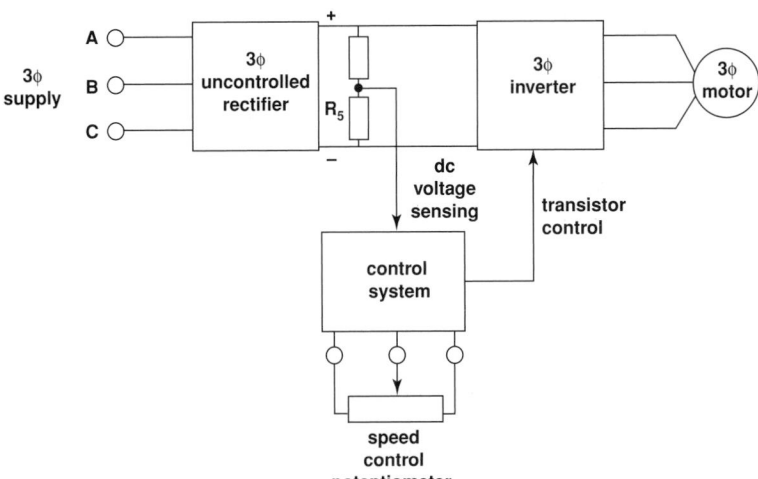

Figure 24.20

The topology for a PWM-type drive.

uncontrolled rectifier remains in the same position relative to line voltage. Typically, the input power factor to a PWM drive is on the order of 0.95 lagging.

PWM drives commonly employ microprocessor technology. As a result, PWM drives are easily adapted to provide features such as variable voltage boost, reduced voltage starting, soft starting, and programmed run. A microprocessor allows the voltage boost to be varied in proportion to the motor speed. As a result, PWM drives are able to maintain motor torque over a wider range of operating frequencies than drives employing six-step inverter technology. Programmed runs are useful in situations where repetitive operating cycles are needed. Depending upon the manufacturer, programmed runs may include multiple acceleration/deceleration profiles, forward/reversing capability, programmed time bases, and the ability to skip programmer-specified frequency bands.

PWM drives are capable of supplying constant torque over a wider range of inverter frequencies (Fig. 24.21). Like the VVI drive, a motor controlled by a PWM drive will produce constant horsepower at frequencies above the rated motor frequency. PWM drives are commonly used in small to medium motor applications.

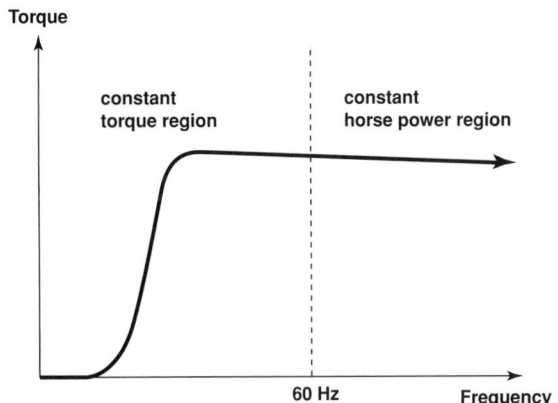

Figure 24.21

The torque-speed characteristics for a three-phase SCIM controlled by a PWM drive.

24.10   The Flux Vector Drive

The **flux vector drive (FVD),** like the VH^{-1} drives, uses a PWM inverter to produce a three-phase output voltage. It differs from these drives in control architecture. The result is an ac motor control system that is more similar to the control of a dc motor than to VVI and PWM techniques used to control a three-phase squirrel-cage induction motor (SCIM).

In a dc motor control system, the armature and field currents are independently controlled. As a result the motor torque can be maintained throughout the motor's operating range. In a three-phase SCIM, the motor is supplied with a single current comprising an in-phase component that controls the strength of the stator field and an out-of-phase or quadrature component that controls the torque-producing flux (Fig. 24.22). The motor line current is the vector sum of these two components. By maintaining a constant quadrature current, the FVD is able to closely approximate the operating behaviour of a dc motor using the less expensive and mechanically simpler 3∅ squirrel-cage induction motor.

In a dc motor the armature and field fluxes are maintained at close to an ideal 90° angle because the armature and field currents are controlled independently. Typically, the field coils are supplied from a fixed dc voltage source, while the armature voltage is varied by changing the armature resistance with a rheostat or by supplying the armature from a variable dc voltage source. This allows the torque angle for the motor to be maintained at a nearly constant 90° throughout its speed range. Consequently, a dc motor is able to produce nearly constant torque at all operating speeds. This differs significantly from a 3∅ induction motor, which operates in a fashion similar to a transformer; a single current is supplied to the stator and the rotor current is induced through transformer action.

Under no-load conditions, the rotor speed in a 3∅ SCIM is close to the synchronous speed of the rotating magnetic field. As the motor load is increased, the rotor frequency, and thus the rotor reactance, increases, causing the rotor current to lag behind the stator current. The lagging rotor current results in a rotor field that lags the stator field; as a consequence, the torque angle of the motor changes with the motor loading. Because a single current supplies the 3∅ SCIM, the torque angle is determined by the angle between the line current and the stator current of the motor. The rotor current is represented by the quadrature component, while the stator current is represented by the in-phase current component. Since the rotor reactance changes with the rotor frequency, the quadrature component of the current will also change with the rotor frequency and therefore the torque angle will change as the motor slip changes. In an FVD, the angle of the line current is controlled in order to maintain a constant quadrature current and the in-phase current

Figure 24.22

The current vector for one phase of a three-phase motor. The in-phase component (I_s) supplies the stator field, while the quadrature component (I_q) supplies the motor magnetizing flux. The motor line current is represented by I_M.

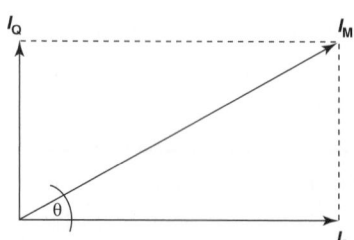

component is allowed to vary. As a consequence, the motor torque can be maintained at a near constant value regardless of the motor operating conditions.

Since the torque produced is dependent upon the slip and the line current, knowledge of these factors must be initially programmed into the FVD control system. This information is supplied to a series of complex mathematical models used to emulate the motor behaviour. The mathematical models are updated using actual data as the motor operates. Line current is easily monitored using a current feedback loop, while slip is monitored using a digital encoder. The digital encoder attached to the shaft of the motor provides data that shows the position of the rotor with respect to the stator.

The block diagram in Fig. 24.23 shows a simplified block diagram of a flux vector drive. Based upon the mathematical model of the motor, the torque command module generates a quadrature current that controls the motor torque as one phase in a two-phase system. The second phase of this system is generated by the operator-controlled speed selection potentiometer. The vector sum of the two current components is converted to a three-phase current that supplies the SCIM. Data from the encoder and current feedback loops is used to update the stator component of the motor current in order to maintain motor torque.

The FVD is able to supply rated torque over a wide range of operating speeds with minimal cogging. It is these characteristics that make the FVD suitable to a wide range of industrial applications involving small to medium motors.

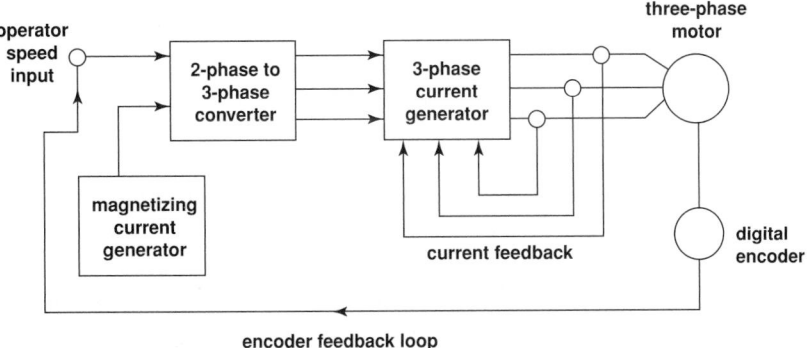

Figure 24.23

A simplified block diagram of a flux vector drive.

24.11 Inverter Types

Variable voltage, pulse width modulation, and flux vector are referred to as the drive topology. Each of these topologies will be one of two types; **current source inverter (CSI)** or **voltage source inverter (VSI)**.

> **CURRENT SOURCE INVERTER (CSI)**
>
> **VOLTAGE SOURCE INVERTER (VSI)**

In a current source inverter (Fig. 24.24(a)), an inductor is series-connected in each of the dc bus lines. The inductor is sized so that it will be able to supply load current over a period of approximately one cycle. In order to accomplish this task, the inductors must be sized to the load. This means that if the motor connected to the drive is changed, the inductors must also be changed. This limits the ease of application for CSI drives; they are not widely used in motor loads.

Figure 24.24

Two types of variable
frequency drives: (a) current
source inverters (CSI) have
inductors series connected
in the dc bus; (b) voltage
source inverters (VSI) have a
capacitor connected across
the dc bus.

(a)

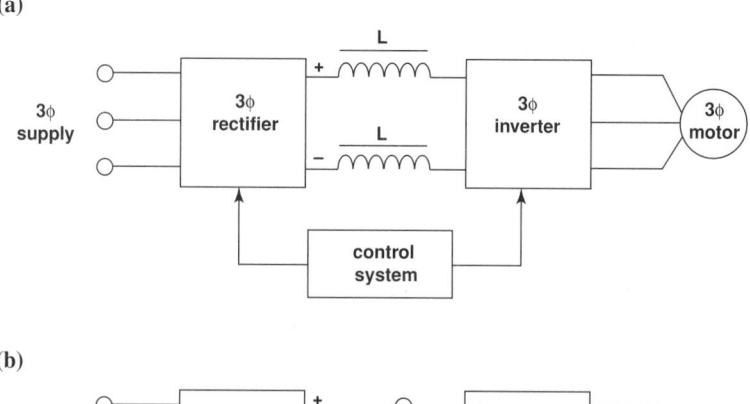

(b)

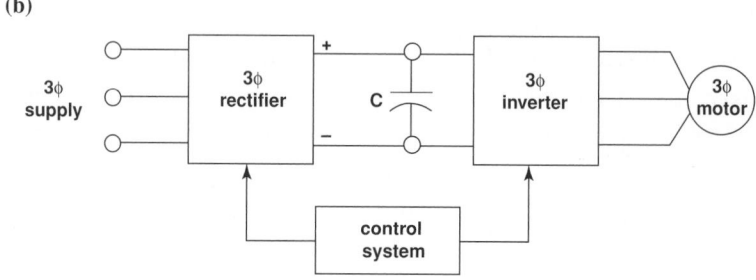

In a voltage source inverter (Fig. 24.24(b)), a capacitor is connected across the lines of the dc bus. The capacitor is sized so that it will maintain the drive output voltage over a period of approximately one cycle. Since capacitor size is independent of the load current, the drive load may be changed without resizing the capacitor. VSI-type drives are the most commonly used for this reason.

24.12 Motors Used with Drives

Three-phase squirrel-cage induction motors are designed to operate with a sinusoidal voltage source, but electronic variable speed drives do not produce a sinusoidal output. This has a number of effects on three-phase motor loads.

Most three-phase motors contain a built-in fan capable of providing adequate cooling at rated speed. When a motor is run at low speeds for extended periods of time, the heat produced may not be adequately dissipated, causing the motor to overheat. In addition, operating a three-phase motor using high-speed switching devices will cause higher eddy-current and hysteresis losses in both the rotor and stator. These increased losses cause excess heat build-up in the motor and thermal breakdown of the insulation resulting in motor failure. Extended low speed operation usually requires the addition of an external cooling means, such as a fan driven by an independent electric motor.

Operating a motor at low frequency, most often 50 or 60 Hz, stresses the motor insulation as the current and voltage continually reverse polarity. Over long periods of time, these stresses can cause insulation breakdown, resulting in motor failure. Proper selection of motor insulation results in a machine able to operate trouble-free for thirty years or more. Electronic drives are very different because they generate high frequency output voltages with very rapid rise times. These rapidly changing voltages will overstress the insulation used in standard three-phase motors in very short periods of time, resulting in short-circuits between windings or between windings and the stator frame. **Inverter rated motors** designed to operate with VFDs use Class F insulation, which is able to withstand the stresses caused by high frequency voltages.

INVERTER RATED MOTOR

24.13 Summary

Upon completion of this chapter you should have learned:

* That three-phase rectifiers can be either controlled or uncontrolled. Uncontrolled rectifiers use diodes to supply a fixed output voltage, while controlled rectifiers use controllable semiconductors, such as SCRs, to supply an output voltage that can be varied.

* That the six-step and pulse width modulation type inverters both use controllable semiconductors, such as transistors, to produce a non-sinusoidal ac voltage. Six-step inverters switch at lower frequencies and use low-speed, high current devices such as SCRs. Pulse width modulation type inverters use low current, high-speed semiconductors such as transistors.

* That a variable voltage inverter (VVI) drive uses a controlled rectifier and a six-step inverter to produce a variable voltage, variable frequency three-phase output.

* That a pulse width modulation (PWM) drive uses an uncontrolled rectifier and a PWM inverter to produce a variable voltage, variable frequency three-phase output.

* That a flux vector drive (FVD) is a complex PWM drive type that maintains motor torque by controlling the motor's torque angle. To accomplish this, the magnetizing current is held at a constant value while the line current is allowed to vary.

* How to explain the difference between a current source inverter (CSI) and a voltage source inverter (VSI).

* That a standard three-phase squirrel-cage induction motor is not designed to operate on a non-sinusoidal source or to run at low speed for extended periods of time. Inverter rated motors have enhanced insulation and cooling.

Key Terms

CURRENT SOURCE INVERTER (CSI):An inverter system that uses inductors to ensure that current can be supplied to the load for a period equal to one cycle.

FLUX VECTOR DRIVE (FVD): A variable frequency drive that maintains motor torque by maintaining a constant magnetizing current.

INVERTER: An electronics circuit used to convert dc to ac.

INVERTER RATED MOTORS: Electric motors specifically designed to operate with VFDs. These motors have enhanced insulation and may include enhanced cooling means for low-speed operation.

OPERATIONAL AMPLIFIER: An integrated circuit amplifier with an inverting and a non-inverting input and a single output. The output voltage is limited to a negative and positive maximum.

POWER ELECTRONICS: The branch of electronics concerned with the control of industrial loads, such as motors.

PULSE WIDTH MODULATION: A means of converting analog information to a series of pulses. The information is coded by varying the width of the pulses rather than the height.

SIX-STEP INVERTER: An inverter system whose output is composed of six 60° steps.

VARIABLE FREQUENCY DRIVE (VFD): Any form of variable speed motor control that is capable of varying the synchronous speed of a motor by changing the frequency of the supply.

VARIABLE VOLTAGE INVERTER (VVI): A form of inverter that changes the inverter output frequency and the voltage of the DC input bus.

VOLTAGE SOURCE INVERTER (VSI): An inverter system that uses a capacitor so that the load voltage can be maintained for a period equal to one cycle of the output frequency.

VOLTS PER HERTZ RATIO: The ratio between the nameplate voltage and frequency of a motor. Maintaining a constant volts per hertz ratio helps maintain a constant motor torque over a range of operating frequencies.

Test Your Knowledge

24.1   The RMS output voltage of a three-phase, half-wave rectifier is ___ of the peak input voltage:
   a. 0.827
   b. 0.955
   c. 0.84

24.2   The six-step inverter uses low-speed, high-current semiconductors.

   true_____   false_____

24.3   The minimum PIV for a rectifying diode in a three-phase full-wave rectifier is:
   a. peak value of the phase voltage
   b. line voltage
   c. peak value of the line voltage

24.4   In any rectifier circuit, the RMS voltage will always be higher than the dc voltage.

   true_____   false_____

24.5   Maintaining a constant volt per hertz ratio helps maintain constant torque in motors connected to both PWM and VVI systems.

   true_____   false_____

24.6   A current source inverter can be used with any three-phase motor.

   true_____   false_____

24.7   A VVI drive controls a motor load by varying both the rectifier output voltage and the output frequency.

   true_____   false_____

24.8   The input power factor to a PWM drive is a constant 0.95 lagging.

   true_____   false_____

24.9   Each diode in a full-wave three-phase rectifier conducts current for only 60°.

   true_____   false_____

24.10   Any motor type can be used with a variable frequency drive.

   true_____   false_____

Questions and Problems

24.11 A three-phase half-wave rectifier is connected to a 347/600 V system. Calculate the dc and RMS output voltages.

24.12 Repeat Problem 24.11 for a full-wave three-phase rectifier.

24.13 A 24 Ω per phase load is connected to the circuit in Problem 24.11. Calculate the total power consumed by the load.

24.14 Repeat Problem 24.13 for the circuit in Problem 24.12.

24.15 A 120/208 V 60 Hz motor is to be connected to a VFD. Calculate the volts per hertz setting for the drive.

24.16 What would be the effect on the motor if the volt per hertz rating were set too low?

Appendix A

Selected Answers

The following numerical answers are usually rounded off to an accuracy of ±1%.

CHAPTER 1

1) false; **2)** c; **3)** b; **4)** b; **5)** a; **6)** d; **7)** c; **8)** false; **9)** d; **10)** c; **11)** c; **12)** a; **13)** c; **14)** c; **15)** a; **16)** a; **17)** c; **18)** b; **19)** c; **20)** b; **21)** c; **22)** c; **23)** c; **24)** a; **25)** a; **26)** a; **27)** c; **28)** true; **29)** false; **30)** false.

CHAPTER 2

1) c; **2)** true; **3)** true; **4)** d; **5)** c; **6)** c; **7)** true; **8)** b; **9)** c; **10)** a; **11)** c; **12)** c; **13)** third orbit has 16 electrons; **14a)** 28; **14b)** 4; **16a)** 960 W; **16b)** 15 Ω; **17)** 240 W; **18)** 2.4 A; **19a)** 3 200 000 MW; **19b)** 12.5 kΩ; Ω; **19c)** 26.67 k.Wh; **20)** 254 V; **21)** $1.21.

CHAPTER 3

1) b; **2)** b; **3)** b; **4)** c; **5)** b; **6)** a; **7)** c; **8)** c; **9)** b; **11)** 180°C; **12)** 160 months; **13a)** 317.5 kV; **13b)** 76.2 kV; **14)** 253 mm²; **16)** No. 1; **17)** 0.04 mm; **18)** No. 34; **19a)** 7.39 km; **19b)** 21.36 kg; **20)** 0.001 59 mm²; **21a)** 358.6 Ω; **21b)** 519.4 Ω; **22a)** 1.333 Ω; **22b)** 160 V, 19.2 kW; **23a)** 2200 Ω ±10%; **23b)** 12 MΩ ±5%; **24)** 2.21 mΩ.

CHAPTER 4

1) false; **2)** a; **3)** b; **4)** c; **5)** a; **6)** false; **7)** false; **8)** false; **9)** c; **10)** true; **11)** true; **12a)** 1.5 A; **12b)** 3 W; **13a)** 1 A; **13b)** 0.67 W; **14a)** 5.1 V; **14b)** 1.7 V; **14c)** 20 h; **15a)** 1.4985 V; **15b)** 133 h; **16)** six groups in parallel; each group consisting of 20 cells in series; **17)** 7.5 A; **18a)** 0.4 A; **18b)** 4 W; **19a)** 900 V; **19b)** 45 kW; **20a)** 125 V; **20b)** 93.75 W; **21)** case 1: 10 V, 1 Ω; case 2: 0.1 W, 10 mA; case 3: 400 V; case 4: 10 Ω, 100 A; case 5: 2000 V, 2 mA; **22)** 5 A; **23)** 5 A flowing away from the common terminal.

CHAPTER 5

1) b; **2)** false; **3)** false; **4)** false; **5)** a; **6)** false; **7)** c; **8)** false; **12)** S pole; **13)** 1250 At; **14)** positive; **15a)** repulsion; **15b)** attraction; **15c)** attraction; **16a)** 10 000 At, 4000 At; **16b)** 1250 W, 1750 W; **16c)** B; **16d)** repel; **16e)** repel; **18)** 0.4 T.

CHAPTER 6

1) true; **2)** true; **3)** b; **4)** true; **5)** false; **6)** true; **7)** c; **9)** upward; **10)** A is a N pole; **11)** away from the reader; **12)** upward; **13a)** cw; **13b)** cw; **14)** 25.4 N; **15a)** 12 N; **15b)** 72 N.m, 53.1 lbf.ft.

CHAPTER 7

1) b; **2)** a; **3)** b; **4)** true; **5)** b; **6)** b; **7)** c; **8)** 20 V; **9a)** increasing **9b)** (−); **10)** 28.3 V; **13)** 25 mV; V_{AB} is positive; the voltage is dc.

CHAPTER 8

1) c; **2)** b; **3)** c; **4)** true; **5)** a; **6)** c; **7)** false; **8)** c; **9)** b; **10)** a; **11)** c; **12)** false; **13)** no; **14)** negative; **18)** −169 V; **19)** 325 V; **20)** 208 V; **21)** 509 V; **22)** 2125 W.

CHAPTER 9

1) true; **2)** true; **3)** a; **4)** true; **5)** b; **6)** b; **7)** b; **8)** true; **9)** a; **10)** b; **11)** 4 H; **12a)** 30 V; **12b)** 20 H; **13)** 40 V; **14)** (−); **15)** 2400 J; **16a)** 180 kJ; **16b)** 24 V; **16c)** 2.5 s; **17a)** 6 A; **17b)** 10 V; **17c)** 2 V; **17d)** 0.5 A/s; **17e)** 50 J; **18)** 0.6 A, 48 A, 360 A, 21 600 A; **19)** 500 V; **20)** 10.7 kV.

CHAPTER 10

1) true; **2)** false; **3)** false; **4)** b; **5)** a; **6)** b; **7)** a; **8)** true; **9)** a; **10)** true; **11)** true; **13a)** 5 min; **13b)** 36 kJ; **14a)** 64 056 v/s; **14b)** 6.4 A; **15a)** 3000 V; **15b)** 270 J; **15c)** 5 μF; **16)** 24 s; **17)** 40 V; **19)** 6 groups in parallel, each group consisting of two capacitors in series; **20a)** 0.248 μF; **20b)** 40 kV; **20c)** 198 J; **21a)** 1.3 MJ; **21b)** 2250 J; **21c)** 578.

CHAPTER 11

1) b; **2)** c; **3)** c; **4)** a; **5)** a; **6)** c; **7)** c; **8)** true; **9)** c; **10)** 120 W; **11b)** +200 V 1 possible with respect to 2; **12a)** 12 A; **12b)** 169.7 V; **13a)** 1136 A; **13b)** 0.3872 Ω; **13c)** 6850 μF; **13d)** 622 V; **13e)** 1325 J; **14a)** 259 A; **14b)** 1642 Ω; **14c)** 4.35 H; **14d)** 366 A; **14e)** 146 kJ.

CHAPTER 12

1) b; **2)** c; **3)** b; **4)** a; **5)** b; **6)** a; **7)** b; **8)** b; **9)** a; **10)** a; **11)** 0.64 lagging; **12a)** 681.8 kVA; **12b)** 323.8 kvar; **13)** 4.3 kvar; **14)** 188.4 Ω; **15a)** 5 A, 2 A; **15b)** 5.38 A; **15c)** 92.8%; **15d)** 18.57 Ω; **16a)** 6 A, 4 A; **16b)** 7.21 A; **16c)** 83.2% leading; **16d)** 16.64 Ω; **17a)** 6 A, 4 A; **17b)** 2 A; **17c)** 0% lagging; **17d)** 60 Ω; **18a)** 25 Ω; **18b)** 28 V, 96 V; **18c)** 112 W; **19a)** 5 Ω; **19b)** 80 V, 90 V; **19c)** 0; **20a)** 37 Ω; Ω **20b)** 140 V, 48 V; **20c)** 182 W; **21a)** 3 A; **21b)** 5A; **21 c)** 5.83 A; **21 d)** 2110 W; **21e)** 450 var; **21f)** 2156 VA; **21g)** 5.83 A; **21h)** 370 V; **21i)** 97.8%; **21j)** 12°; **22a)** 18.97 Ω; **22b)** 30 V; **22c)** 50 V; **22d)** 20 V; **22e)** 0.333 A; **22f)** 6.67 W; **22g)** 30 var; **22h)** 50 var; **22i)** 20 var; **22j)** 21.08 VA; **22k)** 31.6%, leading; **22l)** 71.5°; **23)** 0.571 A.

CHAPTER 13

1) b **2)** c; **3)** true; **4)** a; **5)** b; **6)** c; **7)** b; **8)** b; **9)** false; **10a)** 358 V; **10b)** 23.9 A; **10c)** 25.6 kW; **11a)** 694 A; **11b)** 13.2 kV; **11c)** 9161 kW; **11d)** 100%; **12)** dim; **13)** 23.5 kW; **14)** 0.9 Ω; **16a)** 103.6 kVA; **16b)** 80.4%; **16c)** 61.6 kvar.

CHAPTER 14

1) c; **2)** b: **3)** c; **4)** true; **5)** c; **6)** a; **7)** c; **8)** a; **9)** true; **10)** b; **11)** b, f; **12)** a; **13)** c; **14)** b; **15)** c; **16)** a; **17)** b; **21)** higher; **30)** 120 V; **31)** 60 kV; **32a)** 110.4 V; **32b)** 22.08 A; **33a)** 2420 W; **33b)** 22 A, 11 A; **34)** 50 A, 1250 A; **35a)** zero; **35b)** 520 V; **36a)** short-circuit; **36b)** no change; **38a)** 129 V; **38b)** 93 A; **39a)** 470 kW; **39b)** 99.12%.

CHAPTER 15

1) true; **2)** b; **3)** b; **4)** a; **5)** b; **6)** a; **7)** c; **11a)** 96 V; **11b)** 288 W; **13a)** 4014 At; **13b)** 6814 At.

CHAPTER 16

1) a; **2)** b; **3)** a; **4)** c; **5)** b; **6)** c; **7)** a; **8)** a; **9)** a; **10)** a; **20a)** 490.4 V; **20b)** 789 hp; **20c)** 11.5 kW; **21)** 62.5 kA; **22a)** 600 At; **22b)** 800 At.

CHAPTER 17
1) false; **2)** b; **3)** c; **4)** b; **5)** b; **6)** true; **7)** b; **8)** a; **9)** b; **15)** 69 N, 15.5 lbf;
16a) 514.286 r/min; **16b)** 483.43 r/min; **16c)** 3.6 Hz.

CHAPTER 18
1) false; **2)** b; **3)** c; **4)** false; **5)** c; **6)** b; **7)** a; **8)** c; **9)** b; **10)** a; **16a)** 361 N.m; **16b)** 556 N.m;
16c) 642 N.m; **16d)** 464 N.m, 240 r/min; **16e)** 18.75 hp; **17)** locked rotor torque = 229
N.m; **18)** 3.88 Ω; **19a)** 1453 W; **19b)** 2344 VA; **19c)** 2.94; **20)** 90.3 Ω.

CHAPTER 19
1) true; **2)** true; **3)** b; **4)** b; **5)** c; **6)** b; **7)** a; **12a)** line current increases; **12b)** temperature
increases; **13)** 168 kW; **14a)** 0.08; **14b)** 0.0167; **14c)** 0.004 48.

CHAPTER 20
1) true; **2)** a; **3)** b; **4)** b; **5)** true; **6)** false; **7)** false; **8)** true; **9)** true; **10)** true; **11)** false;
12) b; **13)** false; **14)** true; **17a)** 20 poles; **18)** Excitation must be increased; **21a)** 575 V;
21b) 28.75 V.

CHAPTER 21
1) true; **2)** a; **3)** b; **4)** b; **5)** b; **6)** c; **7)** false; **8)** true; **9)** c; **10)** true; **11)** 720 r/min;
17a) series; **17b)** capacitor-start; **17c)** series; **17d)** shade-pole; **17e)** resistance split-
phase; **17f)** capacitor-run; **17g)** reluctance or hysteresis; **17h)** hysteresis; **18a)** too
hot; **18b)** temperature rise is not defined at no-load; **19a)** 28.6%; **19b)** 55.3%;
19c) 19.2 mN.m; **19d)** 16.9%; **19e)** 56.4°; **19f)** 15 W; **20)** 24 W vs 15 W; **22)** 18°.

CHAPTER 22
1) false; **2)** true; **3)** false; **4)** true; **5)** true; **6)** false; **7)** a; **8)** true; **9)** b; **10)** c; **19)** 548 years;
21) 520 A; **23)** 120 A; **24)** 20 N.m; **26)** V_{cd} is (–); **27)** 600 V.

CHAPTER 23
1) true; **2)** false; **3)** true; **4)** true; **5)** false; **6)** false; **7)** true; **8)** false; **9)** false; **10)** true;
12) 7.54; **13)** β = 0/96, α = 0.906; **14)** 0.1 A; **15)** See Figure below.

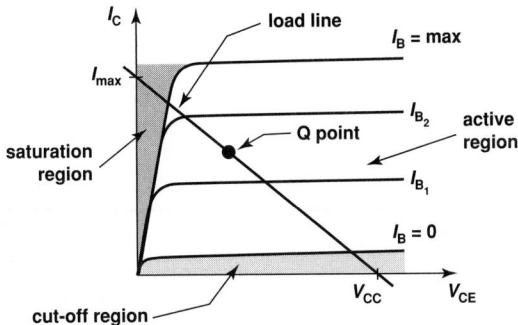

CHAPTER 24
1) C; **2)** true; **3)** c; **4)** true; **5)** true; **6)** false; **7)** true; **8)** true; **9)** false; **10)** false;
11) V_{DC} = 40 5 V, V_{RMS} = 412 V; **12)** V_{DC} = 805 V, V_{RMS} = 810 V; **13)** I_2 = 16.48 A,
P = 6789 W; **14)** I_L = 32.4 A, P = 26 244 W; **15)** 3.466 V/Hz.

Appendix B

Conversion Charts for Units

The relative size of a unit is the key factor that gives us a "feel" for a unit.

The conversion charts in this appendix show the relative size of a unit by the position it occupies on the chart. The largest unit is at the top, the smallest at the bottom, and intermediate units are ranked in between.

The rectangles bearing SI units extend slightly towards the left, to distinguish them from other units.

The units are connected by straight lines, each of which bears an arrow and a number. The number is the ratio of the larger to the smaller of the units so connected, and so its value is always greater than one. The arrow always points toward the smaller of the two units.

In Fig. B-l, for example, five units of length—the mile, metre, yard, inch, and millimetre—are listed in descending order of size. The numbers show the relative size of the connected units; the yard is 36 times larger than the inch, the inch is 25.4 times larger than the millimetre, and so on. With this arrangement, we can easily convert from one unit to any other.

Suppose we want to convert from yards to millimetres. Starting from **yard** in Fig. B-l, we have to move downward and in the direction of the arrows for both lines (36 and 25.4) until we reach **millimetre**. Conversely, if we want to convert from millimetres to yards, we start at **millimetre** and move upward against the direction of the arrows until we reach **yard**. To convert from one unit to another, we apply the following rule:

1. *If, in going from one unit to another, we move in the direction of the arrow, we multiply by the associated number.*

2. *Conversely, if we move against the arrow, we divide.*

In moving from one unit to another, we can follow any path we please; the conversion result is always the same.

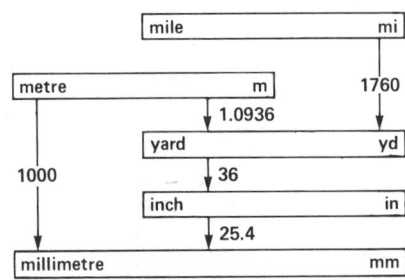

Figure B-1

Units of length.

EXAMPLE B-1

Convert 2.5 yards to millimetres.

SOLUTION:

Starting from **yard** and moving toward **millimetre**, we always move in the direction of the arrows. We must therefore multiply the numbers associated with each line:

2.5 yd = 2.5 × 36 × 25.4 millimetres
    = 2286 mm

EXAMPLE B-2

Convert 2000 metres into miles.

SOLUTION:

Starting from **metre** and moving toward **mile**, we move once with, and once against the direction of the arrows. Consequently, we have:

2000 metres = 2000 × 1.0936 ÷ 1760 miles

$$= \frac{2000 \times 1.0936}{1760}$$

= 1.24 miles

EXAMPLE B-3

Convert 75 100 Btu to kilowatthours.

SOLUTION:

Referring to the ENERGY chart, we now move past three arrows, two of which point opposite to the path we are following. Consequently:

75 100 Btu = 75 000 × 1.055 ÷ 1000 ÷ 3.6
       = 22 kWh

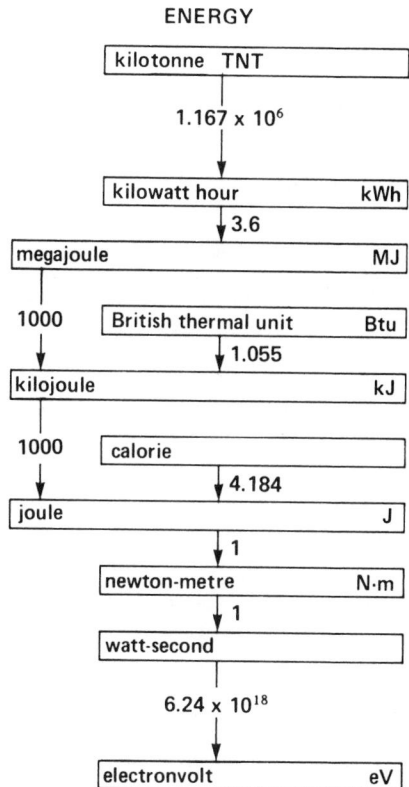

Figure B-2

See Example B-3

Quantities such as AREA, MASS, VOLUME, and so forth, are listed in alphabetical order for quick reference. Multipliers between units are either exact, or accurate to ± 0.1 percent.

Examples at the bottom of each page are intended to assist the reader in applying the conversion rule which basically states:

WITH THE ARROW—MULTIPLY

AGAINST THE ARROW—DIVIDE

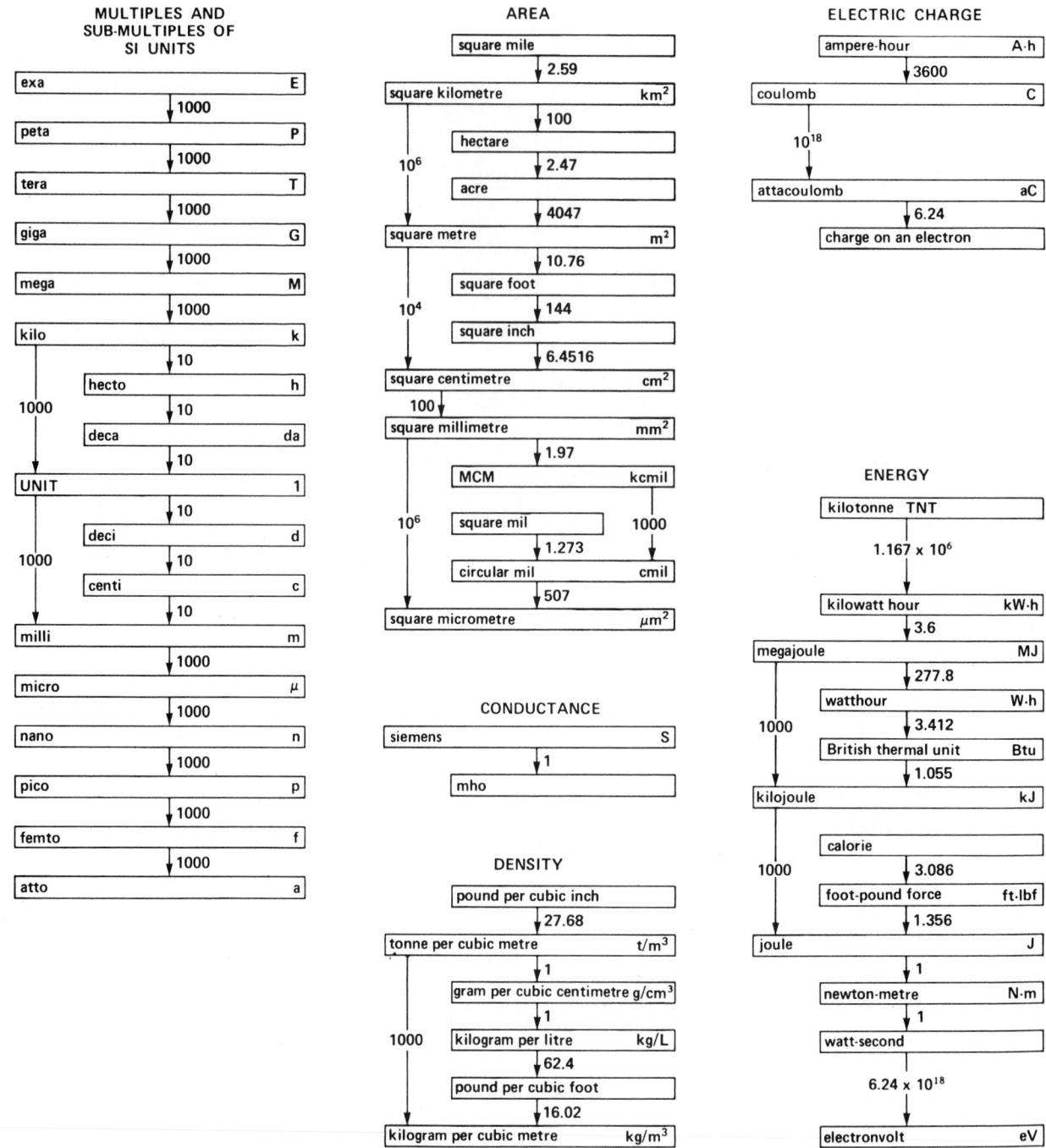

MULTIPLES AND SUB-MULTIPLES OF SI UNITS

exa	E
↓ 1000	
peta	P
↓ 1000	
tera	T
↓ 1000	
giga	G
↓ 1000	
mega	M
↓ 1000	
kilo	k
↓ 10	
hecto	h
↓ 10	
deca	da
↓ 10	
UNIT	1
↓ 10	
deci	d
↓ 10	
centi	c
↓ 10	
milli	m
↓ 1000	
micro	μ
↓ 1000	
nano	n
↓ 1000	
pico	p
↓ 1000	
femto	f
↓ 1000	
atto	a

(1000 from kilo to milli; 1000 from UNIT to milli)

AREA

square mile	
↓ 2.59	
square kilometre	km²
↓ 100	
hectare	
↓ 2.47	
acre	
↓ 4047	
square metre	m²
↓ 10.76	
square foot	
↓ 144	
square inch	
↓ 6.4516	
square centimetre	cm²
↓ 100	
square millimetre	mm²
↓ 1.97	
MCM	kcmil
square mil	1000
↓ 1.273	
circular mil	cmil
↓ 507	
square micrometre	μm²

(10⁶ from square kilometre to square metre; 10⁴ from square metre to square centimetre; 10⁶ from square millimetre to square micrometre)

ELECTRIC CHARGE

ampere-hour	A·h
↓ 3600	
coulomb	C
↓ 10¹⁸	
attacoulomb	aC
↓ 6.24	
charge on an electron	

ENERGY

kilotonne TNT	
↓ 1.167 × 10⁶	
kilowatt hour	kW·h
↓ 3.6	
megajoule	MJ
↓ 277.8	
watthour	W·h
↓ 3.412	
British thermal unit	Btu
↓ 1.055	
kilojoule	kJ
↓ calorie	
↓ 3.086	
foot-pound force	ft·lbf
↓ 1.356	
joule	J
↓ 1	
newton-metre	N·m
↓ 1	
watt-second	
↓ 6.24 × 10¹⁸	
electronvolt	eV

(1000 from megajoule to kilojoule; 1000 from kilojoule to joule)

CONDUCTANCE

siemens	S
↓ 1	
mho	

DENSITY

pound per cubic inch	
↓ 27.68	
tonne per cubic metre	t/m³
↓ 1	
gram per cubic centimetre	g/cm³
↓ 1	
kilogram per litre	kg/L
↓ 62.4	
pound per cubic foot	
↓ 16.02	
kilogram per cubic metre	kg/m³

(1000 from tonne per cubic metre to kilogram per cubic metre)

EXAMPLE: Convert 1590 MCM to square inches.

SOLUTION: 1590 MCM = 1590 (÷ 1.97) (÷ 100) (÷ 6.4516) in² = 1.25 in².

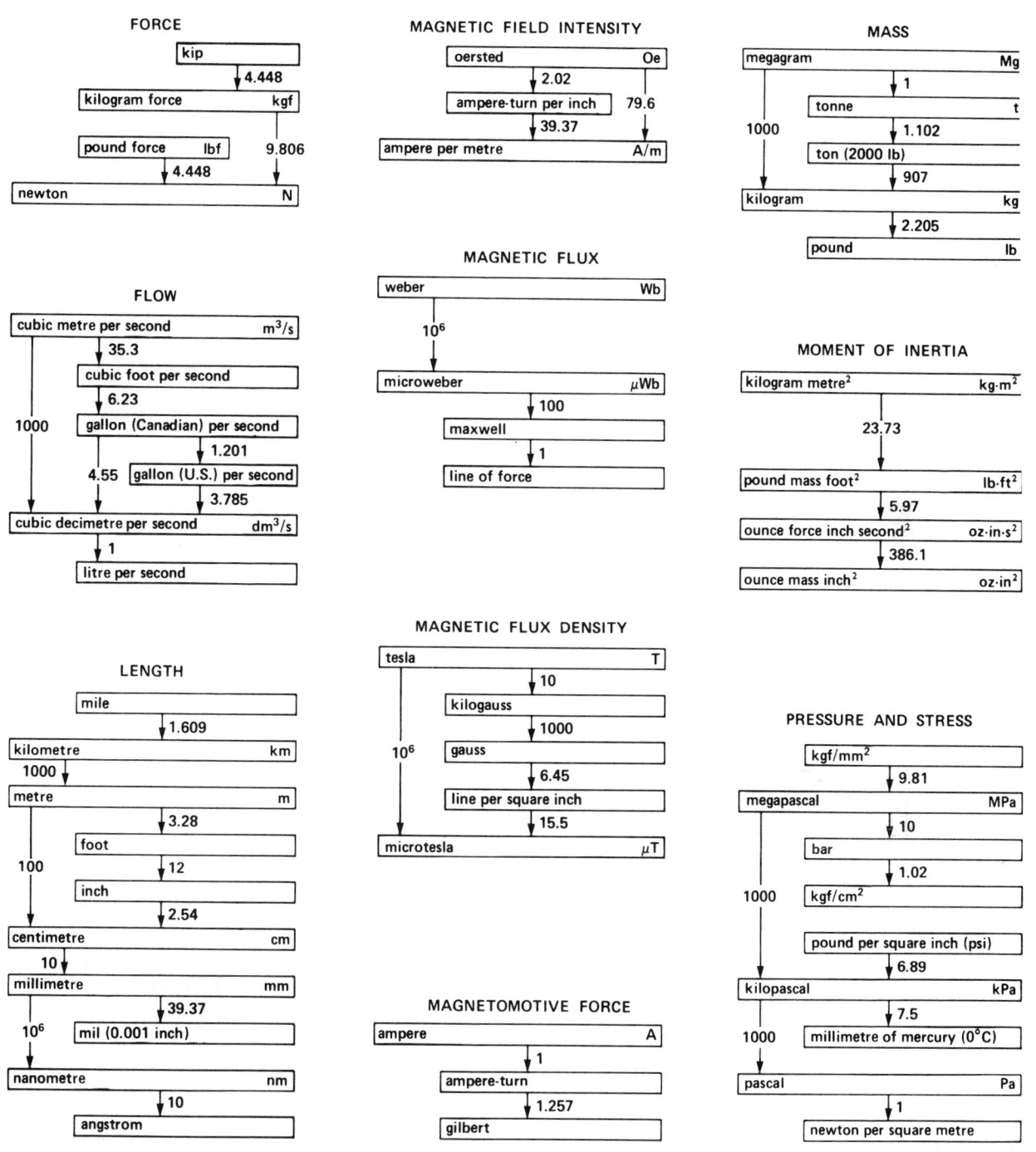

FORCE

kip

↓ 4.448

kilogram force   kgf

pound force   lbf   9.806

↓ 4.448

newton   N

MAGNETIC FIELD INTENSITY

oersted   Oe

↓ 2.02

ampere-turn per inch   79.6

↓ 39.37

ampere per metre   A/m

MASS

megagram   Mg

↓ 1

tonne   t

1000   ↓ 1.102

ton (2000 lb)

↓ 907

kilogram   kg

↓ 2.205

pound   lb

FLOW

cubic metre per second   m³/s

↓ 35.3

cubic foot per second

↓ 6.23

gallon (Canadian) per second

1000   ↓ 1.201

4.55   gallon (U.S.) per second

↓ 3.785

cubic decimetre per second   dm³/s

↓ 1

litre per second

MAGNETIC FLUX

weber   Wb

↓ 10⁶

microweber   μWb

↓ 100

maxwell

↓ 1

line of force

MOMENT OF INERTIA

kilogram metre²   kg·m²

↓ 23.73

pound mass foot²   lb·ft²

↓ 5.97

ounce force inch second²   oz·in·s²

↓ 386.1

ounce mass inch²   oz·in²

LENGTH

mile

↓ 1.609

kilometre   km

1000 ↓

metre   m

↓ 3.28

foot

100   ↓ 12

inch

↓ 2.54

centimetre   cm

10 ↓

millimetre   mm

↓ 39.37

10⁶   mil (0.001 inch)

nanometre   nm

↓ 10

angstrom

MAGNETIC FLUX DENSITY

tesla   T

↓ 10

kilogauss

↓ 1000

10⁶   gauss

↓ 6.45

line per square inch

↓ 15.5

microtesla   μT

PRESSURE AND STRESS

kgf/mm²

↓ 9.81

megapascal   MPa

↓ 10

bar

↓ 1.02

1000   kgf/cm²

pound per square inch (psi)

↓ 6.89

kilopascal   kPa

↓ 7.5

1000   millimetre of mercury (0°C)

pascal   Pa

↓ 1

newton per square metre

MAGNETOMOTIVE FORCE

ampere   A

↓ 1

ampere-turn

↓ 1.257

gilbert

EXAMPLE: Convert 580 psi to megapascals.

SOLUTION: 580 psi = 580 ($\times$ 6.89) ($\div$ 1000) MPa = 4 MPa.

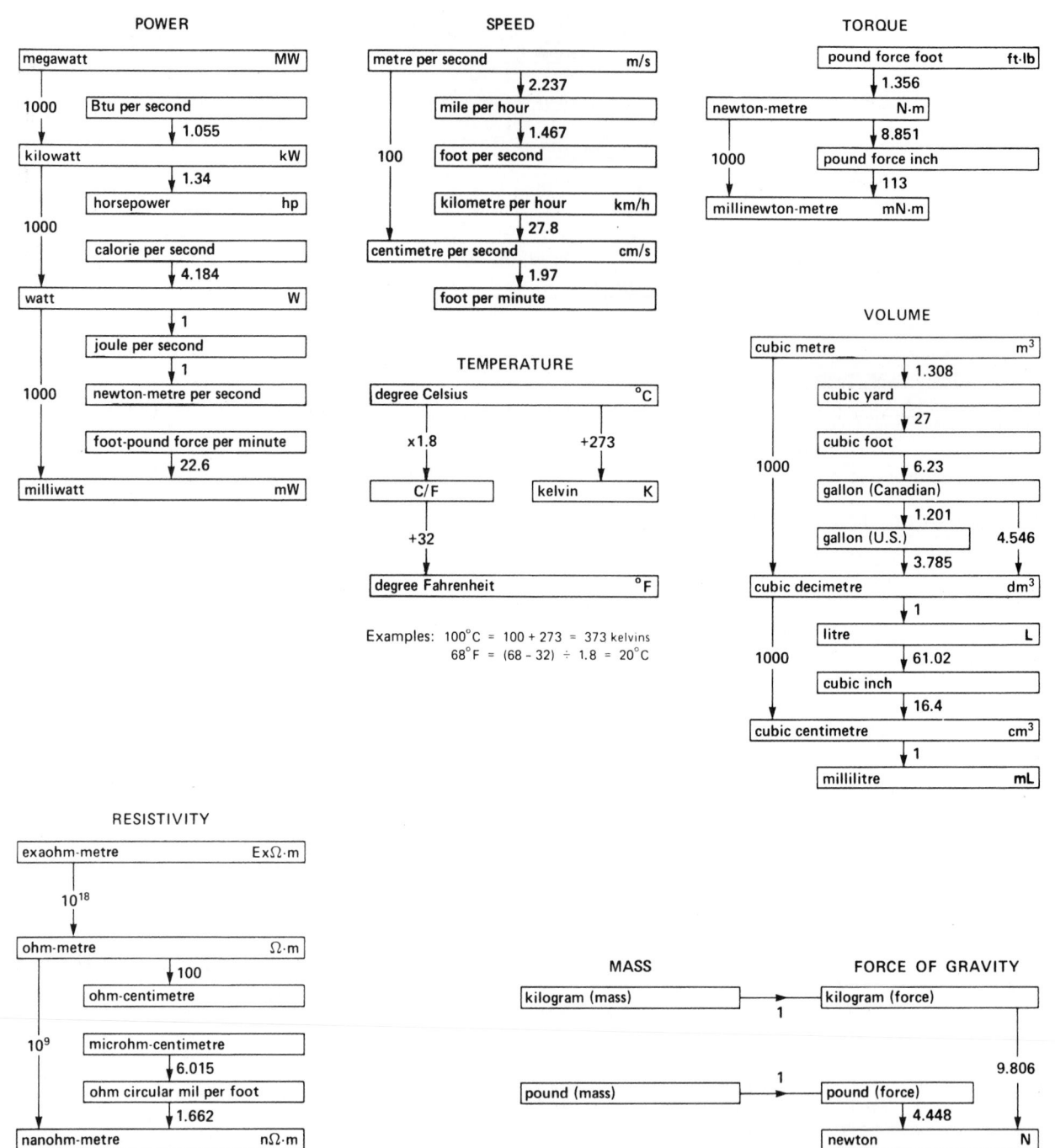

EXAMPLE: Calculate the force of gravity (in newtons) that acts on a mass of 9 lb.

SOLUTION: 9 lbm → 9 (× 1) (× 4.448) N = 40 N.

Appendix C

Properties of Round Copper Conductors

The American wire Gauge system follows a geometric progression in which the diameters of wire gauges No. 0000 and No. 36 are fixed at 460 mils and 5 mils respectively. Because there are 39 wire sizes between No. 0000 and No. 36, the ratio between two successive diameters is $\sqrt[39]{460/5} = 1.1229....$ The corresponding ratio between the cross-sections of two consecutive wire sizes is $(1.1229....)^2 = 1.261$.

For example, the theoretical diameter of a No. 35 wire is $5 \times 1.1229.... = 5.614$ mils. The theoretical cross-section of a No. 35 wire is $5^2 \times 1.261 = 31.52$ circular mils.

In practice, the diameters and cross-sections of the conductors are rounded off according to the values given in the following table.

PROPERTIES OF ROUND COPPER CONDUCTORS

Gauge number AWG/ B & S	Diameter of bare conductor		Cross section		Resistance mΩ/m or Ω/km		Weight g/m or kg/km	Typical diameter of *insulated* magnet wire used in relays, magnets, motors, transformers, etc.
	mm	mils	mm²	cmils	25°C	105°C		
250MCM	12.7	500	126.6	250 000	0.138	0.181	1126	
4/0	11.7	460	107.4	212 000	0.164	0.214	953	
2/0	9.27	365	67.4	133 000	0.261	0.341	600	
1/0	8.26	325	53.5	105 600	0.328	0.429	475	
1	7.35	289	42.4	87 700	0.415	0.542	377	
2	6.54	258	33.6	66 400	0.522	0.683	300	
3	5.83	229	26.6	52 600	0.659	0.862	237	
4	5.18	204	21.1	41 600	0.833	1.09	187	
5	4.62	182	16.8	33 120	1.05	1.37	149	
6	4.11	162	13.30	26 240	1.32	1.73	118	
7	3.66	144	10.5	20 740	1.67	2.19	93.4	
8	3.25	128	8.30	16 380	2.12	2.90	73.8	mm
9	2.89	114	6.59	13 000	2.67	3.48	58.6	3.00
10	2.59	102	5.27	10 400	3.35	4.36	46.9	2.68
11	2.30	90.7	4.17	8 230	4.23	5.54	37.1	2.39
12	2.05	80.8	3.31	6 530	5.31	6.95	29.5	2.14
13	1.83	72.0	2.63	5 180	6.69	8.76	25.4	1.91
14	1.63	64.1	2.08	4 110	8.43	11.0	18.5	1.71
15	1.45	57.1	1.65	3 260	10.6	13.9	14.7	1.53
16	1.29	50.8	1.31	2 580	13.4	17.6	11.6	1.37
17	1.15	45.3	1.04	2 060	16.9	22.1	9.24	1.22
18	1.02	40.3	0.821	1 620	21.4	27.9	7.31	1.10
19	0.91	35.9	0.654	1 290	26.9	35.1	5.80	0.98
20	0.81	32.0	0.517	1 020	33.8	44.3	4.61	0.88
21	0.72	28.5	0.411	812	42.6	55.8	3.66	0.79
22	0.64	25.3	0.324	640	54.1	70.9	2.89	0.70
23	0.57	22.6	0.259	511	67.9	88.9	2.31	0.63
24	0.51	20.1	0.205	404	86.0	112	1.81	0.57
25	0.45	17.9	0.162	320	108	142	1.44	0.51
26	0.40	15.9	0.128	253	137	179	1.14	0.46
27	0.36	14.2	0.102	202	172	225	0.908	0.41
28	0.32	12.6	0.080	159	218	286	0.716	0.37
29	0.29	11.3	0.065	128	272	354	0.576	0.33
30	0.25	10.0	0.0507	100	348	456	0.451	0.29
31	0.23	8.9	0.0401	79.2	440	574	0.357	0.27
32	0.20	8.0	0.0324	64.0	541	709	0.289	0.24
33	0.18	7.1	0.0255	50.4	689	902	0.228	0.21
34	0.16	6.3	0.0201	39.7	873	1140	0.179	0.19
35	0.14	5.6	0.0159	31.4	1110	1450	0.141	0.17
36	0.13	5.0	0.0127	25.0	1390	1810	0.113	0.15
37	0.11	4.5	0.0103	20.3	1710	2230	0.091	0.14
38	0.10	4.0	0.0081	16.0	2170	2840	0.072	0.12
39	0.09	3.5	0.0062	12.3	2820	3690	0.055	0.11
40	0.08	3.1	0.0049	9.6	3610	4720	0.043	0.1

Index